gift

ALTERNATING-CURRENT CIRCUIT THEORY

ALTERNATING-CURRENT CIRCUIT THEORY

SECOND EDITION

by **MYRIL B. REED**

PROFESSOR OF ELECTRICAL ENGINEERING

MICHIGAN STATE UNIVERSITY

HARPER & BROTHERS • PUBLISHERS • NEW YORK

Alternating-Current Circuit Theory, Second Edition

A-F

Library of Congress catalog card number: 56–6091

CONTENTS

PREFACE TO THE FIRST EDITION

The writing of a textbook which includes the many topics deemed essential for an understanding of alternating-current circuit theory, and which treats these topics with sufficient detail and yet sufficient brevity to allow the desired coverage is a difficult task. If only results are given, a student gets no real grasp of the principles involved. If basic principles are considered in too great detail, not enough essential results can be presented. Just how to effect a compromise cannot be determined in such a manner that all teachers are satisfied.

This book has been written with the idea in mind that both basic principles and essential results must be included. It is certain, therefore, that the whole book cannot be covered in the beginning course on a-c circuit theory. Instead particular omissions will have to be made in correspondence with the inclinations of each individual teacher. After the first nine chapters the remainder of the book deals with specialized topics. Different classes, instructors, or curricula will indicate which of these chapters (part or whole) are to be included for study.

The use of this book for more than one course has been found advantageous. The first course should emphasize the fundamental parts or foundation of the knowledge of a-c circuit theory and a following course, using the same nomenclature and basic concepts, should concentrate on the varied applications to special problems.

The exponentials $\epsilon^{j\theta}$ and $\epsilon^{j\omega t}$ rather than $\angle\theta$ or $\angle\omega t$ have been used throughout because such usage corresponds to that of the mathematicians who have developed the mathematics which electrical engineers are finding more and more essential to their professional progress. Since there are already many hurdles in the way of engineers and mathematicians writing for mutual understanding, it seems hardly desirable for engineers to set up deliberately another hurdle consisting of a mathematical nomenclature of their own.

In writing this book particular effort has gone into developing and using an explicit and consistent nomenclature. Also much effort has gone into laying a foundation based on experimental evidence followed by careful and complete mathematical development. It is believed that the precision in thinking which develops as a result of a complete study of this book amply justifies the extra time which will be required for such a study. The author's experience with several classes certainly justifies this conclusion.

A few problems have been scattered throughout the book which are either too long or too difficult for the usual homework assignment. Consequently extra time must be allowed or extra help from the instructor will be required if any of these problems are assigned.

The author would like to acknowledge an indebtedness to Sterling Beckwith, J. E. Hobson, W. A. Lewis, Frank V. Smith, and C. F. Wagner for constructive criticisms on both the contents of this book and the method of treatment. These suggestions have done much to improve the final product.

There is no way to evaluate adequately the assistance of my wife, Georgia. The typing, checking of arithmetic, proofreading, index construction, and much other work have been done by her on the manuscript over a period of several years. Certainly the book would still be in the form of an incomplete manuscript without the continuous help she has given.

MYRIL B. REED

Urbana, Illinois
May, 1948

PREFACE TO THE SECOND EDITION

Since the first appearance of this book, two major additions have been made to the apparatus in common use in the electrical engineering profession—television and computers. Both point in the direction of an increase in complexity and precision in the mathematics and physical apparatus of professional activities. The second edition of *Alternating-Current Circuit Theory* has been made with this fact in mind: that systems of greater complexity must now and in the future be treated with greater precision. To this end

(a) more careful consideration is given to the use and meaning of references to increase the precision of the basis of network theory;

(b) there is a much improved pattern for treating mutual induction, which permits the inclusion of conductors in relative motion into systems with fixed conductors and so sets the stage for consideration of rotating machinery and servomechanisms;

(c) some elementary topology is presented since it is only by this means that it is possible to form such a precise basis for network equations that full advantage can be taken of computers;

(d) the matrix algebra use has been moved from Chapter 13 to Chapter 9, emphasizing the increased importance of this precision tool for handling systems of equations, for suggesting paths for theoretical investigation, and for setting patterns on which computers may be effectively employed;

(e) the m-derived approach to filter design has been completely replaced by the time-tested method, now in use at Bell Telephone Laboratories, based on the symmetric lattice.

MYRIL B. REED

November, 1955

ALTERNATING-CURRENT CIRCUIT THEORY

MATHEMATICAL SYMBOLS

The symbolism in this book differs somewhat from the symbolism in most textbooks in electrical engineering. For example, complex numbers are not represented by the customary bold-face symbols but by italic capital letters, such as I and I_m. Thus the simplest symbols, which can be written on paper or a blackboard, represent the quantities most often considered. Vertical bars are used to represent absolute magnitudes such as $|I|$, and the symbols $i(t)$, $i(x)$, and $I(x, t)$ represent functions which vary with time or space, or both. More explicitly:

I, E, and V represent rms, stationary vectors (complex number) values.

I_m, E_m, and V_m represent maximum value stationary vectors (complex numbers).

$|I|$, $|I_m|$, $|U|$, etc., represent magnitudes of complex or real numbers.

$I(t)$, $V(t)$, etc., represent time varying, i.e., rotating vectors.

$i(t)$, $v(t)$, etc., represent time varying real, i.e., instantaneous values.

i, v, etc., represent horizontal and vertical components of stationary vectors.

E, $e(t)$, e, E_m represent source or internal-generated voltages.

V, $v(t)$, V_m, v represent the voltages which appear across impedances or between any two network points.

$\mathcal{E}$, $\mathcal{I}$, $\mathcal{V}$, etc., represent matrices.

CHAPTER 1

Sine Wave and Vector Representation of an Alternating Current

The first commercial application of electricity—incandescent lighting—was made by means of direct current, i.e., the current which results from a constant rate of average drift of electrons always in a particular direction in a conductor. Direct current was used for several years. As the size of the systems increased, the Edison three-wire circuit was developed in an effort to raise the voltage and thus reduce the current and the attendant line losses and at the same time keep the voltage low enough to minimize the danger to life.

The chronological development of d-c generating devices, from the heyday of direct current to the present time, is shown pictorially in Fig. 1–1. The reciprocating steam engine installation of Fig. 1–1*a* shows purely d-c generating units, and the other installations are conversion devices for changing alternating to direct current. The rectifier units of Figs. 1–1*c* and *d* have no moving parts and are highly successful in converting alternating to direct current.

If a simple and efficient d-c transformer had been found, there is no doubt that direct current would still be in general use. Even today, however, with all the progress of the last fifty years the d-c system is so inflexible as to limit its usefulness seriously. Although many of the electrified railroads, either cross country or city lines, operate on direct current because of the superior characteristics of d-c motors, the energy is usually distributed as alternating current and converted near the point of use. The congested areas of the downtown districts of many of the large cities of the country—New York, Chicago, Los Angeles, Denver, New Orleans, and many others—are supplied largely by direct current. But even here the d-c equipment is gradually being replaced by a-c equipment in spite of the expense of replacement, and practically all new installations are on alternating current.

Since the advent of gas-filled electron tubes, some investigation has been conducted with the intention of making direct current more widely applicable by using these tubes to *convert* alternating current from the large generating stations to high-voltage direct current on the transmission lines, and then to *invert* direct current to alternating current at the end of the lines for distribution. Even so, there are no indications at

Fig. 1–1a. Vertical, cross-compound, direct-connected steam engines at 3000 hp each. (Courtesy, Allis-Chalmers Mfg. Co.)

the present that direct current will supplant alternating current to any extent. The tendency is actually in the other direction.

With the development of the transformer—an efficient, sturdy, simple piece of apparatus with no moving parts—d-c systems were doomed. Two coils of wire wrapped on a piece of iron can be used to increase or decrease the magnitude of the a-c voltage almost at will merely by changing the ratio of the number of turns of the two coils. For example, the modern transformer installations shown in Fig. 1–2 are capable of trans-

Fig. 1–1*b*. Two 3000-kw, 650-volt, 360–rpm rotary converters. (Courtesy, Allis-Chalmers Mfg. Co.)

Fig. 1–1c. Ignitron mercury-arc rectifier. Delivers 60,000 amperes at 645 volts. (Courtesy, Westinghouse Electric & Mfg. Co.)

Fig. 1–1*d*. High-voltage rectifier at the WCBS transmitter. (Courtesy, Columbia Broadcasting System)

forming a large steady flow of electrical energy, at very high efficiency, from one voltage to another widely different one. On the other hand, a d-c voltage can be changed only by introducing a crippling energy loss. The introduction of the rugged and practically foolproof a-c induction motor made the triumph of alternating current complete.

Engineers were extremely skeptical of alternating current when it was introduced. In fact, reference to the files of the *A.I.E.E. Transactions* of the last part of the nineteenth century and the beginning of the twentieth century reveals that the opposition to its use was rather general and caustic. One instinctively feels that the change from the simple steady flow of electrons to the complex alternating flow is bound to introduce complications. In fact it does just that. As will be seen, effects appear in a-c circuits which are unknown in d-c systems. For instance, voltages continually appear in the a-c system the like of which do not occur at all or at most occur but momentarily in d-c systems.

The complications introduced into circuits by the use of alternating current are, however, not serious. In fact, they have been formulated

Fig. 1–2a. A 26,667-kva bank of three transformers and a spare. (Courtesy, Allis-Chalmers Mfg. Co.)

mathematically and studied experimentally until fairly complete, and powerful methods of analysis and excellent techniques in building and handling a-c equipment are available. Vast quantities of energy are transferred daily over long distances from power plants to cities at a-c voltages of more than 200,000 volts. The modern installations shown in Fig. 1–3 show a variety of generating units. The voltages at which these generating stations operate can be changed in magnitude by transformers and distributed to our lights at 110 volts, to our refrigerators at 220 to 110 volts, to large motors at 2300 or more volts, etc.

Alternating current is also used almost entirely in the already vast and still expanding communication systems of the world—radio, telephone, and television. Illustrations of the generating stations for broadcasting

Fig. 1–2*b*. Bank of large power transformers. (Courtesy, Westinghouse Electric & Mfg. Co.)

Fig. 1–3*a*. A 25,000-kw steam turbine installation. (Courtesy, Allis-Chalmers Mfg. Co.)

Fig. 1–3*b*. Interior of large hydro plant. (Courtesy, Allis-Chalmers Mfg. Co.)

systems are shown in Fig. 1–4. The vast network of telephone transmission lines which spreads almost endlessly hardly needs illustration.

In the light of the foregoing statements it should be evident that the study of alternating current is bound to be one of the most essential elements in the training of an electrical engineer. It is with such a study that this book is concerned.

1.1 Alternating Current.

The method of generating an alternating current employed by power engineers is basically simple. In the end view of the alternator (a-c gen-

Fig. 1–3*c*. Interior of large hydro plant showing 190,555-kva generating capacity at 13,350 and 13,800 volts. (Courtesy, General Electric Co.)

erator) shown in Fig. 1–5, it is easily seen that, as the rotor moves, its magnetic poles—alternately north and south—generate a voltage in any of the stationary conductors on the stator. This voltage will have one polarity as a north pole sweeps by a conductor and the opposite polarity as a south pole sweeps by. The proper interconnection of the stationary conductors with the stationary generator terminals establishes an alternating voltage at these terminals. The rapidity with which the voltage alternates is determined by the speed of the rotor. The passage of a north and south pole past a conductor is defined as one cycle. Present-day practice limits the maximum number of cycles per second (cps) to

Fig. 1–3*d*. Reciprocating Diesel engine at 2000 hp driving an electric generator. (Courtesy, Westinghouse Electric & Mfg. Co.)

sixty for most power systems. Higher frequency voltages, such as the 440 cps used in aircraft electrical systems, are also generated by rotating machinery. Obviously there is an upper limit to the speed possible for any machine if it is to remain intact; so there is an upper limit to the number of times its voltage may alternate per second.

The vast telephone networks operate with voltages and currents which alternate at many different values up to 9 million cps. The radio stations which have come into such widespread use operate in the neighborhood of 1 million cps, and the short wave radio stations for experimental and transoceanic communication operate at voltages and currents which alternate somewhere in the range of 6 to 20 million cps. Still higher frequencies are being generated and used in microwave and ultra-high frequency applications.

The generation of the medium frequency voltages used in speech communication systems results from the slight motion of the thin diaphragm in the mouthpiece as the sound waves impinge on it, and it is, therefore,

Fig. 1–4a. Station WCBS on man-made island two miles offshore in Long Island Sound. (Courtesy, Columbia Broadcasting System)

Fig. 1–4*b*. Transmitter room at radio broadcasting station WTAG and WIXTG. (Courtesy, General Electric Co.)

Fig. 1–5. End view of a-c generator (alternator). (Courtesy, Westinghouse Electric & Mfg. Co.)

another form of mechanical device for the generation of alternating electrical impulses.

Voltages of frequencies higher than 1000 cps are usually generated entirely by electrical means rather than by the motion of conductors. The device used is called an oscillator, particular examples of which are shown in Fig. 1–6. The oscillator has no moving parts in the usual sense

Fig. 1–6a. Quartz crystal oscillator for radio transmitter. (Courtesy, General Electric Co.)

to limit its frequency range. However, other considerations, such as the maximum velocity of electrons and the feasible upper limit of the size of the oscillator parts, place a practical upper and *lower* limit to the rapidity of alternations of each such device. Oscillators have been built which generate impulses of over 70,000 million cps and others which generate voltages with frequencies less than 60 cps.

The foregoing discussion is intended to give a rough idea of how an alternating voltage may be obtained, but a really effective explanation of the generating devices must wait until more is known of the behavior of the alternating currents and voltages themselves.

This book is concerned largely with the properties of alternating currents and voltages. Since these properties can only be expressed mathematically, much of the following material will be of necessity somewhat dissociated from physical reality. Whenever possible, however, illustrations from engineering practice will be used to remind the reader that we are not wandering off into the bypaths of the imagination.

Fig. 1–6*b*. Oscillator. (Courtesy, General Electric Co.)

An alternating current, by definition, changes its direction repeatedly. For many commercial applications (power systems) the time the electron drift is in one direction is the same as the time it is in the opposite direction (see curve *a* of Fig. 1–7). In many other applications (some electron tube circuits) the time of electron drift in a particular circuit direction may be different from the time of drift in the opposite direction (see curve *b* of Fig. 1–7). However, the two alternating currents represented by Fig. 1–7 have a common property of repeating a certain variation periodically. Not all alternating currents have this property. There are applications in which the alternating current does not vary periodically, e.g., the current in a radio microphone or telephone transmitter, as shown typically in Fig. 1–8. The current variation in such a system may never repeat over any time interval. Experience has shown that alternating currents of this kind may be treated satisfactorily in terms of sinusoidally varying currents of different frequencies. Therefore, if non-periodic

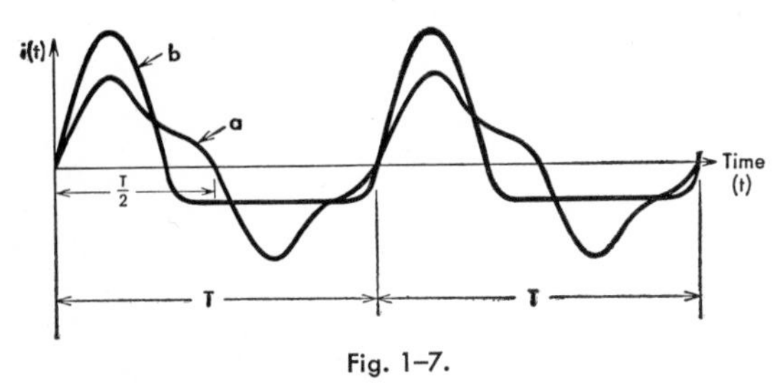

Fig. 1–7.

currents or voltages can be treated in terms of sinusoidal currents or voltages, the study of alternating currents and voltages can be reduced to a study of periodically alternating ones. Furthermore, as will be shown in detail in Chap. 6, *any periodically varying* current or voltage of engineering practice can be considered as a *sum of sinusoidally varying* (sine wave) currents or voltages. It is thus possible to reduce the study of any alternating current or voltage to the study of sinusoidal wave forms.

In addition, although an exact sine wave of current or voltage probably does not exist anywhere in practice, through deliberate design the output

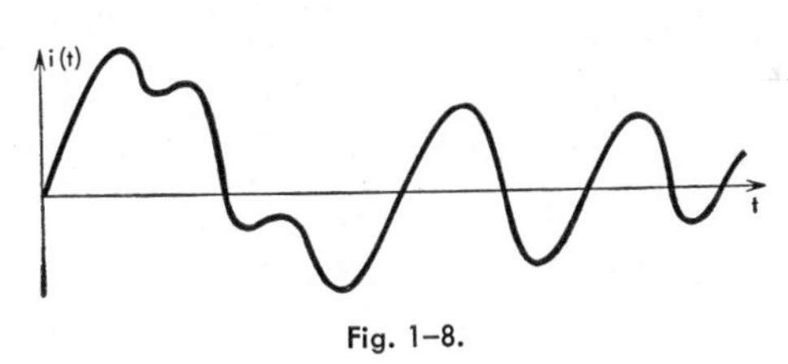

Fig. 1–8.

of the majority of oscillators and alternators is so near a sine wave that calculations based on the assumption of a sine wave are very often as accurate as the meters used to measure the currents and voltages. It is apparent, therefore, that the majority (*but not all*) of the a-c problems of the electrical engineer can be solved on the assumption that the voltage and current or their components vary sinusoidally. For these reasons, sine waves and their properties are of very great importance in the study of a-c phenomena. This book consists largely of a study of sine waves of current and voltage and their behavior in electrical networks.

1.2 Sine Wave Representation of an Alternating Current.

Since any effective treatment of an engineering problem should be capable of mathematical formulation, the first problem that arises in the study of alternating current is the writing of a mathematical expression for an alternating current, or, for the present discussion, of a sine wave of current. Such a wave is shown graphically in Fig. 1–9 and is expressed mathematically by

$$i(t) = |I_m| \sin \omega t \tag{1-1}$$

where $|I_m|$ = maximum value as shown in Fig. 1–9 (the vertical bars indicate the numerical value rather than the complex number value to be used in later parts of the text) and
ω = a constant which will be defined more completely.

Since ωt must range through 2π radians for the sine function to go through one complete variation or cycle—o to b of Fig. 1–9— the current will repeat its complete variation every 2π *seconds* if $\omega = 1$. Furthermore, if $\omega = 2\pi$, the current repeats every second, or the time of a cycle is 1 second. So, to determine an ω which produces a sine wave of period T_p seconds, it is only necessary to solve for ω from $\omega T_p = 2\pi$. Accordingly, to represent an f cycle per second sine wave, i.e., one which goes through a complete cycle f times per second, or one cycle in $1/f$ seconds,

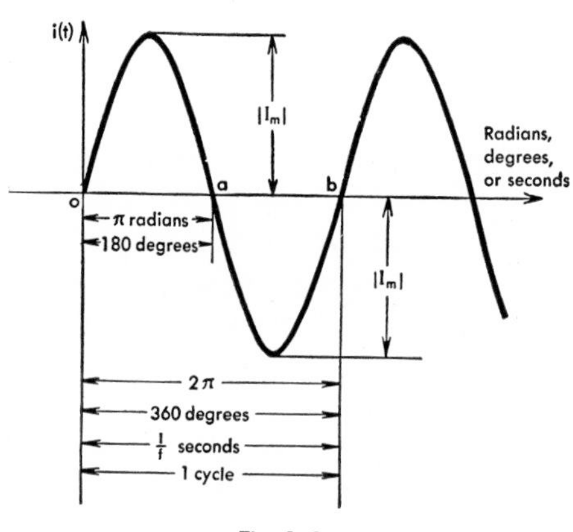

Fig. 1–9.

$$\omega \times \text{time of one cycle} = \omega \frac{1}{f} = 2\pi$$

or

$$\omega = \frac{2\pi}{\text{time of one cycle}} = 2\pi f$$

and equation 1–1 becomes

$$i(t) = |I_m| \sin 2\pi f t = |I_m| \sin \omega t \tag{1-2}$$

where $\omega \equiv 2\pi f$ and is called *angular frequency*.

The symbol f designates cycles or complete variations per second and is called *frequency*.

Note that the sine wave may be plotted with radians, degrees, or seconds as the abscissa or independent variable, as suggested by Fig. 1–9. If degrees or radians are used, it is common practice to write

$$i(\alpha) = |I_m| \sin \alpha \tag{1-3}$$

where, of course, $\alpha = \omega t = 2\pi f t$, from equation 1–2. The degree or radian form of the angle is common because of the form in which the tables of trigonometric functions are given. Seconds, radians, or degrees are used interchangeably in what follows. In fact, they are mixed up in the same expression occasionally, but this should lead to no confusion since the correct interpretation is evident.

The sine wave of Fig. 1–9 and equation 1–2 represents a current with changing (alternating) sense indicated by the positive and negative parts of the curve, and represents an increase and decrease in current alternately in either sense, exactly as desired. However, this particular form of sine wave is not satisfactory for studying alternating currents in general because any current it represents must be zero when $t = 0$. It is a simple matter to avoid such a restriction by writing the sine wave representation in the form

$$i(t) = |I_m| \sin(\omega t + \phi) \qquad (1\text{–}4)$$

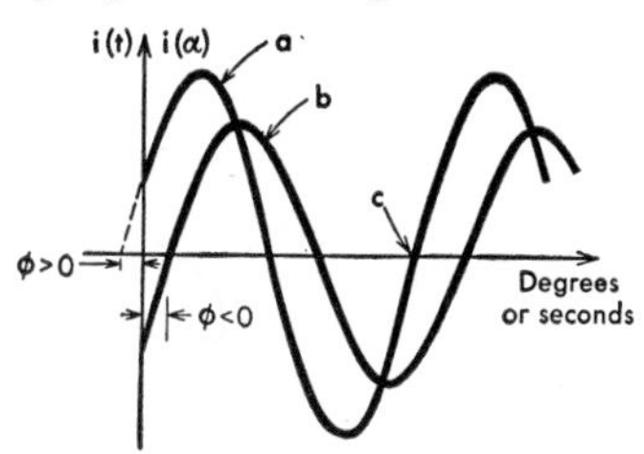

Fig. 1–10.

where ϕ = an offset or phase angle, as shown in Fig. 1–10.

If $\phi > 0$, the sinusoid shown by curve a of Fig. 1–10 results; whereas if $\phi < 0$, curve b of Fig. 1–10 represents equation 1–4. Strictly speaking, ϕ should be expressed in radians, since ωt is in radians, but in what follows ϕ will be expressed in degrees for convenience. The magnitude and proper choice of the sign of the phase angle will evidently shift the zero point of the sine wave to any desired position on the time axis. Equation 1–4 thus represents mathematically any possible sinusoidal current variation, which is exactly what is desired for a study of alternating currents.

1.3 Alternating Current Ampere Effective Value.

The question of what meaning, if any, can be assigned to the term a-c ampere arises in even the most elementary discussion. At any particular instant the current, of course, is simply the negative of the instantaneous, average electron drift in coulombs per second. But is there anything about a continually changing alternating current which corresponds to the constant value of d-c amperes?

The average value of the current cannot be used since frequently the average value is zero—always so for a sinusoid, as may easily be seen by the computation shown in Art. 1–5 or merely by observation of Fig. 1–9. The maximum value does not mean much, as may be seen from Fig. 1–7, since it does not tell much about the overall current or voltage variation. Occasionally the maximum value of voltage is important in determining whether the insulation of a system will break down, but it cannot tell anything about the nature of the current as a whole or its effect. Complete curves of the type shown in Fig. 1–7 could be and are used, but since the variations are so very rapid—tens to millions of cycles per second—pictures must be taken or some repeating device used because the human eye cannot register an image of such short duration. An instrument known as the oscillograph, which gives a picture of instantaneous variations, might be used to measure and record the current at each instant, but the device is relatively complex and the result does not correspond in any way to an ammeter indication. But even if this, or any other, device could give the complete form of current variation in the simplest conceivable manner, the meaning of an a-c ampere would still not be defined.

What is really sought is a single *number*, characteristic of the current variation, sinusoidal or not, which a meter will indicate. The early electrical engineers, when confronted with this problem, acted as men always act. They first tried the various known devices on the new problem. The D'Arsonval meter would not indicate at all on most of the alternating currents. The dynamometer meter—essentially a fixed coil in series with a movable coil with pointer attached—was found to indicate corresponding to a change in the alternating current of the coils. The iron vane instrument—fixed coil and pivoted strip of iron tilted with respect to the coil—also changed in indication corresponding to a change in the alternating current of the coil. Finding an a-c ammeter was thus a relatively simple matter. Determining more exactly what these meters indicated in terms of the actual current variation was not quite so easy, but it was still not very difficult.

In the first place, because the current to be measured is in both coils of a dynamometer meter, the deflection is proportional to the square of the current. Second, because the moving element of the meter, while relatively light in weight, still is very much too heavy to follow very rapid current variations, the meter indicates the *average* of the pull against its restoring spring. Thus the average of the square of the instantaneous current is indicated by the meter needle. But if direct current is observed with this same meter, the deflection is proportional to the square of the direct current also, and if the meter is to be used as an ammeter the scale will have to be drawn so that it extracts the square root in order to indicate $|I|$ and not $|I|^2$. Then, if this meter with the scale marked to measure direct current is used also to measure alternating current, the meter will in effect indicate the square root of the average of the squares of the instantaneous currents.

The mathematical expression for an average of a function is the definite integral of that function divided by the interval between the limits of integration—area divided by the base. On the basis of the foregoing discussion of the properties of a-c ammeters, they indicate in accordance with the expression

$$|I| \equiv \sqrt{\frac{1}{T}\int_0^T i^2(t)\,dt} \tag{1-5}$$

This equation defines the a-c characteristic number. It is usually called the effective current in amperes, or sometimes the root-mean-square (rms) value. The latter designation comes directly from the foregoing mathematical expression, which defines $|I|$ as the square root of the average of the square of the instantaneous current.

There is an alternative method of defining $|I|$ mathematically which was established long after alternating current was in use and which points out in a different manner the properties of rms current. An average drift of electrons through a conductor produces an energy loss no matter what the direction of the electron drift because the electrons will maintain an average position and not drift in either direction unless forced to do so. Accordingly, the instantaneous power is, from the definition of current as the *positive* charge which moves past a point per second and voltage as the work required to move a unit positive charge between two points,

$$p(t) = \frac{d}{dt}\,w(t) = \frac{d}{dt}\,q(t)\,\frac{d}{dq}\,w(q) = i(t)v(t) \text{ (watts)}$$

where $i(t)$ represents the time variation of current, in amperes, through a conductor, and

$v(t)$ represents the time variation of the voltage between two points along the conductor.

If the conductor being considered is a "pure" resistor, according to Ohm's law the voltage across the resistor may be expressed as

$$v(t) = Ri(t) \tag{1-6}$$

where R is a constant and is the conductor resistance in ohms. The numerical value of R actually depends on the particular $i(t)$ used because of skin effect, etc. However, for any particular $i(t)$ a particular constant value of R may be assumed, as has been verified by experiment. The instantaneous power, therefore, may be expressed as

$$p(t) = Ri^2(t) \tag{1-7}$$

Then the total energy loss due to the varying current—alternating or not—over any period of time $(0, T)$ is

$$w(T) = \int_0^T p(t)\,dt = \int_0^T i^2(t)R\,dt \text{ (joules)} \tag{1-8}$$

Now assume, by analogy from the d-c result, that the characteristic number of an a-c ampere $|I|$ is such a number that, if squared and multiplied by the resistance R, will give the average *power* loss in heating this resistor, i.e., $|I|^2R = P$, the average heating loss in watts. Furthermore, if the average power of heating, $|I|^2R$, is multiplied by T (the total heating time) the result is the total energy expended in heat, and if this product is equated to equation 1–8, the result is

$$|I|^2RT = \int_0^T i^2(t)R\,dt$$

Canceling the constant R, which is not a function of time, and rearranging, gives

$$|I| = \sqrt{\frac{1}{T}\int_0^T i^2(t)\,dt} \text{ (amperes)}$$

which is exactly the result already deduced in equation 1–5.

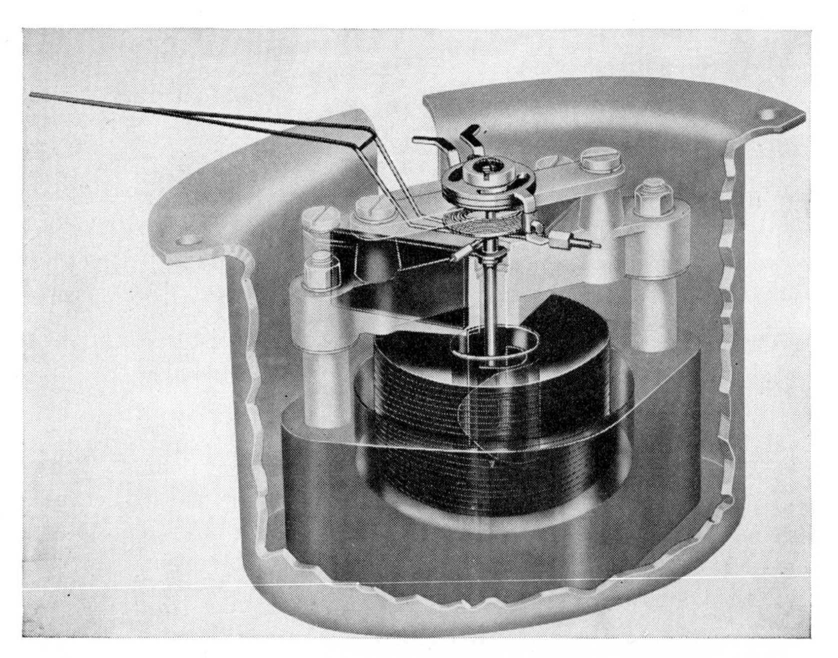

Fig. 1–11. Phantom view of moving iron vane mechanism. (Courtesy, Weston Electrical Instrument Corp.)

By means of equation 1–5, a number characteristic of any alternating (or varying) current may be determined provided the time variation of the current can be determined, and as has already been shown this characteristic number can also be measured directly by an ammeter. The meter shown in Fig. 1–11 illustrates a common variety of a-c ammeter.

1.4 Effective Value of a Sinusoidal Alternating Current.

Since sine waves are to be used in most of what follows, the characteristic number of a sine wave of current will be of particular importance. From the definition of the preceding article the effective value of a sine wave of current is

$$|I| = \sqrt{\frac{1}{T}\int_0^T |I_m|^2 \sin^2 \omega t \, dt} \tag{1–9}$$

The evaluation of this expression is facilitated by the use of the trigonometric substitution

$$\sin^2 \omega t = \frac{1 - \cos 2\omega t}{2}$$

The equation for $|I|$ of a sinusoid is then, after this trigonometric substitution is made and the constant $|I_m|$ is removed from the integral and radical:

$$|I| = |I_m| \sqrt{\frac{1}{T}\int_0^T \frac{1 - \cos 2\omega t}{2} \, dt}$$

Integrating, and substituting the limits, gives

$$|I| = |I_m| \sqrt{\frac{1}{T}\left[\frac{T}{2} - \frac{\sin 2\omega T}{4\omega}\right]} = |I_m| \sqrt{\frac{1}{2} - \frac{\sin 2\omega T}{4\omega T}} \tag{1–10}$$

A simplification of this expression is always used and may be justified in the following discussion. Suppose $f = 60$ cps, with T approximately 1 second and such that $\sin 2\omega T = 1$, a maximum. Then

$$\frac{\sin 2\omega T}{4\omega T} = \frac{\sin 754}{1508} < \frac{1}{1508} \ll \frac{1}{2}$$

according to which the effective value of a sinusoid is practically

$$|I| = \frac{|I_m|}{\sqrt{2}} = 0.707|I_m| \tag{1–11}$$

if the averaging process is carried out for as long as a second on the low frequency of power systems. Higher frequencies will make this last term of equation 1–10 negligible in even a shorter time. Since by the time the ammeter needle has settled to a steady deflection several seconds will always have elapsed, the value given by equation 1–11 is the characteristic number, or effective value, of a sine wave of alternating current within the accuracy of any measuring instrument.

The result given by equation 1–11 may be obtained in another way. Suppose that T of equation 1–10 is taken as $T_p = 1/f$—the time for one cycle of a sine wave according to Fig. 1–9—then for a sine wave

$$|I| = |I_m| \sqrt{\frac{1}{2} - \frac{\sin \frac{2\omega}{f}}{\frac{4\omega}{f}}} = |I_m| \sqrt{\frac{1}{2} - \frac{\sin 4\pi}{8\pi}} = \frac{|I_m|}{\sqrt{2}} = 0.707|I_m| \qquad (1\text{–}12)$$

exactly as given by equation 1–11. Therefore, *it is the usual practice, fully justified by the foregoing, to replace the indefinite limit* T *of equation 1–10 by the definite limit* T_p, *which is the time of a complete cycle or period,* and thus use the expression

$$|I| = \sqrt{\frac{1}{T_p} \int_0^{T_p} |I_m|^2 \sin^2 \omega t \, dt} = \frac{|I_m|}{\sqrt{2}} \qquad (1\text{–}13)$$

to define the effective value, or characteristic number, of a sine wave.

The general equation 1–5 with T replaced by $T_p = 1/f$ is commonly taken as the mathematical definition of the number of amperes of a periodic alternating current *no matter what the wave form.* Thus, in general, for alternating currents, the ampere designation is

$$|I| = \sqrt{\frac{1}{\frac{1}{f}} \int_0^{1/f} i^2(t) \, dt} \qquad (1\text{–}14)$$

A general argument to justify considering only *one cycle* of any periodic current in defining the rms value is not very difficult and should be worked out by the reader on the basis of the area concept of an integral.

Equation 1–14 is one of the most important equations of a-c theory, and the result deduced from it as given in equation 1–11 is used wherever sinusoidal alternating currents are used or discussed. Even if the wave form is not sinusoidal, this defining equation is ordinarily used to compute the effective value. The following example serves to illustrate a non-sine wave application and at the same time emphasizes the fact that $|I_m|/\sqrt{2}$ is the effective value for a sine wave only.

Example 1:1 Suppose an alternating current can be represented by Fig. 1–12. The effective value may be computed as follows:

Solution Equation 1–14 defines the rms value. In order to use this formula, the equation for $i(t)$ must be established. Employing the equation for a straight line gives

$$i(t) = \frac{10}{1/240} t = 2400t, \qquad 0 \leq t \leq \frac{1}{240}$$

$$i(t) = -2400t + 20, \qquad \frac{1}{240} \leq t \leq \frac{1}{120}$$

$$i(t) = -10, \qquad \frac{1}{120} \leq t \leq \frac{1}{60}$$

Then $$\int_0^{1/60} i^2(t)\,dt = \int_0^{1/240} (2400t)^2\,dt + \int_{1/240}^{1/120} (-2400t + 20)^2\,dt + \int_{1/120}^{1/60} (-10)^2\,dt$$

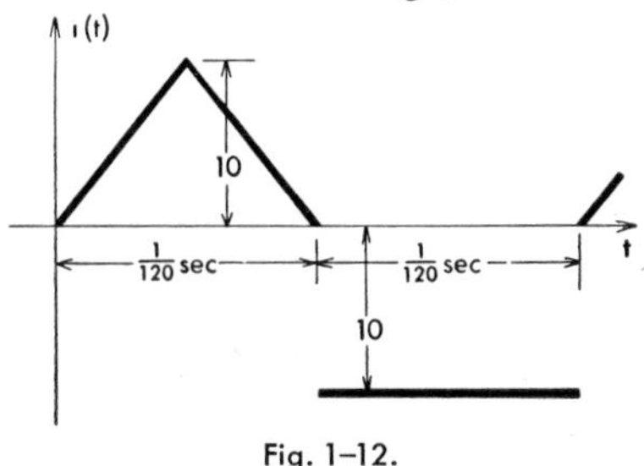

Fig. 1–12.

If the indicated integrations are carried out,

$$\int_0^{1/60} i^2(t)\,dt = (2400)^2 \frac{t^3}{3}\Big|_0^{1/240} + \left[(2400)^2 \frac{t^3}{3} - 96{,}000\frac{t^2}{2} + 400t\right]_{1/240}^{1/120} + 100t\Big|_{1/120}^{1/60}$$

Substituting the limits, and combining the results, gives

$$\int_0^{1/60} i^2(t)\,dt = \tfrac{10}{9}$$

Then, according to equation 1–14,

$$|I| = \sqrt{\frac{1}{\frac{1}{60}} \int_0^{1/60} i^2(t)\,dt} = \tfrac{10}{3}\sqrt{6}$$
$$= 8.16 \neq \frac{|I_m|}{\sqrt{2}}$$

1.5 Average Value of an Alternating Current.

The long-time (i.e., several cycles) average value of a sine wave is practically zero as an examination of a pictorial representation of the wave (Fig. 1–9) or an evaluation of the mathematical definition of the long-time average

$$|I_{\text{av}}| = \frac{1}{t_2 - t_1} \int_{t_1}^{t_2} i(t)\,dt, \quad (t_2 - t_1 \text{ large})$$

will show. Since all sine waves of whatever maximum value or phase position (angle ϕ of equation 1–4) have this same property of zero long-time average value, such an average value cannot be used in any way to differentiate between different sine waves. Non-sine waves, on the other hand, do not necessarily have zero long-time average values (curve b of

Fig. 1–7), and the pulsating (varying unidirectional) current of electron tube rectifiers or converters never has a zero average value. Accordingly, the average value is frequently useful in describing the characteristics of a non-sine wave.

The general form of the average value of any current is by definition expressed as

$$|I_{av}| = \frac{1}{T'}\int_0^{T'} i(t)\,dt \tag{1–15}$$

provided the range 0, T' covers the portion of the current to be averaged.

It is also sometimes useful to determine the average value of a half cycle of an alternating current. Equation 1–15 may be used for such a determination provided the interval $(0, T')$ covers a half cycle. In particular, for a sine wave, if T_p designates the time of a period or complete cycle,

$$|I_{av}| = \frac{1}{\frac{T_p}{2}}\int_0^{T_p/2} |I_m| \sin \omega t\ dt = \frac{2|I_m|}{T_p}\left[-\frac{\cos \omega t}{\omega}\right]_0^{T_p/2}$$

$$= \frac{2|I_m|}{T_p}\left[\frac{-\cos\frac{\omega T_p}{2} + 1}{\omega}\right]$$

Because $T_p = 1/f$, this expression becomes

$$|I_{av}| = \frac{2|I_m|}{\frac{1}{f}}\left[\frac{-\cos\frac{2\pi f}{2f} + 1}{2\pi f}\right] = \frac{2}{\pi}|I_m| \tag{1–16}$$

The ratio of the effective to average value of an alternating current is known as the *form* factor. In particular, for a half wave of a sinusoid:

$$\text{form factor} \equiv \frac{|I|}{|I_{av}|} = \frac{\frac{|I_m|}{\sqrt{2}}}{\frac{2}{\pi}|I_m|} = \frac{\pi}{2\sqrt{2}} = 1.11$$

1.6 Effective or RMS Value of Voltage.

The definition of the voltage characteristic number is more or less arbitrary. But in order to preserve the d-c mathematical expression of Ohm's law as far as possible for alternating current, assume that for a "pure" resistor

$$|V| = R|I| \tag{1–17}$$

where, by definition, $|V|$ = the magnitude of the effective or rms voltage across the resistor.

Fig. 1–13. Voltmeter interior showing high-resistance series resistor. (Courtesy, Westinghouse Electric & Mfg. Co.)

Because of this proportionality relation between $|V|$ and $|I|$ the rms value of $|V|$ is of the same form as that of $|I|$. As a mathematical demonstration of this fact, substituting the definition of $|I|$ (equation 1–14) into the voltage-current relation gives

$$|V| = R|I| = \mathrm{R}\sqrt{\frac{1}{\frac{1}{f}}\int_0^{1/f} i^2(t)\,dt} = \sqrt{\frac{1}{\frac{1}{f}}\int_0^{1/f} R^2 i^2(t)\,dt}$$

which, because $v(t) = R\ i(t)$, gives

$$|V| = \sqrt{\frac{1}{\frac{1}{f}}\int_0^{1/f} v^2(t)\,dt}\ \text{(volts)} \tag{1–18}$$

Hence the *effective value of the voltage is determined by the same formula as the effective value of the current*, with current symbols replaced by voltage symbols. Furthermore, *for a pure resistor, Ohm's law has been retained in terms of the characteristic numbers of the alternating voltage and current and the resistance of the circuit.*

Voltmeters measure the effective or rms values of an alternating voltage. They are simply ammeters in series with resistors, the series combination being connected between the two circuit points at which the voltage is desired. The iron vane instrument of the type shown in Fig. 1–11, with a high resistance in series, is used to measure the voltage between

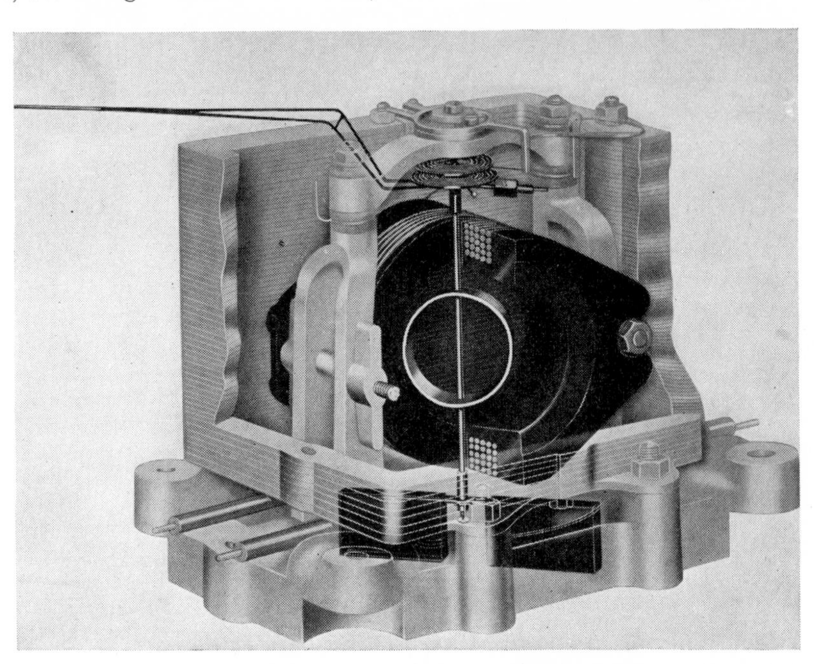

Fig. 1–14. Electrodynamometer mechanism. (Courtesy, Weston Electrical Instrument Corp.)

two circuit points (see Fig. 1–13). Also the dynamometer type meter of Fig. 1–14, with the stationary and movable coils and a high resistance connected in series, is often used to measure voltage.

1.7 Power Supplied to a Circuit in Which Is a Sine Wave of Current and Across Which a Sine Wave of Voltage Is Connected.

In addition to current and voltage, a third fundamental quantity, power, is of prime importance. Indeed, in a sense at least, the power characteristics of electrical apparatus are more important than either the current or voltage, because it is the power control of a system which usually determines its usefulness. Power systems are deliberately designed to transfer energy—control power—from one point to another in the most efficient and effective manner possible. Likewise it is the energy which radio or telephone apparatus delivers to the receivers and loud-speakers which determines the effectiveness of these systems.

At any instant the power associated with two terminals is given by

$$p(t) = v(t)i(t) \text{ (watts)} \tag{1-19}$$

because by *definition* for all possible current and voltage variations

$$\text{watts} = \text{volts} \times \text{amperes}$$

If $i(t)$ and $v(t)$ are both alternating, $p(t)$ will generally be alternating.

Because sinusoidal variations of current and voltage are to form the basis of all subsequent discussions in this book, the instantaneous power for such current and voltage variation will be developed. For the sake of generality, the current-voltage relations

$$v(t) = |V_m| \sin(\omega t + \phi)$$
$$i(t) = |I_m| \sin(\omega t + \phi + \theta)$$

will be used. The phase angle θ may or may not be zero, but it seems evident that the most general approach is to include this angle θ. Then in situations where $\theta = 0$, the derived relations can easily be modified accordingly.

Consider, therefore, the instantaneous power expression,

$$\begin{aligned} p(t) = v(t)i(t) &= |V_m| \sin(\omega t + \phi)|I_m| \sin(\omega t + \phi + \theta) \\ &= |V_m||I_m| \sin(\omega t + \phi + \theta) \sin(\omega t + \phi) \end{aligned} \tag{1-20}$$

From the trigonometric expression

$$\sin(\omega t + \phi + \theta) \sin(\omega t + \phi) = \frac{\cos\theta - \cos(2\omega t + 2\phi + \theta)}{2} \tag{1-21}$$

deduced by subtracting the expression for $\cos(a + b)$ from the expression for $\cos(a - b)$ and setting $a = \omega t + \phi + \theta$ and $b = \omega t + \phi$, equation 1–20 may be written as

$$p(t) = \frac{|V_m||I_m|}{2} \cos\theta - \frac{|V_m||I_m|}{2} \cos(2\omega t + 2\phi + \theta) \tag{1-22}$$

Note the characteristics of this equation. It consists of a *constant* term and a *double-frequency* term symmetric about the t-axis. A typical case is shown plotted in Fig. 1–15a ($\phi = 0$, $\theta \geq 0$).

The instantaneous power $p(t)$ is symmetric about the constant term of equation 1–22 as an axis. Figure 1–15b shows the power plot for $\theta = 90$ and $\phi = 0$ degrees. Note that the constant term of equation 1–22 is now zero and that the power is a *double-frequency* sine wave symmetric about the axis. Figure 1–15c is for $\theta = 0$ and $\phi = 0$ degrees. The power does not alternate for this case but is always positive or zero.

The negative portions of the power waves indicate a flow of energy *from the load to the source*, if, as is the convention being used in this book, a positive $v(t)$ means that the voltage reference is plus to minus in the reference sense of current. Then if both the current $i(t)$ and the voltage $v(t)$ are instantaneously positive, the current is sensed from the plus to

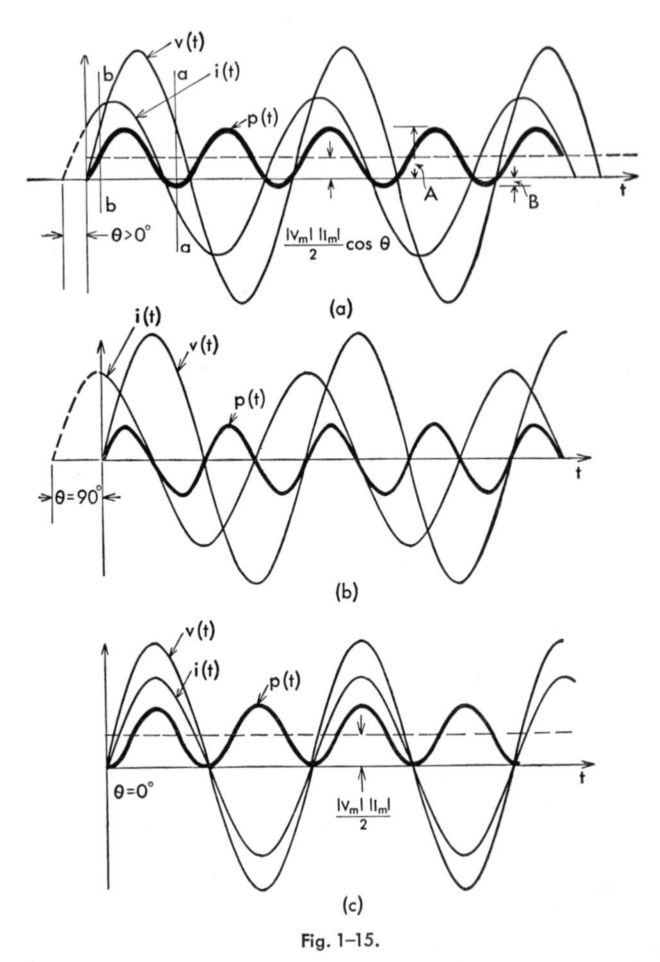

Fig. 1–15.

minus of the voltage, and energy is being absorbed, e.g., as in a resistor. On the other hand, if either the current or voltage, but not both, is instantaneously negative, the instantaneous power is negative, and the current sense is from the minus to plus of the voltage and so represents a delivery of energy, e.g., as in a battery supplying a load.

Just as it is convenient to express the current and voltage in terms of a characteristic number as well as instantaneous values, so a characteristic number which may be associated with alternating or pulsating power is convenient. In order to establish the characteristic number for the power, the following argument may be used. Since the chief concern in using electricity is the transfer of energy from one place to another, the *average* power would seem to be useful since merely multiplying this value by the time will give the energy absorbed or delivered. Furthermore, it is not difficult to build a meter which will measure the average power, and mathematically the average power follows immediately from the calculus definition of an average as (general, not sinusoidal only)

$$P = \frac{1}{T}\int_0^T p(t)\,dt \tag{1–23}$$

The number defined by equation 1–23 may be considered as the characteristic number for the alternating power. Note particularly that the *average power* is used and not the *effective power* in the sense of an effective current.

An indicating wattmeter, a device for measuring average power, is pictured in Fig. 1–14. Since the magnetic field of the pivoted coil is proportional to the voltage and the stationary magnetic field is proportional to the current, the steady deflection of the meter needle is directly proportional to the average product of these two quantities; hence the uniform scale.

The average power defined in equation 1–23 can also be expressed in terms of the resistance of a circuit and the effective current as $P = |I|^2R$. The voltage across the resistor is

$$v_R(t) = Ri(t)$$

Hence, substituting this relation into equation 1–19 and then into equation 1–23, and using equation 1–5, gives

$$P = \frac{1}{T}\int_0^T Ri^2(t)\,dt = R\left[\sqrt{\frac{1}{T}\int_0^T i^2(t)\,dt}\right]^2 = R|I|^2$$

This relation is of fundamental importance and is widely used.

The average power expression for a sine wave of current and voltage, from equations 1–22 and 1–23, is

$$P = \frac{|V_m||I_m|}{T}\int_0^T \frac{\cos\theta - \cos(2\omega t + 2\phi + \theta)}{2}\,dt \tag{1–24}$$

which, on integrating and substituting the limits, becomes

$$\begin{aligned} P &= \frac{|V_m||I_m|}{2T}\left[T\cos\theta - \frac{\sin(2\omega T + 2\phi + \theta) - \sin(\theta + 2\phi)}{2\omega}\right] \\ &= |V||I|\cos\theta + |V||I|\left[\frac{\sin(\theta + 2\phi) - \sin(2\omega T + 2\phi + \theta)}{2\omega T}\right] \end{aligned} \tag{1–25}$$

where $|V_m|/\sqrt{2}$ and $|I_m|/\sqrt{2}$ have been replaced by their equivalent effective value symbols according to equation 1–11.

If the upper limit T of equation 1–24 is taken as the particular time of one cycle, or an integral number n of whole cycles, the bracketed term of equation 1–25 vanishes because substitution of $1/f$ (time of one cycle) or n/f (n any integer) for T makes

$$\sin(2\omega T + 2\phi + \theta) = \sin\left(2\omega \frac{n}{f} + 2\phi + \theta\right) = \sin(4n\pi + 2\phi + \theta)$$
$$= \sin(\theta + 2\phi)$$

and so reduces the numerator of the right-hand term of equation 1–25 to zero, and leaves

$$P = |V||I| \cos \theta$$

If, on the other hand, T is taken equal to any value larger than, say, one second, the bracketed term of equation 1–25 is very small and decreases as T increases, so that it may be neglected. Actually a wattmeter would not indicate it anyway, because the needle takes several seconds to settle to a steady deflection, and by that time the term in question is so small that the meter scale could not be read accurately enough to include it.

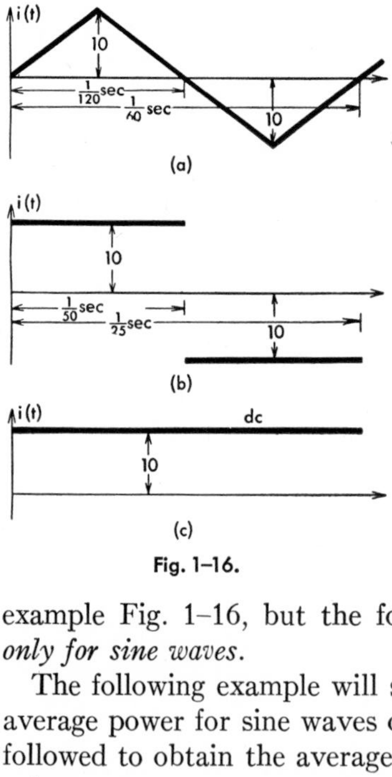

Therefore, in the light of these two immediately preceding conclusions, the average power definition for *sinusoidal currents* and *voltages* is always taken as

$$P = |V||I| \cos \theta \qquad (1\text{–}26)$$

or in integral form

$$P = \frac{1}{T_p} \int_0^{T_p} p(t)\, dt$$
$$= \frac{1}{\frac{1}{f}} \int_0^{1/f} p(t)\, dt \text{ (watts)} \qquad (1\text{–}27)$$

Fig. 1–16.

These integral *definitions* may also be used on periodic non-sine waves, as for example Fig. 1–16, but the form $|V||I| \cos \theta$ of equation 1–26 applies *only for sine waves.*

The following example will serve to emphasize that $|V||I| \cos \theta$ is the average power for sine waves only and to illustrate the procedure to be followed to obtain the average power for non-sine waves of current and voltage.

Example 1:2 Suppose that a voltage wave of the form shown in Fig. 1–16*b* and a current wave shown in Fig. 1–17 represent the voltage across and the current through a circuit element. The average power absorbed by this circuit element is to be determined. The two waves have the same frequency.

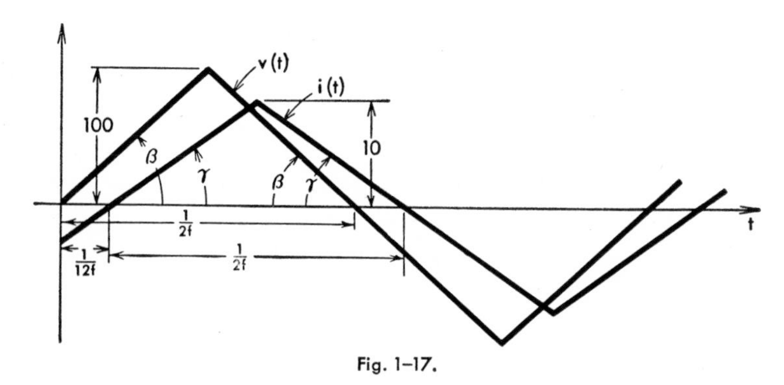

Fig. 1–17.

Solution The mathematical expression for the current and voltage must be established before they can be multiplied.

Because of the breaks in the current and voltage waves the equations differ for various parts of the cycle. Thus from the slope-intercept form of the equation of a straight line

$$\left.\begin{aligned} v(t) &= 10 \\ i(t) &= 40ft - \tfrac{10}{3} \end{aligned}\right] \text{for } 0 \le t \le \frac{1}{3f}$$

$$\left.\begin{aligned} v(t) &= 10 \\ i(t) &= -40ft + \tfrac{70}{3} \end{aligned}\right] \text{for } \frac{1}{3f} \le t < \frac{1}{2f}$$

$$\left.\begin{aligned} v(t) &= -10 \\ i(t) &= -40ft + \tfrac{70}{3} \end{aligned}\right] \text{for } \frac{1}{2f} < t \le \frac{5}{6f}$$

$$\left.\begin{aligned} v(t) &= -10 \\ i(t) &= 40ft - \tfrac{130}{3} \end{aligned}\right] \text{for } \frac{5}{6f} \le t \le \frac{1}{f}$$

The average power from the definition given in equation 1–27 is

$$P = f\left[\int_0^{1/3f} 10(40ft - \tfrac{10}{3})\,dt + \int_{1/3f}^{1/2f} 10(-40ft + \tfrac{70}{3})\,dt \right.$$
$$\left. + \int_{1/2f}^{5/6f} -10(-40ft + \tfrac{70}{3})\,dt + \int_{5/6f}^{1/f} -10(40ft - \tfrac{130}{3})\,dt\right]$$

Performing the indicated integration gives

$$P = f\left[\left(400f\frac{t^2}{2} - \frac{100}{3}t\right)\Bigg|_0^{1/3f} + \left(-400f\frac{t^2}{2} + \frac{700}{3}t\right)\Bigg|_{1/3f}^{1/2f} \right.$$
$$\left. + \left(400f\frac{t^2}{2} - \frac{700}{3}t\right)\Bigg|_{1/2f}^{5/6f} + \left(-400f\frac{t^2}{2} + \frac{1300}{3}t\right)\Bigg|_{5/6f}^{1/f}\right]$$

Substituting the limits, and combining the results, gives

$$P = \tfrac{400}{9} = 44.4 \text{ watts}$$

as the average power.

The expression given by equation 1–26 is of interest for several reasons. First, the average power is not expressed in quite the same manner as it was for direct current. The additional factor, *cos* θ, has now appeared. This factor, known as the *power factor*, is defined as

$$\text{power factor} = \text{pf} \equiv \frac{P}{|V||I|} \text{ (in general)} = \cos\theta \text{ (sine wave)} \tag{1–28}$$

The inclusion of a factor of the nature of $\cos\theta$ in the average power expression means that *average* power for a sinusoidal alternating current may be zero—$\theta = 90$ degrees—even though $|V|$ and $|I|$ are very large. Beginners sometimes injure wattmeters by failing to note that, even though the average power indication is perhaps small enough to be unimportant, the current constitutes a serious overload of the current coil.

As will be shown in detail in subsequent chapters, the range of values of the power factor angle, θ, is, for steady state sine wave operation, between plus and minus 90 degrees. As a result, the power factor ranges between zero and unity. Thus

$$-90^\circ \leq \theta \leq 90^\circ$$

and (1–29)

$$0 \leq \text{pf} = \cos\theta \leq 1$$

Accordingly, the average power is *always* less than or equal to the product of the rms current and voltage

$$P \leq |V||I|$$

for sine waves. This last relation is actually valid for *all wave forms* but this fact is not evident from the foregoing discussion.

In order to demonstrate that $P \leq |V||I|$, an inequality well known to mathematicians may be used. This Schwartzian inequality in integral form is

$$\sqrt{\frac{1}{T_p}\int_0^{T_p} v^2(t)\,dt}\ \sqrt{\frac{1}{T_p}\int_0^{T_p} i^2(t)\,dt} \geq \frac{1}{T_p}\left|\int_0^{T_p} v(t)i(t)\,dt\right|$$

But from the definitions for effective values of current and voltage and average power, the Schwartzian inequality in electrical engineering symbolism becomes

$$|V||I| \geq |P| \tag{1–30}$$

for *all currents and voltages*.

The product $|V||I|$, called the volt-amperes (va) or *apparent* power of a circuit, is symbolized here by

$$|U| \equiv |V||I| \tag{1–31}$$

The designation "apparent power" has no doubt been applied to the volt-ampere product because the first users of alternating current were distressed to discover that the volt-ampere product for alternating current *did not* give the average power as it did for the direct current with which they were familiar. They were very much inclined to consider this trick of alternating current as an apparition on an otherwise peaceful scene.

The fact that $|U| \geq |P|$ inevitably led the ever-curious engineer to investigate and formulate mathematically a discrepancy factor, known as

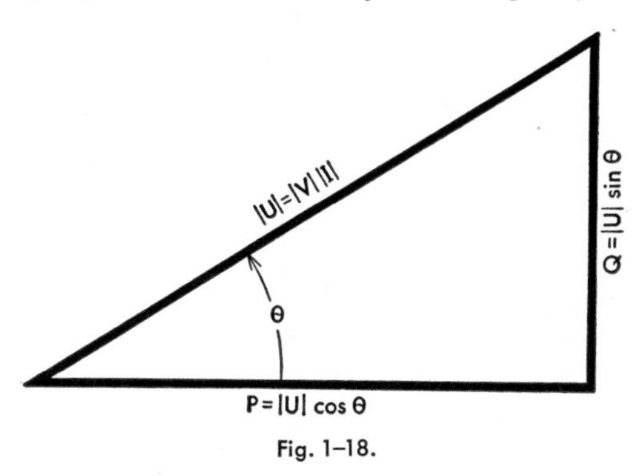

Fig. 1–18.

reactive volt-amperes. For sine waves such a factor is not difficult to define. The power factor, cos θ, of the average power expression suggests a right-triangle relation since

$$P = |V|\,|I| \cos\theta = |U| \cos\theta \tag{1–32}$$

may be considered as the horizontal projection of a vector U located θ degrees from the horizontal (Fig. 1–18). The vertical projection of such a vector is

$$Q = |V||I| \sin\theta = |U| \sin\theta \text{ (vars)} \tag{1–33}$$

and, since $\cos^2\theta + \sin^2\theta = 1$,

$$|U| = \sqrt{P^2 + Q^2} \tag{1–34}$$

Corresponding to the power factor definition of equation 1–28, a *reactive factor* is defined as

$$\text{reactive factor } (rf) = \frac{Q}{|V||I|} = \frac{Q}{|U|} = \sin\theta \tag{1–35}$$

As will be seen often in subsequent parts of this book, the reactive volt-amperes, or vars, Q, play a rather important role in the study of power relations of a-c circuits. In spite of its purely mathematical inception, meters which measure vars have been built and are being constantly used in power systems.

Meters for measuring volt-amperes are also in constant use in power networks. Measurement of volt-amperes requires the product $v(t)i(t)$

to be formed with $v(t)$ and $i(t)$ moved into phase, i.e., a current must be multiplied by a *voltage which may not exist at that instant* (Fig. 1–15). Since electrically such a feat is not possible, mechanical devices are used to combine P and Q to determine $|U|$. One of the several kinds of kilovolt-ampere (kva) meters—*kilo* for thousand—which may be purchased and which is in widespread use is shown in Fig. 1–19. This meter consists essentially of an average power meter and a var meter. The time integrals of P and Q appear on the corresponding dials. The aluminum ball is supported on three small disks. Two rotate independently in proportion to P and Q, and the third one is rotated by the aluminum ball as a result of the motion given it by the P and Q disks. The ball serves to perform the operation indicated in equation 1–34.

Present-day practice tends to rate electrical machines at a certain kva—thousand volt-amperes—rather than *kilowatts* (kw) since voltage usually determines the magnetic field conditions of the machine, and thus the heating effect in the iron, and current determines the heating effect in the conductors. The product of volts and amperes, therefore, is a good criterion of size because machines must be made large enough to radiate sufficient heat to prevent the burning of insulation.

It is of interest to note that the average power and the reactive volt-amperes can be determined directly from the instantaneous power curve.

Fig. 1–19*a*. Kva meter. (Courtesy, Westinghouse Electric & Mfg. Co.)

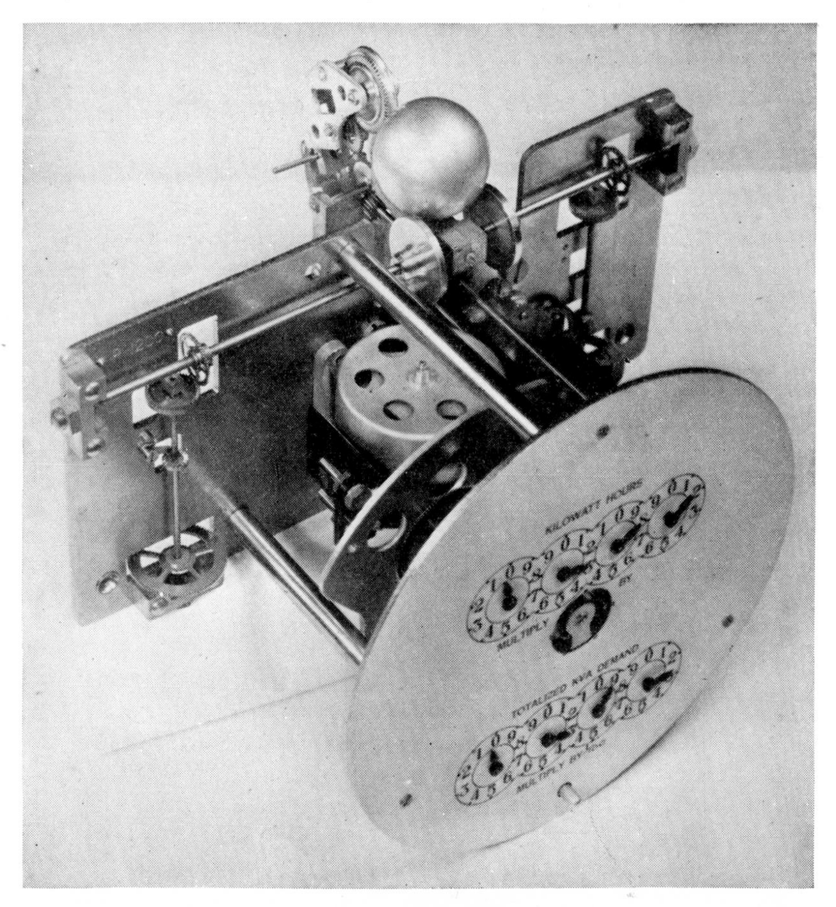

Fig. 1–19b. Detail of ball mechanism of kva meter. (Courtesy, Westinghouse Electric & Mfg. Co.)

Thus (as shown in Fig. 1–15a) the positive maximum of the instantaneous power shown by A is (see equation 1–22)

$$A = |V||I| \cos\theta + |V||I| = |V||I|\,(1 + \cos\theta) \qquad (1\text{–}36)$$

and the magnitude of the negative maximum B is

$$B = |V||I| - |V||I| \cos\theta = |V||I|\,(1 - \cos\theta) \qquad (1\text{–}37)$$

Combining these terms gives

$$P = |V||I| \cos\theta = \frac{A - B}{2} \qquad (1\text{–}38)$$

and

$$|Q| = |V||I| \sin|\theta| = \sqrt{(|V||I|)^2\,(1 - \cos^2\theta)} \qquad (1\text{–}39)$$
$$= \sqrt{AB}$$

1.8 The Energy Supplied to a Circuit by Out-of-Phase Sine Waves of Current and Voltage.

Because power expresses the rate of energy change at any instant,

$$p(t) = \frac{d}{dt} w(t)$$

it in no way represents the energy supplied or used over any period of time. The maximum power or minimum power, while a salient feature of any power expenditure, also does not characterize the power behavior

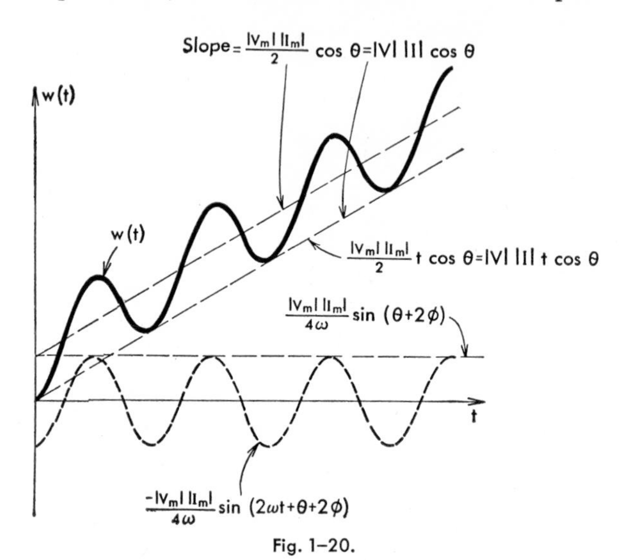

Fig. 1–20.

over any period of time. The average power does, in a sense, characterize the power behavior but only when associated with the time over which the average is computed. In the form of a product, the average power and time give the total energy expenditure, a quantity which is specific for any power variation and time. Accordingly, energy has been long established as one of the bases on which to judge the effectiveness of electrical systems. The energy generated, delivered, and lost is of prime importance in all such systems. Indeed, the energy delivered forms the basis of all financial transactions arising from supplying electricity to any kind of load, through a charge of so much per kilowatthour. The energy lost in a piece of apparatus determines how hot it will get and also determines the discrepancy between the input to the apparatus and its output, and so the efficiency. Innumerable other uses, many of which will appear subsequently, have been found for the energy concept so that energy forms another of the foundation stones of the electrical structure being built in this book.

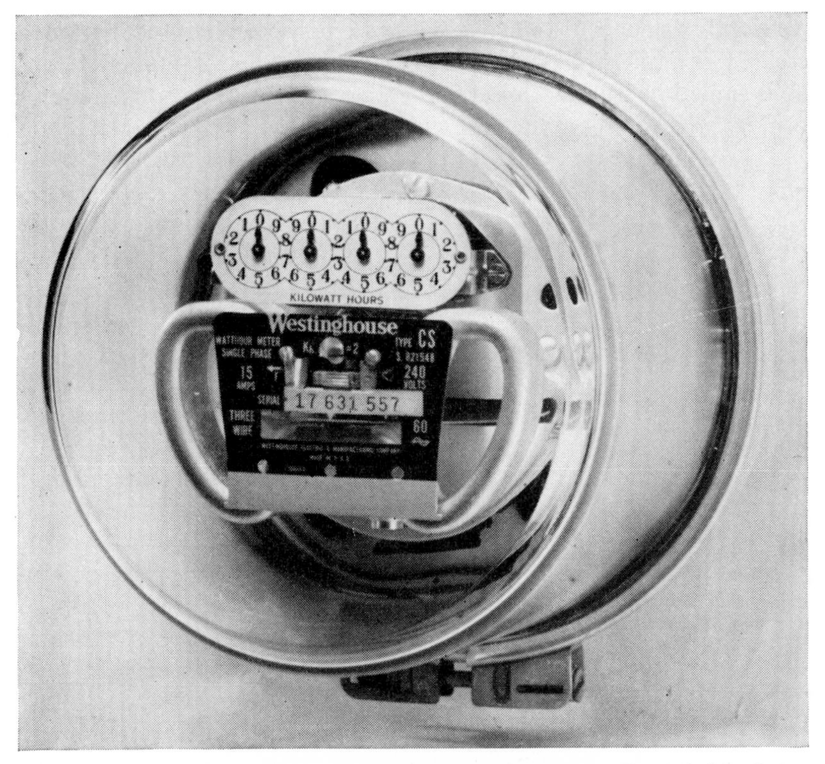

Fig. 1–21a. Single-phase watthour meter. (Courtesy, Westinghouse Electric & Mfg. Co.)

The general definition of the energy supplied to a circuit in t seconds is

$$w(t) = \int_0^t p(t)\, dt \text{ (watt-seconds)} \tag{1–40}$$

If the current and voltage are sinusoidal,

$$w(t) = \int_0^t |V_m| \sin(\omega t + \phi) |I_m| \sin(\omega t + \phi + \theta)\; dt$$

which from equation 1–21 becomes

$$w(t) = |V_m||I_m| \int_0^t \frac{\cos\theta - \cos(2\omega t + 2\phi + \theta)}{2}\, dt$$

Integrating gives

$$w(t) = \left[\frac{|V_m||I_m|}{2}\cos\theta\right] t - \frac{|V_m||I_m|}{4\omega}\left[\sin(2\omega t + 2\phi + \theta) - \sin(\theta + 2\phi)\right] \tag{1–41}$$

A sketch of this equation is shown in Fig. 1–20. Since the power equation is the slope of the energy curve, all regions of the energy curve which have *negative* slope correspond to negative power. Note that the energy increases with time and oscillates about a straight line of slope $|V||I|\cos\theta$.

It is probably true that electrical-energy-measuring meters are among the most widely used and most numerous meters. Every place in the country where electricity is used has at least one of these watthour meters. Illustrations of the small ones used to measure the electrical energy absorbed in a home are shown in Fig. 1–21. These meters are rugged and accurate, and it is on the basis of their indications that nearly all electrical energy is bought and sold.

Fig. 1–21b. Mounted single-phase watthour meter. (Courtesy, General Electric Co.)

The four fundamental concepts—current, voltage, power, and energy—which form the basis of all studies of electricity have now been formulated, and the relations of these concepts with each other have also been established. It can be said without qualification that, if the current, voltage, power, and energy relations of an electrical system of any kind are known, there is no need for further investigation of its electrical properties. All is known about them. All the discussion which follows will, therefore, be concerned with establishing various techniques and results that can be used to determine the current, voltage, power, and energy relations of electrical networks and machines.

1.9 The Addition and Subtraction of Sine Waves.

Some further definitions and defining processes have to be developed before the basic elements entering into the makeup of an electrical network are considered. Often in what follows these definitions will be purely mathematical and will themselves lead to no physical counterpart in a circuit, but they must be developed before a study of the interrelations of electrical quantities in a network is possible. The mathematical process of adding sine waves is an example.

Since it must be possible to add voltages and currents before Kirchhoff's laws can be applied, the sum and difference of sine waves must be developed. Consider two such currents expressed as

$$i_1(t) = |I_{m1}|\sin(\omega t + \phi_1)$$

and

$$i_2(t) = |I_{m2}|\sin(\omega t + \phi_2) \tag{1–42}$$

which are represented graphically in Fig. 1–22. Note that these sinusoids are of the *same* frequency and that their sum is *also a sine wave of the same frequency as each component.* Only waves of the same frequency will be considered until the Fourier series treatment is introduced in Chap. 6. The relation between the component sine waves and their sum may be deduced as follows. If, after being expanded, the equations given by 1–42 are added and some evident combinations made, the following equation results:

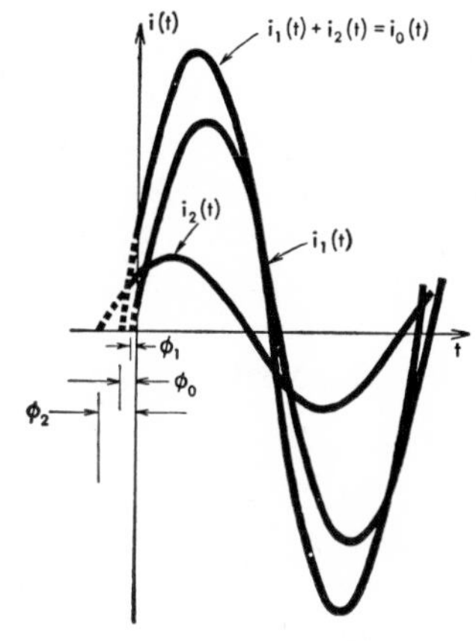

Fig. 1–22.

$$i_0(t) = i_1(t) + i_2(t) = [|I_{m1}| \cos \phi_1 + |I_{m2}| \cos \phi_2] \sin \omega t + [|I_{m1}| \sin \phi_1 + |I_{m2}| \sin \phi_2] \cos \omega t \qquad (1\text{–}43)$$

This sum of two sine waves is to be expressed in terms of a single sine wave, which according to Fig. 1–22 may be expressed as

$$i_0(t) = i_1(t) + i_2(t) = |I_{m0}| \sin (\omega t + \phi_0)$$

Expanding the sine in this equation gives

$$i_0(t) = [|I_{m0}| \cos \phi_0] \sin \omega t + [|I_{m0}| \sin \phi_0] \cos \omega t \qquad (1\text{–}44)$$

But if equations 1–43 and 1–44 are to represent the same sinusoid for all values of time, the coefficients of sin ωt and of cos ωt in these two equations must be equal:

$$|I_{m0}| \cos \phi_0 = |I_{m1}| \cos \phi_1 + |I_{m2}| \cos \phi_2$$

and $\qquad\qquad\qquad\qquad\qquad\qquad\qquad\qquad\qquad\qquad\qquad\qquad$ (1–45)

$$|I_{m0}| \sin \phi_0 = |I_{m1}| \sin \phi_1 + |I_{m2}| \sin \phi_2$$

From this pair of equations the two unknowns $|I_{m0}|$ and ϕ_0 may be found. Squaring equations 1–45, adding, and extracting the square root gives

$$\sqrt{[|I_{m0}| \cos \phi_0]^2 + [|I_{m0}| \sin \phi_0]^2} = \sqrt{[|I_{m1}| \cos \phi_1 + |I_{m2}| \cos \phi_2]^2 + [|I_{m1}| \sin \phi_1 + |I_{m2}| \sin \phi_2]^2}$$

or

$$|I_{m0}| = \sqrt{[|I_{m1}| \cos \phi_1 + |I_{m2}| \cos \phi_2]^2 + [|I_{m1}| \sin \phi_1 + |I_{m2}| \sin \phi_2]^2}$$

$$|I_{m0}| = \sqrt{|I_{m1}|^2 + |I_{m2}|^2 + 2|I_{m1}||I_{m2}| \cos (\phi_1 - \phi_2)} \qquad (1\text{–}46)$$

Furthermore, taking the ratio of the equations given in 1–45 gives

$$\frac{\sin \phi_0}{\cos \phi_0} = \tan \phi_0 = \frac{|I_{m1}| \sin \phi_1 + |I_{m2}| \sin \phi_2}{|I_{m1}| \cos \phi_1 + |I_{m2}| \cos \phi_2}$$

or

$$\phi_0 = \tan^{-1} \frac{|I_{m1}| \sin \phi_1 + |I_{m2}| \sin \phi_2}{|I_{m1}| \cos \phi_1 + |I_{m2}| \cos \phi_2} \qquad (1\text{–}47)$$

Equations 1–46 and 1–47 thus determine the maximum value and phase angle of the sine wave which is the sum of two sine waves.

The formulas for the maximum value and phase angle of the sine wave which is the sum of two other sine waves indicate that the sum of any two like frequency sine waves may be represented by a single sine wave of the same frequency. Note also that the sum of any number of like frequency sine waves is a sine wave, since they may be added two by two to produce one final wave.

These results, which are of very great importance, are considered and interpreted in detail in the next article.

1.10 The Vector Representation of a Sine Wave.

The reader may already have realized that representing alternating currents by sinusoids is likely to become cumbersome mathematically. Equations 1–46 and 1–47 point to this conclusion very strongly. A further simplification which has been one of the major steps forward in the study of electricity was discovered and developed near the beginning of the century. Vectors were used to represent sine waves. Just how this representation works will now be shown, and how it may be employed will be discussed and developed throughout the remainder of this book.

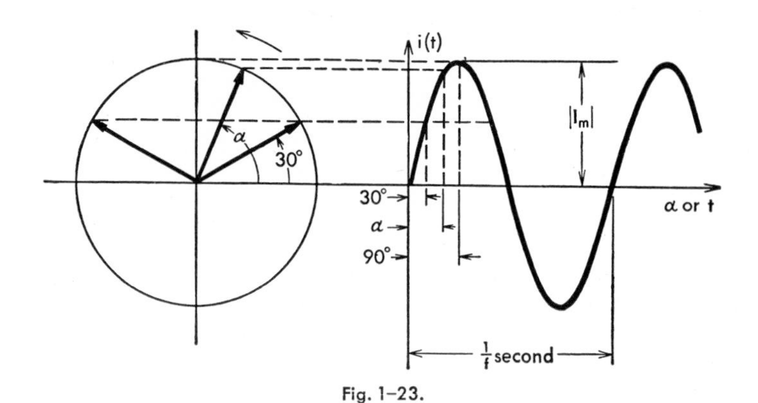

Fig. 1–23.

Consider Fig. 1–23. Imagine that a vector of length $|I_m|$ is rotated *counterclockwise* so that it makes a revolution in $1/f$ seconds. Imagine further that by some means the projection of this vector on the *ordinate*, or *current axis*, is made and plotted against the angle of the vector, or the time taken for the vector to move from some reference position—the horizontal for Fig. 1–23. The result of this plotting is a sine wave of maximum value $|I_m|$. Furthermore (Fig. 1–24), if the reference or starting time ($t = 0$) is taken with the vector in some position other than the horizontal, the sine wave given by the vertical component of the vector, plotted against the angle from the starting position, is a general one of the type considered above, i.e.,

$$i(t) = |I_m| \sin (\omega t + \phi)$$

The virtues of the vector representation become apparent at once. The vector gives very simply, in *pictorial* form, two of the three numbers characteristic of a sine wave which are required to specify the wave,

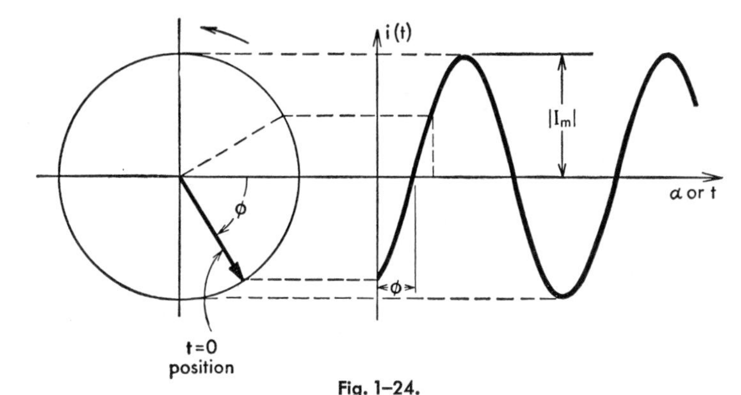

Fig. 1–24.

namely, the phase angle ϕ and the maximum value of the sinusoid. Therefore, *the vector alone may be used to represent the sine wave, but for* ω. Thus the vector in Fig. 1–25 represents a sine wave of maximum value $|I_m|$ with a phase angle of ϕ degrees for any value of ω.

In order for a vector diagram to represent a sine wave, the particular instant which the vector diagram represents *must be given or understood through convention. By common consent it has been agreed that all stationary vector diagrams represent the* $t = 0$ *instant.* Thus from its vector representation the sine wave is completely determined, and may be plotted, or its equation written. Of course, a vector in any particular position represents only the instantaneous $t = 0$ value of the sinusoid and *not* the *whole* wave, as is evident from Figs. 1–23 and 1–24. However, it is easy to determine the whole sine wave graphically or to write its equation from the vector; and there is little doubt that the vector representation is very much simpler.

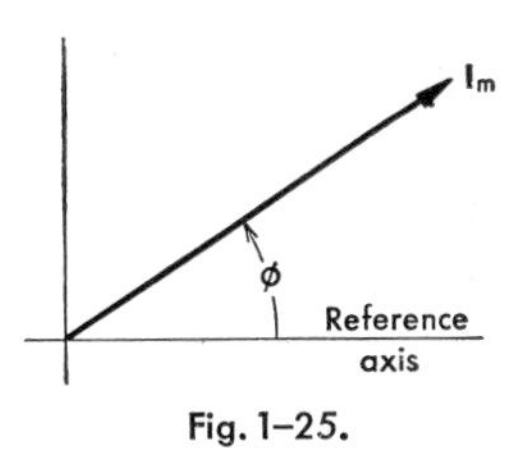

Fig. 1–25.

The simplicity of the vector representation of a sine wave alone would not justify further consideration of the representation were it not for the fact that *the vectors representing sine waves may be added to give a vector which represents the sum of the sine waves.* The vector representation thereby becomes of truly outstanding importance. Evidence of this fact will accumulate throughout the book, but even now the reader can no doubt realize that, because of Kirchhoff's current and voltage laws, the addition and subtraction of currents and voltages—sine waves or their vector representatives—are likely to play a principal role in the study of electric circuits.

Proof of the vector sum and sine wave sum relation may be derived from Fig. 1–26 which shows two vectors and their sum in correspondence with the sine waves of Fig. 1–22. By the cosine law of trigonometry,

$$|I_{m0}| = \sqrt{|I_{m1}|^2 + |I_{m2}|^2 + 2|I_{m1}||I_{m2}| \cos (\phi_2 - \phi_1)} \qquad (1\text{–}48)$$

which is exactly equation 1–46 for the maximum value of the sum of two sine waves, except that $\cos (\phi_2 - \phi_1)$ appears in 1–48 instead of

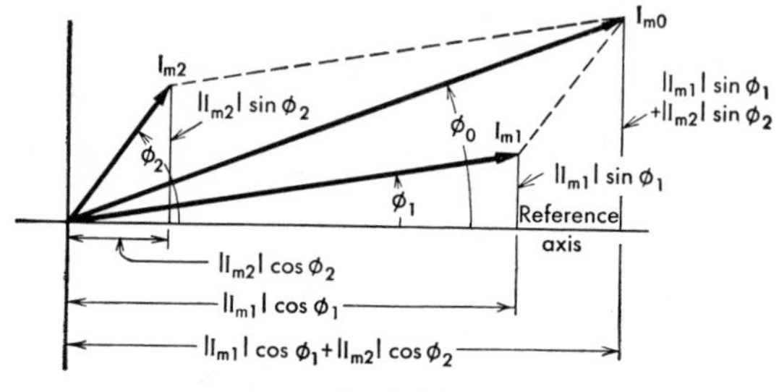

Fig. 1–26.

$\cos (\phi_1 - \phi_2)$ as in equation 1–46. This reversal, however, does not affect the result since $\cos \phi = \cos (-\phi)$. Next consider ϕ_0 in Fig. 1–26. Writing the value of the tangent of ϕ_0 from the figure gives

$$\tan \phi_0 = \frac{|I_{m1}| \sin \phi_1 + |I_{m2}| \sin \phi_2}{|I_{m1}| \cos \phi_1 + |I_{m2}| \cos \phi_2} \qquad (1\text{–}49)$$

which is exactly the equation from which 1–47 was derived. Evidently, therefore, adding either the sine waves or their vector representatives leads to a sine wave, or vector, of the same maximum value, or length, and of the same phase angle.

In a similar manner the equivalence of the *subtraction* of sine waves and of their vector representatives can be shown by actually carrying out the two subtractions and comparing the results. Thus vectors can be used to represent sine waves, and the sum or difference of the vectors gives the vector representation of the sum or difference of the sine waves.

The vector representation of a sine wave, even though affording a marked simplification in pictorial representation over a sinusoid, still requires a graphical treatment or some other method of adding and subtracting vectors. The next great stride was taken when the concept of complex numbers was taken from pure mathematics and applied to the vector representations of sine waves and hence to the solutions of the problems of alternating currents. In the next chapter the complex number representation of a vector will be introduced in order that the reader may have at hand the most effective technique known at present for the solution of a-c circuits.

An important special, and often useful, case of the results given in equations 1–48 and 1–49 arises from adding the vectors representing a *sine* wave and a *cosine* wave. Such a pair of vectors and their sine and

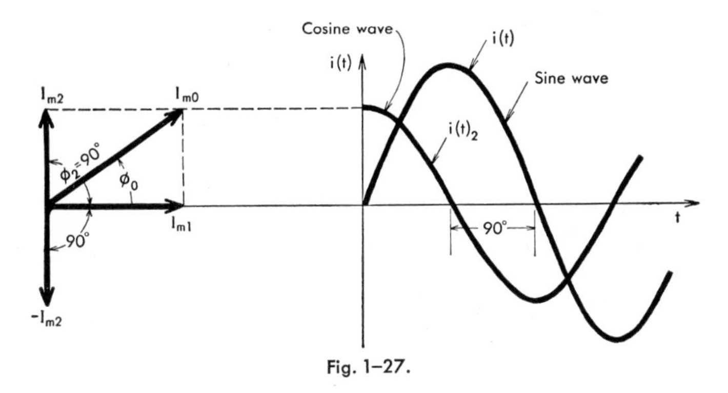

Fig. 1–27.

cosine wave equivalents are shown in Fig. 1–27. Since ϕ_1 is zero and ϕ_2 is 90 degrees, equation 1–48 for the maximum value of the sum of I_{m1} and I_{m2} becomes

$$|I_{m0}| = \sqrt{|I_{m1}|^2 + |I_{m2}|^2} \tag{1–50}$$

and equation 1–49 becomes

$$\tan \phi_0 = \frac{|I_{m2}|}{|I_{m1}|} \tag{1–51}$$

If I_{m1} and $-I_{m2}$ are added, the result is

$$|I_{m0}| = \sqrt{|I_{m1}|^2 + |I_{m2}|^2} \tag{1–52}$$

$$\tan \phi_0 = \frac{-|I_{m2}|}{|I_{m1}|} \tag{1–53}$$

These useful relations for vectors at right angles—sine and cosine waves—are much simpler than the general relations.

In the usage of vectors to represent sine waves, it is common practice for the vectors to have a length $|I_m|/\sqrt{2}$ rather than $|I_m|$. The reason for this custom is apparent on recalling that the characteristic number (rms value) of a sinusoid is $|I_m|/\sqrt{2}$ and that the rms value is indicated by an ammeter. By reducing the vector length by $1/\sqrt{2}$, ammeter and voltmeter indications may be represented directly by vector lengths.

Another fact which should be noted at this point is that the *horizontal component* of a vector may also be used to represent a sine wave. Certainly the projection of a rotating vector onto the horizontal varies sinusoidally as does the vertical projection. Which projection is to be used is entirely a matter of personal choice. In all that follows in this book the vertical component of the rotating vector will be used to represent the sine wave.

Example 1:3 An ammeter indicates a current of 10 amps flowing through a circuit element, and a voltmeter placed across this element indicates 100 volts. An oscillographic view of the current and voltage shows sinusoidal variation with a phase angle of 30 degrees between the current and voltage waves with the voltage positive maximum occurring before the corresponding current maximum. From this information determine the following: (1) $|I_m|$, $|V_m|$; (2) $|U|$, P, Q; (3) power factor, reactive factor; (4) $i(t)$, $v(t)$; (5) $p(t)$, energy absorbed by the circuit element in one cycle of the voltage measured from the point where the voltage is zero and increasing; (6) the two right-angle components of the current and voltage vectors and the angle between these vectors; (7) the actual current and voltage in the circuit at $t = 0$ if curve a of Fig. 1–10 represents the voltage and curve b represents the current with the ϕ of the voltage curve equal to 15 degrees.

Solution (1) Since the ammeter and voltmeter indicate rms values,

$$|I_m| = 10\sqrt{2} = 14.14 \text{ amp}$$
$$|V_m| = 100\sqrt{2} = 141.4 \text{ volts}$$

(2) The apparent power is

$$|U| = |V||I| = 100 \cdot 10 = 1000 \text{ va}$$

The average power is

$$P = |V||I| \cos \theta$$

The power factor angle θ is the angle between the current and voltage sinusoids and is considered *negative if the current maximum occurs later than the voltage maximum*, so

$$P = 100 \times 10 \times \cos(-30°) = 1000 \frac{\sqrt{3}}{2}$$
$$= 866 \text{ watts}$$

The reactive volt-amperes are

$$Q = |V||I| \sin \theta = 100 \times 10 \times \sin(-30°)$$
$$= -500$$

(3) The power factor is

$$\cos \theta = \cos(-30°) = 0.866$$

and the reactive factor is

$$\sin \theta = \sin(-30°) = -0.5$$

(4) The instantaneous current is

$$i(t) = |I_m| \sin (\omega t + \phi_i)$$

where ϕ_i is the angle between the $t = 0$ point and the nearest current zero at which the current is increasing; or $\phi_i = -15$ degrees if the current and voltage are located on the axis as stated in part 7 of this problem. Then

$$i(t) = 14.14 \sin (\omega t - 15°)$$

Note that the $t = 0$ point is actually entirely arbitrary and is located as in the foregoing as a matter of convenience in solving part 7.

The instantaneous voltage equation is

$$\begin{aligned} v(t) &= |V_m| \sin (\omega t + \phi_v) \\ &= 141.4 \sin (\omega t + 15°) \end{aligned}$$

(5) The instantaneous power equation is

$$p(t) = v(t)\, i(t)$$

and from equation 1–22

$$\begin{aligned} p(t) &= \frac{141.4 \times 14.14}{2} \cos (-30°) - \frac{141.4 \times 14.14}{2} \cos 2\omega t \\ &= 866 - 1000 \cos 2\omega t \end{aligned}$$

The energy supplied in one cycle of the voltage from onc zero and increasing value to the next one is (see Fig. 1–10 to determine the limits of integration, say, from point c to a point *one* cycle later)

$$\begin{aligned} w &= \int_{23/24f}^{47/24f} 141.4 \sin (\omega t + 15°) 14.14 \sin (\omega t - 15°)\, dt \\ &= 2000 \int_{23/24f}^{47/24f} \frac{\cos 30° - \cos 2\omega t}{2}\, dt \\ &= 1000 \left[\frac{\sqrt{3}}{2} t - \frac{\sin 2\omega t}{2\omega} \right]_{23/24f}^{47/24f} \\ &= 1000 \left[\frac{\sqrt{3}}{2} \left(\frac{47}{24f} - \frac{23}{24f} \right) - \frac{\sin \frac{47\pi}{6} - \sin \frac{23\pi}{6}}{2\omega} \right] \\ &= 1000 \left[\frac{\sqrt{3}}{2f} - \frac{\sin 1410° - \sin 690°}{2\omega} \right] \\ w &= \frac{866}{f} \text{ watt-seconds} \end{aligned}$$

(6) The two components of the current vector are:

$$\begin{aligned} \text{horizontal component} &= 14.14 \cos (-15°) = 13.66 \\ \text{vertical component} &= 14.14 \sin (-15°) = -3.66 \end{aligned}$$

The two components of the voltage vector are:

$$\begin{aligned} \text{horizontal component} &= 141.4 \cos 15° = 136.6 \\ \text{vertical component} &= 141.4 \sin 15° = 36.6 \end{aligned}$$

The angle between the current and voltage vectors is, of course, 30 degrees.
(7) The actual current and voltage in the circuit may be computed from $i(t)$ and $v(t)$ for $t = 0$. Thus

$$i(0) = 14.14 \sin(-15°) = -3.66 \text{ amp}$$
$$v(0) = 141.4 \sin 15° = 36.6 \text{ volts}$$

These results are also given by the *vertical* components of the corresponding vectors.

PROBLEMS

1–1 Plot sine waves of current from equation 1–1 for $\omega = \frac{1}{2}$ and $\omega = 2$. What is the time required for a cycle in each case? How fast must an a-c generator, with four poles alternately north and south, rotate to produce such currents?

1–2 Sketch a 60-cps, a 25-cps, and a 180-cps sine wave on the same plot. Plot the waves in terms of seconds, degrees, and radians. What length of time in seconds is required for each to complete a cycle? What is the rotation speed of a 6-pole generator in each case?

1–3 Sketch the sine waves represented by equation 1–4 for $\phi = 45°$, $-75°$, $220°$, and $-270°$. Formulate a rule for quickly determining the proper position in which to sketch a sine wave from its general equation 1–4.

1–4 Determine the effective and average values of the currents shown in Fig. 1–16.

1–5 (*a*) Determine the effective value of the alternating current represented by Fig. 1–28. (*b*) Determine the average value of one-half cycle.

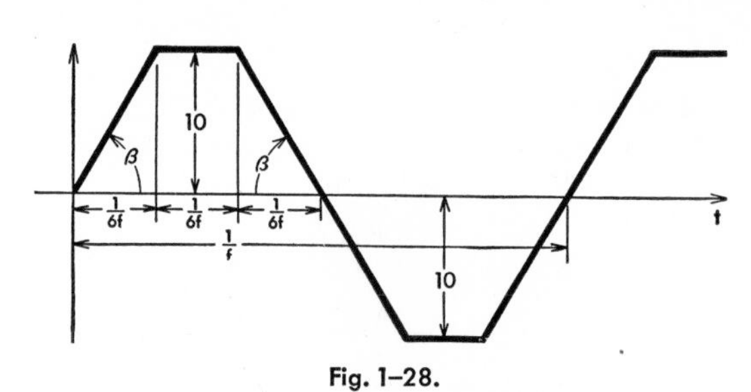

Fig. 1–28.

1–6 The current in an arc lamp may be represented by

$$i(t) = 25 \sin 377t - 10 \sin 1131t \text{ (amperes)}$$

if the sine wave of voltage across the lamp is

$$v(t) = 20 \sin 377t \text{ (volts)}$$

Determine the effective value of the current. Note that the voltage frequency is 60 cps as is one current component; hence use $f = 60$.

1–7 Change the variable of equation 1–13 from t to α ($\alpha = \omega t$). Then carry out the integration and check against equation 1–11. The limits of integration will change to 0 and 2π.

1–8 (*a*) Derive the result of equation 1–16 by changing the variable to $\alpha(\alpha = \omega t)$ and integrating. (*b*) Use equation 1–15 to determine the average of a half cycle of Fig. 1–16*a* and Fig. 1–28.

1–9 (*a*) Determine the average power represented by the current and voltage waves as shown in Fig. 1–17. (*b*) What are the volt-amperes represented by this combination? (*c*) What is the power factor?

1–10 Prove that the relation given by equation 1–21 is correct.

1–11 A 3-hp, single-phase motor of 80 per cent efficiency is driving a fan and operating on a 60 cps sinusoidal voltage of 150 volts maximum value. The input current, of sinusoidal variation, has a maximum value of 15 amp. An oscillograph shows that the positive maximum value of voltage occurs 1/720 sec before the positive maximum current value. What is the power factor? What is the reactive factor? What is the apparent power? Write the instantaneous equations for current and voltage if $t = 0$ when $v(t) = 0$ and increasing. What is the average power taken by the motor? What are the reactive volt-amperes in vars? At what percentage of full load is it operating?

1–12 A system of communication known as carrier current is in common use in power companies. In this system the energy is delivered from a telephone or telegraph transmitter to an antenna, just as in radio, but the antenna instead of sticking up into the sky is hung parallel to the power transmission line for a short distance. The power line *carries* the *carrier* impulses—high-frequency impulse modified (modulated) by the voice or telegraph impulses—to the telephone or telegraph instrument at the far end of the power line.

A particular carrier system delivers the following 100,000 cps current and voltage to its antenna when no signal is modulating the carrier frequency voltage:

$$i(t) = 250 \sin \omega t \text{ (milliamperes)}$$
$$v(t) = 80 \sin (\omega t - 10°) \text{ (volts)}$$

What is the power in watts delivered to the antenna? What is the power factor? Sketch the current and voltage waves and the instantaneous power wave. Show the power wave offset axis. What are $|V|$ and $|I|$?

1–13 Sketch carefully, assuming a maximum value of current of 10 amp and voltage of 100 volts, the current, voltage, power, and energy-supplied waves for $\theta = 0°, -30°, 90°$. Discuss each case, pointing out the characteristics of the energy curve.

1–14 A certain 50-kw radio station operates on 1000 kilocycles per second (kcps). The unmodulated current and voltage at the antenna input are

$$i(t) = 22 \sin (\omega t - 30°) \text{ amperes}$$
$$v(t) = 6200 \sin (\omega t - 35°) \text{ volts}$$

in the pause between program and commercial announcement. (*a*) Sketch the current wave, voltage wave, power variation, and energy-supplied variation. (*b*) What is P, power factor, reactive factor, and how much out-of-phase are the current and voltage? (*c*) What is the total energy supplied to the circuit in 1 min from $t = 0$?

1–15 Show that equation 1–46 comes directly from the equation preceding it. What is the difference between this expression and the cosine law as ordinarily expressed?

1–16 Determine the equation for the resultant sinusoid which is the difference between two sine waves. Show that the difference of two vectors representing the sine waves gives the maximum value and phase angle of the difference of the sine waves.

1–17 Three wires of an electric circuit join at a common point. Ammeters placed in two of these wires indicate $|I_1| = 10$ and $|I_2| = 20$ effective amperes. An oscillograph connected in these same lines indicates that the currents are practically sinusoidal and of the same frequency (60 cps) and that their maximum values are 1/200 sec apart with $|I_{m1}|$ occurring before $|I_{m2}|$. Corresponding terminals on the oscillograph are connected nearest the junction of the wires. Write the instantaneous equations for these two currents, assuming that $t = 0$, 30 degrees after $i_1(t)$ is zero and increasing positively. Add the two currents mathematically (not their vector representatives). What is the sine wave equation of the sum? Sketch the two given currents and their sum. This sum is the current in the third wire. Compare the maximum value of the resultant current with the given currents.

1–18 Draw a vector diagram of the currents of Problem 1–17. Add the vectors to get the maximum value of the sum and determine the phase angle of the resultant sinusoid. Add vectorially a third sine wave

$$i_3(t) = 20 \sin (\omega t - 90°) \text{ amperes}$$

and determine the maximum value and phase angle of the resultant sine wave.

1–19 The voltages across two adjacent elements of a circuit were measured with a vacuum tube voltmeter and found to be 250 and 100 (rms) volts, and a cathode ray oscilloscope showed practically sinusoidal variation of the voltages. A frequency meter indicates 1000 cps. The sum of these two voltages as measured with the vacuum tube voltmeter is 150 volts. If the $t = 0$ point is chosen as coinciding with the zero and negatively increasing instantaneous value of the 250-volt wave, write the equations for the three voltages showing the proper value of ω, ϕ, and $|V_m|$.

A power factor meter—a device used to measure the phase angle between a current and voltage—indicates that the current through the 250-volt circuit element is lagging with respect to this voltage at a power factor of 0.8, i.e., the current maximum occurs later than the voltage maximum. Determine the angle of this current with respect to the other voltages and determine the power represented by this current of rms value 10 amp and each voltage. Use vectors to solve this problem.

1–20 Given three vector representations of currents. These vectors are

	Horizontal Component (amperes)	Vertical Component (amperes)
I_1	10	40
I_2	20	20
I_3	−7	8

Write the sine wave equation for each of the currents and for the sum of all three currents.

1–21 Suppose that the reference axis is changed −30° from the one in Problem 1–20. Give the horizontal and vertical components of each vector and write the equations for each current and the sum.

1–22 Subtract currents I_2 and I_3 from I_1 of Problem 1–20 and write the equation for the resultant sine wave.

1–23 The dial indications of a kw hour and reactive kva-hour meter installed at a factory are, at the first of July: kw hours 7200 and kva-hours reactive 6425. At the first of August these dials indicate, in the same order, 8248 and 7820. On the dials appears the instruction "multiply by 10." What are the average $|U|$, P, and Q if the factory has operated 22 days of 8 hours each? What is the average power factor? What did the energy cost the factory operator if the power company sells it to him for 2 cents per kwhr plus 0.1 cent per kwhr additional for each per cent that the power factor is less than 85 per cent? The system operates at 2300 volts from a bank of transformers connected to a 4000-volt line.

1–24 An ammeter and voltmeter, placed respectively in and across the input lines to a small motor driving a refrigerator, indicate 20 amp and 200 volts. An indicating wattmeter shows 3.2 kw being absorbed by the motor. Motors of the type used to drive refrigerators always operate with the current wave lagging the voltage wave; current positive maximum occurs later than the positive maximum of the voltage. Since the motor is operating from a large power system it is safe to assume sinusoidal variation of current and voltage. The reference point ($t = 0$) is to be taken at a positive maximum of the voltage. Determine the following: $|V_m|$, $|I_m|$, $|U|$, Q, power factor, reactive factor, $p(t)$, energy supplied in kilowatthours to the motor in a 5-min operating period, the two components of the current and voltage vectors, and the actual current and voltage in the circuit at this $t = 0$ instant.

1–25 The mathematical definition of an effective a-c ampere as given in Art. 1–3 postulates that each cycle of the wave form is just like every other cycle. Suppose instead that the alternating current decreases to zero, so that, for $t = 1$ to ∞,

$$i(t) = \frac{10 \sin \omega t}{t} \text{ (amperes)}$$

An ammeter placed in this circuit will show a decreasing effective value of current. Why? Endeavor to show this result mathematically, or at least state how the problem should be approached and what factors should be taken into account. Compare your conclusions with the definition given in the Appendix to the A.I.E.E. Standards on Oil Circuit Breakers. What is the value of the effective current at each instant?

1–26 Consider the three sinusoidal voltage waves

$$\begin{aligned} v_1(t) &= 100 \sin \omega t \\ v_2(t) &= -50 \cos \omega t \\ v_3(t) &= -25 \sin \omega t \end{aligned}$$

Add these waves vectorially and write the sine wave equation for the results according to the following schedule:

$$\begin{aligned} v_1(t) + v_2(t) &= ? \\ v_2(t) + v_3(t) &= ? \\ v_1(t) + v_3(t) &= ? \\ -v_1(t) + v_2(t) &= ? \\ -v_1(t) - v_2(t) &= ? \end{aligned}$$

CHAPTER 2

Algebra of Complex Numbers

This chapter is devoted to the development of the complex number representation of vectors and of the processes using complex numbers which will be needed in later work. The reader's attention should be on the mathematical processes rather than on possible applications, since the application of complex numbers will be treated in considerable detail throughout the remainder of the text in terms of the material presented in this chapter.

Throughout this book unbarred symbols, such as I_m and I, represent vectors, and barred symbols, such as $|I_m|$ and $|I|$, represent magnitudes.

2.1 The Representation of Vectors by Complex Numbers.

Consider the vector I_m shown in Fig. 2–1. In terms of complex numbers the representation of this vector is

$$I_m = i_m + ji_m' \tag{2–1}$$

where the j, or j-operator, as it is called, is simply an indicator showing that the value i_m' is the *vertical* component of the vector.

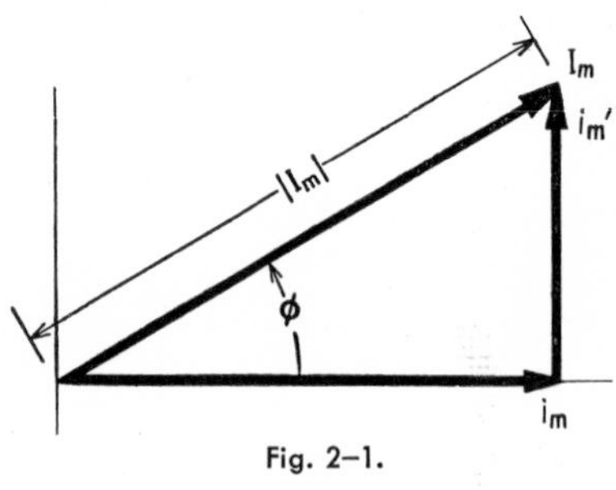

Fig. 2–1.

The j-operator may also be interpreted in another fashion. If the two vector components i_m and i_m' of Fig. 2–1 are themselves considered as vectors along the horizontal, the j-operator may be considered as the operator which, applied to a vector, rotates it through 90 degrees *counterclockwise*. Thus the component, i_m, without the j in front of it, is plotted along the horizontal, and the j indicates that i_m' is rotated through 90 degrees, or is to be plotted on the vertical. Extending this idea, the j-operator applied twice turns a vector through 180 degrees or simply reverses it; and applying the j-operator three times rotates the vector 270 degrees, etc. (see Fig. 2–2). These results may be written as

$$\begin{aligned} j^2 &= -1 \\ j^3 &= -j \\ j^4 &= 1 \\ j^5 &= j \\ &\cdots\cdots \\ j^{2n} &= (-1)^n \\ j^{2n+1} &= (-1)^n j \end{aligned} \qquad (2\text{–}2)$$

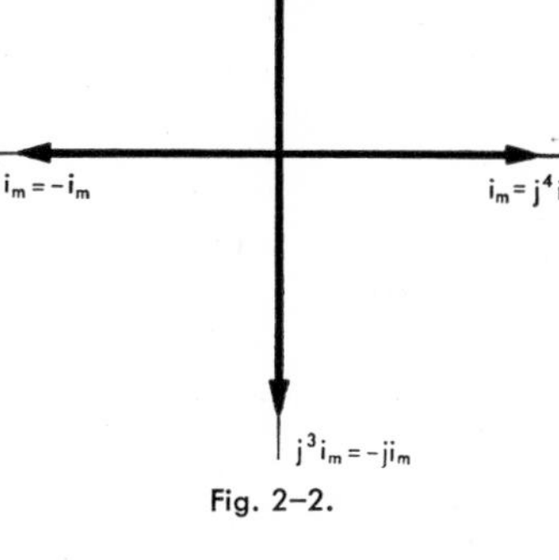

Fig. 2–2.

These relations form the basis of complex number algebra or of the two-dimensional vector algebra used by electrical engineers, and are used frequently for practically all a-c work.

Because the components of a vector when expressed in j-operator form are *always* right-angle components, certain relations can be established between the components $|I_m|$ and ϕ of Fig. 2–1. From this figure

$$i_m = |I_m| \cos \phi \qquad (2\text{–}3)$$

and

$$i_m' = |I_m| \sin \phi \qquad (2\text{–}4)$$

and equation 2–1 becomes

$$I_m = |I_m|(\cos \phi + j \sin \phi) \qquad (2\text{–}5)$$

Still another form of this equation can be developed by considering the trigonometric terms of the equation in more detail. First, the infinite series representations of the trigonometric terms of this last equation are

$$\cos \phi = 1 - \frac{\phi^2}{2!} + \frac{\phi^4}{4!} - \frac{\phi^6}{6!} + \cdots \qquad (2\text{–}6)$$

$$\sin \phi = \phi - \frac{\phi^3}{3!} + \frac{\phi^5}{5!} - \frac{\phi^7}{7!} + \cdots \qquad (2\text{–}7)$$

If equation 2–7 is multiplied by j,

$$j \sin \phi = j\phi - \frac{j\phi^3}{3!} + \frac{j\phi^5}{5!} - \frac{j\phi^7}{7!} + \cdots \qquad (2\text{–}8)$$

but from the relations given by 2–2 this equation may be written as

$$j \sin \phi = j\phi + \frac{(j\phi)^3}{3!} + \frac{(j\phi)^5}{5!} + \frac{(j\phi)^7}{7!} + \cdots \qquad (2\text{–}9)$$

Also $\cos \phi$ may be written from 2–6 and 2–2 as

$$\cos \phi = 1 + \frac{(j\phi)^2}{2!} + \frac{(j\phi)^4}{4!} + \frac{(j\phi)^6}{6!} + \cdots \qquad (2\text{–}10)$$

Then, since the series expansion of an exponential is

$$\epsilon^{j\phi} = 1 + (j\phi) + \frac{(j\phi)^2}{2!} + \frac{(j\phi)^3}{3!} + \frac{(j\phi)^4}{4!} + \cdots \quad (2\text{–}11)$$

the sum of equations 2–9 and 2–10 is exactly equation 2–11. Hence

$$\cos\phi + j\sin\phi = \epsilon^{j\phi} \quad (2\text{–}12)$$

This relation in a more general form, which the reader should develop for practice, is known as Euler's equation and is given in mathematics textbooks as

$$\cos n\phi \pm j\sin n\phi = \epsilon^{\pm jn\phi} \qquad (n = 1, 2, 3, \cdots) \quad (2\text{–}13)$$

Note particularly that the sign preceding the $j \sin \phi$ term and the $j\phi$ term of the exponential is the same.

Equation 2–1 may now be written in the three following equivalent and *very important* forms:

$$I_m = i_m \pm ji_m' = |I_m|(\cos\phi \pm j\sin\phi) = |I_m|\epsilon^{\pm j\phi} \quad (2\text{–}14)$$

The six factors in these equivalent expressions are, of course, related as can be verified by merely examining Fig. 2–1. Thus

$$\begin{aligned} |I_m| &= \sqrt{i_m^2 + i_m'^2} \\ \cos\phi &= \frac{i_m}{|I_m|} \\ \sin\phi &= \frac{i_m'}{|I_m|} \\ \phi &= \tan^{-1}\frac{i_m'}{i_m} \\ i_m &= |I_m|\cos\phi \\ i_m' &= |I_m|\sin\phi \end{aligned} \quad (2\text{–}15)$$

2.2 The Sum or Difference of Two Complex Numbers.

The sum or difference of two vectors is very easily determined by using the complex number representation of these vectors. From the sum or difference of two vectors A and B, by the parallelogram law (Fig. 2–3) it follows that

$$A \pm B = (a \pm b) + j(a' \pm b')$$

where j is inserted in accordance with the convention of complex algebra to show which term is to be plotted on the vertical. If A and B are considered in their complex number form, evidently

$$A \pm B = (a + ja') \pm (b + jb') = (a \pm b) + j(a' \pm b') \quad (2\text{–}16)$$

i.e., addition or subtraction is carried out by adding or subtracting the horizontal and vertical components separately.

Note that there is no way of adding vectors directly if they are expressed in the *exponential* form of 2–14.

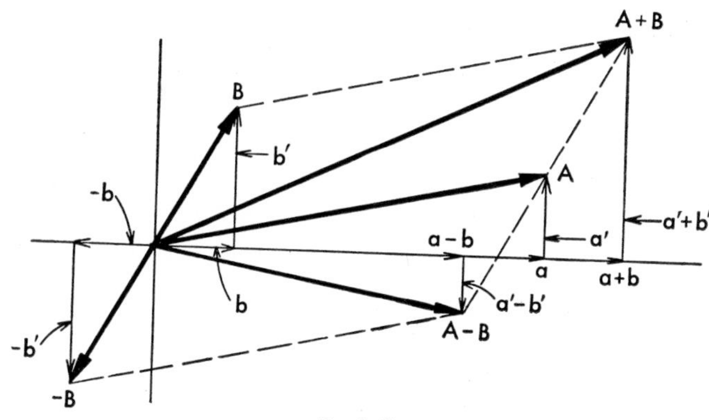

Fig. 2–3.

2.3 The Product of Complex Numbers.

The rectangular form of the product will be considered first. Thus the product

$$BA = AB = (a_1 + ja_2)(b_1 + jb_2) = (b_1 + jb_2)(a_1 + ja_2)$$

gives, by definition,

$$\begin{array}{l} \quad a_1 + ja_2 \\ \quad b_1 + jb_2 \\ \hline a_1b_1 + ja_2b_1 \\ \qquad\quad ja_1b_2 + j^2a_2b_2 \\ \hline a_1b_1 + j(a_2b_1 + a_1b_2) + j^2a_2b_2 \end{array}$$

But from equations 2–2, $j^2 = -1$. Hence

$$AB = (a_1 + ja_2)(b_1 + jb_2) = (a_1b_1 - a_2b_2) + j(a_2b_1 + a_1b_2) \qquad (2\text{–}17)$$

The method of carrying out complex number multiplication is straightforward, but the meaning of the result is not very evident from this equation. However, the use of the exponential form of A and B shows the meaning of the product $AB = BA$ by inspection. Thus, if in exponential form,

$$A = a_1 + ja_2 = \sqrt{a_1^2 + a_2^2}\epsilon^{j\alpha} = |A|\epsilon^{j\alpha} \qquad \alpha = \tan^{-1}\frac{a_2}{a_1}$$

$$B = b_1 + jb_2 = \sqrt{b_1^2 + b_2^2}\epsilon^{j\beta} = |B|\epsilon^{j\beta} \qquad \beta = \tan^{-1}\frac{b_2}{b_1}$$

then

$$AB = |A|\epsilon^{j\alpha}|B|\epsilon^{j\beta} = |A||B|\epsilon^{j\alpha}\epsilon^{j\beta} = |A||B|\epsilon^{j(\alpha+\beta)} \qquad (2\text{–}18)$$

Note that the ordinary rules for multiplication of exponentials is used. Also note how much simpler the exponential form makes the process of multiplication. The meaning of the product of two complex numbers is now easily seen. This product is simply another complex number (see Fig. 2–4), the magnitude of which is the product or the magnitudes of the factors and the angle of which is the sum of the angles of the factors. Or, if the product is looked at from the operator viewpoint, multiplying the vector, or complex number, A by the complex number B gives a vector representing a complex number $C = AB$, $|B|$ times as long as A and shifted through β degrees from its original position. If $\beta < 0$, the product vector is shifted clockwise, and if $\beta > 0$, it is shifted counterclockwise.

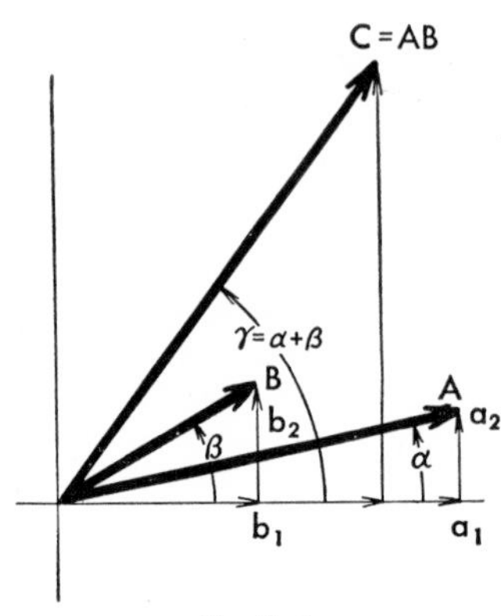

Fig. 2–4.

The equivalence of the two different expressions for the product of two complex numbers given in equations 2–17 and 2–18 may be shown in the following way. If the exponential of equation 2–18 is expressed in the form given by equation 2–12,

$$AB = |A|\,|B|[\cos(\alpha + \beta) + j \sin(\alpha + \beta)]$$

expanding the sine and cosine gives

$$AB = |A|\,|B|[\cos\alpha \cos\beta - \sin\alpha \sin\beta + j(\sin\alpha \cos\beta + \cos\alpha \sin\beta)]$$

and, on rearrangement, this expression becomes

$$AB = [|A| \cos\alpha |B| \cos\beta - |A| \sin\alpha |B| \sin\beta] + j[|A| \sin\alpha |B| \cos\beta + |A| \cos\alpha |B| \sin\beta]$$

If the values of the components a_1, a_2, b_1, and b_2 in terms of vector lengths and angles are noted (see Fig. 2–3), this last equation is

$$AB = a_1b_1 - a_2b_2 + j(a_2b_1 + a_1b_2)$$

which is exactly equation 2–17. Therefore, the products defined in equations 2–17 and 2–18 are equivalent.

Of particular interest is the operator

$$\cos\phi \pm j \sin\phi = \epsilon^{\pm j\phi} \tag{2–19}$$

This multiplying operator is a *unit* operator and $\epsilon^{j\phi}$ changes the *position* of a vector by ϕ degrees (clockwise for $\phi < 0$, counterclockwise for $\phi > 0$) but *does not change its magnitude.*

2.4 Complex Number Conjugate.

The conjugate of a complex number is frequently useful in complex algebra. If a complex number is represented by $B = b + jb'$, its conjugate $\hat{B}$ is

$$\text{B} = b - jb' = |B|\epsilon^{-j\beta} \tag{2-20}$$

Thus the conjugate of a complex number differs from the complex number only in this sign before the j in either rectangular or exponential form.

2.5 The Division and Reciprocal of Complex Numbers.

The ratio of two complex numbers in rectangular form is symbolically

$$\frac{A}{B} = \frac{a_1 + ja_2}{b_1 + jb_2} \tag{2-21}$$

On the supposition that one knew how, dividing as indicated would usually leave a remainder. But such a remainder cannot be interpreted since it is not expressed in terms of components at right angles. Suppose, though, some device is employed to remove the j-operator from the denominator. The result, with a j-operator in the numerator only, can be expressed with the aid of relations 2–2 as two component vectors at right angles and can be represented by a vector which is easily interpreted. An effective method of carrying out the division of equation 2–21 would, therefore, seem to be based on the elimination of the j from the denominator. To this end, note that, the j-operator disappears from the product if the angles given in equation 2–18 are equal and opposite in sign since $\epsilon^{j0} = 1 + j0$. Therefore, if B of equation 2–21 is multiplied by its conjugate, the result is

$$B\hat{B} = (b_1 + jb_2)(b_1 - jb_2) = b_1^2 + b_2^2 = |B|^2$$

or

$$B\hat{B} = |B|\epsilon^{j\beta}|B|\epsilon^{-j\beta} = |B|^2 \tag{2-22}$$

and the j-operator term has vanished.

The denominator of equation 2–21 should accordingly be multiplied by its conjugate, $\hat{B}$, to eliminate the j in the denominator. But to avoid changing the value of this equation, the *numerator* must also be multiplied by $\hat{B}$. In algebra this process is known as rationalizing.

Equation 2–21 may thus be evaluated as follows:

$$\frac{A}{B} = \frac{A\hat{B}}{B\hat{B}} = \frac{(a_1 + ja_2)}{(b_1 + jb_2)}\frac{(b_1 - jb_2)}{(b_1 - jb_2)} \tag{2-23}$$

Multiplying in both numerator and denominator according to the complex number multiplication process of equation 2–17 gives

$$\frac{A}{B} = \frac{A\hat{B}}{B\hat{B}} = \frac{(a_1b_1 + a_2b_2) + j(a_2b_1 - a_1b_2)}{(b_1^2 + b_2^2) + j(b_2b_1 - b_1b_2)} = \frac{a_1b_1 + a_2b_2}{b_1^2 + b_2^2} + j\frac{a_2b_1 - a_1b_2}{b_1^2 + b_2^2} \tag{2-24}$$

which is an ordinary complex number or vector.

An interpretation of the meaning of dividing two complex numbers is simple in terms of exponentials. For example, suppose

$$C = \frac{A}{B} = \frac{|A|\epsilon^{j\alpha}}{|B|\epsilon^{j\beta}} = \frac{|A|}{|B|}\epsilon^{j(\alpha-\beta)} \tag{2-25}$$

The ratio of two complex numbers is, then, a complex number the magnitude of which is the ratio of the magnitudes of the two complex numbers and the position of which is β degrees from A, counterclockwise if $\beta < 0$ and clockwise if $\beta > 0$—just the opposite from multiplication (see Fig. 2–5). Moreover, if B is viewed as an operator affecting A, it is evident that this operator changes A into a complex number C such that $|C| > |A|$ if $|B| < 1$, and $|C| < |A|$ if $|B| > 1$; C is shifted clockwise or counterclockwise depending on the sign of β.

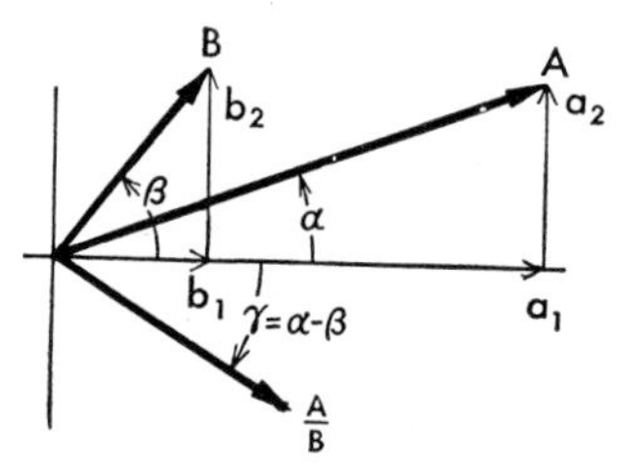

Fig. 2–5.

The equivalence of the two ratios of complex numbers as given in equations 2–24 and 2–25 may be established as follows. If the exponential of equation 2–25 is replaced by its cosine and sine equivalent,

$$\frac{A}{B} = \frac{|A|}{|B|}[\cos(\alpha - \beta) + j\sin(\alpha - \beta)]$$

Then, by expanding the sine and cosine,

$$\frac{A}{B} = \frac{|A|}{|B|}[\cos\alpha\cos\beta + \sin\alpha\sin\beta + j(\sin\alpha\cos\beta - \cos\alpha\sin\beta)]$$

Further multiplying both numerator and denominator on the right by $|B|$, and rearranging, gives

$$\frac{A}{B} = \frac{|A|\cos\alpha|B|\cos\beta + |A|\sin\alpha|B|\sin\beta}{|B|^2} + j\frac{|A|\sin\alpha|B|\cos\beta - |A|\cos\alpha|B|\sin\beta}{|B|^2}$$

But by noting from Fig. 2–5 the values of a_1, a_2, b_1, and b_2 in terms of vector lengths and angles, this last expression becomes

$$\frac{A}{B} = \frac{a_1b_1 + a_2b_2}{b_1^2 + b_2^2} + j\frac{a_2b_1 - a_1b_2}{b_1^2 + b_2^2}$$

which is exactly the same as equation 2–24. The two forms of the complex number ratio given by equations 2–24 and 2–25 are therefore equivalent.

The *unit* operator is also of interest in division, for

$$C = \frac{A}{\epsilon^{\pm j\phi}} = |A|\epsilon^{j(\alpha \mp \phi)} \tag{2-26}$$

is a complex number unchanged in magnitude but shifted in position. Notice that

$$A\epsilon^{\pm j\phi} = \frac{A}{\epsilon^{\mp j\phi}} \tag{2-27}$$

as the law of exponents indicates. Thus division by $\epsilon^{j\phi}$ is the same as multiplication by $\epsilon^{-j\phi}$, and a vector is rotated clockwise through ϕ degrees if $\phi > 0$ and counterclockwise through ϕ degrees if $\phi < 0$ by division with $\epsilon^{+j\phi}$.

Example 2:1 Consider the three complex numbers $A = 10 + j0$, $B = 8 - j6$, $C = 5 + j8.66$. Determine the following: (1) $A + B$, $B - C$; (2) AB, CB; (3) B/A, B/C; (4) the unit operator which rotates A into coincidence with B, and C with A.

Solution (1)

$$A + B = (10 + j0) + (8 - j6) = 18 - j6$$
$$B - C = (8 - j6) - (5 + j8.66) = 3 - j14.66$$

(2)

$$AB = (10 + j0)(8 - j6) = 10\epsilon^{j0}10\epsilon^{-j36.9} = 100\epsilon^{-j36.9}$$

or

$$\begin{array}{r} 8 - j6 \\ 10 + j0 \\ \hline AB = 80 - j60 = 100\epsilon^{-j36.9} \end{array}$$

$$CB = (5 + j8.66)(8 - j6) = 10\epsilon^{j60}10\epsilon^{-j36.9} = 100\epsilon^{j23.1}$$

$$\begin{array}{r} 5 + j8.66 \\ 8 - j6 \\ \hline 40 + j69.28 \\ -j^2 51.96 - j30.0 \\ \hline CB = 91.96 + j39.28 = 100\epsilon^{j23.1} \end{array}$$

(3)

$$\frac{B}{A} = \frac{8 - j6}{10 + j0} = 0.8 - j0.6$$

or

$$\frac{B}{A} = \frac{10\epsilon^{-j36.9}}{10\epsilon^{j0}} = 1.0\epsilon^{-j36.9}$$

$$\frac{B}{C} = \frac{8 - j6}{5 + j8.66} = \frac{10\epsilon^{-j36.9}}{10\epsilon^{j60}} = 1.0\epsilon^{-j96.9}$$

or

$$\frac{B}{C} = \frac{8 - j6}{5 + j8.66} = \frac{8 - j6}{5 + j8.66} \times \frac{5 - j8.66}{5 - j8.66} = \frac{-11.96 - j99.28}{25 + 75}$$
$$= -0.12 - j0.99 = 1.0\epsilon^{-j96.9}$$

(4) Since A is along the horizontal or reference axis, the rotator $\epsilon^{-j36.9}$ if applied to A, gives a vector of magnitude $|A|$ coinciding with B.

If the unit operator ϵ^{-j60} is applied to C, the result is a vector of magnitude $|C|$ coincident with A.

2.6 The a-Operator.

The j-operator has already been shown to be a unit operator which, through multiplication or division, rotates a vector, respectively, 90 degrees counterclockwise or 90 degrees clockwise. Application of the j-operator does not change the magnitude of a vector. Operators which rotate vectors other than 90 degrees are often found to be useful. A 120-degree operator, known as the a-operator, is particularly useful in three-phase studies. This operator is, by definition,

$$a = \epsilon^{j120} = -\tfrac{1}{2} + j\frac{\sqrt{3}}{2} = -0.5 + j0.866 \qquad (2\text{–}28)$$

$$a^2 = \epsilon^{j120}\epsilon^{j120} = \epsilon^{j240} = \epsilon^{-j120}$$

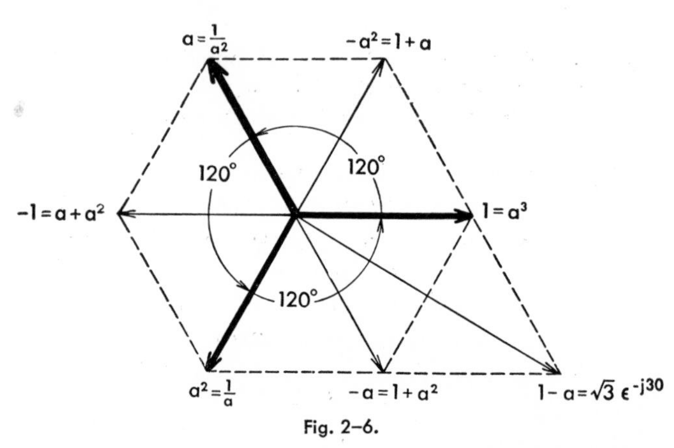

Fig. 2–6.

The algebra of the a-operator, of course, can be derived directly from this mathematical definition, but often a vectorial representation is very much simpler to use. For example, Fig. 2–6 shows the a-operator and some of the properties of this operator in a form which makes the following relations immediately evident:

$$\begin{aligned} a^3 &= 1 \\ -a^2 &= 1 + a \\ 1 - a &= \sqrt{3}\epsilon^{-j30} \\ 1 + a + a^2 &= 0 \\ a^2 &= \frac{1}{a} \\ a &= \frac{1}{a^2} \end{aligned} \qquad (2\text{–}29)$$

2.7 Complex Number Representation of a Rotating Vector.

The complex number representations thus far considered have been of stationary vectors. A more general representation would be that of rotating vector. Such a representation is given by

$$V(t) = |V_m|\epsilon^{j(\omega t+\phi)} = |V_m|\epsilon^{j\phi}\epsilon^{j\omega t} = V_m\epsilon^{j\omega t}$$
$$= |V_m|[\cos(\omega t + \phi) + j\sin(\omega t + \phi)] \qquad (2\text{–}30)$$

This relation gives the magnitude and position of the vector at any time t, starting from an initial position ϕ degrees from the reference axis at $t = 0$. This general representation will be useful later. The capitalized symbol $V(t)$, following the convention adopted, is a complex number varying with time, and $|V_m|$ is its absolute value or magnitude, not varying with time. Note that the *vertical projection of this vector plotted against time gives the sinusoid representing the voltage or current that the vector represents*, or that simply *taking the* j*-part of the rectangular form of the complex number also gives the sinusoid representing the quantity.* Furthermore, the vertical projection of this rotating vector gives the *magnitude* and *circuit polarity* of the voltage at any instant t, and the $t = 0$ value of this equation gives

$$V(0) = V_m = |V_m|\epsilon^{j\phi} \qquad (2\text{–}31)$$

the stationary vector form already considered.

Conversion from the rotating vector form to the sine wave form, and vice versa, is thus simple, e.g., the sine wave which equation 2–30 represents is

$$v(t) = |V_m|\sin(\omega t + \phi)$$

The stationary vectors which have been used in the foregoing are, therefore, the more general rotating vectors of equation 2–30 in their initial—$t = 0$—position.

As already pointed out in the preceding chapter, the horizontal component of a vector may be used instead of the vertical component to represent the instantaneous current or voltage. The component to be used is a matter of personal choice, and, as already pointed out, the vertical component is used here.

Example 2:2 Consider the two sinusoidal voltages $v_1(t) = 100\sin(\omega t + 30°)$ and $v_2(t) = 50\sin(\omega t - 30°)$. Establish: (1) The rotating vector equivalent of these sinusoids; (2) the $t = 0$ stationary forms of these vectors; (3) the actual voltage across the circuit at $t = 0$.

Solution (1) The rotating vectors are

$$V_1(t) = 100\epsilon^{j(\omega t+30)} = 100\epsilon^{j30}\epsilon^{j\omega t}$$
$$= 100(0.866 + j0.5)\epsilon^{j\omega t} = (86.6 + j50)\epsilon^{j\omega t} = V_{m1}\epsilon^{j\omega t}$$
$$V_2(t) = 50\epsilon^{j(\omega t-30)} = 50\epsilon^{-j30}\epsilon^{j\omega t}$$
$$= 50(0.866 - j0.5)\epsilon^{j\omega t} = (43.3 - j25)\epsilon^{j\omega t} = V_{m2}\epsilon^{j\omega t}$$

(2) The $t = 0$ or stationary form of these vectors is obtained by setting $t = 0$ in the rotating vector. Thus

$$V_1(0) = V_{m1} = 100\epsilon^{j30} = 86.6 + j50$$
$$V_2(0) = V_{m2} = 50\epsilon^{-j30} = 43.3 - j25$$

(3) The actual voltage across the circuits at the $t = 0$ instant is simply the vertical or j-component of the stationary *maximum*-value vectors. So

$$v_1(0) = 50 \text{ volts}$$
$$v_2(0) = -25 \text{ volts,}$$

which also follows immediately on setting $t = 0$ in the sinusoidal expressions. Thus

$$v_1(t)_{t=0} = v_1(0) = 100 \sin (0 + 30°) = 50$$
$$v_2(t)_{t=0} = v_2(0) = 50 \sin (0 - 30°) = -25$$

2.8 The Dot or Scalar Product.

By the conventions of three-dimensional vector analysis, a product is defined which is called the *dot* or *scalar* product. This product is defined as

$$I \cdot V = V \cdot I = |V||I| \cos \theta = P \tag{2–32}$$

where θ is the angle between the current and voltage. As indicated, the dot product represents the average power in a circuit across which a sinusoidal voltage is connected and through which a sine wave of current flows (equation 1–26).

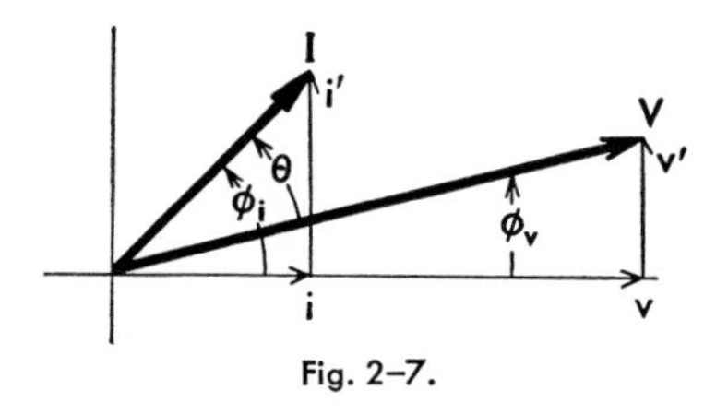

Fig. 2–7.

An alternative expression for the dot product in terms of the components of the two vectors forming the product is very useful and will now be developed. In Fig. 2–7, the angle θ can be replaced by $\phi_i - \phi_v$, and the dot product is

$$V \cdot I = |V||I| \cos (\phi_i - \phi_v)$$

Expanding the cosine gives

$$\begin{aligned} V \cdot I &= |V||I| (\cos \phi_i \cos \phi_v + \sin \phi_i \sin \phi_v) \\ &= |V| \cos \phi_v |I| \cos \phi_i + |V| \sin \phi_v |I| \sin \phi_i \end{aligned}$$

But from Fig. 2–7 the components of the current and voltage vectors are

$$v = |V| \cos \phi_v, \quad v' = |V| \sin \phi_v$$
$$i = |I| \cos \phi_i, \quad i' = |I| \sin \phi_i$$

and the dot product may be expressed as

$$V \cdot I = vi + v'i' = P \tag{2–33}$$

Of interest is the fact that this product consists of adding the products of the *in phase* components of the current and voltage.

The vectors of Fig. 2–7 have lengths corresponding to the effective values of the current and voltage, instead of maximum values as heretofore. This reduction in the length is made as a matter of convenience. Strictly speaking, these vectors will not represent the sine wave correctly. However, if the fact that the vectors are reduced is kept in mind, computations may be made directly from the vector or complex number system to ammeter and voltmeter indications without the $\sqrt{2}$ factor appearing, which is an advantage for computational purposes.

Example 2:3 As an example of the use of the scalar product, suppose that the voltage and current at the input of a small motor are given by

$$V = -50 - j86.6 \text{ and } I = 5 - j8.66$$

The power absorbed by the motor, the rms value of the voltage and current, and the power factor are to be determined.

Solution The power being absorbed by the motor is

$$P = V \cdot I = (-50)(5) + (-86.6)(-8.66) = 500 \text{ watts}$$

From equations 2–14 and 2–15,

$$V = \sqrt{50^2 + 86.6^2}\,\epsilon^{j \tan^{-1} \frac{-86.6}{-50}} = 100\epsilon^{j240}$$
$$I = \sqrt{5^2 + 8.66^2}\,\epsilon^{j \tan^{-1} \frac{-8.66}{5}} = 10\epsilon^{j300}$$

The power factor angle is the difference between the current and voltage angles or $\theta = 60$ degrees, and the power factor $= \cos\theta = 0.5$. Hence the average power, by the volt-ampere-pf method, is

$$P = 100 \times 10 \times 0.5 = 500 \text{ watts}$$

as before.

Note how much more easily the power may be determined from the scalar product than from the power factor, current, and voltage, if the complex number forms of the current and voltage are known.

2.9 Complex Number Form of Trigonometric and Hyperbolic Functions.

Some useful expressions for trigonometric functions may be deduced in terms of the j-operator exponential. From the difference of the two possible forms of equation 2–13 for $n = 1$,

$$\sin\phi = \frac{\epsilon^{j\phi} - \epsilon^{-j\phi}}{2j} \tag{2–34}$$

and, from the sum of the same two forms of equation 2–13,

$$\cos\phi = \frac{\epsilon^{j\phi} + \epsilon^{-j\phi}}{2} \tag{2–35}$$

Example 2:4 As an example of the use of the exponential equivalents of the trigonometric functions, consider

$$\sin\phi\cos\phi = \left(\frac{\epsilon^{j\phi} - \epsilon^{-j\phi}}{2j}\right)\left(\frac{\epsilon^{j\phi} + \epsilon^{-j\phi}}{2}\right)$$
$$= \frac{\epsilon^{2j\phi} - \epsilon^{-2j\phi}}{4j} = \frac{1}{2}\sin 2\phi$$

which gives very readily one of the common transformations of trigonometry.

Other functions sometimes useful are the hyperbolic functions. They are defined as

$$\sinh\phi = \frac{\epsilon^{\phi} - \epsilon^{-\phi}}{2} \qquad (2\text{–}36)$$

and

$$\cosh\phi = \frac{\epsilon^{\phi} + \epsilon^{-\phi}}{2} \qquad (2\text{–}37)$$

Other relations such as $\tanh\phi$, $\operatorname{sech}\phi$, and $\operatorname{csch}\phi$ may be derived from $\sinh\phi$ and $\cosh\phi$ exactly as $\tan\phi$, $\sec\phi$, and $\csc\phi$ may be derived from $\sin\phi$ and $\cos\phi$.

From the relations just given for the trigonometric and hyperbolic functions, functions of a complex angle may be deduced. Thus, from the well-known trigonometric relation for the sine of the sum of two angles,

$$\sin[(a) + (ja')] = \sin a\cos ja' + \cos a\sin ja'$$

Comparing the exponential expressions of equations 2–35 and 2–37, and 2–34 and 2–36 gives

$$\cos ja' = \cosh a' \qquad (2\text{–}38)$$

and

$$\sin ja' = j\sinh a'$$

so that

$$\sin(a + ja') = \sin a\cosh a' + j\cos a\sinh a' \qquad (2\text{–}39)$$

Other similar relations may be deduced with relative ease from the exponentials as they are needed.

2.10 Logarithms of Complex Numbers.

The logarithm of a complex number can be established as follows: Using (1) the exponential form of the complex number, (2) ln to represent logarithms to the base ϵ, and (3) the fact that the logarithm of a product is the sum of the logarithms of the factors of the product,

$$\ln A = \ln|A|\epsilon^{j\alpha} = \ln|A| + \ln\epsilon^{j\alpha}$$
$$= \ln|A| + j\alpha,$$

which is also a complex number. Note that α must be expressed in radians.

The logarithm of a negative number, undefined in the real number system, can be evaluated in terms of complex numbers. Thus

$$\ln(-A) = \ln(-1) + \ln A = \ln \epsilon^{\pm j\pi} + \ln A$$
$$= \ln A \pm j\pi$$

which is also a complex number even if A is real. If A is complex, the logarithm becomes

$$\ln(-A) = \ln A + j(\pm\pi) = \ln|A| + j(\alpha \pm \pi)$$

2.11 Roots and Powers of Complex Numbers.

Occasionally it is necessary to raise a complex number to a certain power or to extract a certain root of a complex number. The technique of both these processes is immediately evident if the exponential form of the complex number is used. Thus the nth power of the complex number A is

$$A^n = (a_1 + ja_2)^n = \left[\sqrt{a_1^2 + a_2^2}\ \epsilon^{j\tan^{-1}\frac{a_2}{a_1}}\right]^n = [|A|\epsilon^{j\alpha}]^n$$
$$= |A|^n \epsilon^{jn\alpha} \tag{2–40}$$

The nth root of a complex number A is

$$\sqrt[n]{A} = \sqrt[n]{|A|\epsilon^{j\alpha}} = \sqrt[n]{|A|}\,\epsilon^{j\frac{\alpha}{n}} \tag{2–41}$$

Example 2:5 Find the fifth power and the cube root of the complex number $8.66 + j5$.

Solution In exponential form

$$8.66 + j5 = 10\epsilon^{j30}$$

Then

$$(8.66 + j5)^5 = (10\epsilon^{j30})^5 = 10^5\epsilon^{j150}$$

and

$$\sqrt[3]{8.66 + j5} = \sqrt[3]{10\epsilon^{j30}} = \sqrt[3]{10}\epsilon^{j10}$$

Example 2:6 Find a symbolic expression for a complex root of a complex number. In particular evaluate $\sqrt[A]{B} = X$.

Solution By employing the usual formula for taking the logarithm of a number, the natural logarithm of X is

$$\ln X = \ln \sqrt[A]{B} = \frac{\ln B}{A} = \frac{\ln|B| + j\beta}{A} = c_1 + jc_2$$

$$\ln X = c_1 + jc_2$$

and

$$X = \epsilon^{c_1 + jc_2} = \epsilon^{c_1}\epsilon^{jc_2} = \epsilon^{c_1}(\cos c_2 + j\sin c_2)$$

To illustrate this process numerically, suppose $A = 3 + j4$ and $B = 1.0 + j1.0$. Then

$$c_1 + jc_2 = \frac{\ln 1.414 + j\pi/4}{3 + j4} = \frac{0.346 + j0.785}{3 + j4} = 0.167 + j0.039$$

Accordingly,

$$\sqrt[3+j4]{1.0 + j1.0} = \epsilon^{c_1}\epsilon^{jc_2} = \epsilon^{0.167}\epsilon^{j0.039}$$
$$= 1.17\epsilon^{j0.039} = 1.17 (\cos 2.2° + j \sin 2.2°)$$
$$= 1.17 + j0.044$$

PROBLEMS

2–1 Given two stationary vector currents

$$I_{m1} = 6 - j8, \quad I_{m2} = 10 + j10$$

(*a*) What is the exponential form of these vector currents?

(*b*) What are the equations in terms of ω of the sine waves which they represent?

2–2 Show that equation 2–13 is correct by a method similar to the one used to derive equation 2–12.

2–3 Express the sum and the difference of the currents of Problem 2–1 in the three forms given by equation 2–14.

2–4 Prove the relations given in equation 2–15.

2–5 Given three currents

$$i(t)_1 = 14.14 \sin (377t - 10°)$$
$$i(t)_2 = 28.28 \sin (377t + 20°)$$
$$i(t)_3 = 10 \sin (377t - 30°)$$

(*a*) Write the three complex number equivalents of equation 2–14 for each of these sine waves.

(*b*) Find $I_1 + I_2 + I_3$ and write the three types of complex numbers of equation 2–14 and the instantaneous or sine wave equation for the result.

2–6 Given the four expressions for currents of the same frequency

$$I_1 = 3 + j4$$
$$i_2(t) = 10 \sin (377t - 30°)$$
$$I_3 = 20 (\cos 60° + j \sin 60°)$$
$$I_4 = 5\epsilon^{-j60}$$

Find the sum of these currents and express the result in the four forms given by these currents.

2–7 Given the complex numbers $A = 8.66 + j5$, $B = 8 - j6$, and $C = 10 + j10$. Multiply each of these numbers by the others in exponential and rectangular form. Check the results by converting the results of the rectangular form multiplications to exponential form.

2–8 Multiply the complex numbers of Problem 2–7 by ϵ^{-j10}. Plot the results vectorially to scale and on the same figure plot the original vectors. The factor ϵ^{-j10} may be thought of as an operator which shifts the vectors or the reference axis. Which way does it shift the vectors for fixed reference axis and which way does it shift the axis for fixed vectors?

2–9 Using the rectangular form evaluate:

$$\frac{1}{\cos \theta + j \sin \theta}, \frac{1}{0 + j1}, \frac{1}{1 + j1}$$

Repeat using the exponential form and check by changing the exponential results into rectangular form.

2-10 Evaluate, by carrying out the complete process of equations 2-23 and 2-24,

$$\frac{3+j4}{8-j6},\quad \frac{2-j10}{4+j1},\quad \frac{7-j7}{2-j2},\quad \frac{10-j0}{0-j6}$$

Repeat using exponentials. Write the sine waves representing these results in terms of ω.

2-11 Suppose the current and voltage vectors derived from a laboratory test of a coil of wire are given by

$$I\ (t) = 10\epsilon^{j(\omega t-30)},\qquad V\ (t) = 100\epsilon^{j(\omega t+15)}$$

where the frequency is 60 cps.

(*a*) Write the sine wave equations of the current and voltage.

(*b*) Draw vector diagrams to scale and plot the positions of these vectors for $t = 0, \frac{1}{60}, \frac{1}{25}$, 0.01, and 0.02 sec.

(*c*) What are the relative positions of I_m and V_m at each of these times?

(*d*) Sketch the sine waves in correct relative positions and mark the time points for each of the above vector positions.

(*e*) What is the dot product of the current and voltage vectors? What is the average power by the power factor method?

(*f*) What is the instantaneous value of the current and voltage at $t = 0$; at $t = \frac{1}{240}$ sec?

2-12 Show graphically and mathematically that the following relations are true:

(*a*) For the j-operator,

$$1 + j + j^2 + j^3 = 0$$
$$1 + j = \sqrt{2}\epsilon^{j45}$$
$$(1 + j)^2 = 2j$$
$$(1 + j)^3 = 2(j + j^2)$$
$$j^4 = (j^2)^4 = (j^3)^4 = 1$$

and $1, j, j^2, j^3$ are the 4 fourth roots of unity.

(*b*) For the a-operator,

$$1 + a^2 - a = -2a$$
$$(1 + a)^2 = a$$
$$a - a^2 = j\sqrt{3}$$
$$a^3 = (a^2)^3 = 1$$

and 1, a, a^2 are the 3 cube roots of unity.

2-13 Determine the 6 sixth roots of unity. Let these roots be symbolized by 1, b, b^2, b^3, b^4, b^5. Then prove the following relations mathematically and graphically:

$$b = \epsilon^{j60}$$
$$1 + b + b^2 + b^3 + b^4 + b^5 = 0$$
$$1 + b = \sqrt{3}\epsilon^{j30}$$
$$(1 + b)^2 = 3b$$
$$1 + b + b^2 + b^3 = j\sqrt{3}$$
$$b^2 + b^4 = b^3$$
$$1 + b^3 + b^4 + b^5 = -j\sqrt{3}$$

2–14 Show that

$$P = V \cdot I = \frac{V_m}{\sqrt{2}} \cdot \frac{I_m}{\sqrt{2}} = \frac{V(t)}{\sqrt{2}} \cdot \frac{I(t)}{\sqrt{2}}$$

where $V(t)$ and $I(t)$ are as given by equation 2–30.

2–15 Show that equations 2–34 and 2–35 are correct.

2–16 Use equations 2–34 and 2–35 and show that:

(*a*) $\cos^2 \phi + \sin^2 \phi = 1$
(*b*) $\cos(\alpha + \beta) = \cos\alpha \cos\beta - \sin\alpha \sin\beta$
(*c*) $\cos(\alpha + \beta) - \cos(\alpha - \beta) = -2 \sin\alpha \sin\beta$

2–17 Show that $\cosh^2 \phi - \sinh^2 \phi = 1$. Evaluate by using exponentials:

$$\cosh(\alpha + \beta) \qquad \sinh(\alpha + \beta) \qquad \sinh\alpha \cosh\beta$$

2–18 What is the infinite series form of $\cosh \phi$ and of $\sinh \phi$? Derive by substituting the appropriate infinite series for the exponentials of equations 2–36 and 2–37. Compare with the series for $\cos \phi$ and $\sin \phi$.

2–19 Show that equation 2–39 is correct by using exponentials.

2–20 Determine the complex number rectangular form of

$$\cosh(a + ja') \text{ and of } \tanh(a + ja') = \sinh(a + ja')/\cosh(a + ja')$$

2–21 Determine the complex number expression for

$$A^B = C = (a + ja')^{(b+jb')} = c + jc'$$

i.e., find c and c'. Evaluate $(8 + j6)^{(8+j6)} = c + jc'$.

2–22 Prove that $AB \cdot AC = |A|^2 B \cdot C$.

2–23 Show that $|A| \sin\alpha + |B| \cos\alpha = \sqrt{|A|^2 + |B|^2} \sin\left(\alpha + \tan^{-1} \frac{B}{A}\right)$.

2–24 Show that $|A| \sinh\alpha + |B| \cosh\alpha = \sqrt{|A|^2 - |B|^2} \sinh(\alpha + \phi)$, and determine the value of ϕ in terms of $|A|$ and $|B|$. Does this formula still hold for $|B| > |A|$? What if $|A| = |B|$?

2–25 Evaluate $\ln \cosh(0.8 + j0.6)$, $\cosh \ln(0.8 + j0.6)$.

2–26 Evaluate $\ln \tanh(0.3 + j0.4)$.

2–27 Evaluate $(3 + j4)^{j6}$, $\sqrt[j6]{8 + j10}$, $\sqrt[1+j1]{4 - j4}$, $\cos^2(0.3 + j0.2)$, $\sqrt{\sin(2 + j4)}$.

CHAPTER 3

The Current, Voltage, Power, and Energy Relations in Resistors, Capacitors, and Inductors (Self and Mutual Induction)

The statement has already been made in Chap. 1 that once the current, voltage, power, and energy relations of an electrical system are known, its complete behavior is determined. In Chap. 1 the manner in which current and voltage are related to power and energy was defined and, in preparation for subsequent use, was expressed mathematically. The next step in establishing the properties of electrical systems is to determine the current, voltage, power, and energy relations in simple electrical systems.

The current and voltage relations of an electrical network depend, among other things, on the resistive, inductive, and capacitive effects of the various elements of the network. These three effects, and the way they determine current, voltage, power, and energy relations, are discussed in this chapter.

As the theory and application of a-c circuits is developed, it will become increasingly evident that actually *every* circuit element is unavoidably resistive, inductive, and capacitive. But because of the complexity both of presenting and of learning the behavior of the general circuit element, and all its current-voltage relations simultaneously, a compromise will be employed. The process here is to study theoretical circuits having pure resistance, inductance, or capacitance characteristics, and then to study combinations of the pure circuit elements to represent *any* existing circuit element. The properties of *all* linear electric circuits may thus be determined. In addition, the knowledge of circuit behavior thus obtained will suggest methods of constructing and using special circuits having properties which approach very closely the properties of any one of the three basic forms. The development of a-c circuit theory accordingly will be started with a study of pure resistors, i.e., resistors which produce no capacitive or inductive effects.

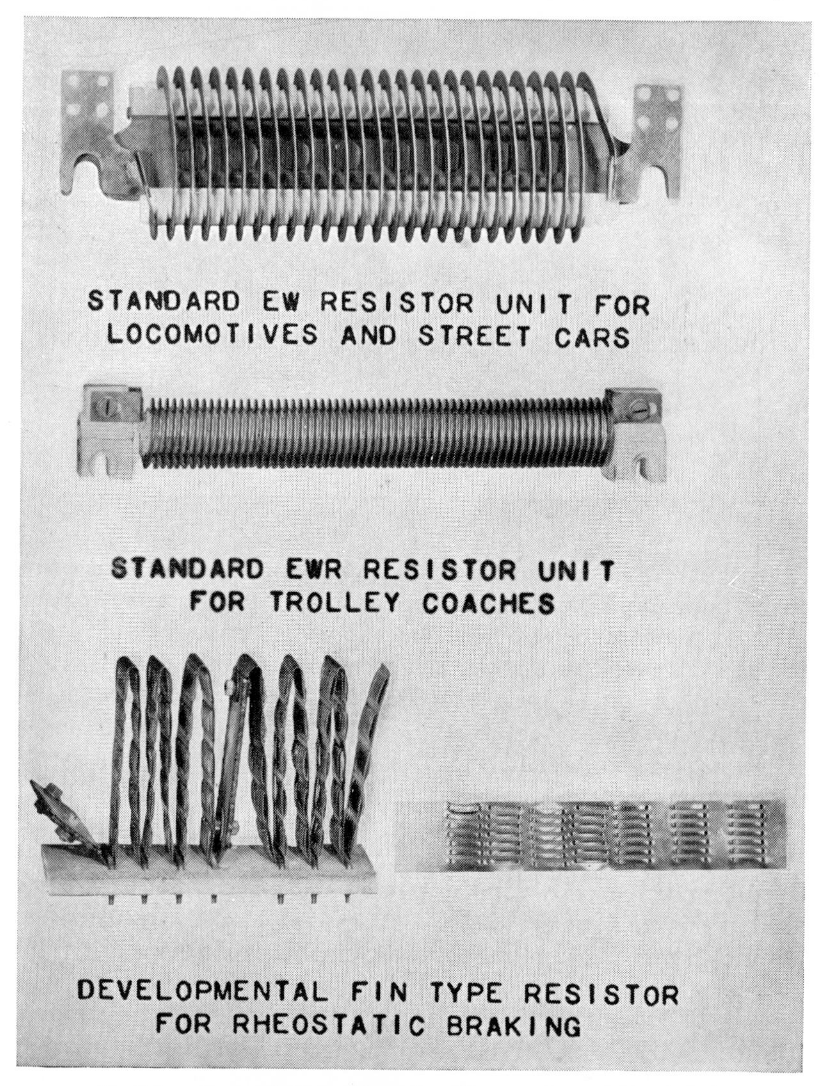

Fig. 3–1a. Transportation resistor units. (Courtesy, General Electric Co.)

3.1 Current Voltage Relation in a Resistor.

A physical unit known as a *resistor* is designed, built, and used subject to the condition that the terminal voltage and current are directly proportional. In so far as this direct proportionality fails, the two-terminal unit fails to be a resistor. The simple mathematical formulation of this current-voltage relation, known as Ohm's law, is (direct current),

$$\text{volts} = \text{resistance} \times \text{amperes}$$

$$V_{dc} = R_{dc}I_{dc} \quad \text{or} \quad \frac{V_{dc}}{I_{dc}} = R_{dc}$$

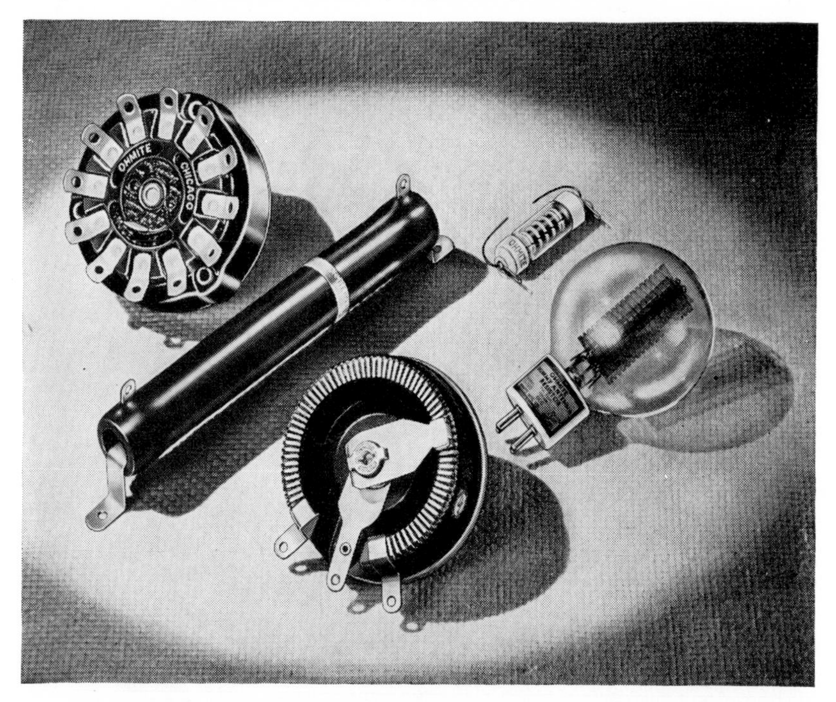

Fig. 3–1b. Fixed and variable resistors. (Courtesy, Ohmite Mfg. Co.)

where R_{dc} is a *constant* of proportionality. Experiment has shown further that Ohm's law for direct current in a solid conductor is substantially correct over the very wide range of current values of present-day usage—microamperes to thousands of amperes. Corresponding to the d-c expression just formulated is the a-c expression

$$\frac{v(t)_{ac}}{i(t)_{ac}} = R_{ac} \tag{3–1}$$

which is valid only for classes of units over restricted ranges of electrical operation. The range of operation for which a unit is a resistor—equation 3–1 is satisfied—can be established only by test. Certain ranges of operation are such that it is impossible to construct a two-terminal unit for which Ohm's law is valid—for example, for direct or alternating currents so small that the behavior of individual electrons becomes important, or for currents such that their time rates of variation cover too wide a range, as for radio, TV, and microwave signals all combined. Furthermore, the capacitive and inductive effects to be discussed in detail in this chapter frequently prevent the Ohm's law expression already given from representing the *whole* of the current-voltage relation of the circuit or any branch of the circuit. In fact, for *sinusoidal* current and voltage variation, the current and voltage of an a-c network branch in which no generator is located is shown subsequently to be

Fig. 3–1c. Motor-operated field resistor. (Courtesy, General Electric Co.)

$$\frac{V}{I} = Z \tag{3–2}$$

where Z (impedance) is a function *not only of the resistance of the circuit branch but of the inductance and capacitance as well.* In order to make the impedance (Z) depend on the resistance only, inductive and capacitive effects must be minimized by proper construction.

Several types of commercial resistors are shown in Fig. 3–1. They range from very high-resistance ones for radio circuits to low-resistance, high-current ones for power applications. It may be pointed out that these particular resistors are made practically purely resistive by using conductor material of high resistance so that not much conductor is needed to build the resistor. The inductive and capacitive effects thus by comparison become unimportant. As the variety of Fig. 3–1 suggests, resistors are very widely used.

The current-voltage relation of a pure resistor has already been given in equation 3–1. Dropping the subscripts, since only alternating current is under consideration, and writing this relation as a voltage equation which varies with time, give

$$v(t) = Ri(t) \tag{3–3}$$

Fig. 3–1d. Power system grounding resistor. (Courtesy, Westinghouse Electric & Mfg. Co.)

where $v(t)$ is the voltage across a "pure" resistor branch of R ohms for a current of $i(t)$ amperes in the resistor. The symbols v, V will be used in all that follows to represent other than source internal-generated voltages. The latter will be represented by e, E, as in Fig. 3–2. This symbolic distinction will simplify the manipulation and interpretation of the equations for electric circuits.

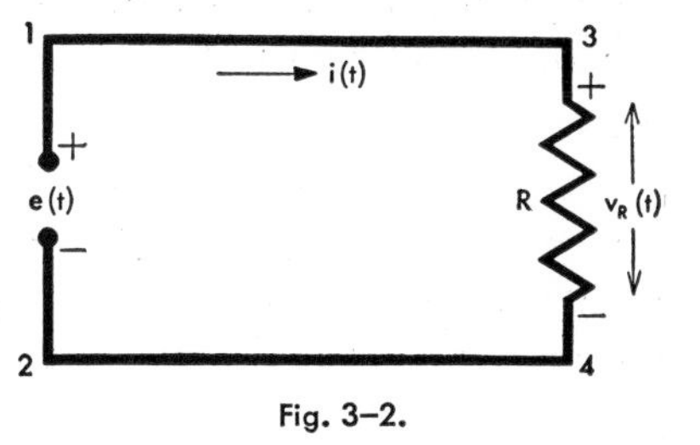

Fig. 3–2.

Confusion always arises in writing, manipulating, and interpreting electric circuit equations unless considerable care is exercised in formulating the fundamental idea of circuit orientation. Both currents and voltages are oriented in all parts of a circuit. It is absolutely necessary, therefore, that the technique employed give, under all circumstances, the magnitude and sense of currents and the magnitude and polarity of voltages.

There are two methods of specifying electric circuit orientations in general use—the double-subscript and the single-subscript methods. Both these methods are used in this book, separately or in combination, whichever is customary or most convenient. The required essentials of the two methods are given here, with a more complete discussion reserved for Chap. 9.

The first and probably the most important fact which must be learned about writing current and voltage equations is that before these equations can be written, *a reference orientation sense must be specified for every current and a reference orienting polarity must be specified for every voltage.* Furthermore, while these reference current orientations and voltage polarities are essential they are also arbitrary, i.e., they can be assumed at will with no knowledge of, or concern with, what the actual current orientations and voltage polarities really are. The solution of the equations for the circuit will specify currents and voltages based on the reference orientations and polarities—a positive result indicating that the actual and reference orientations coincide, and a negative result the contrary.

The double-subscript method is discussed first. The *left to right* order of the double subscripts is used to designate the *reference orientation sense* of the current as well as the *reference plus-to-minus* polarity of voltage. If the current is oriented in the left-to-right subscript order, it is considered positive; if not, it is taken to be negative. For example, in Fig. 3–2, if the current is actually as indicated by the arrow, namely, from 3 to 4, then at the instant t,

$$i(t)_{34} > 0 \text{ (positive)}$$
$$i(t)_{43} < 0 \text{ (negative)}$$

because the reference sense of $i(t)_{34}$ is from 3 to 4 and of $i(t)_{43}$ from 4 to 3.

Correspondingly, because the first of the double subscripts indicates the *reference* (plus polarized) terminal, for a voltage as in Fig. 3–2—plus at 3 and minus at 4—

$$v(t)_{34} > 0 \text{ (positive)}$$
$$v(t)_{43} < 0 \text{ (negative)}$$

If now the current-voltage relation of equation 3–3 for Fig. 3–2 is written in terms of double-subscript notation, under the foregoing relationships and the generally accepted definition that

$$R_{34} = R_{43} > 0 \text{ (positive)} \tag{3–4}$$

the result must be

$$\begin{aligned} v(t)_{34} &= R_{34}i(t)_{34} = R_{43}i(t)_{34} \\ v(t)_{43} &= R_{43}i(t)_{43} = R_{34}i(t)_{43} \end{aligned} \tag{3–5}$$

In passing it may be well to note that relation 3–4 arises from the fact that turning an ordinary resistor end for end in a circuit does not in any way alter the circuit. Therefore, since the resistor is not circuit directional, a reversal of subscripts can have no effect on the sign.

In all that follows here, all voltages (source or otherwise) are treated the same in terms of reference polarities; i.e., the left-hand subscript specifies the *reference plus location* of all voltages. The network equations are written (Kirchhoff's laws): (*a*) about a closed path the voltage-symbol sum, with subscripts in the order of traversing the path, is equated to zero (KVL); (*b*) at a junction the current-symbol sum, with subscripts in the away from (or toward) the junction sense, is equated to zero (KCL). Current and voltage relations are written, therefore, entirely in terms of reference conditions. For example, the voltage equation for the circuit of Fig. 3–2 is

$$e(t)_{21} + v(t)_{34} = e(t)_{21} + R_{34}i(t)_{34} = 0 \tag{3-6}$$

or

$$e(t)_{12} = R_{34}i(t)_{34}$$

The single-subscript method is based on placing voltage reference-plus-marks arbitrarily and current reference arrows with plus mark at the tail of the arrow where associated with the resistor—Fig. 3–2. The closed path voltage equation is formed by equating two sums: (1) all symbols associated with one reference orientation, (2) all other symbols. Thus for Fig. 3–2

$$-e(t) + v_R(t) = -e(t) + Ri(t) = 0$$

or

$$e(t) = Ri(t) \tag{3-7}$$

With these preliminaries, the current-voltage relations of a pure resistor will be developed. The current and voltage relation of a pure resistor is so simple that it is not necessary to refer to the mathematical expression to derive the implications of the equations. To obtain the voltage across a resistor, simply multiply the current by the resistance; and to obtain the current in a resistor, simply divide the voltage across the resistor by the resistance. Furthermore, the wave form of the voltage is the same as that of the current, and the current and voltage are in phase. It is helpful, however, to have available for reference the mathematical expressions for the sine wave current-voltage relation of a resistor.

Accordingly, assume the instantaneous current in a resistor is

$$i(t) = |I_m| \sin (\omega t + \phi) \tag{3-8}$$

In rotating vector form (Art. 2–7) this sinusoidal current is

$$I(t) = I_m\epsilon^{j\omega t} = |I_m|\epsilon^{j\phi}\epsilon^{j\omega t} \tag{3-9}$$

$$= |I_m|[\cos (\omega t + \phi) + j \sin (\omega t + \phi)] \tag{3-10}$$

the j-component of which is the instantaneous equation for the current of equation 3–8. Multiplying the rotating vector current by the resistance gives the rotating vector voltage

$$V(t) = RI(t) = RI_m\epsilon^{j\omega t} = V_m\epsilon^{j\omega t} \tag{3–11}$$

which instantaneously is

$$v(t) = |RI_m| \sin (\omega t + \phi) = |V_m| \sin (\omega t + \phi)$$

As a complex number, stationary vector

$$V_m = RI_m = R|I_m|\epsilon^{j\phi} \tag{3–12}$$

and dividing by $\sqrt{2}$ to obtain the rms values gives

$$V = RI = R|I|\epsilon^{j\phi} \tag{3–13}$$

Also, in terms of magnitudes only,

$$\begin{aligned} |V_m| &= R|I_m| \\ |V| &= R|I| \end{aligned} \tag{3–14}$$

The sinusoid and vector representations of sine waves of current and voltage for a "pure" resistor branch are given in Fig. 3–3. Note that the current and voltage are *in phase*, i.e., the sine

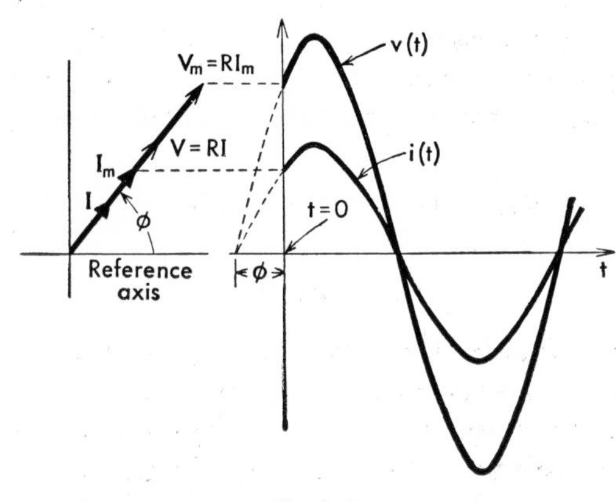

Fig. 3–3.

waves representing them are zero at the same time and positive and negative together, and that the vectors representing these quantities coincide.

If the magnitudes of the vectors representing the maximum values are divided by $\sqrt{2}$, the vector diagram is of effective values as shown.

3.2 Power and Energy Relations in a Resistor.

The power expressions for sinusoidal current in a pure resistor are as follows. First, the instantaneous power is

$$p(t) = v(t)i(t) = Ri^2(t) = R|I_m|^2 \sin^2 (\omega t + \phi)$$
$$= R|I_m|^2 \frac{1 - \cos 2(\omega t + \phi)}{2}$$
$$= \frac{R|I_m|^2}{2} - \frac{R|I_m|^2}{2} \cos 2(\omega t + \phi) \tag{3-15}$$

which has already been illustrated in Fig. 1–15*c*. Second, the average power is

$$P = \frac{1}{\frac{1}{f}} \int_0^{1/f} p(t)\, dt = \frac{R|I_m|^2}{2} = R|I|^2 = |V_R|\, |I| \tag{3-16}$$

as has already been shown by other methods.

The energy supplied to a resistor in t seconds with sinusoidal currents is

$$w(t) = \int_0^t p(t)\, dt = \frac{R|I_m|^2}{2} t - \frac{R|I_m|^2}{4\omega} [\sin 2(\omega t + \phi) - \sin 2\phi] \tag{3-17}$$

Note that this energy expression can never be negative and in fact can never decrease because the derivative of $w(t)$, given as $p(t)$ in equation 3–15, is always positive or zero. The fact that the energy absorbed by a resistor for a sine wave of current never decreases means that of all the supplied energy none is returned. It is simply dissipated in heat. In the next two articles, capacitors and inductors are found to have a different type of power and energy behavior.

Example 3:1 Suppose a heating unit resistor is located between 3 and 4 of Fig. 3–2. The resistance is 20 ohms, and the reference or $t = 0$ time is taken so that the effective value vector form of the current through the resistor is $I_{43} = 10 - j10$ amp. Find the voltage across the resistor, R_{34}, in several different forms. What is the form of the current vector, I_{34}, referred to an axis 30 degrees behind (lagging) the current vector? Determine the average power, and the energy absorbed by the resistor in 10 min from $t = 0$.

Solution Since

$$I = I_{34} = -I_{43} = -10 + j10 = -14.14\epsilon^{-j45} = 14.14\epsilon^{j135}$$
$$V = V_{34} = R_{34}I_{34} = -200 + j200 = 282.8\epsilon^{j135}$$

and the effective value of the resistance voltage is 282.8 volts. Also

$$V_m = \sqrt{2}V = 400\epsilon^{j135} = -282.8 + j282.8$$

and the maximum value of the resistance voltage is 400 volts, and the instantaneous value of this voltage at $t = 0$ is the j-component, 282.8 volts positive at terminal 3.

The rotating vector form of the resistor voltage is

$$V(t) = (-282.8 + j282.8)\epsilon^{j\omega t} = 400\epsilon^{j(\omega t+135)}$$

and the sine wave representation of the voltage across the resistor is the j-component of this rotating vector, i.e.,

$$v(t) = 400 \sin (\omega t + 135°)$$

The current expressed as a rotating vector is

$$I(t)_{43} = \sqrt{2}(10 - j10)\epsilon^{j\omega t} = 20\epsilon^{j(\omega t - 45°)}$$
$$I(t) = I(t)_{34} = -I(t)_{43} = \sqrt{2}(-10 + j10)\epsilon^{j\omega t} = 20\epsilon^{j(\omega t + 135°)}$$

The vector and sine wave diagrams are shown in Fig. 3–4. The correspondence of the various vectors and sine waves is shown in detail in this figure.

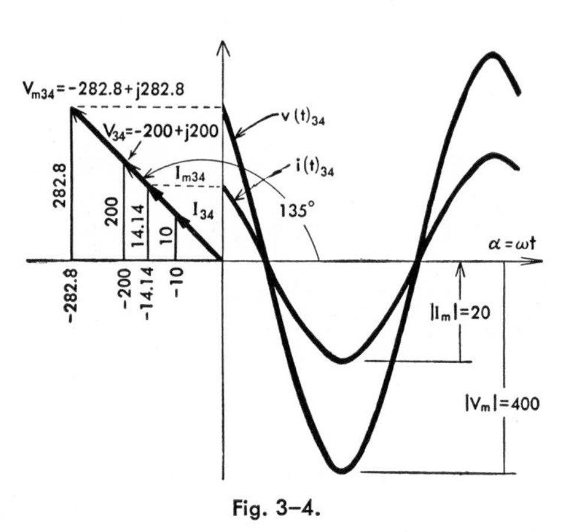

Fig. 3–4.

The current vector, and in fact all the vectors of this example, can be referred to an axis 30 degrees behind the current by multiplying each of the vectors by ϵ^{-j105}. Thus

$$I = I_{34} = 14.14\epsilon^{j135}\epsilon^{-j105} = 14.14\epsilon^{j30}$$

which gives the current referred to an axis 30 degrees behind the current.

The average power is

$$P = |I|^2R = 14.14^2 \times 20 = 4000 \text{ watts}$$

or

$$P = V_{34} \cdot I_{34} = (-200)(-10) + (200)(10) = 4000 \text{ watts}$$

and the energy absorbed in 10 min from $t = 0$ is, from equation 3–17, —$\phi = 135°$—

$$w(600) = \int_0^{600} p(t)\, dt = \frac{R|I_m|^2}{2} t \Big|_0^{600} - \frac{R|I_m|^2}{4\omega} \sin 2(\omega t + 135°)\Big|_0^{600}$$

If the frequency is taken as 60 cps as for a power system, $\omega = 2\pi 60 = 377$, and

$$\begin{aligned} w(600) &= 4000\times 600 - \tfrac{4000}{754} [\sin (4\pi 60 \times 600 + 270°) - \sin 270°] = 2.4\times 10^6 - 0 \\ &= 2{,}400{,}000 \text{ watt-seconds} = 2400 \text{ kilowatt-seconds} \\ &= 2.4 \text{ megawatt-seconds} = \tfrac{2}{3} \text{ kilowatthour} \end{aligned}$$

3.3 The Current-Voltage Relation in a Capacitor.

Having now established the current, voltage, power, and energy relations of a resistor, another of the three fundamental elements of electric circuits, namely, capacitance, will be considered. It is perhaps easier to visualize the capacitive effect than the resistive. In the first place, all capacitive effects arise from the well-known and easily verified fact that electrical charges have a force reaction between them. Moving or stationary electric charges on a conductor (or on an insulator) force moving

Fig. 3–5a. Variable capacitor. (Courtesy, Leeds & Northrup Co.)

or stationary charges on near-by conductors (or insulators) to assume positions or velocities differing from those which would exist without the presence of the first charges. Thus capacitive effects may change currents near by or may actually cause currents where none would otherwise exist. Furthermore, since electric charges are *always* present in *all* electric phenomena, capacitive effects are ever present.

The nature of the capacitive reaction suggests that if capacitance is to be built into a circuit, large areas of conductors close together should be used. Static capacitors are built exactly this way. Several commercial types are shown in Fig. 3–5. All but the picture of Fig. 3–5*d* show static capacitors for a wide variety of uses. Figure 3–5*d* shows a machine known

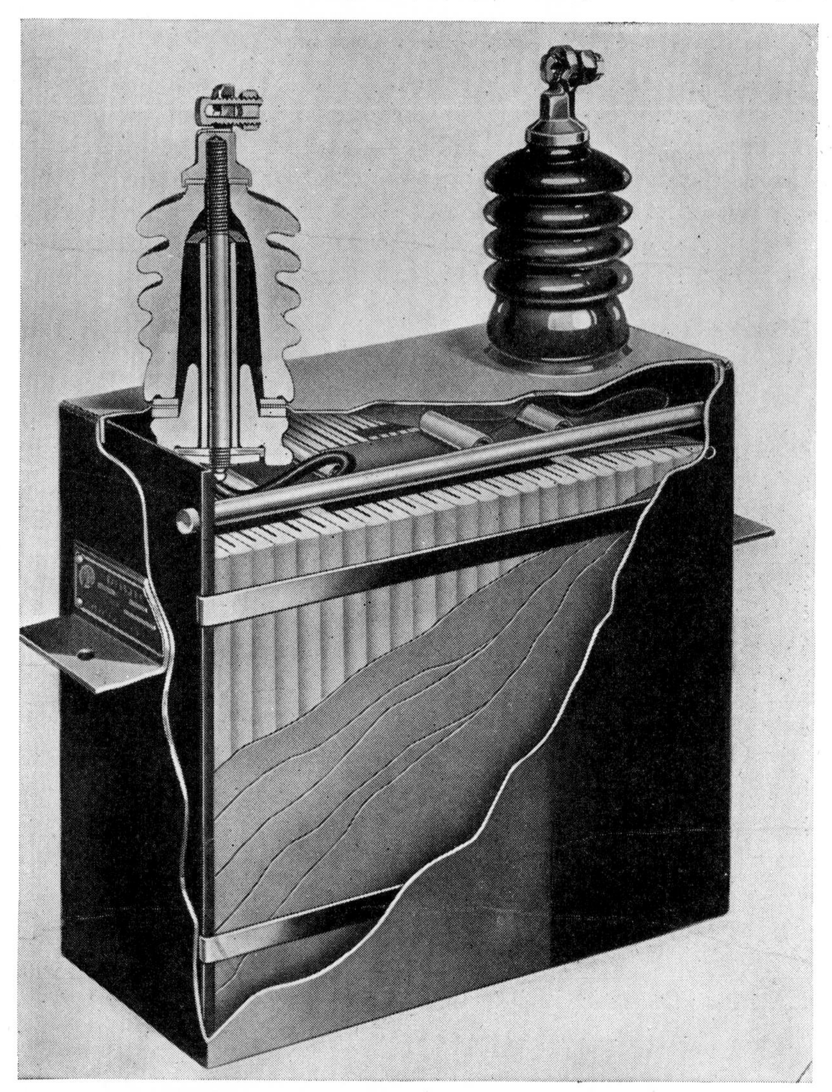

Fig. 3–5b. Cutaway view of capacitor. (Courtesy, Cornell-Dubilier Electric Corp.)

as a synchronous capacitor or, more commonly, synchronous condenser. This unit actually is simply a synchronous motor which can be made to operate with the characteristics of a capacitor; hence its name, synchronous capacitor. Power engineers find such motors with capacitor characteristics very useful. While static and synchronous capacitors have similar electrical behavior, there is not the slightest similarity in the construction of these two devices. More will be given on the use of synchronous capacitors subsequently. For the present, the general properties of static capacitors are discussed.

Fig. 3–5c. High-voltage capacitor. (Courtesy, RCA Mfg. Co.)

Calculation of the capacitance in terms of the physical dimensions of a particular configuration is not attempted here since it requires a certain amount of knowledge of electric field theory which is not discussed in this book.

A capacitor is, by experimental observation, a two-terminal unit such that, with relative reference orientation as illustrated in Fig. 3–6, the current-voltage relation is (single and double subscript forms)

$$i(t) = i(t)_{34} = C_{34} \frac{dv_c(t)_{34}}{dt} = C \frac{dv_c(t)}{dt} \tag{3–18}$$

where $C_{34} = C =$ the factor of proportionality, here considered as a positive constant, known as capacitance (farads).

By definition the capacitor is such that its electrical behavior is not

Fig. 3–5*d*. Outdoor hydrogen-cooled synchronous capacitor, 60,000 kva. (Courtesy, General Electric Co.)

altered by an interchange of terminal connections, hence $C_{34} = C_{43} > 0$.

In addition to the difference in defining equations for a resistor (equation 3–3) and a capacitor (equation 3–18), the capacitor behavior is affected by its past. This effect from the past appears as a direct-voltage component across the capacitor terminals. For the majority of applications, this direct-voltage component vanishes in a very short time after the instant of electrically activating the capacitor. Simple and common situations arise, however, where a direct-voltage component may remain across the capacitor for a long time (theoretically forever). Such an arrangement, capacitors in series, is illustrated by Fig. 8–17 and is discussed in Chap. 8. In all such cases as the latter, complete specification of the capacitor voltage at any time requires the inclusion of a constant in the mathematical description of the capacitor voltage. Therefore, in general, the voltage across the terminals of a capacitor may be represented by

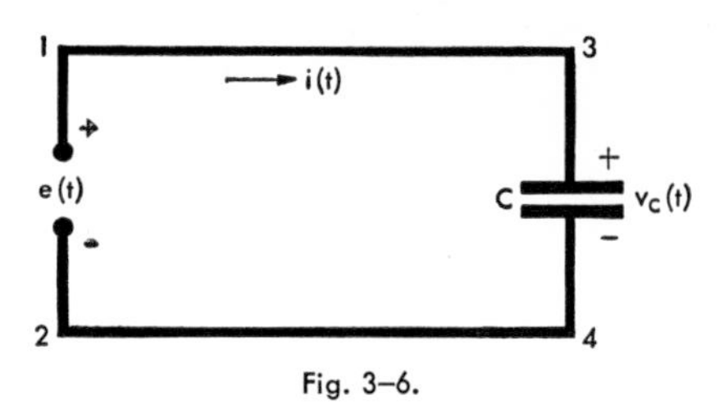

Fig. 3–6.

$$v_c(t) = \frac{q(t)}{C} + v_c(0) \tag{3–19}$$

where $v_c(0)$ is a constant which specifies the direct-voltage component on the capacitor at $t = 0$,

$q(t)/C$ is a function which specifies the time variation of the capacitor voltage exclusive of any direct-voltage component that may be on the capacitor.

Evidently, satisfaction of this last equation at $t = 0$ requires that

$$q(0) = 0$$

A change of variable, widely used because of its convenience, is presented here for completeness and for use in following parts of this book. This change of variable takes the form

$$q_c(t) = q(t) + q_c(0) = Cv_c(t) = Cv(t) + Cv_c(0) \tag{3-20}$$

where

$$\begin{aligned} q(t) &= Cv(t) \\ q_c(0) &= Cv_c(0) \\ q(0) &= 0 \end{aligned} \tag{3-21}$$

Use of equations 3–18, 3–19, and 3–20 specifies that

$$i(t) = C\frac{d\,v_c(t)}{dt} = C\frac{d\,v(t)}{dt} = \frac{d\,q_c(t)}{dt} = \frac{d\,q(t)}{dt} \tag{3-22}$$

An important aspect of this last equation is the fact that $i(t)$ is uniquely determined by $v_c(t)$, whereas $v_c(t)$ is not uniquely determined by $i(t)$. The difference is no more than a constant of integration, but this constant cannot be ignored and indeed may be rather troublesome on occasions. Certain situations arise, such as studying the response of electrical networks to television signals, where this constant markedly affects the situation and must be considered and handled with care. This matter of television signals also makes it impossible to consider an integral solution of equation 3–22 since $v_c(t)$ is defined thereby as being absolutely continuous, whereas observation shows $v_c(t)$ as discontinuous.

The circumstances (fairly general) under which the terminal voltage of a capacitor is sinusoidal are discussed in Chap. 8. At this point and largely in this book, the assumption is made that, for sinusoidal, driving-unit voltages, all steady-state capacitor voltages are sinusoidal. Consider, therefore, the simple but widely representative case in Fig. 3–6 where $e(t) = e(t)_{12} = v_c(t)_{34} = v_c(t)$.

It is not always possible to use the rotating vector to replace the instantaneous sine wave in mathematical manipulations. Where it is possible, though, such a replacement leads to marked simplification. This replacement can be made in derivatives. Therefore, suppose, in anticipation of subsequent results, that $e(t) = v_c(t) = -|E_m| \cos(\omega t + \phi)$ with its rotating vector equivalent (note: $j = \epsilon^{j90}$)

$$E(t) = V_c(t) = |E_m|\epsilon^{j(\phi-90)}\,\epsilon^{j\omega t} = E_m\epsilon^{j\omega t} = V_{mc}\epsilon^{j\omega t}$$

Equation 3–18 then specifies the current by

$$\begin{aligned} I(t) &= j\omega C V_{mc}\epsilon^{j\omega t} = I_m\epsilon^{j\omega t} \qquad (3\text{–}23) \\ &= j\omega C|V_{mc}|[\cos(\omega t + \phi - 90°) + j\sin(\omega t + \phi - 90°)] \\ &= \omega C|V_{mc}|[\cos(\omega t + \phi) + j\sin(\omega t + \phi)] \end{aligned}$$

Alternatively, from equation 3–23

$$V_{mc} = \frac{1}{j\omega C} I_m = j\frac{-1}{\omega C} I_m \qquad (3\text{–}24)$$

The factor $-1/\omega C$ appearing in this last equation is ever present in capacitance calculations; it has been symbolized by (C in farads)

$$X_c \equiv \frac{-1}{\omega C} \equiv \frac{-1}{2\pi f C} \text{ (ohms)} \qquad (3\text{–}25)$$

and is known as *capacitive reactance.*

Several relations for a capacitor which may be taken immediately from the foregoing equations are:

$$V_c = \frac{1}{j\omega C} I = j\frac{-1}{\omega C} I = jX_c I \qquad (3\text{–}26)$$

$$|V_{mc}| = |X_c|\,|I_m| \quad \text{or} \quad |V_c| = |X_c|\,|I| \qquad (3\text{–}27)$$

$$I(t) = \frac{-|V_{mc}|}{X_c}\epsilon^{j(\omega t+\phi+90)} = \frac{|V_{mc}|}{|X_c|}\epsilon^{j(\omega t+\phi+90)} = |I_m|\epsilon^{j(\omega t+\phi+90)}$$

and instantaneously from the j-component of the rotating vector

$$i(t) = \frac{-|V_{mc}|}{X_c}\sin(\omega t + \phi) = |I_m|\sin(\omega t + \phi) \qquad (3\text{–}28)$$

Notice that the stationary vector, or $I(0)$, form of the current must be multiplied by $jX_c = -j|X_c|$ to determine the voltage across the capacitor and not by just X_c as for R of the resistor. The current vector or sine wave, therefore, is 90 degrees *ahead* of the capacitor voltage vector or sine wave and the current and voltage are now *not in phase.* Rather they are 90 degrees out of phase—the current *leading* the voltage. The current *leading* the voltage, which is the same as voltage *lagging* the current, is an important characteristic of capacitive circuits and should be kept in mind. Note particularly that $X_c i(t)$ does not give the instantaneous capacitor voltage because this product is not 90 degrees out of phase with the current as is $v_c(t)$.

The statement is made on p. 77 that experimental observation, plus specified reference orientations, which lead to equation 3–18, define a capacitor. There is no other way to determine whether any particular device may or may not be considered as a capacitor. Ultimately any physical two-terminal unit, constructed following any scheme desired, must be subjected to current and voltage measurements and in so far as the results conform with equation 3–18, or fail to do so, the device is, or fails to be, a capacitor. As the professional problems become increasingly complex it becomes increasingly important that the greatest possible precision be entered into the examination and understanding of the basic concepts of electrical engineering, hence this reëmphasis.

Example 3:2 Suppose a capacitor of 10 = μf capacitance is connected across a voltage source as in Fig. 3–6. Suppose furthermore that a 1000-cps current in the connecting conductors has a maximum value of 14.14 amp and at $t = 0$ has a phase angle of -30 degrees. Find: (*a*) the capacitive reactance; (*b*) the maximum and rms values of the voltage across the capacitor terminals; (*c*) the voltage across the capacitor terminals in complex and real number instantaneous form. (*d*) Draw the vector diagram and plot the sine waves of current and voltage.

Solution (*a*) The capacitive reactance is easily computed from equation 3–25. First, by calculating ω and C,

$$\omega = 2\pi f = 2\pi 1000 = 6283$$

$$C = \frac{10}{10^6} \text{ farads}$$

Therefore,

$$X_c \equiv \frac{-1}{\omega C} = \frac{-10^6}{6283 \times 10} = -15.9 \text{ ohms}$$

(*b*) The maximum value of the voltage across the capacitor is

$$|V_{mc}| = |X_c|\,|I_{mc}| = 15.9 \times 14.14 = 225 \text{ volts}$$

The rms or effective value of this voltage is

$$|V_c| = \frac{|V_{mc}|}{\sqrt{2}} = \frac{|X_c|\,|I_{mc}|}{\sqrt{2}} = 159 \text{ volts}$$

which would be indicated by a voltmeter across the capacitor terminals.

(*c*) In complex number rotating vector form the current is

$$I(t) = |I_m|\,\epsilon^{j\phi}\epsilon^{j\omega t} = 14.14\epsilon^{-j30}\epsilon^{j6283t} = (12.25 - j7.07)\epsilon^{j6283t}$$

or, in still a different form,

$$I(t) = 14.14\,[\cos(6283t - 30°) + j\sin(6283t - 30°)]$$

The capacitor voltage in complex variable form is

$$\begin{aligned} V_c(t) &= jX_cI(t) = (-j15.9)14.14\epsilon^{-j30}\epsilon^{j6283t} \\ &= -j225\epsilon^{-j30}\epsilon^{j6283t} = 225\epsilon^{j(6283t-30-90)} \\ &= 225\epsilon^{j(6283t-120)} \end{aligned}$$

At $t = 0$

$$V_{mc} = V_c(0) = 225\epsilon^{-j120} = -112.5 - j195$$

which is the stationary vector form of the maximum value of capacitor voltage. The complex number effective value of this capacitor voltage is

$$V_c = \frac{V_c(0)}{\sqrt{2}} = \frac{V_{mc}}{\sqrt{2}} = \frac{225}{\sqrt{2}} \epsilon^{-j120} = -79.5 - j138$$

The instantaneous form of the capacitor voltage is the j-component of the rotating vector, i.e.,

$$\begin{aligned} v_c(t) &= X_c|I_m| \cos(\omega t + \phi) = -225 \cos(6283t - 30°) \\ &= 225 \sin(6283t - 120°) \end{aligned}$$

(*d*) The vector diagram and sine waves are shown in Fig. 3–7. The 90-degree phase relation between the capacitor current and voltage, with the current leading the voltage, is in evidence.

Note that because of the 90-degree phase relation, the current of a capacitor and the voltage across the capacitor are not always positive or negative at the same time. For example, at *a–a* of Fig. 3–7 the current

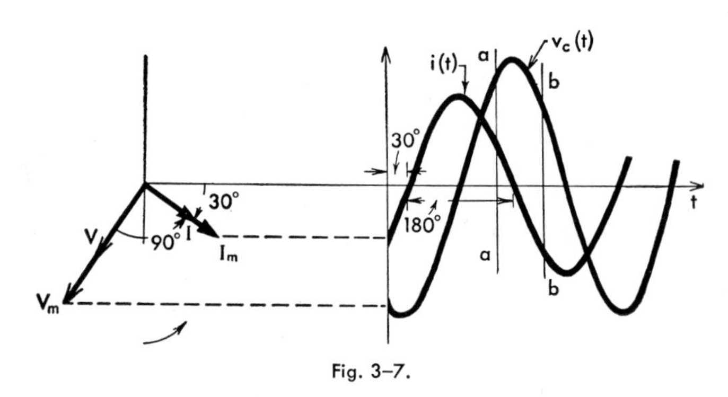

Fig. 3–7.

and voltage are both positive, but at *b–b* the voltage is positive and the current is negative. While this result may seem anomalous on the basis of d-c behavior, it is to be expected for a capacitor, because for a particular voltage across a capacitor the current sense is one way on charge and the other way for discharge.

3.4 Power and Energy Relations of a Capacitor.

The instantaneous power, rate of energy delivery, to a capacitor, for sinusoidal current, is

$$\begin{aligned} p_c(t) &= i(t)v_c(t) = |I_m| \sin(\omega t + \phi)[-|V_{mc}|] \cos(\omega t + \phi) \\ &= -|I_m|\,|V_{mc}| \sin(\omega t + \phi) \cos(\omega t + \phi) \end{aligned}$$

$$p_c(t) = -\frac{|I_m|\,|V_{mc}|}{2} \sin 2(\omega t + \phi) \tag{3–29}$$

The power at the terminals of a capacitor is, accordingly, a double-frequency sine wave of *average* value,

$$P_c = \frac{1}{\frac{1}{f}} \int_0^{1/f} p_c(t)\, dt$$

$$= \frac{|I_m|\,|V_{mc}|}{\frac{2}{f}} \int_0^{1/f} - \sin 2(\omega t + \phi)\, dt = 0 \tag{3-30}$$

On the average, therefore, *a capacitor does not absorb or deliver energy.*

The energy absorbed by capacitor in an interval of $t_2 - t_1$ seconds, for sinusoidal current, is

$$w_c(t_2) - w_c(t_1) = \int_{t_1}^{t_2} p_c(t)\, dt = \frac{|I_m|\,|V_{mc}|}{2} \int_{t_1}^{t_2} - \sin 2(\omega t + \phi)\, dt$$

$$= \frac{|I_m|\,|V_{mc}|}{2} \left[\frac{\cos 2(\omega t + \phi)}{2\omega}\right]_{t_1}^{t_2}$$

$$w_c(t_2) - w_c(t_1) = \frac{|I_m|\,|V_{mc}|}{2} \left[\frac{\cos 2(\omega t_2 + \phi) - \cos 2(\omega t_1 + \phi)}{2\omega}\right] \tag{3-31}$$

The energy absorbed by or delivered to a capacitor over any time interval is thus a function of the time interval, as should be expected.

An important relation for the energy stored in a capacitor will now be derived. Consider first the general expression for the energy *supplied* to a capacitor, in the time interval t–t_1, namely,

$$w_c(t_2) - w_c(t_1) = \int_{t_1}^{t} p_c(t)\, dt = \int_{t_1}^{t} v_c(t) i(t)\, dt$$

But because

$$v_c(t) = \frac{q_c(t)}{C}$$

and

$$i(t) = \frac{dq_c(t)}{dt}$$

this energy-supplied relation becomes

$$w_c(t) - w_c(t_1) = \frac{1}{C} \int_{t_1}^{t} q_c(t) \frac{dq_c(t)}{dt}\, dt = \frac{1}{C} \int_{t_1}^{t} \frac{d}{dt} \frac{q_c(t)^2}{2}\, dt$$

$$= \frac{1}{C} \frac{q_c(t)^2}{2} \bigg|_{t_1}^{t}$$

$$w_c(t) - w_c(t_1) = \frac{1}{2C} [q_c(t)^2 - q_c(t_1)^2] = \frac{C}{2} [v_c^2(t) - v_c^2(t_1)] \tag{3-32}$$

Because the voltage terms of this equation are both squared and so always positive, the energy supplied over any interval t_1 to t is positive or negative, depending on the relative *magnitudes* of $v_c(t)$ and $v_c(t_1)$. Thus, if t_1 is taken at a of Fig. 3–8b and t at b, $v_c(t) < v_c(t_1)$, and the energy supplied to the capacitor over this period is negative. As the energy curve shows, the capacitor discharges over this period. Other time intervals, of course, lead to positive or negative values of $w_c(t)$, depending on whether the capacitor has taken on or given up charge during the interval.

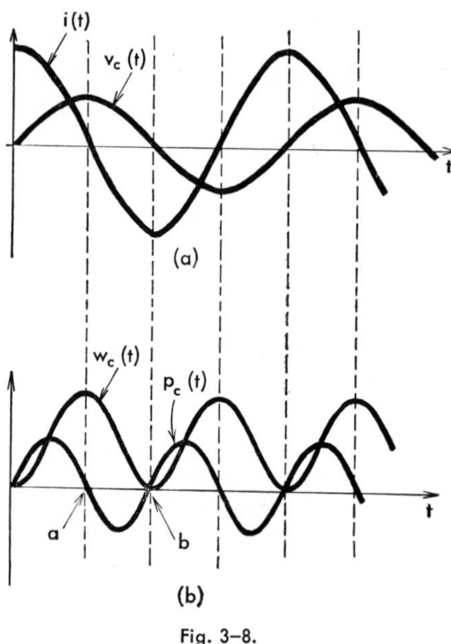

Fig. 3–8.

An important specialization of equation 3–32 leads to a representation of the energy *stored* in a capacitor as follows. It is known from experiment that *if the charge on a capacitor is zero, there is no energy stored in the capacitor*. Suppose, then, that the starting point t_1 of the integration of equation 3–32 is such that the charge on the capacitor at this instant is zero—$q_c(t_1) = 0$. Equation 3–32 then becomes

$$w_c(t) = \frac{q_c(t)^2}{2C} = \tfrac{1}{2}Cv_c(t)^2 \quad (3\text{–}33)$$

But since at the start of the integration the capacitor held no energy this last equation represents the energy actually *stored*. Note that this energy storage at any particular instant depends *only on the value of the capacitor voltage or charge at that instant, and not at all on how the charge or voltage varied before the instant under consideration*.

The curves of Fig. 3–8 show the sinusoidal current, voltage, the double-frequency power, and energy-stored relations. Note that the energy is maximum for maximum $v(t)$, that the energy increases as long as the power is positive, and then decreases as long as the power is negative. Interpreted physically, the capacitor is charged and energy stored as long as the power expression is positive. Then when the power becomes negative, the capacitor is discharging, which means it is *returning energy to the source*. But notice that the energy supplied oscillates between zero and a certain maximum value. The fact that the stored energy returns periodically to zero means that *all* the energy supplied to the capacitor returns to the source, so that the capacitor does not dissipate energy as does a resistor, but merely stores this energy and returns it to the source periodically.

Example 3:3 Suppose that the current function for a capacitor of 100-μf capacitance is

$$i(t) = 10 \sin (1000t + 30°)$$

The voltage across the capacitor is, then,

$$v_c(t) = -100 \cos (1000t + 30°)$$

Determine: (*a*) the energy stored in the capacitor at $t = 0$, and 0.001 sec, (*b*) the energy supplied to the capacitor from $t = 0$ to 0.01 sec later, and from 0.001 sec to 0.01 sec from $t = 0$.

Solution (*a*) Since from equation 3–33 the energy stored in a capacitor at a particular instant depends on the voltage across the capacitor at that instant, the voltages at 0 and 0.001 sec are required. So

$$v_c(0) = -100 \cos 30° = -86.6 \text{ volts}$$

$$v_c(0.001) = -100 \cos \left(1000 \times 0.001 \frac{180}{\pi} + 30°\right)$$

$$= -100 \cos 87.3 = -4.72 \text{ volts}$$

Therefore, at $t = 0$ the energy stored in the capacitor is

$$w_c(0) = \tfrac{100}{2} 10^{-6}(-86.6)^2 = 0.375 \text{ watt-seconds}$$

At $t = 0.001$ sec the energy stored in the capacitor is

$$w_c(0.001) = \tfrac{100}{2} 10^{-6}(-4.72)^2 = 1.11 \text{ milliwatt-seconds}$$

(*b*) The energy supplied may be determined from equation 3–31. First, for the 0 to 0.01 sec interval,

$$w_c(0.01) - w_c(0) = \frac{1000}{2}\left[\frac{\cos 2\left(1000 \times 0.01 \frac{180}{\pi} + 30°\right) - \cos 2(30°)}{2000}\right]$$

$$= -0.272 \text{ watt-seconds}$$

Second, for the interval 0.001 to 0.01 sec,

$$w_c(0.01) - w_c(0.001) =$$

$$\frac{1000}{2}\left[\frac{\cos 2\left(1000 \times 0.01 \frac{180}{\pi} + 30°\right) - \cos 2\left(1000 \times 0.001 \frac{180}{\pi} + 30°\right)}{2000}\right]$$

$$= 0.102 \text{ watt-seconds}$$

is the total energy supplied to the capacitor between $t = 0.001$ and $t = 0.01$ sec.

Note the negative value of energy supplied in the 0 to 0.1 sec interval. It means that the circuit during this interval did not absorb energy but returned the amount calculated, to the source, i.e., the capacitor discharged some of its energy.

3.5 The Current Voltage Relation in Inductors.

In addition to resistors and capacitors, a third basic unit (coil of wire, fundamentally) often called a *reactor* (inductor) is used in constructing electrical networks. Typical examples of reactors from practice are shown in Fig. 3–9. The physical simplicity of a reactor is in direct correspondence with the physical simplicity of resistors and capacitors. The current-voltage relation of a reactor is, however, slightly more complex. Thus if the voltage reference plus is at the tail of the current-sensing arrow, the terminal voltage and current functions are related by

$$v(t) = A\frac{di(t)}{dt} + B\,i(t) \tag{3–34}$$

where A and B are positive constants. These constants, from long usage, are designated by R and L, so that the current-voltage equation for a reactor is

$$v(t) = L\frac{di(t)}{dt} + R\,i(t) \tag{3–35}$$

where L and R are positive, real constants. It is important to note that this last equation, in the precise form given, applies to reactors only for the reference orientation specified, namely, reference plus at the tail of the reference arrow.

Because of the plus sign in equation 3–35, the voltage of a reactor may be considered as consisting of two components of voltage which may be considered separately for the purposes of mathematical analysis. Because

Fig. 3–9a. Inductor. (Courtesy, Bud Radio, Inc.)

Fig. 3–9b. Inductor. (Courtesy, General Radio Co.)

of the appearance of the $Ri(t)$ term in equation 3–35, the reactor is said to have a resistive component of voltage. The $L\,di(t)/dt$ term is said to indicate a self-inductive component of voltage and it is common practice to designate as an *inductor* a device for which the R-coefficient of equation 3–35 may be considered as sufficiently small to be neglected for the purposes at hand. Considering the terminal voltage of a reactor as consisting of two components which may be treated separately, on the basis of a common $i(t)$ as in equation 3–35, requires that the reference plus for each component be located at the tail of the reference arrow. A very simple and hence useful identity in reference alignments for all the basic network elements—resistors, capacitors, and reactors (inductors)—is thus established. With this pattern of reference alignments the resistive, capacitive, and self-inductive components may be incorporated into the equations of Kirchhoff's voltage law on a simple basis of identical treatment. The utility of this simplicity is evident even at an elementary level of discussion, and at the level of theoretical investigation or practical usage this simplicity may mean the difference between success and failure.

If a physical element is to be constructed for which the R-coefficient of equation 3–35 is small enough to be neglected, special care must be exercised in this construction. Some inductor construction techniques are as follows: forming the coil of a wire made of twisted strands of very fine enamel-covered wire; giving the coils special shapes; using shielding cans of special material which are as large as space restrictions permit, etc. In addition to making an inductor for a small R-coefficient, the construction is also usually directed toward making the L-coefficient as large as possible. The shaping of the coil is largely utilized for this purpose. However, the two aims of making R small and L large are not independent of each other, so compromise designs must be made. In effect, the design and construction of inductors are complex and very often require the services of a professional expert to realize stringent requirements. Attention must even be given to avoiding introducing capacitive effects from the proximity of the turns of the coil as well as the materials in and about the coil.

Fig. 3–9c. Power system reactor inductor for 300 amperes, 243 volts. (Courtesy, General Electric Co.)

It is possible, in spite of the fact that many complexities arise, to construct coils such that the terminal voltage-current relation for the reference orientations of Fig. 3–10 is practically

$$v_L(t) = v_L(t)_{34} = L_{34}\frac{di(t)_{34}}{dt}$$

$$= L\frac{di(t)}{dt} \qquad (3\text{–}36)$$

The coefficient of self-induction, L, is *by definition always positive* and non-directional so that $L_{34} = L_{43} > 0$.

In terms of sinusoidal operation, which is the theme of this book, for a sinusoidal current function expressed in equivalent complex variable form, i.e.,

$$I(t) = I_m\epsilon^{j\omega t} = |I_m|\,\epsilon^{j\phi}\epsilon^{j\omega t} \qquad (3\text{–}37)$$

Fig. 3–9d. Variable inductor. (Courtesy, General Radio Co.)

the inductor voltage may be expressed as (Fig. 3–10)

$$\begin{aligned} V_L(t) &= V_L(t)_{34} \\ &= L\frac{d}{dt}I_m\epsilon^{j\omega t} \\ &= j\omega L I_m\epsilon^{j\omega t} \end{aligned} \tag{3–38}$$

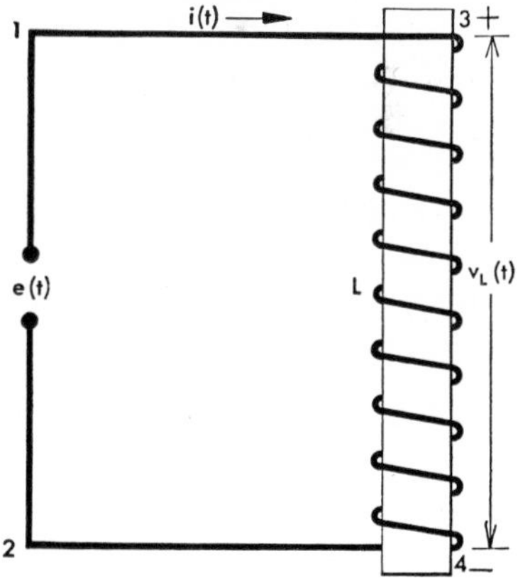

Fig. 3–10.

or, in terms of a reactance symbol,

$$\begin{aligned} V_L(t) &= jX_L I_m\epsilon^{j\omega t} \\ &= X_L|I_m|\epsilon^{j(\omega t+\phi+90)} \\ &= X_L|I_m|[\cos(\omega t+\phi \\ &\quad +90)+j\sin \\ &\quad (\omega t+\phi+90)] \\ &= X_L|I_m|[-\sin(\omega t+\phi) \\ &\quad +j\cos(\omega t+\phi)] \end{aligned} \tag{3–39}$$

where, by definition, for L in henries,

$$X_L \equiv \omega L = 2\pi f L \text{ (ohms)} \tag{3–40}$$

and is called the *inductive reactance* in exact correspondence with the similar definition for the capacitor. An important difference in X_L and X_C should be noted—X_L varies *directly* with the frequency and X_C varies inversely. Also, by definition, note that

$$X_L > 0 \text{ (positive)}$$
$$X_C < 0 \text{ (negative)}$$

Certain immediately evident relations appear from equations 3–37 through 3–40, namely,

$$V_{mL} = j\omega LI_m = jX_LI_m$$
$$V_L = j\omega LI = jX_LI \tag{3–41}$$

and in terms of magnitudes only

$$|V_{mL}| = X_L|I_m|$$
$$|V_L| = X_L|I| \tag{3–42}$$

The real variable or instantaneous sine wave form of the inductor current-voltage relation follows from taking the vertical or j-component of the complex variable expression, so that from equation 3–39

$$v_L(t) = v_L(t)_{34} = X_L|I_m| \cos(\omega t + \phi) \tag{3–43}$$

Thus, as with the capacitor, a cosine wave of voltage arises from a sine wave of current. Note, however, that for the inductor the cosine wave is positive and not negative as for the capacitor. The inductor voltage, therefore, leads the current, or the *current lags the voltage* as it is commonly stated, by 90 degrees. Also, to determine the complex number form of the inductor voltage, the current is to be multiplied by jX_L. This multiplying factor is symbolically just like the similarly used factor for a capacitor, namely, jX_C, but has a different effect because of the difference in the definitions of X_L and X_C.

Example 3:4 A coil of wire has an inductance $L = \dfrac{10}{2\pi}$ mh. A sine wave of current of frequency 1000 cps and effective value of 20 amp is assigned to this coil. The current has a time phase shift of 15 degrees. Determine the reactance and various forms of the voltage across the terminals of the inductor. Assume no resistance in the coil.

Solution Because the inductance is given in millihenrys, it must be converted to henries by dividing by 1000 in order to compute the reactance in ohms. Then

$$X_L \equiv \omega L = \frac{2\pi 1000}{1000}\,\frac{10}{2\pi} = 10 \text{ ohms}$$

The rotating vector form of the inductor voltage is

$$\begin{aligned} V_L(t) &= jX_LI(t) = j10I(t) = j10 \times 20\sqrt{2}\epsilon^{j6283t}\epsilon^{j15} \\ &= 282.8\epsilon^{j(6283t+105)} \\ &= 282.8\,[\cos(6283t + 105°) + j\sin(6283t + 105°)] \end{aligned}$$

The stationary vector rms value form of this voltage is

$$V_L = jX_LI = j10 \times 20\epsilon^{j15} = j200\epsilon^{j15}$$
$$= 200\epsilon^{j105} = -51.8 + j193.2$$

The sine wave form of the inductor voltage is

$$v_L(t) = X_L|I_m| \cos(\omega t + \phi)$$

which may be taken directly from the complex variable form of the voltage as

$$v_L(t) = 282.8 \sin(6283t + 105°)$$
$$= 282.8 \cos(6283t + 15°)$$

Of course, the rms value of the inductor voltage is

$$|V_L| = X_L|I| = 10 \cdot 20 = 200$$

and the maximum value is

$$|V_{mL}| = 200\sqrt{2} = 282.8$$

The vector diagram and sine waves of Fig. 3–11 represent the inductor current and voltage relations.

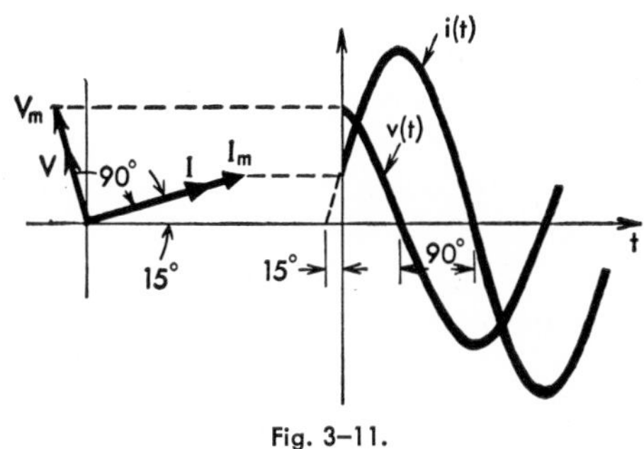

Fig. 3–11.

A brief comparative summary of the current-voltage relations of resistors, capacitors, and inductors should serve at this point to fix them more firmly in mind. Assuming a *sine wave* of current:

(1) The resistor, capacitor, and inductor voltages are all *sine waves*—the resistor voltage *in phase* with the current, the capacitor voltage *lagging* the current by 90 degrees (negative cosine wave), and the inductor voltage *leading* the current by 90 degrees (positive cosine wave).

(2) These voltages may be obtained by multiplying the *complex number* form of the current by a factor—a real number $R(R > 0)$ for the resistor, a pure imaginary $jX_C(X_C < 0)$ for a capacitor, and a pure imaginary $jX_L(X_L > 0)$ for an inductor.

(3) The effective or maximum values of the resistance, capacitance, or inductance voltages may be calculated by merely multiplying the effective or maximum value of the current by R, $|X_C|$, or X_L, respectively.

(4) Of course, dividing the proper voltage by the corresponding factor of (2) and (3) determines the current of the resistor, capacitor, or inductor.

A brief comparative summary of the physical aspects of resistors, capacitors, and inductors should serve at this point also to help orient the beginner in the direction of abstraction which the profession of electrical engineering is unquestionably going. As pointed out in the foregoing, determination of whether a two-terminal electrical network unit is an R-element (resistor), a C-element (capacitor), an L-element (inductor), or perhaps a combination of these basic elements can only be accomplished by: (1) measurements on the physical unit with an ammeter and a voltmeter; and (2) correlation of these observations with the mathematical relations of equations 3–1, 3–22, or 3–36 or with a sum formed from some combination of these same mathematical relations. There is a distinct tendency to lose sight of this fact as two-terminal units labeled, specifically or by implication, as resistors, capacitors, or inductors are casually used to form electrical networks in all fields of practical electrical usage as well as in all electrical laboratories.

One of the principal sources of certainty that a two-terminal network element may be classed as an R-element, a C-element, an L-element, or a combination of them is familiarity with the physical forms which these elements commonly assume. For many ordinary uses, conducting plates separated by non-conducting plates are unquestionably considered as capacitors—Fig. 3–5*a*. Or coils of wire are with certainty taken as inductors. The familiar physical forms of resistors are more varied and so not so easily recognized. The heavy grids of Figs. 3–1*c* and 3–1*d* might be interpreted unquestionably as resistors, although only by an expert in the field of electrical engineering practice. Apparently, familiarity serves to identify certain physical forms of two-terminal elements but with reservations. These reservations become even more impressive on recognition of the fact that a two-terminal element which behaves as an R-element, a C-element, an L-element, or a particular combination of them, in say a 60 cps power system, would not behave even remotely in the same manner if incorporated into a radio system. Perhaps this particular example is extreme enough to seem completely beyond the realm of reasonableness. Consider, instead then, the interchange of some set of basic elements from a two-wire telephone system into one of the micro-wave telephone systems. There is no assurance that an R-element of one system will be an R-element in the other. The C-elements and L-elements similarly do not retain their electrical properties unaltered through such a transfer.

Appearances are also very deceptive in another sense. Precisely the same appearance of a two-terminal electrical network element may cover a radical change in the materials of which the device is constructed. For example, a non-magnetic supporting mechanism may replace a similarly constructed one of magnetic material. A coil then changes its electrical behavior so drastically that there is some question whether it can in any

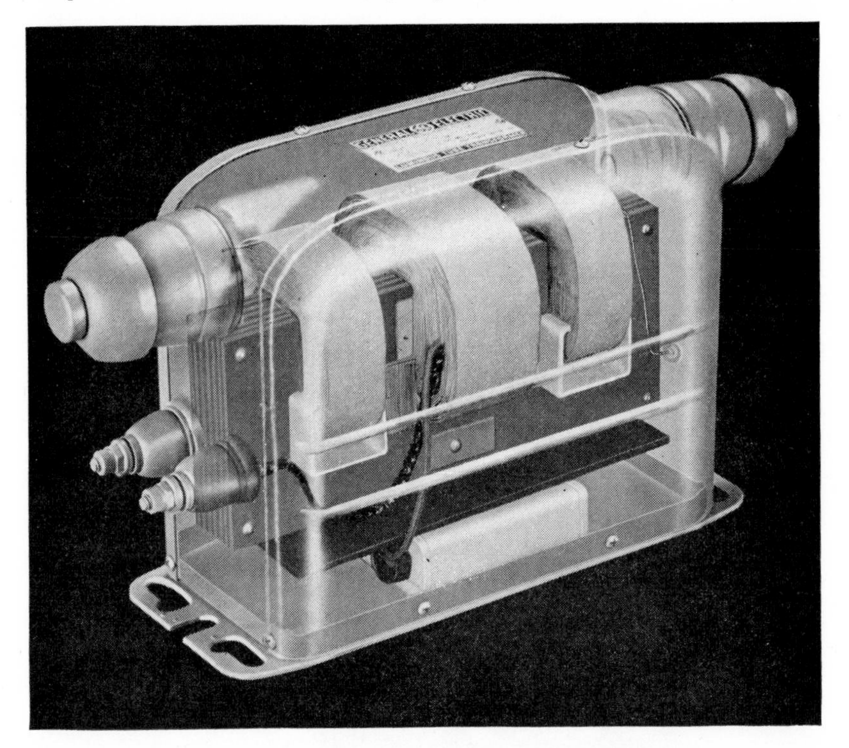

Fig. 3–12a. Phantom view of 0.250–kva transformer; 15,000/115 volts, 300 milliampere secondary. (Courtesy, General Electric Co.)

real sense still be called an inductor. The iron-cored coil is said to be inductive, but users of such coils are very careful to avoid the mistake of assuming that the coil behaves electrically like a coil which has no magnetic material associated with it.

Unquestionably, therefore, the final and conclusive criterion for the R, C, L characterization of a two-terminal electrical network element is that of correlation of ammeter and voltmeter observations with particular mathematical relations.

3.6 The Current-Voltage Relation of Mutual Induction.

Very early in experimental observations of the electrical behavior of coils of wire near each other, it was found that a voltage may be measured across the open-circuited terminals of one coil for a varying current of the other coil. Such voltages are named *mutual induction* voltages, in contrast to the self-induction voltages, $v_L(t)$, discussed in the preceding section. The terms self and mutual are used to describe the location of the induction voltage—self being applied to induction voltages of the conductor with the varying current, and mutual to induction voltages of con-

Fig. 3–12*b*. Cutaway view of distribution transformer. (Courtesy, Westinghouse Electric & Mfg. Co.)

ductors other than the one with varying current. The application of the principle of mutual induction appears in the literally hundreds of thousands of transformers being used today, typical illustrations of which, as used in practice, are shown in Fig. 3–12.

Various factors in the physical make-up of two coils and their surroundings affect the pattern of mutual induction. The space position of the coils with respect to each other, the direction of winding of the coils, the material in and about the coils, and the material of which the coils are wound are all such factors.

Fig. 3–12c. Large power transformer. (Courtesy, Westinghouse Electric & Mfg. Co.)

Also the relative alignment of references is determining in so far as signs in equations are concerned. On the whole the mutual induction problem seems complex. Careful consideration of the situation, however, leads to a final technique which is very simple.

A physical arrangement, illustrated by Fig. 3–13—two coils located in space just as shown—is found experimentally to specify a mathematical relation between $i_1(t)$ and $v_2(t)$ and between $i_2(t)$ and $v_1(t)$ under the following restrictions: for the reference orientations shown (non-magnetic media throughout)

$$\frac{v_2(t)}{\dfrac{di_1(t)}{dt}} = \frac{v_1(t)}{\dfrac{di_2(t)}{dt}} = \text{same real constant}$$

or in alternative forms: for coil A open, and D operative

$$v_{21}(t) = v_1(t) = M_{AD}\frac{di_2(t)}{dt} = M_{AD}\frac{di_{43}(t)}{dt},\ M_{AD} > 0 \qquad \text{(3–44)}$$

and for coil D open, coil A operative

$$v_{43}(t) = v_2(t) = M_{AD}\frac{di_1(t)}{dt} = M_{AD}\frac{di_{21}(t)}{dt}, \; M_{AD} > 0 \qquad (3\text{–}45)$$

The most effective way to treat the general pattern of mutual induction is to consider deviations from a basic arrangement such as Fig. 3–13.

Experimental observation indicates that reversing the direction of winding of either coil of Fig. 3–13 has the sole effect of changing the sign of equations 3–44 and 3–45. Further, experimental observation shows that as the coils are shifted in space with respect to each other only two effects are noted: the numerical value of the constant and the sign of equations 3–44 and 3–45 change. Thus the sole effect on equations 3–44 and 3–45 of winding reversal or space relocation is simple, although exactly which sign is to be used in a particular case is not simple to determine until certain conventions are firmly established. No consideration is given here to assigning numerical magnitudes to the M-coefficient.

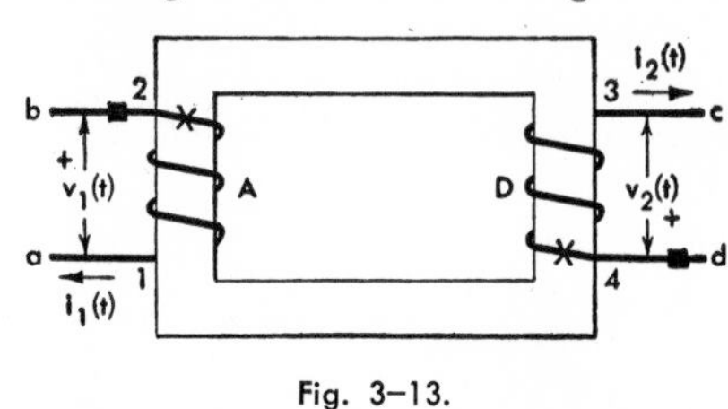

Fig. 3–13.

Consider then the problem of choice of signs to be used in the mutual induction equations. The basis from which a start is here made is given in Fig. 3–13. The rectangular marks in the figure—*actual* mutual induction polarity marks—are so established, by convention, for a particular winding pattern and space location that, with reference plus at these marks and current reference arrows directed into a coil at such a mark, equations 3–44 and 3–45 are *always* valid exactly as given. Methods of locating the actual mutual-induction polarity marks are discussed in the next section.

While it is possible to establish the current-voltage equations from the known location of *actual* mutual-induction polarity marks, it is more convenient and, indeed, almost mandatory to use *reference* mutual-induction polarity marks for general situations such as conductors moving with respect to each other in space. This more general approach of using reference mutual induction marks also makes all problems dealing with mutual induction simpler; so, contrary to many situations, the most general approach simplifies both the very complex and the very simple problems.

The *reference* mutual induction marks may be assigned arbitrarily, as may those for the current and voltage, but the most convenient scheme is to fix these reference mutual induction marks at the tail of current-sensing arrows along with reference plus for voltage. Thus the mutual-induction reference marks are *always* to be located at the tail of the reference arrow of the element as by the x marks of Fig. 3–13. In addition, the mutual induction coefficient, M, carries a sign when in numerical form according to:

$M > 0$ if reference and actual mutual induction marks coincide on both coils or fail to coincide on both coils;

$M < 0$ if only one reference and its corresponding actual mutual induction mark do not coincide.

For the arrangement in Fig. 3–13, $M_{AD} = M_{DA} > 0$.

Location of the reference mutual induction marks always at the tail of the reference arrow in effect *always* presents the basic situation of Fig. 3–13. Therefore, equations 3–44 and 3–45 may be used without exception to specify the mutual-induction current-voltage relation with no concern over the actual alignment of coils until numerical computations are to be performed. The sign of M is then easy to establish from the relative alignment of *reference* and *actual* mutual induction marks.

Example 3:5 Establish the Kirchhoff voltage equations for Fig. 3–14 where the actual mutual-induction polarity marks (squares) are associated with the

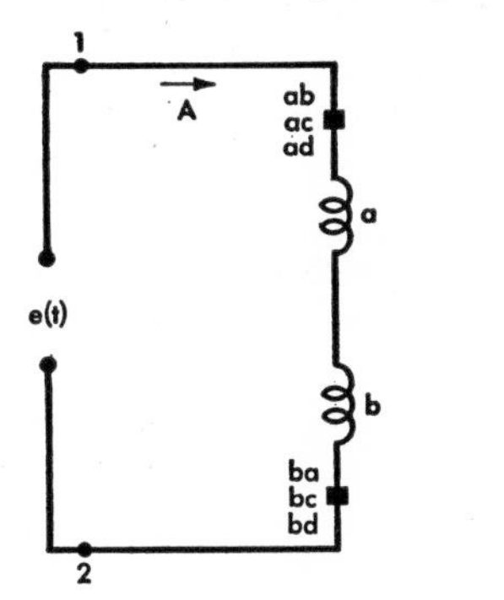

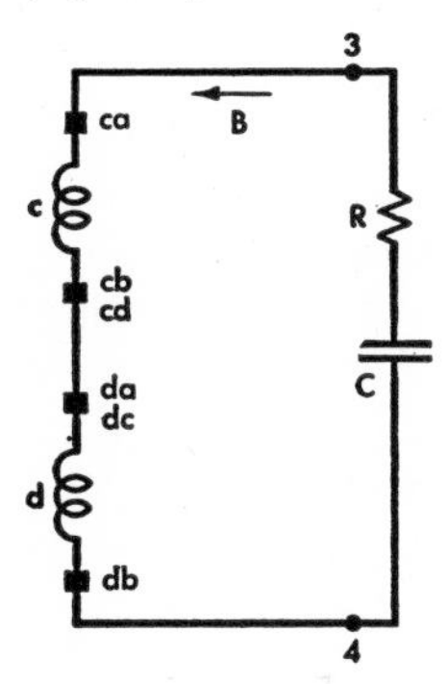

Fig. 3–14.

proper coils by the pairs of letters; i.e., *ab* and *ba* at squares indicate the actual mutual-induction polarity marks for coils *a* and *b*. The elaborateness of this pattern of *actual* mutual-induction polarity marks is another reason for avoiding consideration of this pattern when it is possible to do so. Incidentally the pattern of actual mutual-induction polarity marks in Fig. 3–14 is precisely that required for four coils with one particular and possible space orientation.

Solution The KVL (Kirchhoff voltage law) equations do not depend on the complex pattern of actual mutual-induction polarity marks but only on the simple alignment of reference marks here set—all at the tail of sensing arrows, hence all aligned the same way with respect to the two circuits.

The equation for the A circuit of Fig. 3–14 is, first in terms of voltage symbols—all voltage references at the tail of the A arrow—with double subscripts on the M's indicating the two coils under consideration and not the location of references

$$e(t) + v_{Ra}(t) + v_{La}(t) + v_{ab}(t) + v_{ac}(t) + v_{ad}(t) + v_{Rb}(t) + v_{Lb}(t) + v_{ba}(t) + v_{bc}(t) + v_{bd}(t) = 0$$

or in terms of the $i(t)$

$$e(t) + R_a i_A(t) + L_a \frac{di_A(t)}{dt} + M_{ab}\frac{di_A(t)}{dt} + M_{ac}\frac{di_B(t)}{dt} + M_{ad}\frac{di_B(t)}{dt}$$

$$+ R_b i_A(t) + L_b \frac{di_A(t)}{dt} + M_{ba}\frac{di_A(t)}{dt} + M_{bc}\frac{di_B(t)}{dt} + M_{bd}\frac{di_B(t)}{dt} = 0 \qquad (3\text{–}46)$$

Similarly, only plus signs appear in the equation for the B circuit, which is

$$Ri_B(t) + \frac{q_B(t)}{C} + v_c(0) + R_c i_B(t) + L_c\frac{di_B(t)}{dt} + R_d i_B(t) + L_d\frac{di_B(t)}{dt}$$

$$+ M_{cd}\frac{di_B(t)}{dt} + M_{ca}\frac{di_A(t)}{dt} + M_{cb}\frac{di_A(t)}{dt} + M_{dc}\frac{di_B(t)}{dt}$$

$$+ M_{da}\frac{di_A(t)}{dt} + M_{db}\frac{di_A(t)}{dt} = 0 \qquad (3\text{–}47)$$

In terms of the variable $q(t)$, this last equation is, if $\dot{q}(t)$ and $\ddot{q}(t)$ indicate respectively the first and second derivatives with respect to t,

$$R\dot{q}_B(t) + \frac{q_B(t)}{C} + v_c(0) + R_c\dot{q}_B(t) + L_c\ddot{q}_B(t) + R_d\dot{q}_B(t) + L_d\ddot{q}_B(t)$$

$$+ M_{cd}\ddot{q}_B(t) + M_{ca}\ddot{q}_A(t) + M_{cb}\ddot{q}_A(t) + M_{dc}\ddot{q}_B(t)$$

$$+ M_{da}\ddot{q}_A(t) + M_{db}\ddot{q}_A(t) = 0 \qquad (3\text{–}48)$$

Notice that the *actual* mutual-induction polarity marks do not enter the problem of forming the foregoing equations. Only at the stage where numerical values are to be assigned to the M-coefficients need the actual mutual-induction polarity marks be considered. Then, based on the conventions regarding reference alignments—voltage plus and mutual induction x at the tail of the sensing arrow

$$M_{ab} = M_{ba} < 0;\ M_{ac} = M_{ca} > 0;\ M_{ad} = M_{da} > 0;\ M_{bc} = M_{cb} > 0;$$
$$M_{bd} = M_{db} > 0;\quad M_{cd} = M_{dc} < 0$$

3.7 Some Methods of Locating Actual Mutual-Induction Polarity Marks.

The actual mutual-induction polarity marks may be placed on a pair of coils by inspection provided the coils have a common or very nearly common axis, as coils a, b, c of Fig. 3–15. The actual mutual-induction polarity marks are located as shown—on like terminals for the same direction of winding, and on opposite terminals for opposite directions of winding.

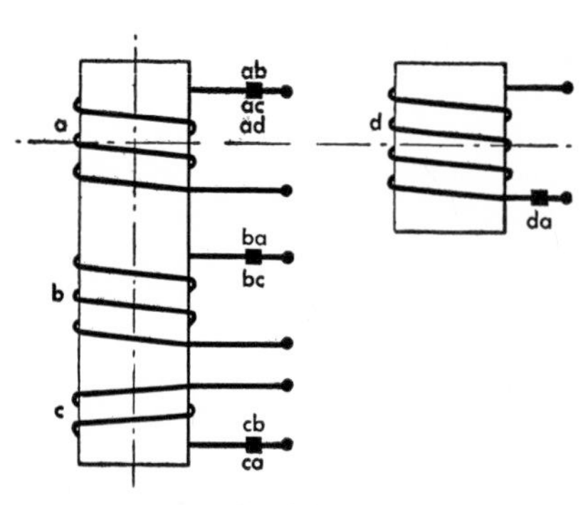

Fig. 3–15.

If the windings have a common center line, as coils a and d in Fig. 3–15, or very nearly so, the coils may be imagined as moved onto a common axis along the center line. If the winding directions are the same for this imagined coincidence, non-corresponding terminals in the common axis position (coils a and d of Fig. 3–15) are marked; if the winding directions are not the same in the common axis position, corresponding terminals in the common axis position are marked.

In practice it is usually difficult to determine the exact relation of the coils if they are not marked when wound. They are submerged in oil, wrapped in varnished cambric, buried in wax, or otherwise covered with insulation so that it is almost necessary to destroy the coils to determine their relation to each other. Often the manufacturer marks mutual induction devices for polarity by attaching some sort of marker to the

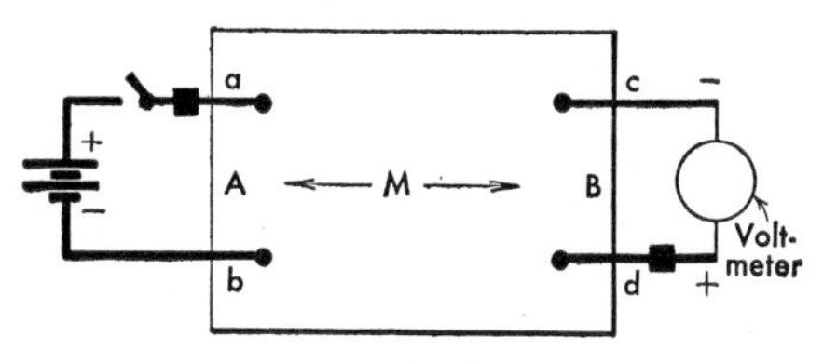

Fig. 3–16.

proper leads or by using colored wires. Where the coils are not marked for polarity and where it is difficult or impossible to tell from inspection the relative orientation of the coils, the following electrical tests may be used.

The arrangement shown in Fig. 3–16 can be used to determine the proper polarity marking. A battery and a D'Arsonval voltmeter are connected to the four terminals of the magnetically coupled elements. When the switch is closed to the battery a momentary deflection of the voltmeter can be noted. When the direction of this deflection is positive,

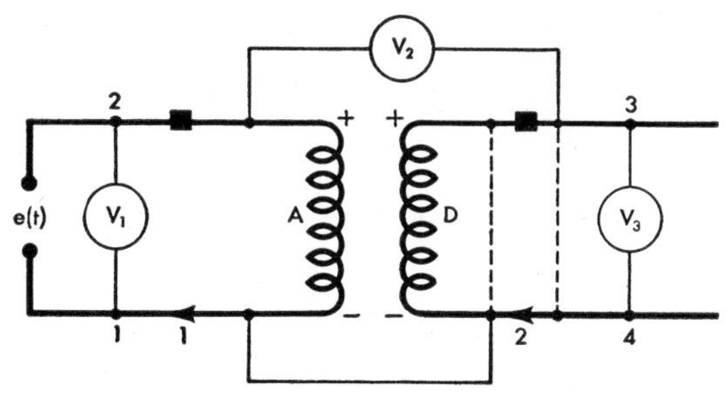

Fig. 3–17.

the polarity marks are located at the positive terminals as shown in Fig. 3–16. If the deflection is negative, the coil polarity mark is placed at the negative voltmeter terminal.

A widely used alternative technique for determining the polarity marking of magnetically coupled windings may be deduced as follows. As shown in Fig. 3–17, because the current in coil 3–4 is zero, the voltage across coil 2–1 does not include a mutual induction voltage but is (neglecting resistance for the moment)

$$E(t)_{21} = V(t)_{21} = V_{m21}\epsilon^{j\omega t} = j\omega L_{21} I_{m21}\epsilon^{j\omega t} \tag{3–49}$$

The voltage due to mutual induction which appears across coil 3–4 is, in accordance with the polarity mark convention already established,

$$V(t)_{34} = V_{m34}\epsilon^{j\omega t} = j\omega M_{DA} I_{m21}\epsilon^{j\omega t} \tag{3–50}$$

But these last two equations show that the voltages V_{34} and V_{21} are in phase, i.e., the terminals 2 and 3 are always either both positive or both negative. But note that these same terminals are also polarity marked for magnetic coupling. Because of this correspondence in magnetic coupling polarity marks and voltage polarity, a voltmeter can be used to establish the magnetic coupling polarity marks as follows. If terminals 1 and 4 are connected as shown in Fig. 3–17, the voltmeter indications $|V_1|$, $|V_2|$, and $|V_3|$ are related by

$$|V_2| \simeq ||V_1| - |V_3|| \tag{3–51}$$

because $|V_2|$ is the rms value of the *difference* between the two coil voltages. If, as is always the case in practice, resistive effects are present, the voltmeter indication $|V_2|$ will not be exactly equal to the difference between $|V_1|$ and $|V_3|$ but it will be near enough so that $|V_2|$ is obviously the difference rather than the sum of $|V_1|$ and $|V_3|$. On the other hand, if terminal 1 is connected to 3 rather than 4, approximately the voltage *sum* $|V_1| + |V_3|$ appears on a voltmeter $|V_2|$ connected to the two terminals not already joined (2 and 4). Accordingly, if *any* two of the terminals (one from each coil) of two magnetically coupled windings are connected and a voltmeter is connected to the remaining two terminals: (*a*) the two terminals to which the voltmeter is connected should be polarity marked if the voltmeter indication is approximately the difference between the voltages of the two windings; (*b*) if the voltmeter indicates approximately the sum of the two coil voltages, one of the terminals to which the voltmeter is connected and the terminal on the other winding to which the voltmeter is *not* connected should be polarity marked.

The sine wave, mutual induction voltage relation follows immediately from assuming a sinusoidal current in rotating vector form in one coil, say 3–4, of Fig. 3–17, i.e.,

$$I(t)_{34} = I_{m34}\epsilon^{j\omega t} = |I_{m34}|\epsilon^{j\phi}\epsilon^{j\omega t}$$

Once more it should be noted that the replacement of the sine wave by a rotating vector is valid only because the j-component of

$$\frac{d}{dt} I_m\epsilon^{j\omega t} = \frac{d}{dt}|I_m| \cos(\omega t + \phi) + j\frac{d}{dt}|I_m| \sin(\omega t + \phi)$$

is exactly the same as the derivative of the sinusoid, namely,

$$\frac{d}{dt}|I_m| \sin(\omega t + \phi)$$

Then, from Fig. 3–17, $M_{AD} < 0$.

$$V_{M1}(t) = M_{AD} \frac{d}{dt} I_{m2}\epsilon^{j\omega t} = j\omega M_{AD} I_{m2}\epsilon^{j\omega t}$$

which will be written as

$$V_{M1}(t) = jX_{AD} I_{m2}\epsilon^{j\omega t} \tag{3–52}$$

from which

$$\begin{aligned} V_{M1}(t) &= X_{AD}|I_{m2}|[\cos(\omega t + \phi + 90°) + j\sin(\omega t + \phi + 90°)] \\ &= X_{AD}|I_{m2}|[-\sin(\omega t + \phi) + j\cos(\omega t + \phi)] \end{aligned} \tag{3–53}$$

and instantaneously

$$v_{M1}(t) = X_{AD}|I_{m2}|\cos(\omega t + \phi)$$

Note that

$$X_{AD} = \omega M_{AD} = 2\pi f M_{AD} \tag{3–54}$$

is the mutual induction reactance in exact correspondence with the self-induction reactance.

The stationary vector and magnitude relations for mutual induction current and voltage are

$$\begin{aligned} V_{mM1} &= jX_{AD} I_{m2} \\ V_{M1} &= jX_{AD} I_2 \end{aligned} \tag{3–55}$$

and

$$\begin{aligned} |V_{mM1}| &= X_{AD}|I_{m2}| \\ |V_{M1}| &= X_{AD}|I_2| \end{aligned} \tag{3–56}$$

3.8 Power and Energy Relations in Inductors.

The equation for the instantaneous power for an inductor is

$$\begin{aligned} p_L(t) &= v_L(t)i(t) = |V_{mL}|\cos(\omega t + \phi)|I_m|\sin(\omega t + \phi) \\ &= \frac{|V_{mL}|\,|I_m|}{2} \sin 2(\omega t + \phi) \end{aligned} \tag{3–57}$$

and the terminal instantaneous power of an inductor for sinusoidal current variation is a double-frequency sine wave identical, except for the minus sign, with the corresponding expression for the instantaneous power of a capacitor (equation 3–29).

By simply adding the minus sign to the corresponding capacitor relations (equations 3–30 and 3–31) the average power for an inductor for sinusoidal current variation is

$$P = \frac{1}{\frac{1}{f}} \int_0^{1/f} p(t)\, dt = 0 \tag{3–58}$$

and the total energy supplied in $t_2 - t_1$ seconds is

$$w_L(t_2) - w_L(t_1) = \frac{-|I_m|\,|V_{mL}|}{2}\left[\frac{\cos 2(\omega t_2 + \phi) - \cos 2(\omega t_1 + \phi)}{2\omega}\right] \quad (3\text{–}59)$$

Because the only difference between the energy supplied to or absorbed by an inductor and that supplied to or absorbed by a capacitor is a negative sign, there would seem to be little more to say about the inductor power and energy relations that has not already been said about the corresponding capacitor relations. However, an examination of the physical properties of an inductor suggests a possible difference. Because there is no magnetic field about an inductor when the current is zero, there can be no energy stored in the magnetic field or associated with the inductor when the current is zero. Suppose, therefore, the starting point for computing the energy stored in, or absorbed by, the inductor is taken at the current zero. Then if t_1 is such that $i(t_1) = 0$,

$$w_L(t) - w_L(t_1) = \int_{t_1}^{t} p_L(t)\,dt = \int_{t_1}^{t} v_L(t)i(t)\,dt$$

But because

$$v_L(t) = L\,\frac{di(t)}{dt}$$

the inductor energy equation becomes

$$w_L(t) - w_L(t_1) = \int_{t_1}^{t} L\,\frac{di(t)}{dt}\,i(t)\,dt = L\int_{t_1}^{t} \frac{d}{dt}\,\frac{i(t)^2}{2}\,dt \quad (3\text{–}60)$$

Carrying out the indicated integration gives

$$w_L(t) - w_L(t_1) = \frac{L}{2}\,[i(t)^2 - i(t_1)^2] \quad (3\text{–}61)$$

and for $i(t_1) = 0$,

$$w_L(t) = \tfrac{1}{2}Li(t)^2 \quad (3\text{–}62)$$

The energy stored in an inductor at any instant, therefore, is directly proportional to the square of the current in the inductor at that instant and in no way depends on the manner of variation of the current.

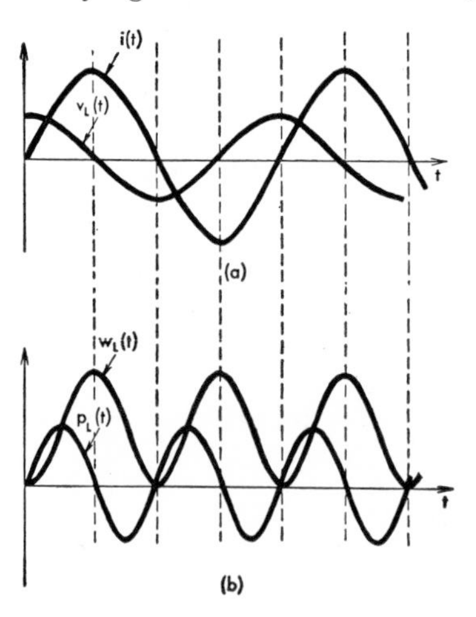

Fig. 3–18.

The curves of Fig. 3–18 show the sinusoidal current, voltage, power, and stored-energy relations of an inductor. Note that the energy is a maximum for maximum $i(t)$. Also the sign of the $p(t)$ determines whether energy is being absorbed—positive power—by the magnetic field of the inductor, or whether the field is returning the energy—negative power—to the source. As with the capacitor, the energy supplied oscillates between a constant maximum value and zero. Hence, as for a capacitor, the inductor does not dissipate any energy but returns it to the source.

Consider once more the fact that the power and energy relations of capacitors and inductors, when expressed from a common $t = 0$ point (equations 3–29, 3–31, 3–57, and 3–59), are simply the negative of each other. It is often said that if a pure inductor and capacitor are connected in series so that the same current is in each, the energy must be passed back and forth from the electric field of the capacitor to the magnetic field of the inductor, and vice versa. Consequently, as might be expected, series circuits containing capacitors and inductors have some unusual properties, which are discussed in the next chapter.

A comparison of the energy relations of resistors, capacitors, and inductors shows that *on the average* resistors return none of the energy they absorb whereas capacitors and inductors return all the energy they absorb. Instantaneously, resistors still do not return any energy to the source whereas capacitors and inductors may be absorbing energy or returning it, depending on the instant of consideration.

Example 3:6 The current in coil 3–4 of Fig. 3–19 is $i(t)_{dc} = 10 \sin(377t - 30°)$. The circuit constants are $L_{12} = 0.02$ henry, $L_{34} = 0.04$ henry, $|M_{ab}| = |M_{ba}| = 0.01$ henry, and $R = 10$ ohms. Assume all other resistances zero in order to emphasize as much as possible the inductive effects. Determine the voltages $v(t)_{ab}$ and $V(t)_{ab}$, and draw the complete vector diagram. What is the energy stored in each coil when $t = 0$? What is the energy supplied by the generator in 0.03 sec from $t = 0$? Determine the magnitude and polarity of each of the induction voltages at $t = 0$.

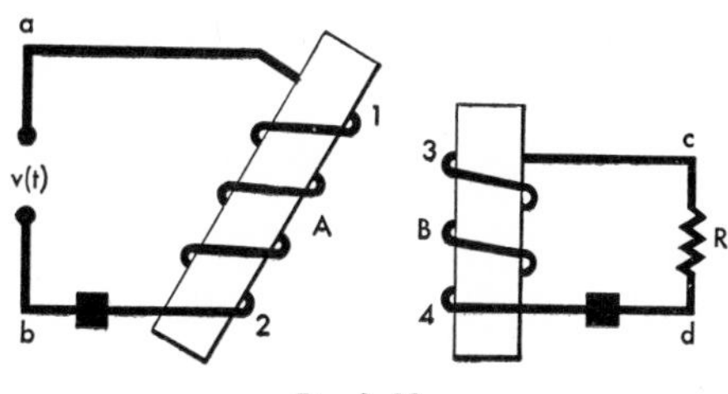

Fig. 3–19.

Solution In order to solve this problem, the Kirchhoff voltage equations must be used. The voltage equation for the 3–4–d–c mesh is

$$v(t)_{dc} + v_L(t)_{34} + v_M(t)_{34} = 0$$

or, in terms of the current,

$$R_{dc}i(t)_{34} + L_{34}\frac{di(t)_{34}}{dt} + M_{BA}\frac{di(t)_{12}}{dt} = 0 \tag{3-63}$$

where $M_{BA} = 0.01 > 0$ because the reference mutual induction marks are at 1 and at 3, first of subscripts, so neither coincides with the actual mutual induction marks. Since all the factors of this equation are known except $i(t)_{12}$, the equation may be used to solve for $i(t)_{12}$. The process of solution will be easier if complex numbers are used. Equation 3–63 may be written in complex variable as

$$R_{dc}I(t)_{34} + L_{34}\frac{dI(t)_{34}}{dt} = -M_{BA}\frac{dI(t)_{12}}{dt} \tag{3-64}$$

The known factors in this equation are

$$I(t)_{dc} = I(t)_{34} = 10\epsilon^{j(377t-30)} = (8.66 - j5)\epsilon^{j377t}$$
$$V(t)_{dc} = R_{cd}I(t)_{34} = 100\epsilon^{j(377t-30)} = (86.6 - j50)\epsilon^{j377t}$$
$$V_L(t)_{34} = L_{34}\frac{dI(t)_{34}}{dt} = j377 \times 0.04(8.66 - j5)\epsilon^{j377t} = (75.4 + j130.6)\epsilon^{j377t}$$
$$= 151\epsilon^{j(377t+60)}$$

Substituting these results in equation 3–64 and solving for the derivative of the current give

$$\frac{dI(t)_{12}}{dt} = \frac{-1}{0.01}[(86.6-j50)\epsilon^{j377t}+(75.4+j131)\epsilon^{j377t}] = -(16{,}200+j8076)\epsilon^{j377t}$$

Integrating this result to find $I(t)_{12}$, and assuming the integration constant as zero, since direct current does not exist in the circuit, gives

$$I(t)_{12} = -\frac{16{,}200 + j8076}{j377}\epsilon^{j377t} = -(21.4 - j43)\epsilon^{j377t} = 48\epsilon^{j(377t+116.5)}$$

To proceed now to the mesh a–b–2–1, the voltage equation, in complex form, is

$$V(t)_{ab} = V(t)_{12} = V_L(t)_{12} + V_M(t)_{12} = L_{12}\frac{dI(t)_{12}}{dt} + M_{AB}\frac{dI(t)_{34}}{dt}$$

Substituting known values on the right-hand side of this equation gives

$$V(t)_{ab} = -0.02(16{,}200 + j8076)\epsilon^{j377t} + 0.01(1885 + j3265)\epsilon^{j377t}$$
$$= -(305.2 + j128.6)\epsilon^{j377t} = 331\epsilon^{j(377t+202.8)}$$

The sine wave form of this equation is

$$v(t)_{ab} = 331 \sin(377t + 202.8°)$$

If the complex number expression for the total voltage of this circuit looking in at the a–b terminal is divided by the complex number form of the current at this point, a complex number is determined which is called impedance and is symbolized by $Z_0 = R_0 + jX_0$. This relation is treated in detail in the next chapter. For the present the ratio indicated is

$$Z_0 = \frac{V_{12}}{I_{12}} = \frac{V_{ab}}{I_{ba}} = \frac{V_{mab}}{I_{mba}} = \frac{331\epsilon^{j202.8}}{48\epsilon^{j116.5}} = 6.89\epsilon^{j86.3}$$
$$= 0.434 + j6.8 = R_0 + jX_0$$

Now to show that R_0 is an equivalent resistance, multiply this value by $|I_{12}|^2$ and compare with the power loss in the load resistor R. The result is

$$P_0 = R_0|I_{12}|^2 = 0.434\left[\frac{48}{\sqrt{2}}\right]^2 = 500$$

and the loss in the resistor R is

$$P_R = R|I_{cd}|^2 = 10\left[\frac{10}{\sqrt{2}}\right]^2 = 500 \text{ watts}$$

Since these two power losses are equal, evidently the factor R_0 is an equivalent resistance.

The energy stored in coil A at $t = 0$ is from equation 3–62

$$w_L(0)_{12} = \tfrac{1}{2}L_{12}i^2(0)_{12}$$

Since the instantaneous current in a circuit is the vertical component of the rotating vector representing that current at that instant, at $t = 0$,

$$I(0)_{12} = -21.4 + j43$$

and

$$i(0)_{12} = 43$$

so

$$w_L(0)_{12} = \tfrac{1}{2}\,0.02(43)^2 = 18.49 \text{ watt-seconds}$$

The energy stored in coil B at $t = 0$ is

$$w_L(0)_{34} = \tfrac{1}{2}L_{34}i^2(0)_{34}$$

The current $i(0)_{34}$ is from the sine wave given in the problem statement,

$$i(0)_{34} = i(0)_{dc} = 10 \sin(-30°) = -5 \text{ amp}$$

Accordingly,

$$w_L(0)_{34} = \tfrac{1}{2}\,0.04(-5)^2 = 0.50 \text{ watt-seconds}$$

The energy supplied to the circuit in 0.03 sec from $t = 0$ may be obtained from

$$w(0.03) = \int_0^{0.03} p(t)\,dt$$

The instantaneous power is the product

$$p(t)_{12} = v(t)_{12}i(t)_{12}$$

which from already calculated results is

$$\begin{aligned} p(t)_{12} &= 331 \sin(377t + 202.8°)48 \sin(377t + 116.5°) \\ &= \frac{15{,}888}{2}[\cos 86.3° - \cos(754t + 319.3°)] \\ p(t)_{12} &= 512.4 - 7944 \cos(754t + 319.3°) \end{aligned}$$

The energy is then

$$\begin{aligned} w_0(0.03) &= \int_0^{0.03} [512.4 - 7944 \cos(754t + 319.3°)]\,dt \\ &= 15.37 - \tfrac{7944}{754} \sin(754t + 319.3°)\Big|_0^{0.03} \\ &= 15.37 - 10.53[\sin(1295° + 319.3°) - \sin 319.3°] \\ &= 15.37 - 10.53[\sin 1614.3° - \sin 319.3°] \\ &= 15.37 - 10.53(0.753) \\ &= 7.44 \text{ watt-seconds supplied by the source} \end{aligned}$$

in 0.03 sec from $t = 0$.

The polarity and magnitude of the induction voltages may be readily obtained from their vector forms as follows. The current derivatives are

$$\frac{dI(t)_{dc}}{dt} = \frac{dI(t)_{34}}{dt} = \frac{d}{dt}[10\epsilon^{j(377t-30)}]$$
$$= j3770\epsilon^{j(377t-30)} = j(3265 - j1885)\epsilon^{j377t}$$

and, as already computed,

$$\frac{dI(t)_{12}}{dt} = (-16{,}200 - j8076)\epsilon^{j377t}$$

The induction voltages are then at $t = 0$.

$$V_{mM34} = M_{BA}\frac{dI(0)_{12}}{dt} = -162 - j81$$
$$V_{mM12} = M_{AB}\frac{dI(0)_{34}}{dt} = 18.85 + j32.65$$
$$V_{mL12} = L_{12}\frac{dI(0)_{12}}{dt} = -324 - j162$$
$$V_{mL34} = L_{34}\frac{dI(t)_{34}}{dt} = 75.4 + j130.6$$

From the fact that the *vertical* or *j-component* of these maximum value vectors represents the instantaneous circuit condition at $t = 0$, the mutual induction voltage in coil B is 81 volts positive at terminal 4. At $t = 0$ the mutual induction voltage in coil A is 32.65 volts positive at terminal 1. At $t = 0$ the self-induction voltage in coil B is 130.6 volts positive at terminal 3. And at $t = 0$ the self-induction voltage in coil A is 162 volts positive at terminal 2.

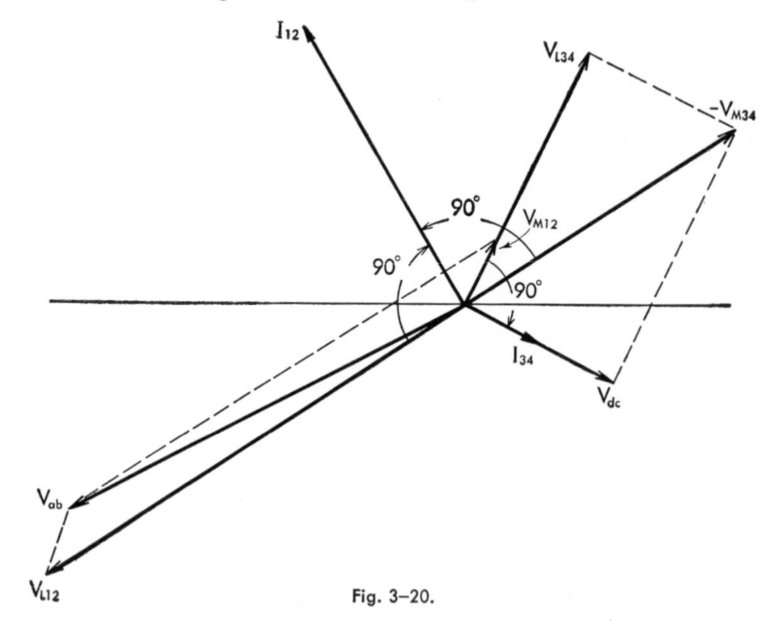

Fig. 3–20.

An overall view of these results can be shown on such a vector diagram as Fig. 3–20. This vector diagram may be considered as being of either maximum or effective values. Multiplying or dividing by $\sqrt{2}$ is all that is required to change from one to the other.

PROBLEMS

3–1 A current, in milliamperes, of $i(t) = 14.14 \sin (10^6 t - 45°)$ is to be in a non-inductive 10-ohm resistor of a radio set. (*a*) What is the sine wave equation for the voltage across the resistor? (*b*) Sketch the current and voltage waves and draw, to scale, the maximum and effective value vector diagram (Fig. 3–3). (*c*) What are the complex numbers representing the current and voltage? Take the ratio of these complex numbers, V/I. To what physical factor of the circuit does this ratio correspond? (*d*) What is the power supplied to the resistor? What is the energy supplied in 1 sec, from $t = 0$? What is the power factor? What are the volt-amperes $|U|$, and the reactive volt-amperes Q?

3–2 Repeat Problem 3–1 if the resistor is now replaced by a 2-μf capacitor of a telephone circuit and the current is given in milliamperes. Telephone circuits operate on a band of frequencies—audio frequencies—of about 60 to 8000 cps. An average performance is sometimes calculated on the assumption that $f = 1000$. This problem may be worked out on such an assumption. What is the energy stored in the capacitor at $t = 0$?

3–3 A capacitor is sometimes connected across the terminals of a motor to improve the power factor. Suppose that such a capacitor of 100 μf is left across the line to help improve the power factor of a factory even though its particular motor is being repaired. The line connecting the capacitor to the substation—power company terminals—has a resistance of 5 ohms. The current in the line and capacitor is

$$i(t) = 2.83 \sin (377t - 30°) \text{ amperes}$$

(*a*) What are the sine wave equations for each of the voltages and the total voltage? (The voltages may be added as $v_0(t) = v_R(t) + v_c(t)$, and the resultant sine wave determined as in Chap. 1.) (*b*) Sketch the current, each component voltage (resistor and capacitor), and the total voltage in terms of sinusoids, and (to scale) the complete maximum and effective value vector system. Mark all angles, magnitudes, etc. (*c*) What are the complex numbers representing each of the four quantities of (*b*)? Evaluate the ratio of V/I for the complex numbers for the total voltage and the current. To what do the two components thus determined correspond in this problem? This factor is known as the impedance and is symbolized by Z. It is considered in detail in the next chapter. (*d*) What is the instantaneous and average power supplied to the resistor? To the capacitor? To the whole circuit? What is the energy supplied in 1.11 seconds from $t = 0$ to the resistor and to the capacitor? What is the power factor? What are the total volt-amperes?

3–4 Coils may be constructed which, at radio frequencies, may be considered purely inductive. Such inductors, connected across (in parallel with) a capacitor, are in common use in radio and telephony as so-called tuning circuits. Suppose a coil of 0.016 henry is used in such a tuning circuit with a capacitor of 1.66 $\mu\mu$f. The frequency is 10^6 cps and the current in the inductor

$$i(t) = 1.5 \sin (\omega t + 15°) \text{ (milliamperes)}$$

(*a*) What is the voltage across the inductor in the forms V_m, V, $V(t)$, $v(t)$? (*b*) What is the current through the capacitor in the forms I_m, I, $I(t)$, $i(t)$? (*c*) Add the inductor and capacitor currents to form the total current and express in the forms I_{m0}, I_0, $I_0(t)$, $i_0(t)$. (*d*) Find the ratio V/I_0. This result should equal the reciprocal of $(1/jX_L) + (1/jX_C)$, which is the impedance of the L and C parallel circuit.

3–5 Short sections—up to about 30 miles—of the two-wire rural electrification power lines, forming a vast network over the rural areas of the country, can be represented electrically by a non-inductive resistor in series with a pure inductor. Suppose a short circuit is accidentally placed on the end of a section of such a line. The line has a resistance of 5 ohms and an inductance of 0.2 henry. The current in the short circuit is

$$i(t) = 283 \sin (377t - 45°) \text{ amperes}$$

Answer the questions of Problem 3–3 with the required modification in the problem statement.

3–6 Assume a 1000-cps current $i(t) = 28.28 \sin \omega t$(ma) is desired in a series tuning circuit of a 10-ohm resistor, a 5-ohm inductive reactor, and a 10-ohm capacitive reactor. Repeat Problem 3–3, but now in terms of the three circuit elements and the four voltages.

3–7 Give an argument proving that equation 3–45 is correct for the assumptions: (*a*) $i(t)_{21} > 0$ and decreasing; (*b*) $i(t)_{21} < 0$ and increasing; and (*c*) $i(t)_{21} < 0$ and decreasing.

3–8 Suppose the current in coil B of Fig. 3–19 is $I_{34} = 1 - j1$ amperes, and in coil A, $I_{12} = -10 + j20$ amperes. Suppose also $L_{12} = 0.02h$, $L_{34} = 0.04h$, and $|M_{AB}| = 0.01h$, $\omega = 377$. Find: (*a*) V_{M12}, V_{L34}, V_{M34}, and V_{L12}. (*b*) From the j-components of the maximum value vectors determine the actual self and mutual induction voltages in the circuit at $t = 0$. Mark these four voltages with magnitude and polarity on a diagram.

3–9 A D'Arsonval voltmeter connected across a circuit terminal cd, as in Fig. 3–16, indicates a positive polarity at c when a battery with plus at a is connected to terminals ab. The polarity marking of the two coils of the circuit is thereby determined. Suppose this circuit is then connected to a generator and load so that the currents in the load and generator are

$$\begin{aligned} i(t)_{ab} &= 3.6 \sin (10^6 t + 30°) \text{ milliamperes} \\ i(t)_{cd} &= 2.0 \sin 10^6 t \text{ milliamperes} \\ L_{ab} &= 3\mu\text{h} \\ L_{cd} &= 5\mu\text{h} \\ |M_{AB}| &= |M_{BA}| = 2\mu\text{h} \end{aligned}$$

Find: (*a*) V_{Mab}; V_{Lab}; V_{Mcd}; V_{Lcd}. (*b*) Show on a diagram the polarity and magnitude of these voltages at $t = 0$. (*c*) What is the energy stored in each coil due to the current in that coil one-fourth cycle after $t = 0$?

3–10 The currents in the circuit of Fig. 3–21 are

$$I_{ab} = 10 + j0$$
$$I_{cd} = 3 + j4$$
$$I_{ef} = 8 - j6$$

Also $L_A = 0.1h$, $L_B = 0.2h$, $L_C = 0.3h$, $|M_{AB}| = 0.1h$, $|M_{AC}| = 0.15h$, $|M_{BC}| = 0.25h$, $\omega = 377$. (*a*) Find: V_{Mab}, V_{Lab}, V_{Mcd}, V_{Lcd}, V_{Mef}, V_{Lef}. (*b*) Indicate on a diagram the instantaneous polarity and magnitude of each of these voltages at $t = 0$. (*c*) What is the energy stored in each coil at $t = 0$ due to the current in that coil? Note in part (*a*) that V_{Mab}, V_{Mcd}, and V_{Mef} are each the sum of two mutual induction voltages.

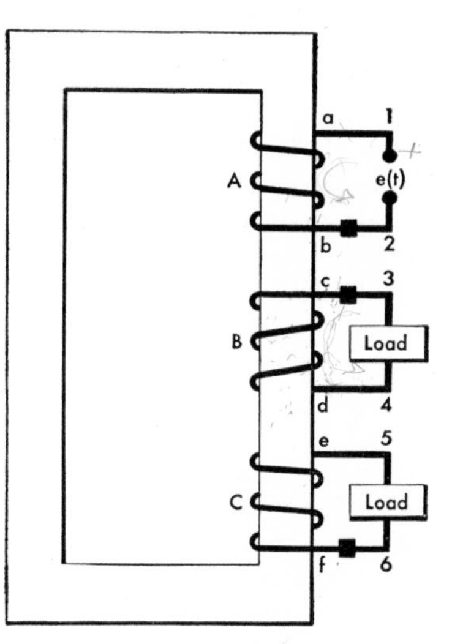

Fig. 3–21.

3–11 Three winding transformers are in common use in both power and communication systems. Such a transformer may be represented diagrammatically by Fig. 3–21. Write the equations for V_{34} and V_{56} of this transformer if the generator terminal voltage is sinusoidal. Assume different values of mutual induction between each pair of coils. Pay particular attention to the signs of the mutual induction terms.

3–12 Repeat the preceding problem for a four-winding transformer. Coils A and B are wound in one direction and coils C and D in the other direction. Generators are located in coils A and C.

3–13 The two windings of a transformer connected in series as in Fig. 3–22 form a reactor which in emergencies may be useful since four values of reactance may be obtained by using each coil separately or the two coils in series aiding or

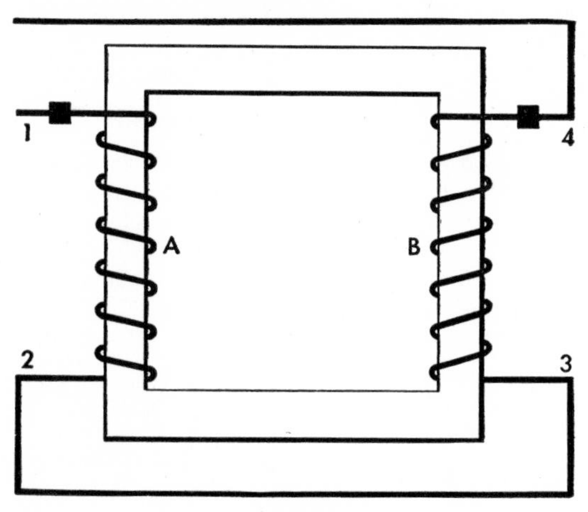

Fig. 3–22.

opposing. To demonstrate the latter possibilities, derive the expressions for the equivalent coefficient of self-induction for a circuit of two transformer coils electrically in series—aiding magnetically and opposing magnetically. Show that the equivalent L_0 for coils aiding is (refer to Fig. 3–22)

$$L_0 = L_{12} + 2M_{AB} + L_{34}, M_{AB} > 0$$

and for coils opposing

$$L_0 = L_{12} + 2M_{AB} + L_{34}, M_{AB} < 0$$

3–14 Suppose that the two-winding power transformer illustrated in Fig. 3–22 is in use as a reactor. Assume the circuit constants are $L_A = 0.05$ henry, $L_B = 0.03$ henry. $|M_{AB}| = 0.02$, $R_A = 2$ ohms, and $R_B = 5$ ohms. The current in coil A is $I(t)_{12} = (6 + j8)\epsilon^{j377t}$ amperes. (*a*) Find $V(t)_{31}$, $v(t)_{31}$, V_{12}, V_{23}, and total P. What is the energy stored in each coil one half cycle after $t = 0$ due to the current in that coil? What is the energy supplied to the whole circuit in 0.01 sec from $t = 0$? Draw the complete vector diagram. (*b*) Repeat part (*a*) if 2 is connected to 4 rather than 3.

3–15 Assume a current $i(t)_{cd} = 20 \sin 1000t$ amperes in coil B of the three winding transformer of Fig. 3–21. The circuit parameters $L_{56} = 0.05$ henry, $L_{34} = 0.01$ henry, $L_{ab} = 0.08$ henry, $L_{cd} = 0.05$ henry, $L_{ef} = 0.1$ henry. $|M_{AB}| = 0.057$ henry, $|M_{BC}| = 0.054$ henry, and $|M_{AC}| = 0.044$ henry. Neglect all resistances. Determine $v(t)_{56}$ and $V(t)_{56}$ and draw the complete vector diagram. What is the energy stored in each coil one quarter cycle after $t = 0$ due to the current in that coil? What is the energy supplied by the generator in 0.02 sec from $t = 0$?

3–16 Sketch free-hand but carefully the current, voltage, power, and energy curves for a current of

$$i(t) = 10 \sin (\omega t + 30°) \text{ amperes}$$

through a 10-ohm resistor. Place the curves so that their values can be compared at corresponding instants. Trace step by step for at least one cycle the significance of the curves and their relations to each other. Particular attention should be paid to the energy curve.

3–17 Repeat the preceding problem for an inductor.

3–18 Repeat Problem 3–16 for a capacitor.

CHAPTER 4

The General Series Circuit of Constant Circuit Elements

In the preceding chapters it was pointed out that a sinusoid is a good approximation to the usual commercial alternating current and voltage. It was further noted that, even if the alternating current could not be represented satisfactorily by a single sine wave, the sum of several different frequency sine waves could be used to represent any periodic a-c voltage or current variation. The characteristics of the sinusoid were studied and, to make the formulas more compact and hence simpler and more effective, the vector representation of a sine wave was considered. To still further facilitate the treatment of alternating currents, the complex number treatment of two-dimensional vectors was introduced and the method of transforming from the complex number to the sinusoid, and vice versa, was considered.

The four fundamental quantities—current, voltage, power, and energy—and their interrelations were introduced and defined and the results were applied to the three basic circuit elements—resistance, inductance, and capacitance. The next step is naturally a study of the current, voltage, power, and energy relations of combinations of resistors, inductors, and capacitors. This chapter is devoted to the simplest type of such a combination—the series circuit. Examples of resistors, capacitors, and inductors installed in practice are shown in Fig. 4–1.

4.1 The Solution of the Equation for a Series Circuit.

A detailed study of a complete series circuit is essential for two reasons. First, by means of such a study the foundation may be laid for studying more complicated networks. Also all networks are constructed of branches in which usually more than one of the three fundamental circuit elements are present. And last, a general series circuit, as is shown subsequently, has some very interesting properties which are extremely useful in certain circumstances but are to be avoided in others.

The series circuit represented in Fig. 4–2*a* may be considered to be the most general possible since it contains all the basic circuit elements—

Fig. 4–1a. Resistors, inductors, and capacitors as installed in the final amplifier of the WCBS 50-kw transmitter. (Courtesy, Columbia Broadcasting System)

resistance, capacitance, self-inductance, and mutual inductance. This circuit may be simplified to the form shown in Fig. 4–2*b* without any loss of generality by combining the three induction coefficients into a single term as given by Problem 3–13.

The series resistance indicated in Fig. 4–2 represents the total resistance and includes the resistance of the capacitor as well as the resistance of the coil. Actually, of course, it is not possible to separate a coil or

Fig. 4–1b. Inductors, capacitors, and resistor installations.

capacitor and its resistance in any such manner. However, for the purposes of computation and visualization this representation is very useful, for it serves to simplify the appearance of the circuit and its equations.

Since Kirchhoff's voltage and current laws form the basis of all network studies, it is with Kirchhoff's voltage law that the study of a series circuit is started. This equation for the general series circuit of Fig. 4–2*b* is

$$v_0(t) = R\dot{q}(t) + L\ddot{q}(t) + \frac{1}{C}\,q(t) + v_c(0)$$

or, if the equation is written in complex variable or rotating vector form,

$$V_0(t) = R\dot{Q}(t) + L\ddot{Q}(t) + \frac{1}{C}\,Q(t) + V_c(0) \tag{4–1}$$

This is the differential equation of the general series circuit.

The complete solution of this differential equation is given in full detail in Chap. 8. For the present, only the steady state solution (i.e., the usual operating condition) will be considered. Since the current in a resistor, inductor, or capacitor was shown in the preceding chapter to be sinusoidal if the connected voltage is sinusoidal or vice versa, there is little doubt that the current through a complete series circuit, such as shown in Fig. 4–2*b*, will be sinusoidal if the voltage across its terminals is sinusoidal. Accordingly, if the terminal voltage of the circuit is assumed to be sinusoidal and of the rotating vector form,

$$V(t) = V_m\epsilon^{j\omega t} = |V_m|\epsilon^{j\phi}\epsilon^{j\omega t}$$

a sinusoidal response, which in rotating vector form may be expressed as

$$\begin{aligned} Q(t) &= |Q_m|\ \epsilon^{j(\phi+\theta-90)}\ \epsilon^{j\omega t} + Q_0 = Q_m\ \epsilon^{j\omega t} + Q_0 \\ I(t) &= \dot{Q}(t) = j\omega Q_m\,\epsilon^{j\omega t} = I_m\,\epsilon^{j\omega t} \end{aligned} \tag{4–2}$$

8-50

may be expected in the circuit. The angles θ and $-90°$ are added in anticipation of the results to be obtained. Determination of Q_m and Q_0 by substitution of the assumed solution in equation 4–1 establishes equation 4–2 as a solution. Thus equation 4–1 becomes

$$V_m\,\epsilon^{j\omega t} = j\omega\left(R + j\omega L + \frac{1}{j\omega C}\right)Q_m\,\epsilon^{j\omega t} + V_c(0) + \frac{Q_0}{C}$$

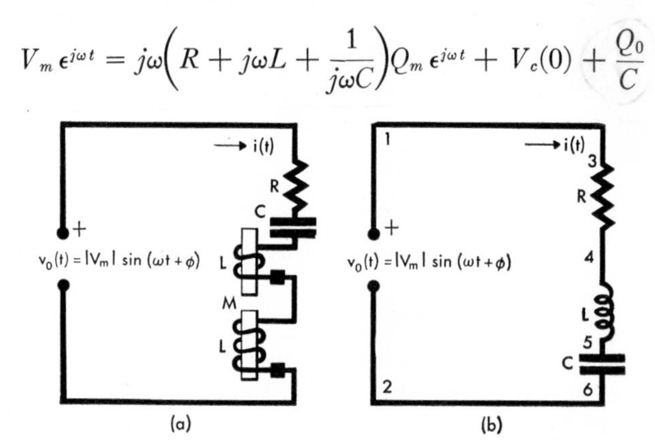

Fig. 4–2.

Since this relation must hold for *all values of t*, the equations

$$\begin{aligned} V_m &= \left(R + j\omega L + \frac{1}{j\omega C}\right)I_m = ZI_m = Zj\omega Q_m \\ Q_0 &= -CV_c(0) \end{aligned} \tag{4–3}$$

define Q_m and Q_0 so that equation 4–2 is a solution of equation 4–1; i.e., this solution is (verify by substitution in equation 4–1)

$$Q(t) = \frac{V_m}{j\omega Z}\,\epsilon^{j\omega t} - CV_c(0) \tag{4–4}$$

The factor

$$Z \equiv R + j\omega L + \frac{1}{j\omega C} \tag{4–5}$$

is known as the *impedance* of the circuit. Alternative forms of the impedance from this last equation are

$$Z \equiv R + j\left(\omega L - \frac{1}{\omega C}\right) = R + j(X_L + X_C) = R + jX_0$$
$$= \sqrt{R^2 + (X_L + X_C)^2}\epsilon^{j\sigma} = \sqrt{R^2 + X_0{}^2}\epsilon^{j\sigma} = |Z|\epsilon^{j\sigma} \quad (4\text{–}6)$$

where

$$X_0 \equiv X_L + X_C \quad (4\text{–}7)$$

is the total or equivalent reactance of the circuit, and

$$\sigma \equiv \tan^{-1}\frac{X_L + X_C}{R} = \tan^{-1}\frac{X_0}{R} \quad (4\text{–}8)$$

is the impedance angle.

From equation 4–3 the impedance also may be expressed as

$$Z = |Z|\epsilon^{j\sigma} = \frac{V_m}{I_m} = \frac{V}{I} = \frac{|V_m|\epsilon^{j\phi}}{|I_m|\epsilon^{j\phi}\epsilon^{j\theta}} = \frac{|V_m|}{|I_m|}\epsilon^{-j\theta} \quad (4\text{–}9)$$

which is the Ohm's form for the current-voltage relation. Note that the impedance angle σ is

$$\sigma = -\theta \quad (4\text{–}10)$$

and that θ is *the phase angle between the voltage and current.* This phase angle θ is positive if the current *leads* the voltage and *negative* if the current *lags* the voltage.*

The angle θ, known as the power factor angle, has already been discussed in Art. 1–7 in connection with power relations. Because of the definition of Z as given in equation 4–6, the graphical representation of Fig. 4–3 relates the resistance, reactances, impedance, power factor angle, and impedance angle. Thus, because $\cos\theta = \cos(-\theta)$

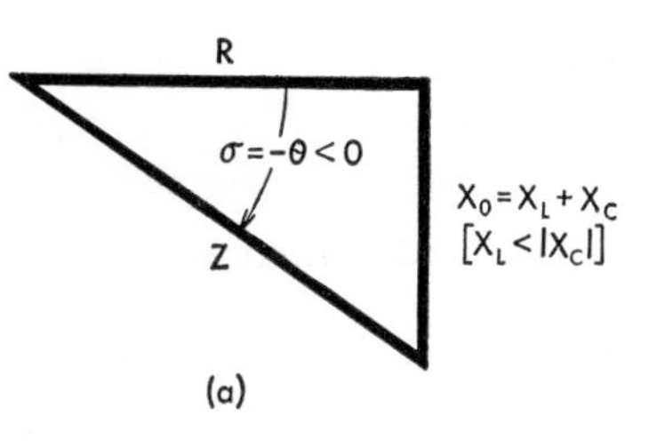

(a)

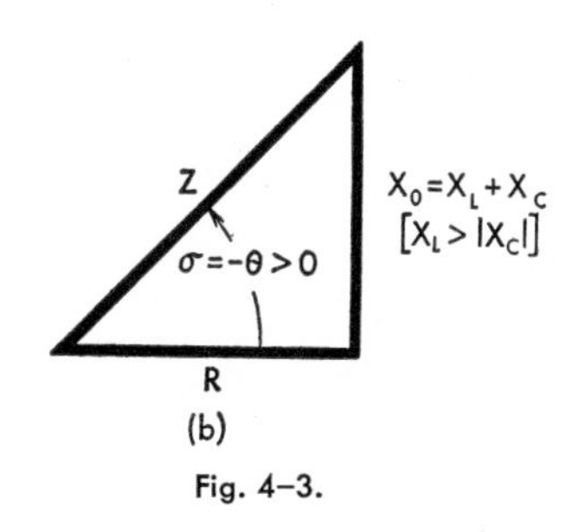

(b)

Fig. 4–3.

$$\text{power factor} = pf = \cos\theta = \cos\sigma = \frac{R}{|Z|} \quad (4\text{–}11)$$

* The power factor angle definition in use in this book fits the present international agreement to represent the reactive factor ($\sin\theta$) as negative for lagging current. The AIEE is at the moment in the process of attempting to change this definition. Since it will not be possible to present both definitions and since the change from one to the other is so simple, which definition is presented is relatively unimportant as long as it is used consistently. Consequently the existing standard will be used in this book.

from which, of course,

$$R = |Z| \cos \sigma = |Z| \cos \theta$$

Also from equations 4–6 and 4–10, or Fig. 4–3,

$$X_0 \equiv X_L + X_C = |Z| \sin \sigma = - |Z| \sin \theta \qquad (4\text{–}12)$$

or

$$-X_0 \equiv -(X_L + X_C) = |Z| \sin \theta$$

and

$$\text{reactive factor} = rf = \sin \theta = \frac{-X_0}{|Z|} = -\sin \sigma \qquad (4\text{–}13)$$

Because

$$\theta = -\sigma = -\tan^{-1}\frac{X_0}{R} = -\tan^{-1}\frac{X_L + X_C}{R} \qquad (4\text{–}14)$$

and R is always positive, σ must be a first or fourth quadrant angle and so must θ. It is also evident from equation 4–16 and the discussion immediately following equation 4–10 that

if $|X_C| > X_L$ or $X_L = 0$, then $\frac{\pi}{2} \geq \theta > 0$, the current *leads* the voltage

if $|X_C| < X_L$ or $X_C = 0$, then $-\frac{\pi}{2} \leq \theta < 0$, the current *lags* the voltage

if $|X_C| = X_L$, then $\theta = 0$, the current is *in phase* with the voltage

In addition to specifying the current of the circuit, the complex constant I_m specifies the voltages according to

$$V_R(t) = RI(t) = RI_m\epsilon^{j\omega t} \qquad (4\text{–}15)$$

$$V_L(t) = L\dot{I}(t) = j\omega LI_m\epsilon^{j\omega t} = jX_LI_m\epsilon^{j\omega t} \qquad (4\text{–}16)$$

$$V_C(t) = \frac{Q_c(t)}{C} = \frac{Q(t) + CV_c(0)}{C} = \frac{V_m}{j\omega CZ}\epsilon^{j\omega t}$$

$$= jX_CI_m\epsilon^{j\omega t} \qquad (4\text{–}17)$$

Note also that the current and voltage *vectors*, or *complex numbers*, or the ones which rotate, bear a constant relation to each other, i.e., they are separated by a constant angle, have a constant magnitude ratio, and rotate together. The vector diagrams which are drawn to illustrate circuit relations are of necessity stationary and should be considered as being instantaneous snapshots, taken at $t = 0$, of a system of vectors rotating *counterclockwise* at f revolutions per second.

The vector diagram of a series circuit of R, L, and C, $X_L > |X_C|$, is shown in Fig. 4–4*a*. A case of special interest is given by the vector diagram of Fig. 4–4*b*. This diagram represents the $t = 0$ position of the rotating vector system as occurring at the instant the current vector is horizontal or the instantaneous current is zero, i.e., the current vector coincides with the axis of reference. Note that the only difference between the vector diagrams of Fig. 4–4 is the position of the vectors with respect to the reference axis. The effect of the angles θ and ϕ are clearly shown by the vector diagrams. They serve to locate the current and voltage vectors with respect to the $t = 0$ reference axis and each other. The vector diagram of Fig. 4–4 also serves to show typically all the voltages

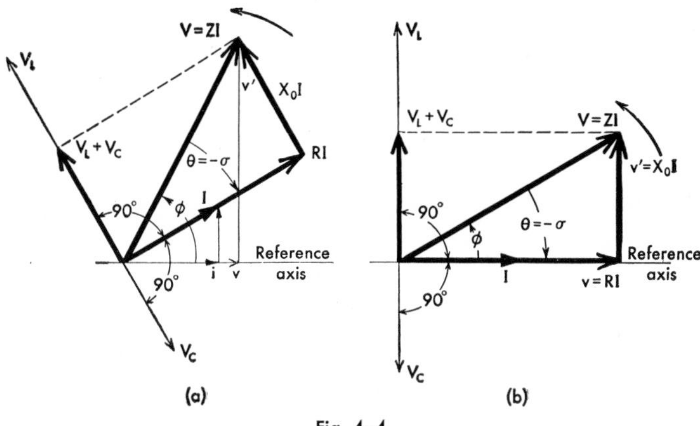

Fig. 4–4.

and the current of a series circuit of R, L, and C. The voltage across the resistor is in phase with the current, the voltage across the inductor leads the current by exactly 90 degrees, and the capacitor voltage lags the current by exactly 90 degrees. The resultant reactance voltage—sum of capacitor and inductor voltages—is at right angles to the current and resistor voltage as shown. This resultant reactance voltage will lead or lag the current depending on whether the inductor voltage or the capacitor voltage is greater.

Example 4:1 The total voltage and current of the laboratory test circuit—R, L, C series as in Fig. 4–2*b*—are given in complex variable form (rotating vector) by

$$I(t) = I(t)_{34} = 14.14\epsilon^{j(377t-20)} \text{ amperes}$$
$$V_0(t) = V(t)_{36} = 282.8\epsilon^{j(377t+10)} \text{ volts}$$

Determine: V_0, Z_0, I, R, X_0, P, Q, $|U|$, V_R, V_X, pf, rf, f, X_L, X_C, θ, σ, and $|Z_0|$. Draw the complete vector diagram. Determine the values of $i(0)$, $v_X(0)$, $v_R(0)$, and $v(0)_{36}$, and write the equations for $v_X(t)$, $v_R(t)$, and $i(t)$.

Solution The $t = 0$, effective value vector for the total impedance voltage is

$$\frac{V_0(0)}{\sqrt{2}} = V_0 = \frac{|V_m|}{\sqrt{2}}\epsilon^{j\phi} = \frac{282.8}{\sqrt{2}}\epsilon^{j10} = \frac{282.8}{\sqrt{2}}(\cos 10° + j \sin 10°)$$
$$V_0 = 197.0 + j34.7 = 200\,\epsilon^{j10}$$

The $t = 0$, effective value vector for the current is

$$\frac{I(0)}{\sqrt{2}} = I = \frac{14.14}{\sqrt{2}}[\cos(-20°) + j \sin(-20°)]$$

$$I = I_{34} = 9.4 - j3.42 = 10\epsilon^{-j20}$$

Then the impedance is the ratio of this voltage and current

$$Z_0 = \frac{V}{I} = \frac{197 + j34.7}{9.4 - j3.42} = \frac{200\epsilon^{j10}}{10\epsilon^{-j20}} = 20\epsilon^{j30} = 17.32 + j10$$

from which

$$|Z| = \sqrt{R^2 + X_0^2} = 20 \text{ ohms}$$
$$R = 17.32 \text{ ohms}$$
$$X_0 = 10 \text{ ohms}$$
$$\sigma = \tan^{-1}\frac{X_0}{R} = 30 \text{ degrees}$$

The total average power is

$$P = |V_0||I| \cos\theta = 10 \times 200 \times 0.866 = 1732 \text{ watts}$$

or

$$= V_0 \cdot I = 197 \times 9.4 + 34.7 \times (-3.42) = 1732 \text{ watts}$$

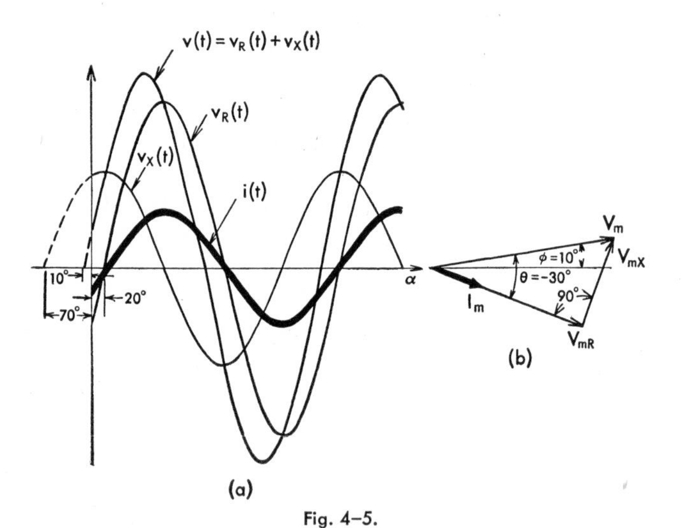

Fig. 4–5.

The apparent power is

$$|U| = |V_0||I| = 2000 \text{ va} = 2 \text{ kva}$$

The reactive factor is, since $\theta = -\sigma = -30°$,

$$rf = \sin\theta = \sin(-30°) = \frac{-X_0}{|Z|} = -0.5,$$

and the power factor is

$$pf = \cos\theta = \cos(-30°) = \frac{R}{|Z|} = 0.866$$

The reactive volt-amperes are

$$Q = |V_0||I|\sin\theta = -1000 \text{ vars}$$

In order to express V_R and V_X as complex numbers, equation 4–9 may be used. The *impedance of the resistor only* is $Z_R = R$, hence

$$V_R = Z_R I = (R + j0)I = 17.32 \times 10\epsilon^{-j20} = 173.2\epsilon^{-j20} = 162.8 - j59.2.$$

Also, the impedance of the total reactance is $Z_X = 0 + jX_0$, so

$$V_X = Z_X I = jX_0 I = 10\epsilon^{j90}\,10\epsilon^{-j20} = 100\epsilon^{j70}$$
$$= j10(9.4 - j3.42) = 34.2 + j94$$

These relations are shown on the vector diagram of Fig. 4–5*b* and the sine waves of Fig. 4–5*a*.

The instantaneous values of the current and voltages at $t = 0$ may be determined immediately from the complex numbers, for, from definition, the projection of a maximum value current or voltage vector onto the vertical axis gives the instantaneous current or voltage. Therefore,

$$i(0)_{34} = -3.42\sqrt{2} = -4.8 \text{ amp}$$

which is a current of 4.8 amp from 4 to 3 of Fig. 4–2*b* at the $t = 0$ instant. The instantaneous voltage across the total reactance—both L and C—at $t = 0$, from the vertical or j-component of V_X, is

$$v_X(0)_{46} = 94 \times \sqrt{2} = 132.9 \text{ volts}$$

that across the resistor, from the j-component of V_R, is

$$v_R(0)_{34} = -59.2 \times \sqrt{2} = -83.7 \text{ volts}$$

and that across the total series circuit, from the j-component of V_0, is

$$v(0)_{36} = 34.7 \times \sqrt{2} = 49.2 \text{ volts}$$

Note that the instantaneous voltage sum, at $t = 0$,

$$v_R(0)_{34} + v_X(0)_{46} = -83.7 + 132.9 = 49.2 = v(0)_{36}$$

The equation for $v_X(t)$ may be written immediately from the expression for V_X, since V_X gives the position of the V_X vector at $t = 0$. Hence

$$V_X(t) = \sqrt{2}V_X\epsilon^{j\omega t} = \sqrt{2}\,100\epsilon^{j70}\epsilon^{j377t} = 141.4\epsilon^{j(377t+70)}$$

and the vertical or j-component is

$$v_X(t) = 141.4\sin(377t + 70°)$$

The frequency is, from the coefficient of t already given in the expression for $I(t)$ or $V(t)$,

$$\omega = 2\pi f = 377$$
$$f = \frac{377}{2\pi} = 60 \text{ cps}$$

The individual reactances X_L and X_C cannot be computed from the data given. Because the current lags the total voltage by 30 degrees the circuit is certainly predominantly inductive. However, there may not be any capacitance in the circuit from all that can be determined from the given current and voltage. If capacitance is present, it is only possible to say that $X_L > |X_C|$.

The instantaneous current may be taken directly from the given $I(t)$ as

$$i(t) = 14.14 \sin (377t - 20°)$$

And finally the instantaneous equation for the voltage across the resistance is simply $i(t)$ multiplied by R, which is

$$\begin{aligned} v_R(t) &= 17.32 \times 14.14 \sin (377t - 20°) \\ &= 245 \sin (377t - 20°) \end{aligned}$$

4.2 Admittance, Conductance, and Susceptance.

In considering the Ohm's law equation for a direct current, conductance is defined as the reciprocal of the resistance. Correspondingly, in the symbolic treatment of a-c circuits the reciprocal of the impedance, called *admittance*, is useful. Later in this book, it will be found that the use of the admittance symbol condenses some formulas considerably and, therefore, aids in circuit analysis because the simpler the formula the easier it is to be interpreted.

The admittance for a series circuit is defined as

$$Y \equiv \frac{1}{Z} \equiv \frac{1}{R + jX_0} \text{ mhos}$$

which, if rationalized, becomes

$$Y \equiv \frac{R}{R^2 + X_0^2} + j\frac{-X_0}{R^2 + X_0^2} = \frac{R}{|Z|^2} + j\frac{-X_0}{|Z|^2} \equiv G_0 + jB_0 \quad (4\text{–}18)$$

According to this definition, Y has two components which are designated by

$$G_0 \equiv \frac{R}{|Z|^2} \text{ conductance (mhos)} \quad (4\text{–}19)$$

which for zero frequency gives the d-c form of conductance; and

$$B_0 \equiv \frac{-X_0}{|Z|^2} \text{ susceptance (mhos)} \quad (4\text{–}20)$$

which is zero for zero frequency.

Ohm's law may be expressed in terms of the admittance as

$$I = YV \quad (4\text{–}21)$$

Hence *the admittance is used to multiply voltage to give current.*

As exponentials

$$Y = \frac{1}{|Z|\epsilon^{j\sigma}} = |Y|\epsilon^{-j\sigma} = |Y|\epsilon^{j\theta}$$

and, because $\epsilon^{j\theta}$ has no effect on the *magnitude* of the number—real or complex—which it multiplies, the admittance and impedance are numerical reciprocals

$$|Y| = \frac{1}{|Z|} \tag{4–22}$$

as well as complex number reciprocals. Note that according to equation 4–19, R and G are *not* reciprocals, except for the special case $X_0 = 0$.

Some of the typical and occasionally useful relations in terms of Y, B, G, and Z, X, R are

$$\begin{aligned} pf &= \cos\theta = \frac{G}{|Y|} = \frac{R}{|Z|} \\ rf &= \sin\theta = \frac{B_0}{|Y|} = \frac{-X_0}{|Z|} \\ \theta &= \tan^{-1}\frac{B_0}{G} = \tan^{-1}\frac{-X_0}{R} = -\tan^{-1}\frac{X_0}{R} \\ Q &= B_0|V|^2 = -X_0|I|^2 \text{ vars} \\ P &= G|V|^2 = R|I|^2 \text{ watts} \\ |U| &= |V|\,|I| = |Y|\,|V|^2 = |Z|\,|I|^2 \text{ volt-amperes} \end{aligned} \tag{4–23}$$

Example 4:2 A series circuit is found in the laboratory to have an admittance of

$$Y = 0.08 + j0.06 \text{ mhos}$$

and the connected voltage in the form of the $t = 0$ value of the rotating vector voltage divided by $\sqrt{2}$, i.e., the rms complex number voltage, is

$$V = 80 - j60 \text{ volts}$$

Find: Z, I, $|I|$, $I(t)$, $|I_m|$, V, $V(t)$, $|V_m|$, pf, rf, P, $|U|$, Q, $i(t)$, $v(t)$, V_R, and V_X. Draw the vector diagram.

Solution From the definition,

$$Z \equiv \frac{1}{Y} = \frac{1}{0.08 + j0.06} = \frac{0.08 - j0.06}{0.01}$$

$$Z = |Z|\epsilon^{j\sigma} = 8 - j6 = 10\epsilon^{-j36.9}$$

hence

$$R = 8 \text{ ohms},\ X_0 = -6 \text{ ohms}$$

and the circuit is predominantly capacitive because $X_0 = X_L + X_C = \omega L - 1/\omega C$ is negative only if $1/\omega C > \omega L$.

The power factor is

$$pf = \cos\theta = \frac{R}{|Z|} = \frac{G}{|Y|} = \frac{8}{10} = 0.8$$

and

$$\theta = -\tan^{-1}\frac{X_0}{R} = \tan^{-1}\frac{-X_0}{R} = \tan^{-1}\frac{B_0}{G} = -\tan^{-1}\frac{-6}{8} = \tan^{-1}\frac{0.06}{0.08} = 36.9°$$

or simply from the exponential Z

$$\theta = -\sigma = 36.9°$$

The reactive factor is

$$rf = \sin\theta = \sin 36.9° = 0.6$$

The current is

$$\begin{aligned} I &= YV = (0.08 + j0.06)(80 - j60) = 0.1\epsilon^{j36.9}\, 100\epsilon^{-j36.9} \\ &= 10\epsilon^{j0} = 10 + j0 \end{aligned}$$

and

$$|I| = 10, \; |I_m| = 14.14, \; I_m = 14.14 + j0 = 14.14\epsilon^{j0}$$

The rotating vector current is, therefore,

$$I(t) = (14.14 + j0)\epsilon^{j\omega t} = 14.14\epsilon^{j\omega t},$$

and the total impedance voltage of the series circuit is

$$V(t) = Z\,I(t) = 10\epsilon^{-j36.9}\, 14.14\epsilon^{j\omega t} = 141.4\epsilon^{j(\omega t - 36.9)}$$

Then immediately

$$|V_m| = 141.4 \text{ volts and } |V| = 100 \text{ volts}$$

The average power is

$$P = V \cdot I = 80 \times 10 + (-60)(0) = 800 \text{ watts}$$

or

$$P = |V||I|\cos\theta = 100 \times 10 \times 0.8 = 800 \text{ watts}$$

or

$$P = G|V|^2 = 0.08(100)^2 = 800 \text{ watts}$$

The apparent power is

$$|U| = |V||I| = 1000 \text{ va}$$

and the reactive volt-amperes are

$$Q = |U|\sin\theta = 600 \text{ vars}$$

or

$$Q = B_0|V|^2 = 0.06 \times (100)^2 = 600 \text{ vars}$$

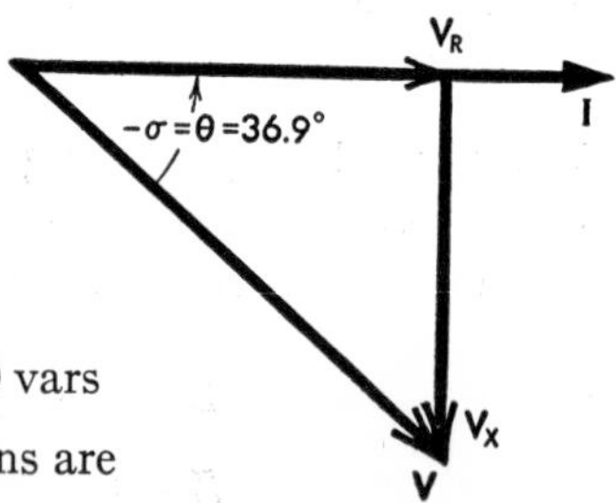

Fig. 4–6.

The instantaneous current and voltage equations are

$$\begin{aligned} i(t) &= 14.14 \sin \omega t \\ v(t) &= 141.4 \sin(\omega t - 36.9°) \end{aligned}$$

and

$$\begin{aligned} V_R &= RI = 80 + j0 \text{ volts} \\ V_X &= jX_0 I = 0 - j60 \text{ volts} \end{aligned}$$

The vector diagram is shown in Fig. 4–6. Note that the current leads the total voltage as must be true for capacitive circuits.

4.3 Series Circuit Resonance.

An R, L, and C series circuit has some interesting and useful properties. These properties become more evident in terms of ammeter and voltmeter indications than in terms of complex numbers. Therefore, the magnitude of the current in such a circuit will be examined in detail.

As already established, the complex number representation of the current in a series R, L, and C circuit is

$$I = \frac{V}{Z} = VY = \frac{v + jv'}{R + jX_0}$$

or, in terms of magnitudes only,

$$|I| = |V|\,|Y| = \frac{|V|}{\sqrt{R^2 + X_0^2}}$$

which in detail is

$$|I| = \frac{|V|}{\sqrt{R^2 + (X_L + X_C)^2}} = \frac{|V|}{\sqrt{R^2 + \left(2\pi fL - \dfrac{1}{2\pi fC}\right)^2}} \qquad (4\text{–}24)$$

If this current magnitude is viewed as a function of all the circuit elements which may affect it, evidently $|I|$ is a function of five variables $|V|$, R, L, C, and f. Because of the effectiveness of picturing functions graphically, a graphical method will be used in conjunction with a mathematical discussion. However, since there is no way of plotting a function in terms of five variables, of necessity two-dimensional sections will be considered. In order to do this, all the variables but one will be assumed constant and the change in current magnitude will be considered in terms of the single remaining variable. Such a variation corresponds to the usual laboratory technique of varying one circuit element at a time, as well as to the method used in practical applications.

When the R, L, and C circuit was first used in radio circuits it was tuned by varying L, largely because variable capacitors were not being manufactured and could not be readily constructed by the many experimenters in radio, whereas a variable inductor could readily be constructed by winding some wire on two concentric cylinders which could be moved with respect to each other. At the present time variable capacitors are widely used (see Fig. 4–1, for example).

Corresponding to the several parameters which may be varied, the sets of curves shown in Figs. 4–7, 4–8, 4–9, and 4–10 show the behavior of an R, L, and C series circuit when it is treated as a function of R, L, C, or f alone. In all these curves, except the one for R as the independent variable (relatively unimportant) the current magnitude reaches a maximum for a certain value of the circuit parameters. A more explicit formulation of the circuit properties represented by these curves may be ob-

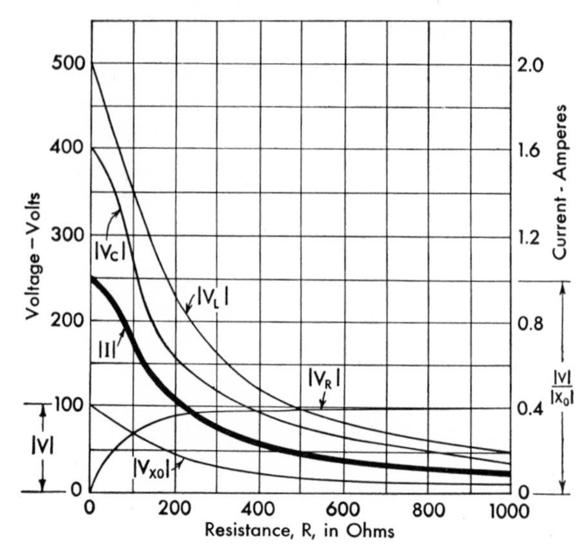

Fig. 4–7.

tained by a mathematical study of equation 4–24. An examination of this equation shows that because of the constant numerator the current will be a maximum when the denominator is a minimum. Therefore, for constant R, the minimum of the denominator will occur when $X_0 = 0$, i.e., when

$$\omega L = \frac{1}{\omega C} \tag{4–25}$$

Therefore, for constant R and $|V|$ the current will be a maximum when

$$\begin{aligned} &\text{if } L \text{ varies,} \quad && L_r \equiv \frac{1}{\omega^2 C} \\ &\text{if } C \text{ varies,} \quad && C_r \equiv \frac{1}{\omega^2 L} \\ &\text{and if } f \text{ varies,} \quad && f_r \equiv \frac{1}{2\pi\sqrt{LC}} \end{aligned} \tag{4–26}$$

But notice that because these relations were determined by setting $X_0 = 0$, equation 4–24 becomes, if $L = L_r$, $C = C_r$, or $f = f_r$,

$$|I| = \frac{|V|}{R} \tag{4–27}$$

Therefore, in addition to taking maximum current from a constant voltage source and fixed R, the R, L, and C series circuit which satisfies any

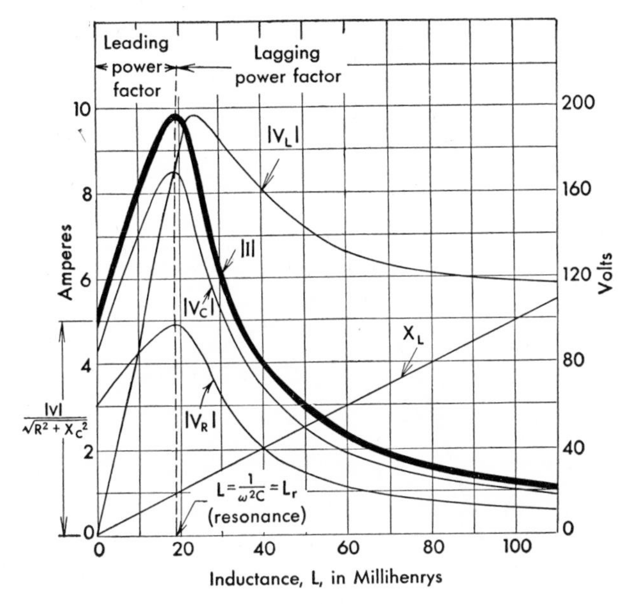

Fig. 4–8.

of the equations 4–26 takes this current at *unity power factor*. Such a circuit is said to be *resonant* or *tuned* when its power factor is unity.

According to equation 4–27 the total generator terminal voltage will appear across the *resistance alone* at resonance. But this does *not* mean that no voltage will appear across the inductor and capacitor. In fact, these voltages may be very much in evidence. They are shown plotted in typical form in Figs. 4–8, 4–9, and 4–10. These reactance voltage curves all show peaks which may, under circumstances discussed subsequently, represent very high voltages. Note, however, that *all the reactance voltage peaks do not occur at resonance where the current is a maximum* even though the reactance voltages are obtained by multiplying the current magnitude by the reactance.

Example 4:3 Determine the salient characteristics of the rms voltage functions $|V_L|$ and $|V_C|$ for a series R, L, C circuit as ω is varied.

Solution First note that

$$|V_L| = X_L|I| = \frac{\omega L|V|}{\sqrt{R^2 + \left(\omega L - \frac{1}{\omega C}\right)^2}}$$

and

$$|V_C| = |X_C|\,|I| = \frac{|V|}{\omega C\sqrt{R^2 + \left(\omega L - \frac{1}{\omega C}\right)^2}}$$

for Fig. 4–2*b* if $|I|$ is as given by equation 4–24. If now $|X_C|\,|I|$ and $X_L|I|$ are differentiated with respect to ω, the results equated to zero, and $\omega_{C\max}$ and

$\omega_{L\max}$, respectively, obtained from these equations, the result is, for $\omega_r = 1/\sqrt{LC}$,

$$\omega_{C\max} = \omega_r \sqrt{1 - \frac{CR^2}{2L}}$$

$$\omega_{L\max} = \frac{\omega_r}{\sqrt{1 - \frac{CR^2}{2L}}}$$

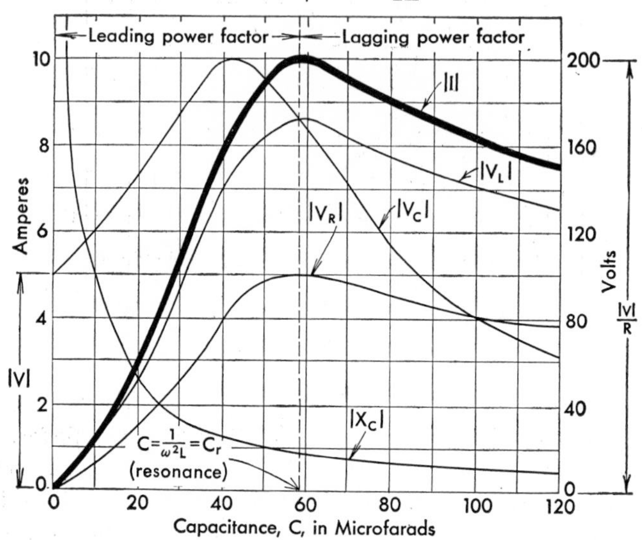

Fig. 4–9.

These two values of ω locate the maximum values of $|V_C|$ and $|V_L|$ respectively —see Fig. 4–10—whenever $\omega_{C\max}$ and $\omega_{L\max}$ are real.

If $R^2 = 2L/C$, these last two equations indicate that the maxima (zero derivatives) occur at $\omega = 0$ and $\omega = \infty$. Moreover, since

$$\lim_{\omega\to\infty}|V_L| = \lim_{\omega\to 0}|V_C| = |V|$$

the maxima of $|V_L|$ and $|V_C|$ are equal for $R^2 = 2L/C$. If $R^2 > 2L/C$, $\omega_{C\max}$ and $\omega_{L\max}$ are imaginary and there are no zero derivatives. However, the maxima of $|V_C|$ and $|V_L|$, both equal to $|V|$, still occur at $\omega = 0$ and $\omega = \infty$, respectively. If $R^2 < 2L/C$, the maxima of $|V_C|$ and $|V_L|$ occur at the above defined real values of $\omega_{C\max}$ and $\omega_{L\max}$. Furthermore, for $R^2 < 2L/C$, these equations indicate that always

$$\omega_{L\max} > \omega_{C\max}$$

since then the radicals are less than one.

If $|V_C|$ and $|V_L|$ are evaluated at $\omega_{C\max}$ and $\omega_{L\max}$ by substituting the values of $\omega_{C\max}$ and $\omega_{L\max}$ given above in the equations for $|V_C|$ and $|V_L|$, the result is

$$|V_C|_{\max} = |V_L|_{\max} = \frac{\omega_r L}{R} \frac{|V|}{\sqrt{1 - \frac{CR^2}{4L}}}$$

which indicates that once more the maxima of $|V_L|$ and $|V_C|$ are the same. Evidently, therefore, it is always true that $|V_C|_{max} = |V_L|_{max}$.

At resonance, since $|X_L| = |X_C|$ by definition, $|V_L|_r = |V_C|_r$ always; i.e., $|V_C|$ and $|V_L|$ at resonance are also always equal.

Although the reactance voltages $|V_L|$ and $|V_C|$ do not always have maximum values at resonance, in all cases the inductive and capacitive voltages at resonance *are equal* in magnitude and of opposite sign, i.e.,

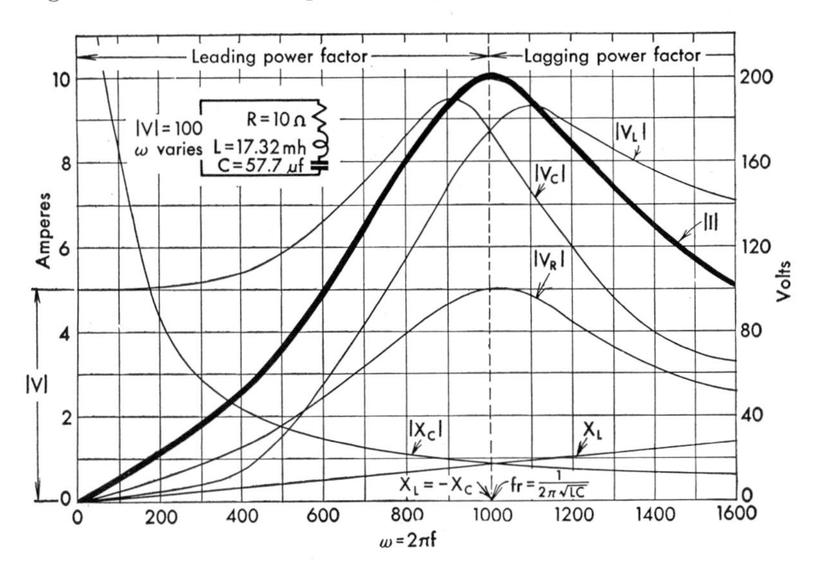

Fig. 4–10.

oppositely directed in the circuit at resonance, and so cancel so far as the external circuit is concerned no matter what their magnitude. The appearance of the total applied voltage across the resistance only is thus accounted for.

The vector diagrams of Figs. 4–11*a*, *b*, and *c* illustrate: (1) resonance with V_L and V_C equal and opposite but each *larger* than the source terminal voltage $V = IR$, (2) non-resonance with $|V_L| > |V_C|$, and (3) non-resonance with $|V_C| > |V_L|$. The non-resonance diagram of Fig. 4–11*b* represents a lagging power factor condition, which from Figs. 4–8, 4–9, and 4–10 indicates that L, C, and f are greater than their resonant values L_r, C_r, and f_r. Similarly, the vector diagram of Fig. 4–11*c* represents the below resonance condition of leading power factor.

Example 4:4 Suppose a static capacitor is connected across the end of a two wire rural transmission line, in parallel with the daytime load. The capacitor assists in keeping up the load voltage, as shown in a later chapter. The line is short enough—30 miles—to be considered as an inductor and resistor in series, with $R = 30$ ohms and $L = 0.1173$ henry for the two wires. The capacitance is 60 μf.

Suppose, furthermore, that a short circuit develops in the load and burns off the main line and load connection, leaving the capacitor connected as shown in Fig. 4–12. What is the current, and what are the circuit voltages?

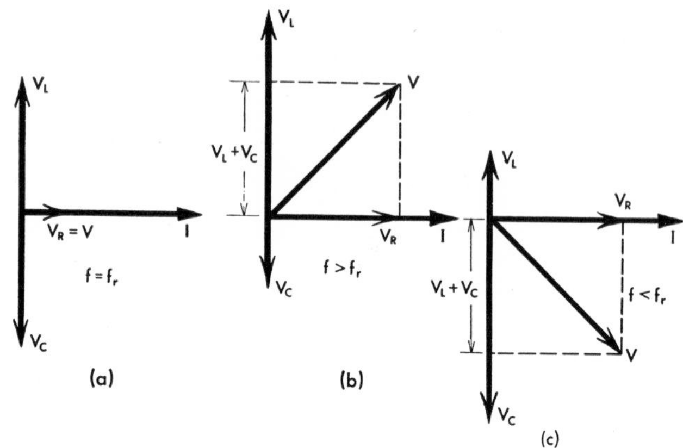

Fig. 4–11.

Solution First, the impedance of the circuit is

$$Z = R + j\left(\omega L - \frac{1}{\omega C}\right) = 30 + j\left(377 \times 0.1173 - \frac{10^6}{377 \times 60}\right)$$
$$= 30 + j(44.2 - 44.2) = 30 + j0$$

The line and capacitor are evidently in *resonance* because the capacitor and line inductor reactances are equal in magnitude.

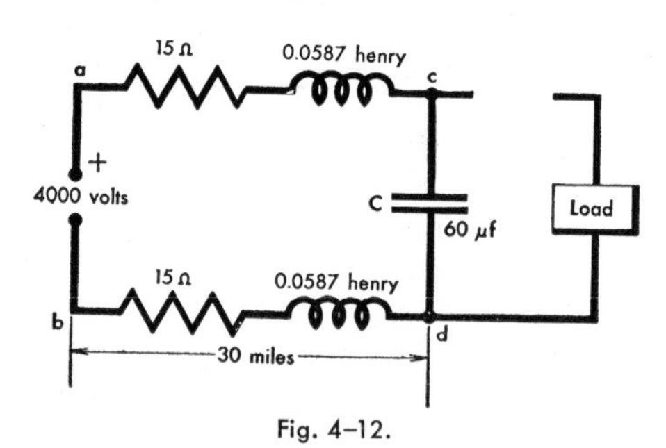

Fig. 4–12.

The current, if the voltage is taken as the reference axis, is

$$I = \frac{V}{Z} = \frac{4000 + j0}{30 + j0} = 133.3 + j0 \text{ amperes}$$

The voltage across the capacitor is

$$V_C = jX_C I = -j44.2 \times 133.3 = 0 - j5893 \text{ volts}$$

as compared to a normal 4000 volts or less. Along the transmission line the voltage is

$$V_l = Z_l I = (30 + j44.2)(133.3 + j0) = 4000 + j5893 = 7122\epsilon^{j55.8}$$

This line impedance voltage is, of course, split between the two wires of the line, so that $|V_{ac}| = |V_{bd}| = 3561$ volts. If a 10 per cent impedance voltage is allowed along the line, which is plenty under normal operation, these normal voltages will be

$$|V_{ac}|_n = |V_{bd}|_n = \frac{4000 \times 0.10}{2} = 200 \text{ volts}$$

which is very much less than 3561 volts.

Therefore, whether the capacitor or the line is considered, the voltages, when the load burns loose from the line, are greater than normal and would almost certainly lead to further trouble.

Any disastrous effect from series resonance may be caused by either the excessive current burning the equipment or the excessive voltage breaking down the insulation. Sufficient extra resistance in the circuit,

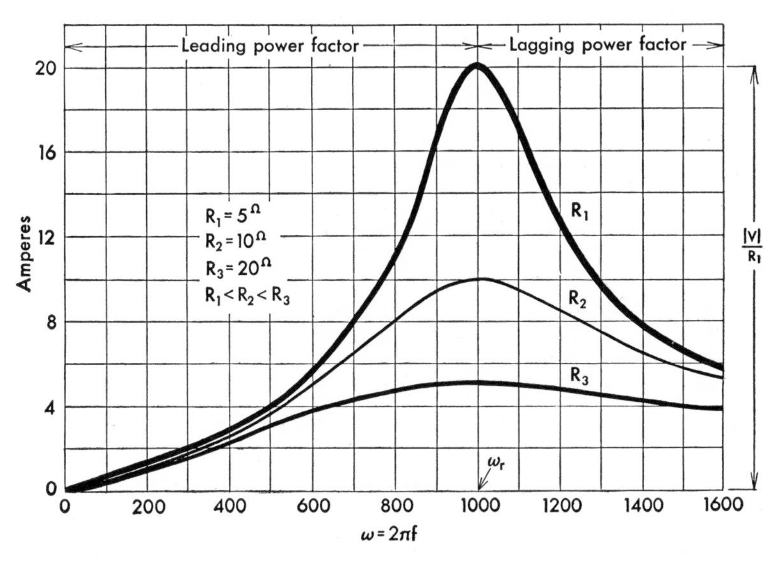

Fig. 4–13.

as equation 4–27 indicates, will of necessity reduce the current at resonance to any desired value; and, since a reduction in resonant current also reduces the reactance voltages at resonance, the resonant condition may thereby be rendered harmless. The curves of Fig. 4–13 show the effect of changing the resistance.

Series resonance is not always to be avoided, or its effects suppressed by adding resistance. In fact, increasing use is being made of series capacitance in power systems.

In addition to the properties of the series resonant or tuning circuit already developed, other important frequency characteristics may be developed as follows: the resonant frequency of the last of equations 4–26 is evidently unchanged by changing L and C if the product LC is kept constant. If, therefore, $LC = b$ (a constant) and then $C = b/L$ is substituted into equation 4–24, the result is

$$|I| = \frac{|V|}{\sqrt{R^2 + L^2\left(2\pi f - \dfrac{1}{2\pi b f}\right)^2}} \tag{4–28}$$

Increasing L in this equation decreases the $|I|$ for any non-resonant value of f. Hence, if curves of $|I|$ vs. f are plotted for different inductors and capacitors, ($LC = b$—a constant), the results are as shown typically

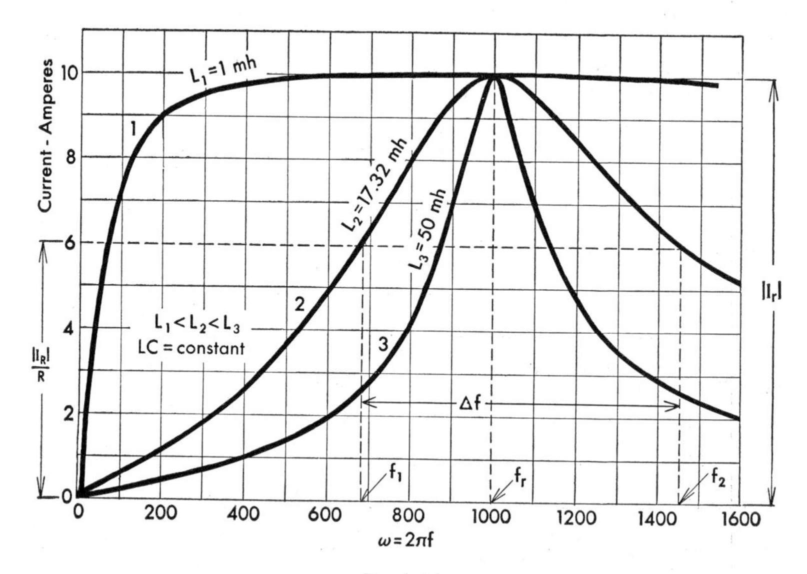

Fig. 4–14.

in Fig. 4–14. Note that the coefficients of self-induction for these curves are related by $L_3 > L_2 > L_1$. A circuit which has an $|I|$ vs. f curve as shown in 3 of Fig. 4–14 is said to be more *sharply* tuned than the circuit with a current curve as given by 2 or 1. Evidently the higher the inductance of a circuit, with the restriction that the product LC be maintained constant, the sharper the tuning.

In order to establish a measure of what may be considered the degree of tuning, i.e., to determine whether a circuit will respond according to curve 3 or curve 1 of Fig. 4–14, the frequency band—range of frequencies between, say, f^1 and f^2—for which the current magnitude is greater than a particular fraction $1/k(k > 1)$ of the current at resonance will be determined. At the frequencies f^1 and f^2 of Fig. 4–14,

$$|I_k| = \frac{|I_r|}{k} = \frac{|V|}{\sqrt{R^2 + \left(\omega L - \dfrac{1}{\omega C}\right)^2}} \tag{4–29}$$

But $|I_r|$ may be eliminated from this expression by using the resonance relation

$$|I_r| = \frac{|V|}{R} \tag{4–30}$$

to replace $|I_r|$. Thus equation 4–29 becomes

$$\frac{|V|}{kR} = \frac{|V|}{\sqrt{R^2 + \left(\omega L - \dfrac{1}{\omega C}\right)^2}} \tag{4–31}$$

from which the frequencies at which $|I| = |I_k| = |I_r|/k$ may be determined as follows.

Solving equation 4–31 for the frequency leads to

$$f = \left[\pm R\sqrt{k^2 - 1} \pm \sqrt{R^2(k^2 - 1) + \frac{4L}{C}}\right]\frac{1}{4\pi L} \tag{4–32}$$

But since a negative frequency is non-physical and because the right-hand radical is greater than the left-hand radical, the two values of frequency which will satisfy the condition $f > 0$ and equation 4–32 are

$$f_1 = \frac{1}{4\pi L}\left[-R\sqrt{k^2 - 1} + \sqrt{R^2(k^2 - 1) + \frac{4L}{C}}\right] \tag{4–33}$$

and

$$f_2 = \frac{1}{4\pi L}\left[R\sqrt{k^2 - 1} + \sqrt{R^2(k^2 - 1) + \frac{4L}{C}}\right] \tag{4–34}$$

These two frequencies are shown for curve 2 on Fig. 4–14.

Since $f_1 < f_2$, the difference divided by f, the so-called band width, is

$$\frac{\Delta f}{f} = \frac{f_2 - f_1}{f} = \frac{R\sqrt{k^2 - 1}}{2\pi f L} = \frac{R\sqrt{k^2 - 1}}{\omega L} \tag{4–35}$$

This band of frequencies, Δf, then, is such that for a particular R, L, and C series circuit the current $|I|$, over the frequency range Δf, will be greater than $(1/k)$th of the current at resonance. It is evident from

Fig. 4–14 that, if k is large and Δf small, the circuit will be sharply tuned as in curve 3 of this figure.

Suppose, as a further consideration of equation 4–35, that two circuits are at hand and the relative sharpness of tuning of the two circuits is to be determined. If k is assigned any value greater than unity and R and L of the two circuits are substituted into equation 4–35 the circuit with the smaller resultant Δf is the more sharply tuned.

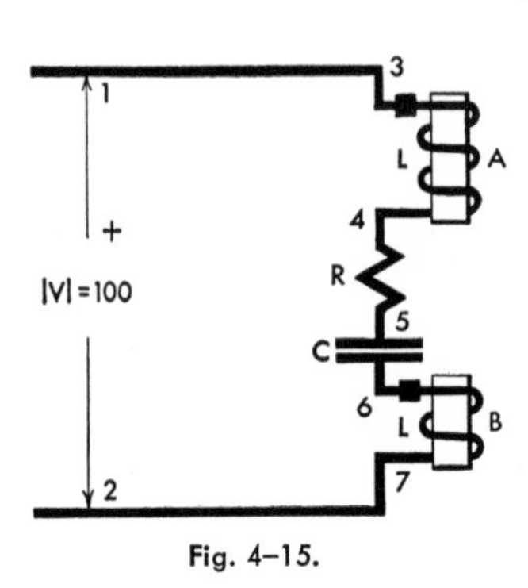

Fig. 4–15.

Further consideration is given the implications of equation 4–35 in part (d) of the following example.

Example 4:5 The characteristics of a laboratory test circuit are to be computed. The circuit is shown in Fig. 4–15, and the parameters are: $R_0 = 5$ ohms, $L_{34} = 0.15$ henry, $L_{67} = 0.25$ henry, $|M_{AB}| = 0.05$ henry, and $C = 2\mu$f. (a) What is the resonant frequency? What is the effect on the resonant frequency of turning one of the coils end for end? (b) What is the current at resonant frequency? (c) What is the reactance voltage across each of the inductors, and the capacitor, at resonance, for 100 volts total impedance voltage? Assume that the capacitor has zero resistance and that the 5-ohm resistance is divided between the two coils as $R_{34} = 2$ ohms and $R_{67} = 3$ ohms. (d) What is the smallest current in a 10-cps band of frequency about resonance? (e) Draw the vector diagram. Show V_C and V_L on this diagram.

Solution (a) Since the two coils are connected so as to be aiding magnetically with currents from 3 to 4 and from 6 to 7, or since the polarity marks are on leads 3 and 6, $M_{BA} > 0$ and according to Problem 3–13,

$$L_{37} = L_{34} + 2M_{BA} + L_{67} = 0.5 \text{ henry}$$

The resonant frequency is, therefore (equation 4–26), in terms of this equivalent inductance

$$f_r = \frac{1}{2\pi\sqrt{LC}} = \frac{1}{2\pi\sqrt{0.5 \times 2 \times 10^{-6}}} = \frac{1000}{2\pi} = 159.15 \text{ cps}$$

and

$$\omega_r = 1000$$

If one of the coils is turned end for end but otherwise is exactly in the same position, the equivalent coefficient of self-induction is, since $M_{BA} < 0$,

$$L_0 = L_{34} + 2\text{M}_{BA} + L_{67} = 0.3 \text{ henry}$$

and the resonant frequency now is

$$f_r = \frac{1}{2\pi\sqrt{0.3 \times 2 \times 10^{-6}}} = \frac{1000}{2\pi\sqrt{0.6}} = 205 \text{ cps}$$

(*b*) The current at resonance is the total impedance voltage divided by the total resistance, i.e.,

$$|I_r| = \frac{|V_0|}{R_0} = \frac{100}{5} = 20 \text{ amp}$$

(*c*) The voltage across the capacitor at resonance is

$$V_C = Z_{56}\, I_{56} = (0 + jX_C)I = 0 - j\frac{I}{2\pi f_r C} = 0 - j\frac{I}{\omega_r C}$$

If I_{37} is taken as reference, i.e., $I_{37} = 20 + j0$, since $\omega_r = 1000$, the voltage across the capacitor at resonance is

$$V_C = V_{56} = 0 - j10{,}000 \text{ volts.}$$

The voltage across coil 3–4 at resonance—$\omega_r = 1000$—is, if the coil internal resistance of 2 ohms is also included,

$$V_{34} = Z_{34}\, I_{37} = [R_{L34} + j(X_{L34} + X_{AB})]I_{37}$$

Substituting in this equation

$$V_{34} = [2 + j(150 + 50)](20 + j0) = 40 + j4000 \text{ volts}$$

Also the voltage across coil 6–7 and its resistance, at resonance, is

$$V_{67} = Z_{67}\, I_{37} = [R_{67} + j(X_{L67} + X_{BA})]I_{37}$$
$$= [3 + j(250 + 50)](20 + j0) = 60 + j6000 \text{ volts}$$

The total impedance voltage in this circuit due to the coils may be computed by adding the two voltages just computed. Hence

$$V_{34} + V_{67} = 100 + j10{,}000$$

is the total voltage due to the inductance of the coils and their internal resistance.

Notice that the voltages of the coils for this circuit are very high, and that the sum of the capacitor and inductor voltages is simply 100 volts, as, of course, it must be. Furthermore, there seems to be little doubt that operating the circuit of Fig. 4–15 under the conditions indicated by the problem solution is distinctly undesirable. While the overall voltage is low, and relatively harmless, contact across either coil or the capacitor might be fatal. The probabilities are that the circuit itself would break down under the excessive electric field present both in the coils and capacitor with such high voltages across their terminals.

Note furthermore that the coils being connected through a mutual magnetic field adds 1000 volts to the voltage across each coil or 2000 volts to the total inductance voltage. If the coils were in opposition magnetically, the mutual induction voltages would subtract from the total inductance voltage (see Problem 4–12).

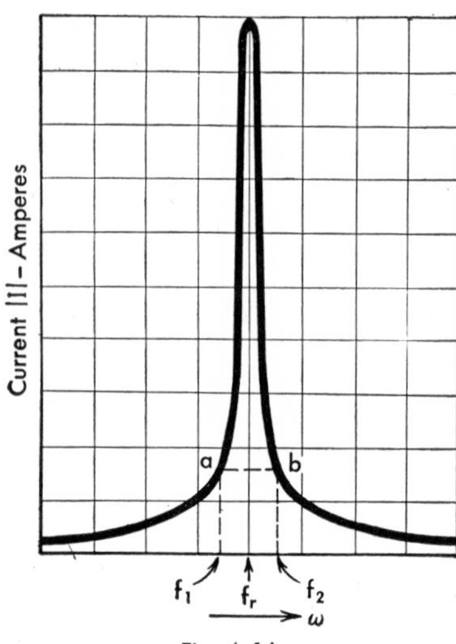

Fig. 4–16.

(*d*) From equation 4–35, by substitution, for $\Delta f = 10$

$$10 = \frac{5\sqrt{k^2 - 1}}{2\pi 0.5}$$

from which,

$$k = 6.36$$

Hence the current in the 10 cps band about resonance—shown at *a* and *b* of Fig. 4–16—is greater than

$$|I_k| = \frac{20}{6.36} = 3.15 \text{ amp}$$

(*e*) The circuit vector diagram shown in Fig. 4–17 represents the general nature of the results of this problem. The diagram is *not* to scale. Angles and lengths are both exaggerated.

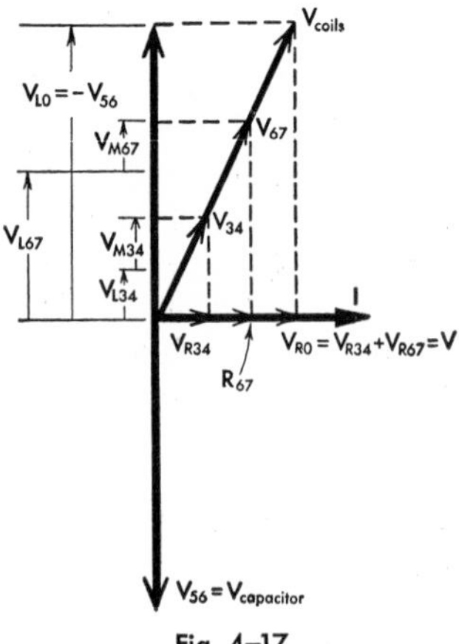

Fig. 4–17.

4.4 Impedances in Series.

Consider a circuit represented by Fig. 4–18, where each rectangle represents any constant impedance—a non-inductive resistor, an inductor, a capacitor, or any combination of the three. Evidently

$$V_k = Z_k I, \quad (k = 1, 2, 3, \cdots) \tag{4-36}$$

But from Kirchhoff's voltage law,

$$V_1 + V_2 + V_3 + \cdots + V_n = \sum_{k=1}^{n} V_k = V_0 = V_{ab} \tag{4-37}$$

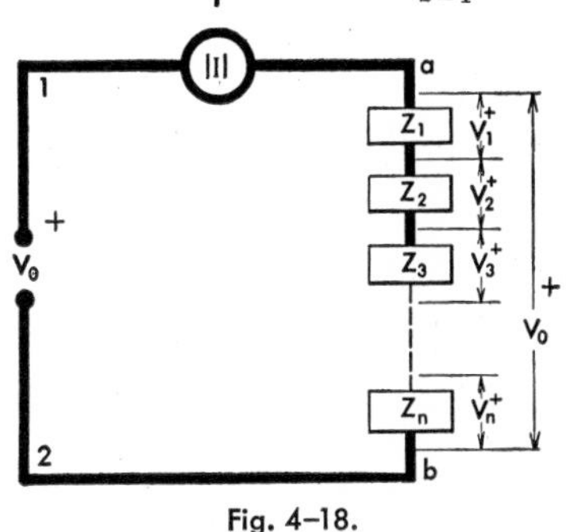

Fig. 4–18.

Hence, substituting from 4–36,

$$V_0 = I \sum_{k=1}^{n} Z_k = IZ_0 \tag{4-38}$$

where the equivalent or total impedance of the circuit is

$$Z_0 = \sum_{k=1}^{n} Z_k = Z_1 + Z_2 + \cdots + Z_n \tag{4-39}$$

The total impedance of a set of impedances in series is, therefore, the *complex number sum of the individual impedances*. The beginner should note that this sum is *always* the *complex number sum*, *never* the *real number* sum, except where the ratio X_0/R is the same for each impedance.

Evidently,

$$\sum_{k=1}^{n} Z_k = \sum_{k=1}^{n} R_k + j \sum_{k=1}^{n} X_{0k} \tag{4-40}$$

where

$$X_{0k} = X_{Lk} + X_{Ck}$$

A series circuit made up of several impedances will be in resonance if

$$\sum_{k=1}^{n} X_{0k} = \sum_{k=1}^{n} X_{Lk} + \sum_{k=1}^{n} X_{Ck} = 0$$

In fact, a series circuit of many elements may be replaced by a single R, L, and C, in series, and there will be no way of detecting the difference if the terminals a and b of Fig. 4–18 were the only ones available.

4.5 Power and Energy in a Series Circuit.

The expressions for the power and energy in a series circuit are not different from the expressions derived in Arts. 1–7 and 1–8. The discussion in Art. 4–1 gives completely the characteristics and method of computing the power factor angle θ. The determination of the power is simple if this angle is known, or if the complex form of the current and voltage, referred to any axis, is known. In the latter case the scalar product gives the power.

In Art. 1–7 the average power absorbed by the circuit of a pure resistor was shown to be $|I|^2 R$ for any wave form of current. A like expression may be shown to apply to a circuit of constant elements R, L, and/or C, through which a sine *wave of current flows*. For, from Chap. 1, on the assumption of sine waves,

$$P = |V|\,|I| \cos\theta$$

but for a circuit containing L and C as well as R

$$|V| = |I|\,|Z| \quad \text{and} \quad \cos\theta = \frac{R}{|Z|}$$

Hence, substituting in the power expression, the average power loss in the circuit is

$$P = |I|\,|V| \cos\theta = |I|\,|Z|\,|I| \frac{R}{|Z|} = |I|^2 R$$

even though inductance and capacitance may be in the circuit. This result should be expected from the fact that the capacitor and inductor, on the average, return to the source all the energy taken from it.

4.6 Series Circuits of a Resistor and Inductor or Resistor and Capacitor in Series.

As has already been pointed out, series circuits of R and L, or R and C, in series are special cases of the R, L, and C series circuit.

If the series circuit consists of R and L only, the capacitive reactance is zero since C is infinite. The current lags the voltage and the impedance is

$$Z_L = R + jX_L = |Z_L|\epsilon^{j\sigma_L}$$

where

$$\sigma_L = \tan^{-1}\frac{X_L}{R} = -\theta_L$$

$$|Z_L| = \sqrt{R^2 + X_L{}^2}$$

By general agreement communication engineers have adopted the symbolism

$$Q \equiv \frac{X_L}{R} \equiv \frac{\omega L}{R} \tag{4-41}$$

so that

$$Q = \tan \sigma \tag{4-42}$$

This definition determines the Q of a coil as it is ordinarily used. A coil of high Q is particularly desirable for many purposes since the inductive effect of a high Q coil is much greater than the resistive.

$\frac{1}{Q_R} = \frac{\Delta f}{f_R}$

It is perhaps unfortunate that the symbol Q should have been adopted to represent three distinct relations, namely, charge, reactive volt-amperes, and $\tan \sigma$ for an inductive reactor. Because the three uses of Q occur in such widely separated fields of electrical engineering, however, there is actually no confusion.

If a series circuit consists of R and C only, the inductive reactance is zero since L is zero. The current leads the voltage and the impedance is

$$Z_C = R + jX_C = |Z_C|\epsilon^{j\sigma_C}$$

$$\sigma_C = \tan^{-1}\frac{X_C}{R} = -\theta_C$$

$$|Z_C| = \sqrt{R^2 + X_C^2}$$

4.7 Locus Diagrams for a Series Circuit.

The discussion of Art. 4–3 gives in detail the characteristics of the *magnitude* of the current in an R, L, and C series circuit. Further useful ideas can be derived by a consideration of the variation of the *vector* current in this same circuit. This vector variation is known as a locus diagram.

The series circuit locus diagram of interest here is a curve along which the *terminus of the current vector* must move as one of the elements of the circuit is varied independently, say V_0, R, L, C, or f. The equation for this current vector is

$$I = i_1 + ji_2 = \frac{V_0}{Z} = V_0\frac{R}{|Z|^2} + jV_0\frac{-X_0}{|Z|^2} \tag{4-43}$$

But two vectors are equal if and only if their corresponding components are equal. Therefore, with V_0 taken as along the reference axis so $V_0 = |V_0| + j0$, equation 4–43 requires that

$$i_1 = \frac{R}{|Z|^2}|V_0| = \frac{R}{R^2 + X_0^2}|V_0| \tag{4-44}$$

$$i_2 = \frac{-X_0}{|Z|^2}|V_0| = \frac{-X_0}{R^2 + X_0^2}|V_0| \tag{4-45}$$

Suppose these two equations are used to form one equation in terms of i_1 and i_2 by eliminating R. The ratio of these equations gives

$$R = -X_0\frac{i_1}{i_2} \tag{4-46}$$

For an inverse transformation in the complex plane, $Z = \frac{1}{Y}$ circles go into circles.

which, if substituted into equation 4–45 gives, after a little manipulation,

$$X_0 i_1^2 + X_0 i_2^2 + |V_0| i_2 = 0 \tag{4-47}$$

Completing the squares of this equation leads to

$$i_1^2 + \left(i_2 + \frac{|V_0|}{2X_0}\right)^2 = \left(\frac{|V_0|}{2|X_0|}\right)^2 \tag{4-48}$$

But this is the equation of a circle of radius $|V_0|/2|X_0|$ with a center on the i_2 axis a distance $-|V_0|/2X_0$ from the origin. The semicircles of Fig. 4–19 represent the two possible cases. As the resistance is varied

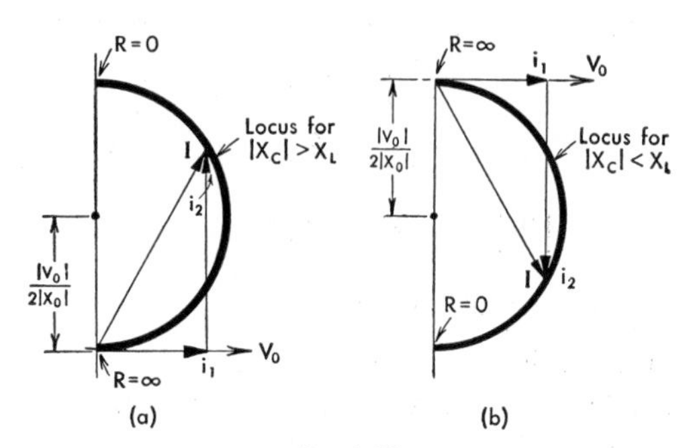

Fig. 4–19.

from ∞ to 0 the current vector follows the semicircular locus from zero length to the length $|V_0|/|X_0|$. The phase position of the current with respect to the voltage also changes, during this resistance variation, from practically in phase at low currents (high R) to 90 degrees lead or lag, depending on the sign of X_0. Note also that this diagram indicates immediately that no matter what the value of R, unity power factor cannot occur, and the maximum current occurs for $R = 0$. The curve of Fig. 4–7 shows these same conclusions in a form not so easy to reproduce as the simple locus diagram.

If the reactance is eliminated from equations 4–44 and 4–45 the result is

$$\left(i_1 - \frac{|V_0|}{2R}\right)^2 + i_2^2 = \left(\frac{|V_0|}{2R}\right)^2 \tag{4-49}$$

Three possible forms which this locus can take are shown in Fig. 4–20. The locus as L varies is shown in Fig. 4–20a. Evidently at $L = 0$, $X_L = 0$, and X_C determines the current which then leads the voltage. Note that this locus diagram shows immediately that maximum current occurs at unity power factor, i.e., resonance, and that the maximum value of this current is $|V_0|/R$.

The locus as C varies (Fig. 4–20*b*) is similar to the one obtained as L varies. Once more this locus diagram shows immediately that maximum current occurs at resonance and has a value $|V_0|/R$.

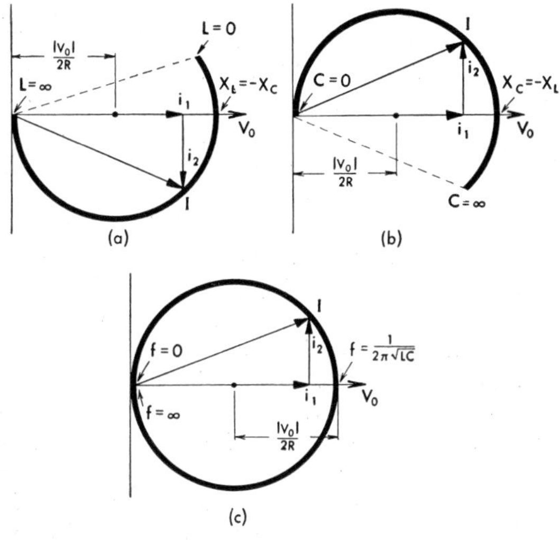

Fig. 4–20.

The locus of I as frequency varies includes the whole circle as shown in Fig. 4–20*c*. This diagram shows once more that resonance and maximum current occur together.

It seems evident that the locus diagram leads to more certain results than plotting curves, as in Figs. 4–7, 4–8, 4–9, and 4–10. These curves can be plotted only from particular values of the circuit parameters R, L, C, and f. On the other hand, the locus diagrams show the total range of possible variation and so all the possibilities on the one simple diagram.

PROBLEMS

4–1 Suppose that the voltage, impedance, and reactive factor of an R, L, and C series tuning circuit are: $v(t) = 14.14 \sin(6282t + 60°)$ volts, $|Z| = 1000$ ohms, $rf = -0.8$. Determine: V_m, I_m, I, V_R, V_X, $|V_R|$, $|V_X|$, V, Z, θ, $i(t)$, $v_R(t)$, $v_X(t)$, $p(t)$, pf, f, R, $X_L + X_C$, Y, G, B, P, $|U|$, (vars). Sketch the sine waves for the current and all the voltages. Is this circuit acting as an inductor or a capacitor? Draw a complete vector diagram.

4–2 Show that the total impedance voltage in a series circuit is $|V|^2 = |V_R|^2 + |V_X|^2$. Also show that $pf = |V_R|/|V|$, and $|rf| = |V_X|/|V|$, and hence that $|V_R| = |V| \cos\theta$, and $|V_X| = |V| \sin|\theta|$.

4–3 Consider a circuit of a resistor and inductor in series. Write the fundamental differential equation and solve by assuming the complex variable form of the current as in equation 4–2. Consider the steady state only. Determine the impedance and show that it is a special case of equation 4–6.

4–4 Repeat Problem 4–3 for a resistor and capacitor in series.

4–5 Prove that the relations given by equations 4–23 are correct.

4–6 A current-limiting reactor used in power systems (Fig. 3–9*d*) to limit the current in the event of a short circuit is simply an R and L series circuit. Suppose such a circuit has $R = 5$ ohms and $L = 0.1$ henry and is connected, as a result of a short circuit, to a voltage $v(t) = 2000 \sin 377t$. Find: $V(t)$, V, $i(t)$, $I(t)$, I, pf, θ, rf, P, $|U|$, Q, Y. Draw the vector diagram.

4–7 A wattmeter, voltmeter, ammeter, and power factor meter are used to measure the input to a two-terminal circuit. The wattmeter indicates 1000 watts, $|I| = 14$, $|V| = 100$, and the power factor meter indicates lead. A vibrating reed frequency meter indicates 59.6 cps. Use the current vector as the reference axis and find: pf, rf, $|U|$, Q, V, I, $V(t)$, $I(t)$, $i(t)$, $v(t)$, V_R, V_X, Z, Y, θ, L, or C, σ. Draw the vector diagram.

4–8 (*a*) Plot curves of $|V_C|$ and $|V_L|$ vs. C and L for a series circuit if $R = 10$ ohms, $L = 0.1$ henry when C varies, and $C = 10\ \mu$f when L varies. Where are the maximum and minimum values? What are they? Do they occur at resonance? $|V_0| = 100$ volts, $\omega = 1000$.

4–9 A series circuit of a radio receiver has parameter values of $R = 4$ ohms, $L = 150\mu$h, and is resonant at 1000 kcps. This tuning circuit under test has a constant source voltage of 100 volts, at all frequencies, connected to it. Plot curves of X_L, X_C, $|Z|$, $|V_R|$, $|V_C|$, $|V_L|$, and $|I|$ vs. f. Be sure to include the current maximum in the plot. Do the maximum values of $|V_C|$ and $|V_L|$ occur at resonance? Why?

4–10 Find the frequency of resonance from $d|I|/df = 0$—the necessary condition for a maximum or minimum—use equation 4–24.

4–11 A series circuit has a resistance of 10 ohms, $X_L = |X_C| = 1000$ ohms. The connected voltage is 100. What is the current, the voltage across X_L and X_C, and what is the total power? How do $|V_C|$ and $|V_L|$ compare? Find $i(t)$, $v_L(t)$, $v_C(t)$, and $v(t)$. I reference.

4–12 Work out the problem of Example 4–5 for the condition of the two coils in magnetic opposition. Answer all pertinent questions asked in the example. Show the effect of the mutual induction on this circuit. Does the lower equivalent L make this circuit a more desirable one to operate at resonance than the one of the example? Why?

4–13 Determine the frequencies at which $|V_L|$ and $|V_C|$ are a maximum in an R, L, and C series circuit. Show that for $R = 0$ these maxima occur at resonance and that for any other value of R they do not occur at resonance. Also show that increasing R makes the maximum value of $|V_C|$ occur at lower frequencies and of $|V_L|$ at higher frequencies. Are the maximum values of $|V_C|$ and $|V_L|$ equal? Assume, of course, a constant source voltage and constant R, L, and C.

4–14 When a 100-volt, 60-cps voltage is connected to a circuit containing R, L, and C in series, the current is 1.9 amp and the average power is 100 watts. When a 100-volt, 30-cps voltage is connected to this same circuit the current and power are unchanged. What are the values of R, X_L, and X_C at 60 cps?

4–15 Show that equation 4–32 is the solution of equation 4–31.

4–16 (a) Specify the change in R in a radio tuning circuit of $R = 10$ ohms, $L = 0.2$ mh, $C = 127\ \mu\mu$f $= 127 \times 10^{-6}\ \mu$f $= 127 \times 10^{-12}$ farads and $|V_0| =$ 0.1 volt in order that the minimum current in a total band of 200 cps about resonance is 20 per cent of the resonant current. (*b*) Repeat (*a*) for a change in L and C so that the frequency of resonance does not change. (*c*) What is the 1,000,000-cps current through each circuit? (*d*) What is V_L, V_C, and V_R for the unchanged circuit of part (*a*) at this same frequency? Use I as reference.

4–17 A series circuit is to resonate at 1000 cps and is to be tuned sharply enough so that in a 10-cps band about resonance the current is greater than 0.1 of the current at resonance. The total resistance of the circuit is to be 20 ohms. What are the values of L, C, and $Q = \omega L/R$ (at resonance) of the circuit? Find the two frequencies which bound the 10-cps region. Is the resonant frequency at the center of this band? Prove your answer.

4–18 Show that, if $R_1L_2 < R_2L_1$ of two series circuits 1 and 2, circuit number 1 is the more sharply tuned.

4–19 Show that the frequency of resonance is or is not at the center of the Δf band given by equation 4–35. Which frequency point f_1 or f_2 is farther from f_r? Derive a relation which shows how much greater the frequency interval from f_1 to f_r is than that from f_2 to f_r. As a suggestion, find a form for $\dfrac{f_2 - f_r}{f_1 - f_r}$. Another more useful or simpler form may occur to the reader. If so, he should work it out.

4–20 Three impedances in series—$Z_1 = 8 - j6$, $Z_2 = 3 + j4$, and $Z_3 = 10 + j0$—have a total voltage of $V_0(t) = 150\epsilon^{j(\omega t+70)}$ volts across their terminals. (*a*) What is the current in the circuit—$|I|$, I, $i(t)$? (*b*) What is the voltage across each of the impedances—$|V|$, V and $v(t)$? (*c*) What is the power factor and reactive factor of each impedance? What is the total power factor and reactive factor? (*d*) Draw the complete vector diagram showing the voltage drop across each impedance.

4–21 Show, if a current and voltage in complex form when referred to a particular reference axis have a ratio $V/I = Z$, that changing the reference axis does not change Z. In other words, show that the impedance and admittance are independent of the axis to which the current and voltage are referred.

4–22 A circuit with 5 ohms resistance and $X_L = 10$ ohms has a current of 10μa with frequency at 10^6 cps. The voltage is kept constant and a capacitor is placed in series with R and L. The current is then 5μa. What is the capacitance? Draw the vector diagram using an axis of reference 30 degrees ahead of the current. Find: $i(t)$, $v_R(t)$, $v_C(t)$, I, V_L, V_C, V_R, P, Q(vars), $|U|$ for the R, L, and C circuit.

4–23 The current in the circuit shown in Fig. 4–21 is $I_{13} = 5 + j7$ at $\omega = 1000$. Find: V_0, Z_0, $i(t)$, and $v_0(t)$. Draw the complete vector diagram and show on it that the sum of all the impedance voltages—seven of them—add to V_0. What is the frequency of resonance of this circuit? How wide a band of frequency is required so that the minimum current in this band is 0.2 of the resonant current?

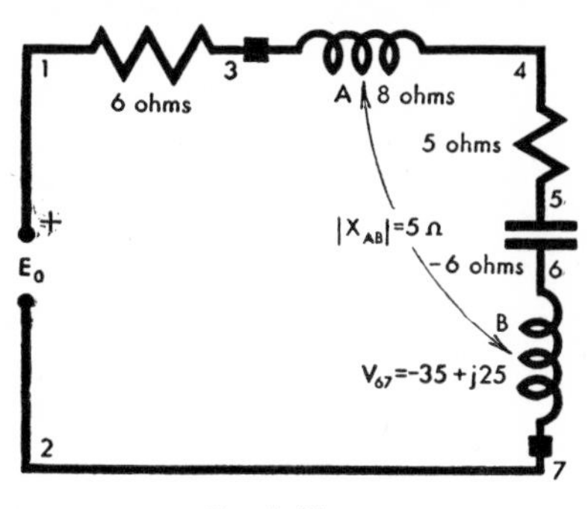

Fig. 4–21.

4–24 Determine R and X_0 in terms of G and B for an R, L, and C circuit.

4–25 A series circuit with a conductance of 0.08 mho and susceptance of 0.06 mho has an impedance voltage across its terminals of $V_0 = 30 + j40$. Find I, V_R, V_X, R, X, Z, P, $Q = \tan \sigma$, and θ.

4–26 The Q of a series circuit at resonance is 70. The coil Q is 75. The series circuit resonates at 1100 kcps. Determine the capacitance, the total resistance, R_0, and the coil resistance R_L. The current is 0.01 ma, and the average power is 0.02 microwatt at resonance.

4–27 Draw to scale the locus diagram for varying R in a series circuit of $L = 1$ henry, $C = 10\ \mu$f, and $\omega = 1000$. The terminal voltage is $|V_0| = 100$. Locate points on the current vector locus for which $R = 10$, 100, 200, 300, 500, 2000, 5000, 10,000 ohms. Note that the current vectors do not progress uniformly for uniform resistance change.

4–28 Draw to scale a locus diagram for an R, L, and C series circuit for C the variable. Assume $|V_0| = 100$, R $= 500$ ohms, $L = 0.1$ henry, $\omega = 10{,}000$. Locate the fourth quadrant limiting point of this locus carefully. Locate on the locus points corresponding to $C = 0.02$, 0.05, 0.1, 0.15, 0.2 μf.

4–29 Draw to scale a locus diagram as ω varies for a series circuit of $R = 10$ ohms, $L = 0.1$ henry, $C = 0.1\ \mu$f, and $|V_0| = 100$. Locate points on the diagram of $\omega = 700$, 1000, 1200, 1500. $\omega_R = 10{,}000$.

9950, 10 000, 10 025

CHAPTER 5

The Parallel and Series-Parallel Electric Circuit

The current, voltage, power, and energy relations of resistors, inductors, and capacitors alone and in series combination have been studied, and the sine wave form of these relations has been developed in detail. It would seem logical at this point to delve further into the current, voltage, power, and energy relations of R, C, L, and M circuits, provided there are other relations of importance. It happens that there are. Furthermore, many ideas and relations have already been introduced which are of such a fundamental nature that they should be learned thoroughly. To facilitate the acquisition of a real grip on these fundamental relations, this chapter is devoted to reviewing many of them while still extending current, voltage, power, and energy relations to other types of circuits.

Next to a series circuit, probably the simplest possible combination of R, C, L, and M circuit elements is the very commonly employed parallel circuit. This chapter is devoted to a study of the parallel circuit.

5.1 Parallel Circuit Current and Voltage Relations.

The parallel circuit with no mutual induction, shown in Fig. 5–1, is considered first. Assume that the terminal voltage is maintained constant to facilitate studying the properties of the circuit without having to consider the properties of the generator at the same time. Since the two impedances in parallel *in no way* affect each other, for a specified terminal voltage, they may be treated separately, and the stationary vector method for series circuits may be applied to the separate series circuits. The currents of the two branches which are in parallel combine into the generator current. The determination of the generator current, therefore, requires the addition of the two branch currents. It was shown in Arts. 1–9 and 1–10 that, if added, two stationary vectors representing sine waves give a stationary vector

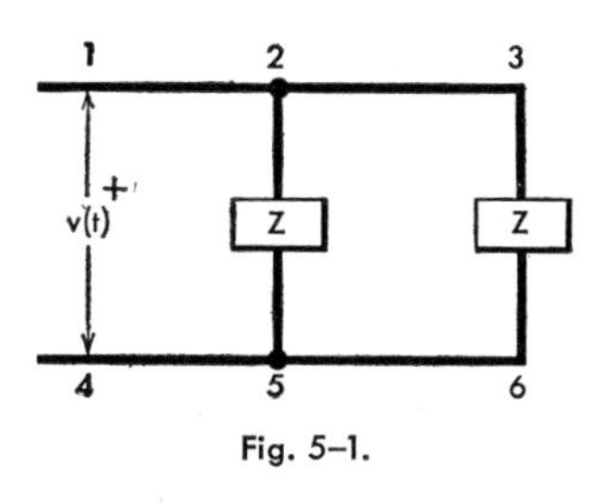

Fig. 5–1.

representing the sum of the two sine waves. Accordingly, the sum of the stationary or rotating vectors representing the two branch currents will be a vector representing the total current.

Note that these vectors must be combined properly, i.e., double subscripts or an equivalent method must be used to indicate whether to add or to subtract the complex numbers. See Fig. 5–2 for an illustration of

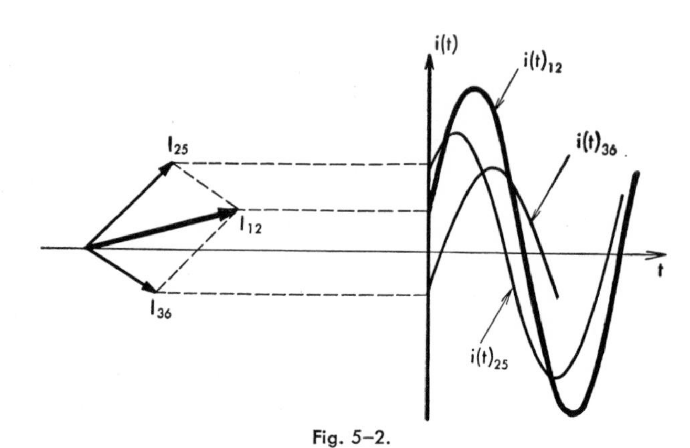

Fig. 5–2.

the sine waves and their vector representation of the currents of Fig. 5–1. To proceed then from these conclusions, the branch currents for Fig. 5–1 in effective-value, stationary vector form, in terms of the generator *terminal* voltage, are

$$I_{25} = \frac{V_{14}}{Z_{25}} = \frac{V_{25}}{Z_{25}}$$

which in terms of the admittance of equation 4–18 may be written as

$$I_{25} = V_{14}\left[\frac{R_{25}}{|Z_{25}|^2} + j\,\frac{-X_{25}}{|Z_{25}|^2}\right] = [G_{25} + jB_{25}]V_{14} = Y_{25}V_{14} \quad (5\text{–}1)$$

Similarly,

$$I_{36} = \frac{V_{14}}{Z_{36}} = (G_{36} + jB_{36})V_{14} = Y_{36}V_{14} \quad (5\text{–}2)$$

The current through the source is

$$I_{12} = I_{25} + I_{36} \quad (5\text{–}3)$$

or, by substitution from equations 5–1 and 5–2,

$$\begin{aligned} I_0 = I_{12} &= (Y_{25} + Y_{36})V_{14} = [(G_{25} + G_{36}) + j(B_{25} + B_{36})]V_{14} \\ &= \left[\left(\frac{R_{25}}{|Z_{25}|^2} + \frac{R_{36}}{|Z_{36}|^2}\right) + j\left(\frac{-X_{025}}{|Z_{25}|^2} + \frac{-X_{036}}{|Z_{36}|^2}\right)\right]V_{14} \end{aligned} \quad (5\text{–}4)$$

If there are several branches, say n, in parallel, the source or total current is, by simple extension of equation 5–4,

$$I_0 = V \sum_{k=1}^{n} Y_k \tag{5-5}$$

a very important expression showing that *admittances* in parallel *add* as do *impedances* in *series*. The expression for the *equivalent impedance* of a two-branch parallel circuit may be derived from equation 5–4. Thus

$$Z_0 = \frac{V_{14}}{I_0} = \frac{1}{Y_0} = \frac{1}{Y_{25} + Y_{36}}$$

which gives

$$Z_0 = \frac{1}{\dfrac{1}{Z_{25}} + \dfrac{1}{Z_{36}}} = \frac{Z_{25}Z_{36}}{Z_{25} + Z_{36}} \tag{5-6}$$

Note that this equation is similar to the equivalent resistance expression for d-c parallel circuits except that *complex numbers* have replaced the real number resistance values.

Other relations analogous to the d-c relations may be deduced for a-c parallel circuits, e.g., since

$$V_{14} = V_{25} = Z_0 I_{12} = Z_{25} I_{25} = Z_{36} I_{36}$$

then

$$\frac{Z_{25}}{Z_{36}} = \frac{Y_{36}}{Y_{25}} = \frac{I_{36}}{I_{25}} \tag{5-7}$$

or

$$\frac{Z_0}{Z_{25}} = \frac{Y_{25}}{Y_0} = \frac{I_{25}}{I_{12}} = \frac{I_{25}}{I_0} \tag{5-8}$$

Example 5:1 The circuit of Fig. 5–3 represents three loads in parallel connected to a two-wire line in the secondary distribution system of a large city.

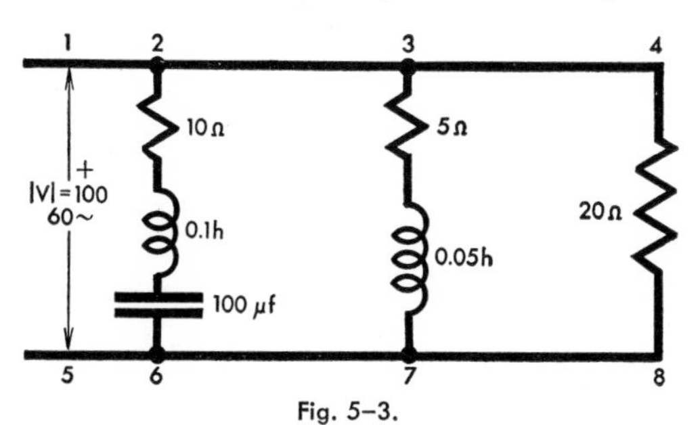

Fig. 5–3.

Determine the following relations: I_{12}, $I_{12}(t)$, I_{26}, $I_{26}(t)$, I_{37}, I_{48}, V_{L37}, V_{L26}, V_{C26}, P_0, $|U_0|$, $i_{12}(t)$, $i_{26}(t)$. Draw the complete vector diagram, using the source voltage as reference.

Solution Stationary vectors are used since it has already been shown (chaps. 3 and 4) that they determine all the required relations for sinusoidal source voltages. For convenience, the generator terminal voltage is used as the reference axis; hence

$$V_{15} = V_{26} = V_{37} = V_{48} = 100 + j0 = 100\epsilon^{j0}$$

The impedances and admittances of the circuit are

$$Z_{26} = 10 + j(37.7 - 26.5) = 10 + j11.2 = 15\epsilon^{j48.2}$$
$$Y_{26} \equiv \frac{1}{Z_{26}} = 0.0667\epsilon^{-j48.2}$$
$$Z_{37} = 5 + j18.85 = 19.5\epsilon^{j75.14};\ Y_{37} = 0.051\epsilon^{-j75.14}$$
$$Z_{48} = 20 + j0 = 20\epsilon^{j0};\ Y_{48} = 0.05\epsilon^{j0}$$

The branch currents may then be computed as

$$I_{26} = V_{26}Y_{26} = 100\epsilon^{j0}0.0667\epsilon^{-j48.2} = 6.67\epsilon^{-j48.2} = 4.45 - j4.98$$
$$I(t)_{26} = \sqrt{2}(6.67\epsilon^{j\omega t}\epsilon^{-j48.2}) = \sqrt{2}\,6.67\epsilon^{j(\omega t-48.2)}$$
$$I_{37} = V_{37}Y_{37} = 100\epsilon^{j0}0.051\epsilon^{-j75.14} = 5.1\epsilon^{-j75.14} = 1.3 - j4.93$$
$$I(t)_{37} = \sqrt{2}\,5.1\epsilon^{j\omega t}\epsilon^{-j75.14} = \sqrt{2}\,5.1\epsilon^{j(\omega t-75.14)}$$
$$I_{48} = V_{48}Y_{48} = 100\epsilon^{j0}0.05\epsilon^{j0} = 5.0\epsilon^{j0} = 5 + j0$$
$$I(t)_{48} = \sqrt{2}\,5\epsilon^{j\omega t}$$

The total current is, by Kirchhoff's current law,

$$I_{12} = I_{26} + I_{37} + I_{48} = 10.75 - j9.91 = 14.62\epsilon^{-j42.7}$$

and

$$I(t)_{12} = \sqrt{2}\,14.62\epsilon^{j\omega t}\epsilon^{-j42.7} = \sqrt{2}\,14.62\epsilon^{j(\omega t-42.7)}$$

The impedance voltages required by the problem statement are

$$V_{L37} = jX_{37}I_{37} = 18.85\epsilon^{j90}5.11e^{-j75.14} = 96.1\epsilon^{j14.86} = 92.9 + j24.7$$
$$V_{L26} = jX_{L26}I_{26} = 37.7\epsilon^{j90}6.67\epsilon^{-j48.2} = 251.5\epsilon^{j41.8} = 187.4 + j167.6$$
$$V_{C26} = jX_{C26}I_{26} = 26.5\epsilon^{-j90}6.67\epsilon^{-j48.2} = 176.7\epsilon^{-j138.2} = -131.7 - j117.7$$

The average power and apparent power are

$$P_0 = V_{26} \cdot I_{26} + V_{37} \cdot I_{37} + V_{48} \cdot I_{48} = 445 + 130 + 500 = 1075 \text{ watts}$$

and

$$|U_0| = |V_{26}||I_{12}| = 100 \times 14.62 = 1462 \text{ va}$$

The average power may be found in other ways, thus

$$P_0 = |I_{26}|^2R_{26} + |I_{37}|^2R_{37} + |I_{48}|^2R_{48} = 6.67^2\times10 + 5.1^2\times5 + 5^2\times20 = 1075 \text{ watts}$$

Also the expression $|V||I| \cos \theta$ may be used, as the reader should verify.

The sine wave equations to be determined are simply the j-components of the rotating vectors already computed in the foregoing:

$$i_{12}(t) = \sqrt{2}\,14.62 \sin(\omega t - 42.7°) = 20.7 \sin(\omega t - 42.7°)$$
$$i_{26}(t) = \sqrt{2}\,6.67 \sin(\omega t - 48.2°) = 9.4 \sin(\omega t - 48.2°)$$

Note that the various voltages are shown on the vector diagram of Fig. 5–4 and that the equivalent resistance and reactance voltages V_{R0} and V_{X0}, respectively, are shown forming a right triangle with V_{15} as the hypotenuse and with the $V_{R0} = I_0 R_0$ voltage in phase with I_0.

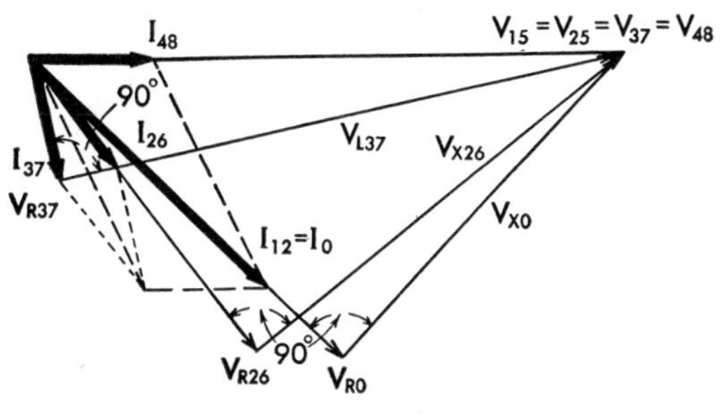

Fig. 5–4.

5.2 Parallel Circuit with Mutual Induction.

There is no essential difference in the treatment of parallel circuits in which the branches are magnetically connected, or coupled, and those in which they are not. However, the circuit shown in Fig. 5–5 will be considered in order to illustrate inclusion of mutual-induction voltages in the equations of a circuit.

Assuming the terminal voltage of the generator constant,

$$\begin{aligned} V_{14} &= V_{25} = R_{25}I_{25} + jX_{25}I_{25} + jX_{AB}I_{36} \\ V_{14} &= V_{36} = R_{36}I_{36} + jX_{36}I_{36} + jX_{BA}I_{25} \end{aligned} \tag{5–9}$$

which in terms of impedance symbols may be written as

$$\begin{aligned} V_{25} &= Z_{25}I_{25} + Z_{AB}I_{36} \\ V_{36} &= Z_{BA}I_{25} + Z_{36}I_{36} \end{aligned} \tag{5–10}$$

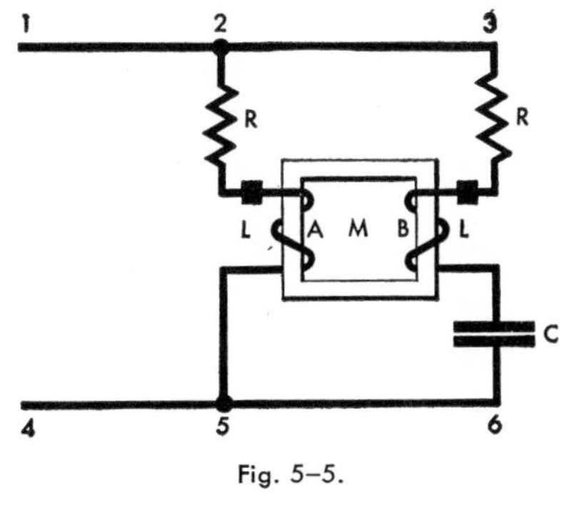

Fig. 5–5.

where

$$\begin{aligned} Z_{25} &= R_{25} + jX_{25} \\ Z_{AB} &= jX_{AB}, \text{ etc.} \end{aligned}$$

The solution of the pair of equations 5–10 is

$$I_{25} = \frac{\begin{vmatrix} V_{25} & Z_{AB} \\ V_{36} & Z_{36} \end{vmatrix}}{\begin{vmatrix} Z_{25} & Z_{AB} \\ Z_{BA} & Z_{36} \end{vmatrix}} = \frac{V_{25}Z_{36} - V_{36}Z_{AB}}{Z_{25}Z_{36} - Z_{AB}Z_{BA}}$$

from which, because $V_{14} = V_{25} = V_{36}$, and if $Z_{250} = 1/Y_{250}$

$$I_{25} = \frac{V_{14}(Z_{36} - Z_{AB})}{Z_{25}Z_{36} - Z_{AB}Z_{BA}} = V_{14}\frac{1}{Z_{250}} = V_{14}Y_{250} \tag{5–11}$$

Likewise,

$$I_{36} = \frac{V_{36}Z_{25} - V_{25}Z_{BA}}{Z_{25}Z_{36} - Z_{BA}Z_{AB}} = \frac{V_{14}(Z_{25} - Z_{BA})}{Z_{25}Z_{36} - Z_{AB}Z_{BA}} = V_{14}\frac{1}{Z_{360}} = V_{14}Y_{360} \quad (5\text{–}12)$$

The admittance, conductance, and susceptance were defined in Chap. 4 and given a particular form there. Admittance will *always* be defined, wherever it appears, as the reciprocal of impedance. Accordingly, the admittances for the circuit of Fig. 5–5 are, from equations 5–11 and 5–12,

$$Y_{250} = \frac{Z_{36} - Z_{AB}}{Z_{25}Z_{36} - Z_{AB}Z_{BA}} = \frac{1}{Z_{250}} \quad (5\text{–}13)$$

$$Y_{360} = \frac{Z_{25} - Z_{BA}}{Z_{25}Z_{36} - Z_{AB}Z_{BA}} = \frac{1}{Z_{360}} \quad (5\text{–}14)$$

The total admittance of the circuit viewed from the terminals 1–4 has already been shown in Art. 5–1 to be the sum

$$Y_0 = Y_{250} + Y_{360} = \frac{Z_{25} + Z_{36} - Z_{AB} - Z_{BA}}{Z_{25}Z_{36} - Z_{AB}Z_{BA}} = \frac{1}{Z_0} \quad (5\text{–}15)$$

These equations can be modified slightly in an evident manner for circuits in which $Z_{AB} = Z_{BA}$, i.e., for a circuit in which the magnetic permeability is constant.

The reciprocals of these three admittances of equations 5–13, 5–14, and 5–15 are the impedances of the two branches 2–5 and 3–6, and of the circuit as a whole measured from the terminals 1–4. Note that the inclusion of mutual induction has made Y_{250} different from the reciprocal of Z_{25}, and that only if Z_{BA} is zero is Y_{250} the reciprocal of Z_{25}. Because in all cases the reciprocal of any combination of impedances is considered an admittance if the combination is itself an impedance, and vice versa, the immediately foregoing results show that the admittance of a branch in a circuit may not be simply the reciprocal of the self-impedance of that branch.

Example 5:2 Suppose the circuit of Fig. 5–5 has a terminal voltage of $V_{14} = 20 + j20$, and that $Z_{25} = 2 + j4$, $Z_{36} = 3 + j(3 - 5)$, $Z_{AB} = Z_{BA} = j2$ ohms. Determine all the currents and draw the complete vector diagram.

Solution From equations 5–11 and 5–12,

$$I_{25} = \frac{(20 + j20)(3 - j4)}{14 + j8 + 4} = \frac{140 - j20}{18 + j8} = 6.08 - j3.81 = 7.17\epsilon^{-j32.1}$$

$$I_{36} = \frac{(20 + j20)(2 + j2)}{18 + j8} = \frac{0 + j80}{18 + j8} = 1.65 + j3.71 = 4.06\epsilon^{j66}$$

and the sum of these currents gives the total current as

$$I_{12} = I_{25} + I_{36} = 7.73 - j0.10 = 7.73\epsilon^{-j0.73}$$

In order to draw the vector diagram the voltages must be calculated. These voltages are:

$$\begin{aligned}
V_{R25} &= R_{25}I_{25} = 2(7.17\epsilon^{-j32.1}) = 14.34\epsilon^{-j32.1} \\
V_{L25} &= jX_{25}I_{25} = (j4)7.17\epsilon^{-j32.1} = 28.68\epsilon^{j57.9} \\
V_{M25} &= Z_{AB}I_{36} = (j2)4.06\epsilon^{j66} = 8.12\epsilon^{j156} \\
V_{R36} &= R_{36}I_{36} = 3(4.06\epsilon^{j66}) = 12.18\epsilon^{j66} \\
V_{X36} &= jX_{36}I_{36} = (-j2)4.06\epsilon^{j66} = 8.12\epsilon^{-j24} \\
V_{M36} &= Z_{BA}I_{25} = (j2)(7.17\epsilon^{-j32.1}) = 14.34\epsilon^{j57.9}
\end{aligned}$$

The vector diagram for this example is shown in Fig. 5–6.

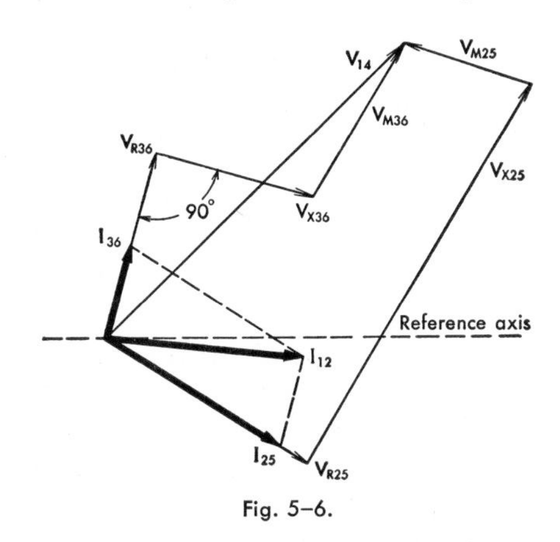

Fig. 5–6.

5.3 Resonance in a Two-Branch Parallel Circuit.

If a parallel circuit has more than two branches, the problem of determining its complete behavior is very complex. Even the problem of studying, more or less completely, a two-branch parallel circuit, each

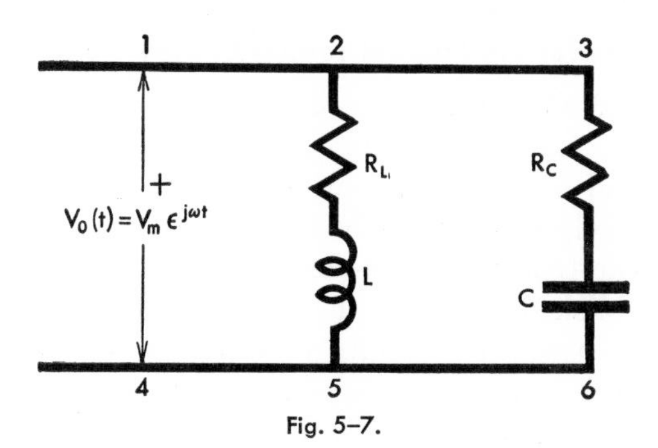

Fig. 5–7.

branch of which contains R, L, and C, is extremely complicated so that only the less complex two-branch parallel tuning circuit of Fig. 5–7 will be studied in detail. This latter circuit is of considerable importance in network applications.

Corresponding to the definition of resonance for a series circuit given in Chap. 4, *a parallel circuit will be considered to be in resonance when the total current and terminal voltage are in phase;* that is, when the power factor of the circuit viewed from the source is unity. A mathematical definition of resonance in the parallel tuning circuit of Fig. 5–7 may be obtained from a consideration of equation 5–4 particularized for this circuit. The resulting equivalent admittance is

$$Y_{14} = Y_0 \equiv G_0 + jB_0 = \left[\frac{R_L}{|Z_L|^2} + \frac{R_C}{|Z_C|^2}\right] + j\left[\frac{-X_L}{|Z_L|^2} + \frac{-X_C}{|Z_C|^2}\right] \tag{5–16}$$

In order for the total current and terminal voltage to be in phase, from the equation

$$I_0 = Y_0 V_0$$

Y_0 must be a real number, hence the imaginary part of Y_0 must be equal to zero, or

$$B_L + B_C = \frac{-X_L}{|Z_L|^2} + \frac{-X_C}{|Z_C|^2} = 0 \tag{5–17}$$

Substituting the values of the symbols of this equation in terms of the symbols for the circuit elements leads to

$$\frac{-X_L}{|Z_L|^2} + \frac{-X_C}{|Z_C|^2} = \frac{-2\pi fL}{R_L^2 + 4\pi^2 f^2 L^2} + \frac{\dfrac{1}{2\pi fC}}{R_C^2 + \dfrac{1}{4\pi^2 f^2 C^2}} = 0 \tag{5–18}$$

Whenever the circuit parameters are such that this equation is satisfied, the tuning circuit is in resonance. This equation will be useful in what follows.

5.4 The Equations for the Parallel Tuning Circuit.

Probably the most immediately evident method of establishing the properties of the parallel tuning circuit is to write the equation for the current into it and determine the mathematical properties of this equation. This method, while entirely feasible, offers some mathematical difficulties. In the treatment to be employed here, the current equation will first be established and then the locus diagrams similar to those of Art. 4–7 will be used to facilitate determining the properties of the equation.

Since the source terminal voltage will be considered constant, the current magnitude varies directly as the equivalent admittance magnitude and may be written from equation 5–16 and Fig. 5–7 as

$$|I_0| = |V|\,|Y_0| = |V|\sqrt{\left[\frac{R_L}{|Z_L|^2} + \frac{R_C}{|Z_C|^2}\right]^2 + \left[\frac{-X_L}{|Z_L|^2} + \frac{-X_C}{|Z_C|^2}\right]^2} \tag{5–19}$$

Recalling the fact that the X's and the Z's are functions of L, C, and f, this equation is a function of the five independent variables, R_L, R_C, L, C, and f.

Adequate treatment in terms of these five independent variables would require a six-dimensional space—one for each of these variables and one for the admittance. But, since for practical purposes only two dimensions are available for demonstration, equation 5–19 will have to be studied in sections, i.e., it will be necessary to assume that all the independent

Fig. 5–8a. Radio frequency amplifier; one type of circuit in which the parallel tuning circuit is used. (Courtesy, Bud Radio, Inc.)

variables, or parameters, but one are maintained constant and the resultant two-dimensional relation will be studied. Any other method leads to practically insurmountable algebraic difficulties, in addition to which the two-dimensional method corresponds to the actual method of using the circuit, e.g., in tuning the circuit, L or C, or f or perhaps one of the R's is varied while all other parameters are held constant. Thus, fortunately, the practical technique permits the use of the simplest mathematical procedure to study the circuit.

The properties of the total power factor angle are of interest and may be determined by evaluating the expression for θ of equations 4–23 in terms of the conductance and susceptance of the parallel tuning circuit. The result is

$$\theta_0 \equiv \tan^{-1} \frac{|X_C|\,|Z_L|^2 - X_L|Z_C|^2}{|R_C|\,|Z_L|^2 + R_L|Z_C|^2} \tag{5–20}$$

A thorough investigation of the two equations of this article will establish the properties of the parallel tuning circuit. Such an investigation is carried out in the next few articles.

It is not possible to overemphasize the practical importance of the two-branch parallel tuning circuit. Some mention has already been made of its widespread use in both power and communication systems. The networks of Fig. 5–8 illustrate the type of equipment with which parallel tuning circuits at high frequencies are constructed. Equipment which is used to form parallel tuning circuits in power systems is shown in Fig. 5–19. The synchronous condenser of Fig. 5–19*a*, which parallels a load at

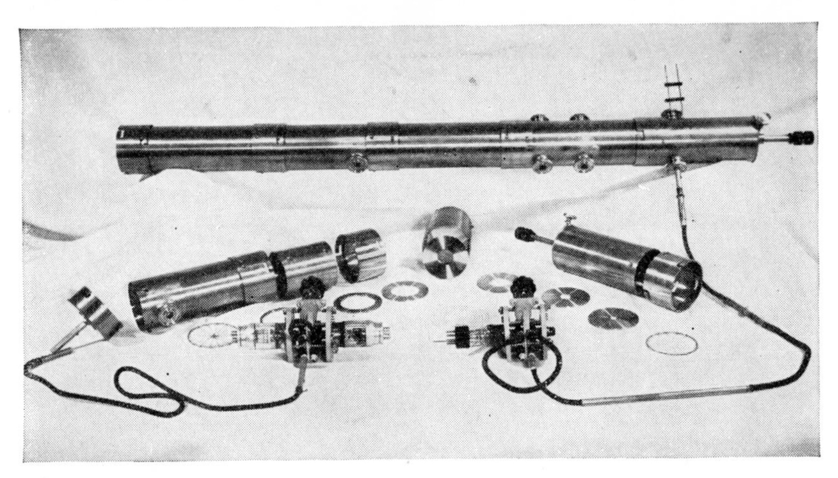

Fig. 5–8*b*. Klystron tubes and ultrahigh frequency wave guides.

the end of a transmission line, shows one of the important types of power system uses of the parallel tuning circuit. It is evident from the size of this installation that electrical engineers find the parallel tuning circuit important enough to spend considerable money on a single installation. A less expensive but equally important power system installation is shown in Fig. 5–19*b*. The static capacitors shown, parallel a load to tune, or partially tune, the combination to a power factor more nearly unity than could be attained by the load alone.

5.5 Properties of the Parallel Tuning Circuit as a Function of R_L Only.

Suppose that the resistance of the inductor branch of the parallel tuning circuit is varied from zero to open circuit and that the characteristics of the resultant total input current variation are desired. A locus vector diagram is the simplest device to use to determine the current variation.

Since the capacitor branch does not vary with R_L, the current through this branch is represented by a constant vector as shown by I_C of Fig. 5–

9*a*. The vector representing the current in the inductor branch varies along a semicircle in accordance with the locus diagram derived in Art. 4–7 and shown in Figs. 4–19*b* and 5–9*a*. If I_C and I_L are added to determine the total current, the locus of I_0 is shown by the heavy semicircle of Fig. 5–9*a*. A study of this locus will serve to reveal the properties of I_0.

The maximum value of the total current $|I_0|$ can be determined as indicated in Fig. 5–9*c*, by a line *od* from the origin through the center of the locus curve of I_0. That this line determines the maximum length of

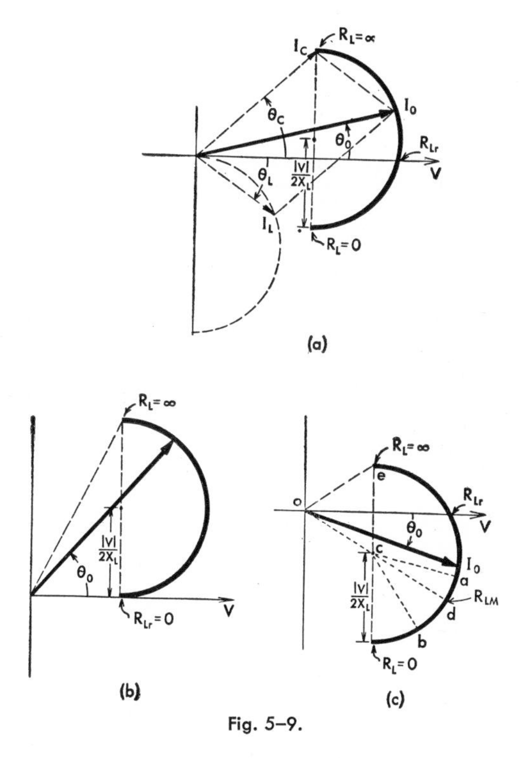

Fig. 5–9.

I_0 is evident from the fact that any value of I_0 is the sum of two vectors: the constant vector *oc* and a vector from the center *c* to the semicircle, of length equal to the radius of the semicircle, e.g., *ca*, *cb*, or *cd*. Obviously such a vector sum is of greatest length when the two vectors lie on the same straight line; i.e., *oc* plus *cd*. Also for any locus, such as those in Fig. 5–9, located any place in the first or fourth quadrant a maximum value of $|I_0|$ exists. Accordingly, the curve of $|I_0|$ vs. R_L will *always* be concave down, i.e., have a maximum at a value of R_L different from 0 or ∞, and may or may not have a resonant value of R_L, depending on whether the diameter of the locus diagram is respectively greater than, equal to, or less than the *j*-component of I_C (see Figs. 5–9 and 5–10).

A more complete quantitative discussion of the $|I_0|$ vs. R_L relation will now be given. Consider first the determination of the value of R_L which will produce the maximum value of $|I_0|$. Setting the first derivative

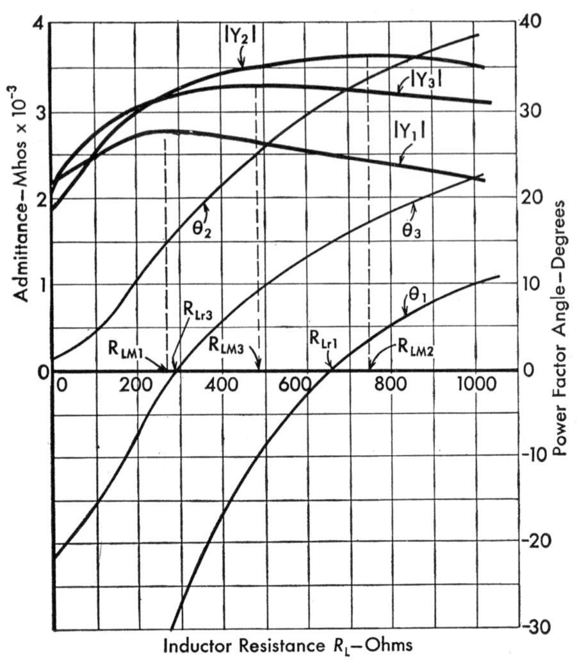

Fig. 5–10.

with respect to R_L of equation 5–19 equal to zero, and solving for R_L, results in

$$R_{LM} = \frac{-|Z_C|^2 + 2X_L|X_C| + \sqrt{(|Z_C|^2 - 2X_L|X_C|)^2 + 4X_L{}^2R_C{}^2}}{2R_C} \tag{5–21}$$

where R_{LM} symbolizes the value of R_L to make $|I_0|$ a maximum.

The value of R_L to produce resonance may be obtained by solving equation 5–18 for R_L. The result is

$$R_{Lr} = \sqrt{\frac{X_L(|Z_C|^2 - X_L|X_C|)}{|X_C|}} \tag{5–22}$$

If it exists resonance will, of course, occur when I_0 coincides with V on the locus diagram, and according to this last equation, R_{Lr} is real and so resonance exists if $X_L|X_C| < |Z_C|^2$.

If, next, the locus diagram is used for the determination of further properties of the parallel tuning circuit, the location of the center of the semicircular locus of I_0 serves to subdivide the discussion conveniently.

First suppose that the center of the locus lies on the voltage vector V. Such a condition arises if the radius $|V|/2X_L$ of the locus is equal to the j-component of the capacitor branch current I_C (see Fig. 5–9). From this locus it is evident that if the center is on the vector V, *the maximum value of* $|I_0|$ *occurs at resonance.*

More precisely in mathematical form, the j-component of I_C from the diagram is $|I_C| \sin \theta_C$ and, since

$$|I_C| = \frac{|V|}{|Z_C|} \text{ and } \sin \theta_C = \frac{|X_C|}{|Z_C|}$$

immediately

$$|I_C| \sin \theta_C = \frac{|V|\,|X_C|}{|Z_C|^2}$$

Equating this j-component of I_C to the radius of the semicircle $|V|/2X_L$ gives the parameter relation

$$\frac{|X_C|}{|Z_C|^2} = \frac{1}{2X_L}$$

from which

$$2|X_C|X_L = |Z_C|^2 \tag{5–23}$$

if the locus center lies on V. Substituting this condition into the equations for the values of R_L to produce a maximum $|I_0|$ and resonant $|I_0|$ (equations 5–21 and 5–22) shows them to be the same and such that

$$R_{Lr} = R_{LM} = X_L$$

Suppose next that the radius of the semicircle is greater than the vertical component of I_C. Then in correspondence with the derivation of equation 5–23,

$$2|X_C|X_L < |Z_C|^2 \tag{5–24}$$

and the semicircle is located as in Fig. 5–9c with center below V. The maximum value of $|I_0|$ will then occur when the vector I_0 is in the fourth quadrant, and from the locus diagram $R_{Lr} > R_{LM}$.

If the radius of the semicircle is less than the imaginary component of I_C, but the diameter is greater or equal,

$$\frac{|V|}{2X_L} < |I_C| \sin \theta_C \leqslant \frac{|V|}{X_L}$$

or substituting alternative values for $|I_C|$ and $\sin \theta_C$, canceling $|V|$, and taking reciprocals

$$2X_L|X_C| > |Z_C|^2 \geqslant X_L|X_C| \tag{5–25}$$

This condition corresponds to the location of the center of the semicircle above V as in Fig. 5–9a, but not farther above than given by the limiting position of Fig. 5–9b. Evidently $|I_0|$ will have a maximum value for I_0 in the first quadrant so that $R_{LM} > R_{Lr}$.

Finally, if the diameter of the semicircle is less than the imaginary component of I_C,

$$X_L|X_C| > |Z_C|^2 \tag{5–26}$$

and the semicircle will never intersect V, so that resonance will not occur for any R_L.

It is evident from the locus diagrams that, if $R_L < R_{Lr}$, the current I_0 lags V; if $R_L > R_{Lr}$, the current I_0 leads V; and, of course, if $R_L = R_{Lr}$, I_0 and V are in phase.

A résumé of the foregoing conclusions may be put in the following compact form:

$$\left.\begin{array}{l} \text{If } |Z_C|^2 > 2X_L|X_C|, \\ \text{then } R_{Lr} > R_{LM} \\ \text{If } |Z_C|^2 = 2X_L|X_C|, \\ \text{then } R_{Lr} = R_{LM} = X_L \\ \text{If } 2X_L|X_C| > |Z_C|^2 \geq X_L|X_C|, \\ \text{then } R_{Lr} < R_{LM} \end{array}\right\} \left\{\begin{array}{l} \text{For } R_L < R_{Lr}, \; -\dfrac{\pi}{2} < \theta < 0 \text{ (lag)} \\ \text{For } R_L = R_{Lr}, \; \theta = 0 \\ \text{For } R_L > R_{Lr}, \; \dfrac{\pi}{2} > \theta > 0 \text{ (lead)} \end{array}\right. \tag{5–27}$$

$$\text{If } |Z_C|^2 < X_L|X_C| \begin{bmatrix} \text{No resonance, but} \\ \text{maximum} |I_0| \text{at } R_{LM} \end{bmatrix}; \text{ for all } R_L, \; \frac{\pi}{2} > \theta > 0 \text{ (lead)}$$

Example 5:3 As an illustration of the use of the results given by 5–27, consider a particular circuit in which $X_L = 400$ ohms, $|X_C| = 300$ ohms, and $R_C = 600$ ohms. Using these numbers gives

$$|Z_C|^2 = 450{,}000$$
$$2|X_C|X_L = 240{,}000$$

hence

$$|Z_C|^2 > 2|X_C|X_L$$

According to the first row of relations 5–27 and Fig. 5–9c, the circuit may be adjusted to produce a maximum current or a resonant current by the proper value of R_L; resonance occurs at a higher resistance than that required to produce maximum current; and at values of R_L above the resonant value the current leads the voltage, and at values of R_L below the resonant value the current lags the voltage. All these points are shown on the locus diagram or in the curves of θ_1 and $|Y_1|$ of Fig. 5–10, drawn for the conditions of this example.

Other rectangular coordinate curves of different shape than those of Fig. 5–10 may be obtained by fixing the parameters, X_C, X_L, and R_C, at different values. Criteria 5–27 apply, however, no matter what the values assigned to these parameters.

5.6 Parallel Tuning Circuit Admittance a Function of Capacitor Branch Resistance (R_C) Only.

The admittance, or the current, of the parallel tuning circuit, as a function of R_C only is so similar to the R_L equation, so far as mathematical treatment, locus diagrams, and conclusions are concerned, that only the results will be given. In brief, the circuit can always be adjusted to produce a maximum current, but not always to resonance.

As with the R_L variable, use of a combination of mathematics and locus diagrams permits a detailed specification of the behavior of the circuit under consideration. Accordingly, the value of R_C to produce a maximum is (see Problem 5–20)

$$R_{CM} \equiv \frac{-|Z_L|^2 + 2|X_C|X_L + \sqrt{(|Z_L|^2 - 2|X_C|X_L)^2 + 4|X_C|^2 R_L^2}}{2R_L} \qquad (5\text{–}28)$$

The value of R_C to produce resonance, from equation 5–18, is

$$R_{Cr} \equiv \sqrt{\frac{|X_C|(|Z_L|^2 - |X_C|X_L)}{X_L}} \qquad (5\text{–}29)$$

Also

$$\left.\begin{array}{l} \text{If } |Z_L|^2 > 2|X_C|X_L, \\ \text{then } R_{Cr} > R_{CM} \\ \text{If } |Z_L|^2 = 2|X_C|X_L, \\ \text{then } R_{Cr} = R_{CM} = X_C) \\ \text{If } |X_C|X_L \leq |Z_L|^2 < 2|X_C|X_L, \\ \text{then } R_{Cr} < R_{CM} \end{array}\right\} \left\{\begin{array}{l} \text{For } R_C < R_{Cr},\ \dfrac{\pi}{2} > \theta > 0 \text{ (lead)} \\ \text{For } R_C = R_{Cr},\ \theta = 0 \\ \text{For } R_C > R_{Cr},\ -\dfrac{\pi}{2} < \theta < 0 \text{ (lag)} \end{array}\right. \qquad (5\text{–}30)$$

$$\text{If } |Z_L|^2 < |X_C|X_L \left[\begin{array}{l}\text{No resonance but} \\ \text{maximum } |I_0| \text{ at } R_{CM}\end{array}\right] \text{for all } R_L,\ -\pi < \theta < 0 \text{ (lag)}$$

Note that this system of relations is *very* similar to the system of the preceding article for R_L as the variable.

5.7 Parallel Tuning Circuit Input Current as a Function of Inductance (L) Only.

If the inductance of branch 2–5 of the parallel tuning circuit of Fig. 5–7 is considered as the only variable, a locus diagram may be established as shown in Fig. 5–11. The heavy-lined semicircle is the locus of the input current and is formed by adding the constant capacitor branch current I_C to the semicircular locus of I_L as given by Fig. 4–20*a*. Only a semicircle is used in Fig. 5–11 because there is no capacitor in the inductor branch to extend the locus beyond the semicircle.

An examination of this locus indicates certain facts immediately;

namely, that the variation of $|I_0|$ vs. L has a minimum value at the point where a line through the origin and center of the locus semicircle intersects the locus—point d of Fig. 5–11, since $oc + cd$ is less than any other

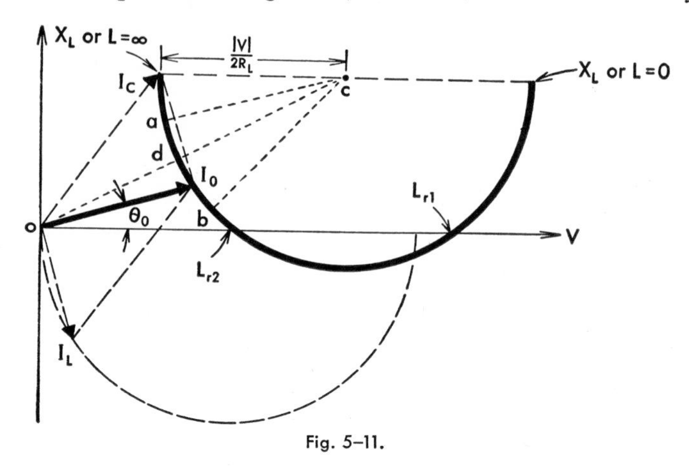

Fig. 5–11.

sum such as $oc + ca$, $oc + cb$, etc.—and that resonance may occur at *two*, *one*, or *no* values of L, depending on the relative values of the imaginary component of I_C and the radius of the locus semicircle. The locus diagram also shows that resonance and minimum $|I_0|$ can never coincide because I_0 cannot be perpendicular to the locus and at the same time in phase with V. Note, however, that as R_L decreases, the radius of the semicircle—$|V|/2R_L$—increases, and in the limiting case of $R_L = 0$ the radius is infinite and the locus of I_L is a vertical straight line. Minimum $|I_0|$ then occurs at resonance as shown in Fig. 5–12.

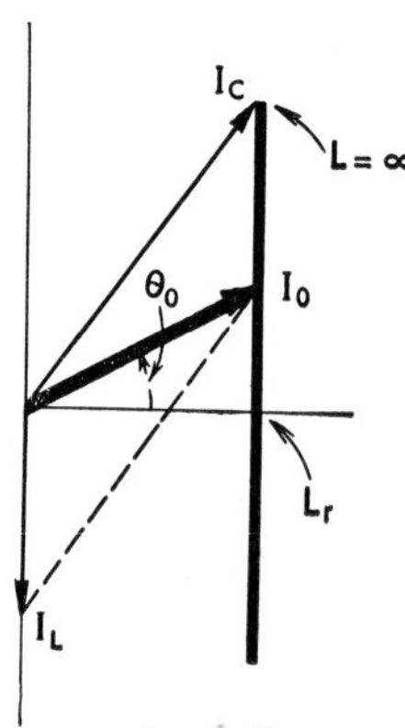

Fig. 5–12.

The two values of L to produce resonance may be obtained by solving equation 5–18 for L. A quadratic in L results, and the two L values are

$$L_{r1} \equiv \frac{|Z_C|^2 - \sqrt{|Z_C|^4 - 4|X_C|^2 R_L^2}}{2\omega|X_C|} \tag{5–31}$$

$$L_{r2} \equiv \frac{|Z_C|^2 + \sqrt{|Z_C|^4 - 4|X_C|^2 R_L^2}}{2\omega|X_C|} \tag{5–32}$$

Both these values of inductance will produce resonance if $|Z_C|^2 > 2|X_C|R_L$; and, of course, there is only one value of L—which will be indicated by L_{r0}—which will produce resonance if $|Z_C|^2 = 2|X_C|R_L$, namely,

$$L_{r0} \equiv \frac{|Z_C|^2}{2\omega|X_C|} = \frac{R_L}{\omega} \tag{5–33}$$

The value of inductance to produce a minimum input current may be derived by forming the derivative, with respect to L, of equation 5–19, equating the result to zero, and solving for L. The result is

$$L_m \equiv \frac{|Z_C|^2 + 2R_CR_L + \sqrt{(|Z_C|^2 + 2R_CR_L)^2 + 4|X_C|^2R_L^2}}{2\omega|X_C|} \tag{5–34}$$

The locus diagram shows that this value of L gives a minimum $|I_0|$ rather than a maximum.

The locus diagram of Fig. 5–11 makes it evident that resonance and minimum inductances are related according to

$$\begin{aligned} L_m &> L_{r0} \\ L_m &> L_{r2} > L_{r1} \end{aligned} \tag{5–35}$$

Any other characteristics of the parallel tuning circuit, under a variation of L only, can be deduced by using a combination of locus diagrams and mathematics. A brief résumé of the outstanding properties of the parallel tuning circuit under variation of L is given in the following:

$$\begin{array}{l} \text{If } |Z_C|^2 > 2|X_C|R_L, \\ \text{then } L_{r1} < L_{r2} < L_m, \text{ and} \end{array} \left[\begin{array}{ll} \text{for } L < L_{r1}, & 0 < \theta < \frac{\pi}{2} \text{ (lead)} \\ \text{for } L_{r1} < L < L_{r2}, & 0 > \theta > -\frac{\pi}{2} \text{ (lag)} \\ \text{for } L > L_{r2}, & 0 < \theta < \frac{\pi}{2} \text{ (lead)} \end{array}\right. \tag{5–36}$$

$$\text{If } |Z_C|^2 = 2|X_C|R_L \left[\begin{array}{l} L_{r0} < L_m \\ X_L = R_L \text{ at resonance } 0 \le \theta < \frac{\pi}{2} \text{ (lead)} \end{array}\right.$$

$$\text{If } |Z_C|^2 < 2\,|X_C|R_L \left[\begin{array}{l} \text{No resonance but a} \\ \text{minimum } |I_0| \text{ at } L_m \end{array}\right] 0 < \theta < \frac{\pi}{2} \text{ (lead)}$$

Example 5:4 As an example of the use of the foregoing set of inequalities, consider the circuit in which $X_C = -400$ ohms, $R_L = 500$ ohms, $R_C =$ 600 ohms, and $\omega = 250$. Then

$$|Z_C|^2 = 520{,}000 > 2|X_C|R_L = 400{,}000$$

and from 5–36 and the equations 5–34, 5–31, and 5–32, the circuit has two resonant values of L at $L_{r1} = 0.94$ henry and $L_{r2} = 4.26$ henrys; a minimum admittance at $L_m = 11.5$ henrys (see curve Y_1 of Fig. 5–13). From 5–36 the total current is leading for L below L_{r1}, lagging for L between L_{r1} and L_{r2}, and again leading for L above the higher resonant inductance L_{r2}, as is shown in curve θ_1 of Fig. 5–13 or as indicated by the locus diagram.

5.8 Parallel Tuning Circuit Admittance as a Function of Capacitance (C) Only.

The characteristics of the admittance of the parallel tuning circuit as a function of capacitance only are similar to the characteristics of the

L-variation of admittance discussed in the preceding article. The locus diagram is simply Fig. 5–11 inverted. Accordingly $|I_0|$ will have a minimum where the line from the origin to the center of the semicircle intersects the semicircle, resonance may occur at *two*, *one*, or *zero* values of C,

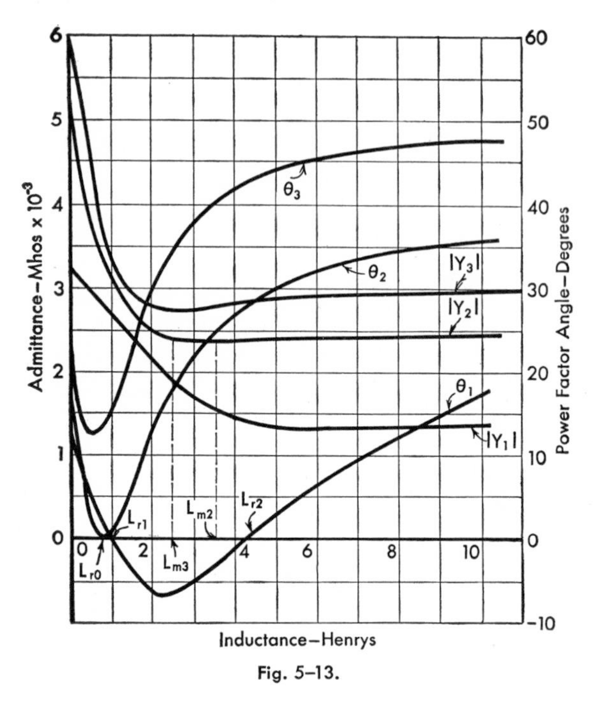

Fig. 5–13.

and minimum $|I_0|$ and resonance can never occur at the same value of C. The curves of Fig. 5–14 show typical admittance and power factor angle variations.

The method of determining the C-variation characteristics by a combination of mathematics and locus diagram is also very similar to the method of the preceding article; hence only a bare outline of the method is given here.

Setting the partial derivative, with respect to C, of the current $|I_0|$ of equation 5–19 equal to zero, solving for the positive value of C which satisfies this relation, and noting from a locus diagram that a *minimum* value of $|I_0|$ results show that

$$C_m \equiv \frac{-(|Z_L|^2 + 2R_CR_L) + \sqrt{(|Z_L|^2 + 2R_CR_L)^2 + 4R_C^2X_L^2}}{2\omega R_C^2X_L} \tag{5–37}$$

is the value of C which makes the admittance, as a function of C only, a *minimum* (see Fig. 5–14 also).

The values of C which will make the parallel circuit resonant may be determined by solving equation 5–18 for C. The result is

$$C_{r2} \equiv \frac{|Z_L|^2 + \sqrt{|Z_L|^4 - 4X_L^2R_C^2}}{2\omega X_L R_C^2} \tag{5-38}$$

and

$$C_{r1} \equiv \frac{|Z_L|^2 - \sqrt{|Z_L|^4 - 4X_L^2R_C^2}}{2\omega X_L R_C^2} \tag{5-39}$$

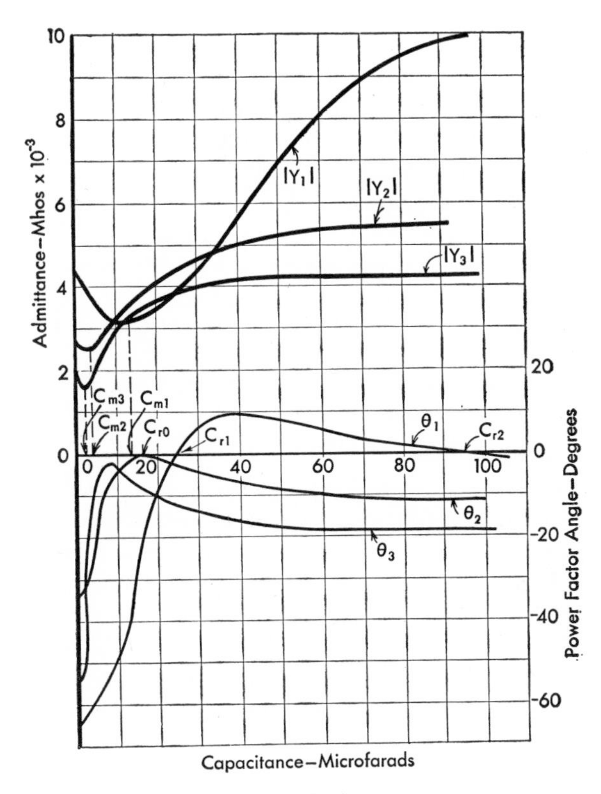

Fig. 5–14.

Examination of these relations shows that for a C to exist which will produce resonance, i.e., C_{r1} and C_{r2} not imaginary, the square root must be real or $|Z_L|^2 \geq 2X_LR_C$. Therefore, two values of resonance will exist only if $|Z_L|^2 > 2X_LR_C$; and only one value of C, namely, $C_{r0} = 1/\omega R_C$, produces resonance if $|Z_L|^2 = 2X_LR_C$.

In compact form the characteristics of the parallel tuning circuit for C as a variable are:

$$\text{If } |Z_L|^2 > 2X_LR_C, \text{ then } C_{r2} > C_{r1} > C_m, \text{ and } \begin{cases} \text{for } C < C_{r1} & 0 > \theta > \dfrac{-\pi}{2} \text{ (lag)} \\ \text{for } C_{r1} < C < C_{r2}, & 0 < \theta < \dfrac{\pi}{2} \text{ (lead)} \\ \text{for } C > C_{r2} & 0 < \theta < \dfrac{-\pi}{2} \text{ (lag)} \end{cases} \quad (5\text{–}40)$$

$$\text{If } |Z_L|^2 = 2X_LR_C \begin{Bmatrix} C_{r0} > C_m \\ X_C = R_C \text{ at resonance} \end{Bmatrix} 0 \geq \theta > \frac{-\pi}{2} \text{ (lag or zero)}$$

$$\text{If } |Z_L|^2 < 2X_LR_C \begin{bmatrix} \text{no resonance but a} \\ \text{minimum } |I_0| \text{ at } C_m \end{bmatrix} 0 < \theta < \frac{-\pi}{2} \text{ (lag)}$$

The curves of Fig. 5–14 illustrate typical forms of the $|Y|$ vs. C curves, the general characteristics of which may be determined from 5–40. Curves $|Y_1|$ and θ_1 are plotted for a circuit of $X_L = 200$ ohms, $R_C = 100$ ohms, $R_L = 100$ ohms, and $\omega = 210$; $|Y_2|$ and θ_2 for $X_L = 200$ ohms, $R_L = 300$ ohms, $R_C = 325$ ohms, and $\omega = 210$; and $|Y_3|$ and θ_3 for $X_L = 400$ ohms, $R_L = 300$ ohms, $R_C = 350$ ohms, and $\omega = 400$.

The relations of 5–40 and the curves of Fig. 5–14 show that the θ_0 vs. C curve, concave down, crosses the abscissa twice for two resonant values of C, is just tangent for only one resonant value of C, and is wholly below the axis if variation of C will not produce resonance. The locus diagram should be constructed to verify all these conclusions.

5.9 Parallel Tuning Circuit Admittance a Function of Frequency (*f*) Only.

The admittance of the parallel tuning circuit as a function of frequency is very much more complex than any of the other functions considered in the foregoing. The locus diagram is not simple enough to warrant spending much time on it since a mathematical analysis is needed to supplement the locus diagram anyway. Therefore, only the mathematical treatment will be considered, and this treatment will be presented briefly.

Evaluating the first partial derivative of $|I_0|$ of equation 5–19 with respect to frequency, equating to zero, and dropping a non-zero, positive multiplying factor gives

$$16\pi^4C^2L^2\left[\left(R_C^2 + \frac{L}{C}\right)^2 - 2R_C^2(R_C^2 + R_CR_L)\right]f^4 + 8\pi^2L^2(R_L^2 - R_C^2)f^2 - \left[\left(R_L^2 + \frac{L}{C}\right)^2 - 2R_L^2(R_L^2 + R_LR_C)\right] = 0 \quad (5\text{–}41)$$

a quartic in f which may be treated as a quadratic in f^2. Solving this equation for f^2 and extracting the positive square root gives

$$f_0 = \sqrt{\frac{b \pm \sqrt{b^2 + ad}}{4\pi^2CLa}} \quad (5\text{–}42)$$

where

$$a \equiv \left(R_C^2 + \frac{L}{C}\right)^2 - 2R_C^2(R_C^2 + R_CR_L) \qquad (5\text{–}43)$$

$$b \equiv \frac{L}{C}(R_C^2 - R_L^2) \qquad (5\text{–}44)$$

$$d \equiv \left(R_L^2 + \frac{L}{C}\right)^2 - 2R_L^2(R_L^2 + R_LR_C) \qquad (5\text{–}45)$$

as the value of f for which the admittance, or current, curve has a zero slope.

The relative magnitudes of the ratio L/C and the product R_LR_C prove on investigation to be very important in the analysis of the rather complex equation 5–42. Hence the final results given below in 5–49 are under the headings of the three possible relations for these two quantities; namely, $L/C > R_CR_L$, $L/C = R_CR_L$, and $L/C < R_CR_L$, with the various possible relations between L/C, R_C, and R_L under each. The system of inequalities in 5–49 have been worked out through symbolic manipulation of the total admittance equation. The results only are given here, and they will be interpreted in the following discussion.

An extensive study of equations 5–42 and 5–19 leads to the conclusion that the admittance as a function of frequency only may be classified in *five* types of variation—an increasing function, a decreasing function, a function which attains a maximum, a function which attains a minimum, and an admittance which is constant and resonant for all values of frequency. These curves are illustrated by $|Y_1|$, $|Y_2|$, $|Y_3|$, $|Y_4|$, and $|Y_5|$, respectively, of Fig. 5–15, and the circuit parameter restrictions to produce a particular one of these admittance functions are given in the tabular form 5–49. The frequency at which a maximum occurs is designated by f_M and is the value of f_0 (equation 5–42) for a circuit with an admittance vs. frequency curve as shown by $|Y_3|$ of Fig. 5–15. Correspondingly, f_m designates the value of f_0 at which the minimum admittance occurs for circuits with admittance curves of the form given by the $|Y_4|$ curve of Fig. 5–15.

To turn next to a consideration of the frequency to produce resonance, from equation 5–18,

$$f_r \equiv \frac{1}{2\pi\sqrt{LC}}\sqrt{\frac{R_L^2 - \frac{L}{C}}{R_C^2 - \frac{L}{C}}} \qquad (5\text{–}46)$$

is the one and only value of f which will make the power factor unity. Note that f_r is real and, therefore, corresponds to a real frequency, only if R_L^2 and R_C^2 are *both* less than, *both* greater than, or *both* equal to L/C. Note that in this latter case f_r is indeterminate from equation 5–46 (see Problem 5–28).

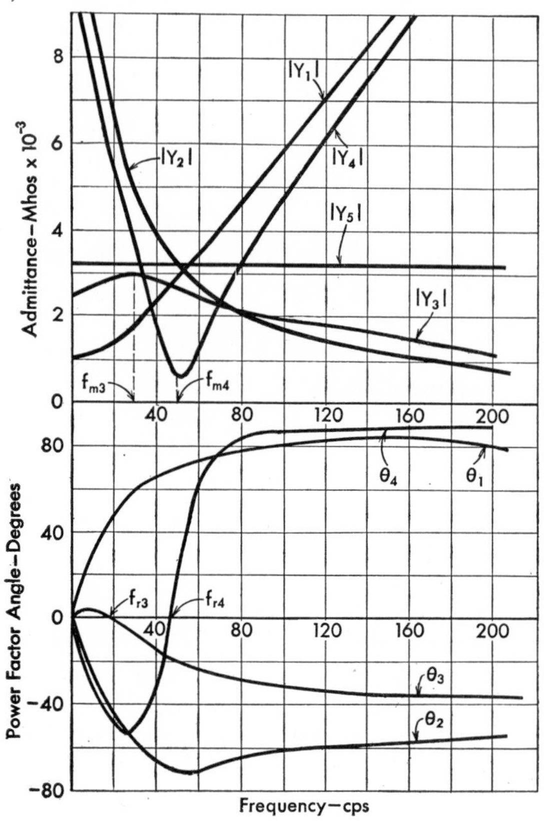

Fig. 5–15.

Equating f_r of equation 5–46 to f_0 of equation 5–42 establishes the condition for resonance to coincide with the zero derivative value f_0. The result is

$$f_0 = f_r, \text{ if } R_L = R_C \tag{5–47}$$

Hence *resonance will occur at the zero slope point on the* $|Y|$ *vs.* f *curve—a maximum or minimum point—only if* $R_L = R_C$. Note furthermore that if the resistances are equal and not equal to $\sqrt{L/C}$, the frequency of resonance, from equation 5–46, is ($R_L = R_C \neq \sqrt{L/C}$).

$$f_r = \frac{1}{2\pi\sqrt{LC}} \tag{5–48}$$

which is the same as the series circuit resonant frequency. Therefore, *if resonance coincides with a maximum or minimum admittance it will do so at the resonant frequency of the* L *and* C *in series.*

From the system of inequalities 5–49, it is apparent that *only the* $|Y(f)|$ *relations which have a maximum or minimum can be made resonant.* In other words, *for the decreasing and increasing functions, resonance will not exist for any frequency.* The only exception is the circuit which has a constant admittance and is resonant at all frequencies. This circuit is specified in the last relation of Case II of 5–49. Note, in addition, that, while only curves with maxima or minima have resonance, *not all* curves with maxima or minima have resonance (e.g., see the last two sections of Case I and Case III of 5–49).

That the relative magnitudes of the ratio L/C and the product $R_C R_L$ are a natural basis for analysis of equation 5–42 is apparent on examination of the results in 5–49. Thus, $L/C > R_C R_L$ makes a *maximum* admittance *impossible*, whereas $L/C < R_C R_L$ makes a *minimum impossible.*

The curves of θ vs. f of Fig. 5–15 have been plotted from equation 5–20, and the θ vs. f relations of 5–49 have been derived from this same equation.

Example 5:5 Some numerical examples are now given to illustrate further the use and meaning of the system 5–49. Suppose that $L = 1$ henry, $C = 10^{-5}$ farad, $R_C = 10$ ohms, and $R_L = 1000$ ohms. Then

$$R_C R_L = 10^4 < 10^5 = \frac{L}{C}$$

$$R_C^2 = 10^2 < \frac{L}{C}, \text{ and } R_L^2 = 10^6 > \frac{L}{C}$$

Then from the last two rows of Case I of 5–49 the curve may have a minimum or be an increasing curve, but since

$$\left(R_L^2 + \frac{L}{C}\right)^2 = 121 \times 10^{10} < 202 \times 10^{10} = 2R_L^2(R_L^2 + R_C R_L)$$

the admittance equation is an increasing function—shown by $|Y_1|$ of Fig. 5–15 —which, as 5–49 indicates, will never be in resonance. Since $R_L > R_C$, from 5–49, the power factor angle θ is positive or leading for all frequencies, as is shown by curve θ_1 of Fig. 5–15.

Again assume $R_C = 2000$ ohms, $R_L = 100$ ohms, $L = 1$ henry, and $C = 10^{-5}$ farad. Then

$$R_C R_L = 2 \times 10^5 > 10^5 = \frac{L}{C}$$

$$R_C^2 = 4 \times 10^6 > \frac{L}{C}, \quad \text{and} \quad R_L^2 = 10^4 < \frac{L}{C}$$

$$\left(R_L^2 + \frac{L}{C}\right)^2 = 121 \times 10^8 > 42 \times 10^8 = 2R_L^2(R_L^2 + R_C R_L)$$

Hence the third from the last row of Case III of 5–49 specifies that the admittance equation is a decreasing function (see $|Y_2|$ of Fig. 5–15) which will never be in resonance, and, since $R_C > R_L$, $\theta < 0$, or the circuit power factor is lagging for all frequencies (see curve θ_2 of Fig. 5–15).

If $R_C = 1000$ ohms, $R_L = 400$ ohms, $C = 10^{-5}$ farad. $L = 1$ henry.

$$R_C R_L > \frac{L}{C};\ R_L{}^2 > \frac{L}{C};\ R_C{}^2 > \frac{L}{C}$$

hence from Case III of 5–49—first group of terms—the admittance takes on a maximum value at $f_M = 23.4$ cps determined from equation 5–42 which gives the frequency for either a maximum or minimum. See curve $|Y_3|$, of Fig. 5–15. Also since $R_C > R_L$, $f_M > f_r$ and the maximum admittance is at a higher frequency than resonance—$f_r = 13$ (equation 5–46). Also from the table—illustrated in curve θ_3 of Fig. 5–15—the power factor angle is leading for frequencies below resonance and lagging for frequencies above resonance.

One further illustration of the use of the tabular system of 5–49 will be given. Suppose a two-branch parallel circuit is desired which will have a *minimum admittance and resonance* at f_1 cycles per second. In order for the admittance curve to have a minimum, the parameter conditions of Case I must be satisfied, so that $R_C R_L < L/C$. As shown in the third row of Case I, $f_m = f_r$ if $R_L = R_C$, i.e., resonance and minimum admittance occur at the same frequency if $R_C = R_L$. Therefore, if

$$R_C R_L = R_C{}^2 = R_L{}^2 < \frac{L}{C}$$

the circuit will be resonant at minimum current. The frequency of minimum admittance and resonance is, as shown in Case I, third line,

$$f_m = f_r = f_1 = \frac{1}{2\pi\sqrt{LC}}$$

The desired circuit may be established from the foregoing conclusions. It is possible, in fact, to establish from these relations an unlimited number of circuits which are resonant at minimum current at a particular frequency. Thus, for any particular L or C, at the specified frequency a C or L can be determined from the resonant frequency equation. The ratio L/C then follows for each arbitrary choice of L or C, and the resistances R_C and R_L may, therefore, be taken as any equal values, subject only to the restriction that their squares are less than L/C.

The question of whether the minimum current obtained at resonance is lower or higher than any particular value cannot be answered by using the foregoing relations. Something may be said of this aspect of the problem if note is taken of the fact that $f = 1/2\pi\sqrt{LC}$ is the condition which makes $|X_C| = X_L$, as a simple substitution will show; and an examination

ADMITTANCE, RESONANCE AND PHASE RELATIONS FOR PARALLEL CIRCUIT

(f_m and f_M determined by equation 5–42 and f_r by equation 5–46)

Circuit Element Relations		Response-Frequency Relation	Resonance and Phase Relations
Case I —	$R_C R_L < L/C$		
$R_L^2 < L/C$, $R_C^2 < L/C$	$R_L > R_C; f_m > f_r$		Circuit is resonant. $f < f_r; \theta < 0$
	$R_L = R_C; f_m = f_r = \dfrac{1}{2\pi\sqrt{LC}}$		$f = f_r; \theta = 0$
	$R_L < R_C; f_m < f_r$	Curve has a minimum at f_m.	$f > f_r; \theta > 0$
$R_L^2 = L/C$;	$R_C^2 < L/C$		Circuit is not resonant.
$R_L^2 < L/C$;	$R_C^2 = L/C$		
$R_L^2 < L/C$, $R_C^2 > L/C$	$(R_C^2 + L/C)^2 > 2R_C^2(R_C^2 + R_C R_L)$		
	$(R_C^2 + L/C)^2 \leqq 2R_C^2(R_C^2 + R_C R_L)$	$\lvert Y_0\rvert$ decreases; curve has no maximum or minimum.	$R_L > R_C; \theta > 0$
$R_L^2 > L/C$, $R_C^2 < L/C$	$(R_L^2 + L/C)^2 \leqq 2R_L^2(R_L^2 + R_C R_L)$	$\lvert Y_0\rvert$ increases; curve has no maximum or minimum.	$R_L < R_C; \theta < 0$
	$(R_L^2 + L/C)^2 > 2R_L^2(R_L^2 + R_C R_L)$	Curve has a minimum at f_m.	
Case II —	$R_C R_L = L/C$		
	$R_L^2 < L/C,\ R_C^2 > L/C$	$\lvert Y_0\rvert$ decreases; curve has no maximum or minimum.	Circuit is not resonant. $R_L < R_C; \theta < 0$
	$R_L^2 > L/C,\ R_C^2 < L/C$	$\lvert Y_0\rvert$ increases; curve has no maximum or minimum.	$R_L > R_C; \theta > 0$ (5–49)
	$R_L^2 = R_C^2 = L/C$	$\lvert Y_0\rvert = \sqrt{C/L}$, and curve is constant for every frequency.	Circuit is resonant at every frequency. $\theta = 0$ always.
Case III —	$R_C R_L > L/C$		Circuit is resonant.
$R_L^2 > L/C$, $R_C^2 > L/C$	$R_L > R_C; f_M < f_r$		$f = f_r; \theta = 0$
	$R_L = R_C; f_M = f_r = \dfrac{1}{2\pi\sqrt{LC}}$		$f > f_r; \theta < 0$
	$R_L < R_C; f_M > f_r$	Curve has a maximum at f_M.	$f < f_r; \theta > 0$
$R_L^2 = L/C$;	$R_C^2 > L/C$		
$R_L^2 > L/C$;	$R_C^2 = L/C$		
$R_L^2 < L/C$, $R_C^2 > L/C$	$(R_L^2 + L/C)^2 < 2R_L^2(R_L^2 + R_C R_L)$		Circuit is not resonant.
	$(R_L^2 + L/C)^2 \geqq 2R_L^2(R_L^2 + R_C R_L)$	$\lvert Y_0\rvert$ decreases; curve has no maximum or minimum.	$R_L > R_C; \theta > 0$
$R_L^2 > L/C$, $R_C^2 < L/C$	$(R_C^2 + L/C)^2 \geqq 2R_C^2(R_C^2 + R_C R_L)$	$\lvert Y_0\rvert$ increases; curve has no maximum or minimum.	$R_L < R_C; \theta < 0$
	$(R_C^2 + L/C)^2 < 2R_C^2(R_C^2 + R_C R_L)$	Curve has a maximum at f_M.	

* Myril B. Reed, Electronics Reference Sheet, August, 1941.

of equation 5–19 will show that when $|X_C| = X_L$ the limit of $|Y_0|$ as the equal R's approach zero is zero. Therefore, the *minimum admittance may be made as small as desired by reducing the equal* R's *far enough.*

5.10 Further Discussion of the Parallel Tuning Circuit.

A brief summary of the conclusions reached in the foregoing discussion of the parallel tuning circuit will serve to make the outstanding properties of this circuit more evident.

(*a*) If R_L or R_C only is varied, the total admittance can always be adjusted to a *maximum* admittance or current. Resonance may or may not occur *at* the *maximum* admittance, or resonance may not occur at any value of R_L or R_C, depending on the relations between the constant parameters of the circuit.

(*b*) If L or C only is varied, the total admittance can always be adjusted to a *minimum* and resonance can *never* be made to coincide with this minimum, although it will be near the minimum if R_L, X_C, or $|Z_C|$ is very small for the L-variation, or if R_C, X_L, or $|Z_L|$ is very small for the C-variation. There may be two, one, or no resonance points as L or C is varied, depending on the relations of the other circuit parameters. The value of L to make the admittance a minimum is always *greater* than the value or values of L to make the circuit resonant. Conversely, the value of C to make the admittance a minimum is always *less* than the value or values of C to make the circuit resonant.

(*c*) The variation of the frequency of the voltage connected to a parallel tuning circuit leads to several possible modes of variation. There are five different types of curves possible as f is varied, the particular type obtained being dependent on the other circuit parameter relations; namely, an increasing or a decreasing function, a variation leading to a maximum at other than zero or infinite frequency, a variation leading to a minimum at other than zero or infinite frequency, or, finally, a straight line which means constant admittance at all frequencies. Resonance and maximum or minimum admittance may or may not coincide, or resonance may not be possible—again depending on the other circuit parameter relations.

The parallel and series tuning circuits behave somewhat differently at resonance. If these circuits are considered as functions of frequency, it will be recalled that the *series tuning circuit always has a minimum impedance*, i.e., *maximum admittance at resonance.* The parallel tuning circuit, on the other hand, may or may not have a maximum admittance. As this parallel circuit is used in practice, it is designed to produce a *minimum* admittance. If the resistances are kept relatively low, minimum admittance is always available but not exactly at resonance unless $R_L = R_C$. If the two resistances are made very low (see Problem 5–34) the current, or admittance, of the parallel circuit will be nearly zero, and so will serve practically to block currents of resonant and near-resonant frequencies. It is this particular property of the parallel tuning circuit which is used most frequently in the application of the circuit.

It will be recalled that the series resonant condition is accompanied by excessive voltage in many instances and, therefore, must be applied with caution, particularly in systems where the normal voltages are high. The parallel tuning circuit does not have either excessive voltages or currents, even at resonance, for *constant terminal voltage* and linear R, L, and C. This fact is evident immediately from Fig. 5–7. Each branch of the circuit is connected directly across the source so that its current is determined by the relation of the branch impedance and source voltage and so cannot be excessive unless the circuit is originally badly designed.

5.11 Series-Parallel Circuit — Equivalent Impedance Method.

Consider the circuit represented by Fig. 5–16. This circuit may be solved by employing facts already deduced; namely, that impedances add in series and admittances add in parallel. In particular for this circuit, from equation 5–6, the parallel branches may be replaced by an equivalent impedance of

$$Z_p = \frac{1}{Y_p} = \frac{1}{Y_{25} + Y_{36}} = \frac{Z_{25}Z_{36}}{Z_{25} + Z_{36}} \tag{5–50}$$

Adding this impedance to the impedance Z_{12} gives the total impedance of the circuit, if viewed from the generator terminals,

$$Z_0 = Z_{14} = Z_{41} = Z_{12} + \frac{Z_{25}Z_{36}}{Z_{25} + Z_{36}} \tag{5–51}$$

The input current I_{12} therefore will be the voltage at the terminals divided by this *equivalent* impedance. So

$$I_{12} = \frac{V_{14}}{Z_{14}} = \frac{V_{14}}{Z_0} = \frac{V_{14}}{Z_{12} + \dfrac{Z_{25}Z_{36}}{Z_{25} + Z_{36}}} \tag{5–52}$$

The branch currents may be determined then from equations 5–8 and 5–3, or from the fact that the voltage equation around the path 1–2–5–4 of Fig. 5–16 is

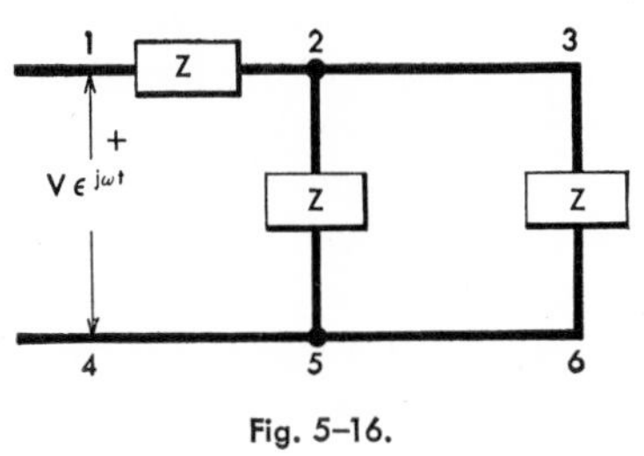

Fig. 5–16.

$$V_{14} = Z_{12}I_{12} + Z_{25}I_{25}$$

which may be rearranged into

$$I_{12} = \frac{V_{14} - Z_{25}I_{25}}{Z_{12}}$$

and

$$I_{25} = \frac{V_{14} - Z_{12}I_{12}}{Z_{25}} \tag{5–53}$$

The series-parallel circuit may be considered as a representation of an alternator with an internal impedance Z_{12} connected to a two-branch parallel circuit. This is illustrated in the following example.

Example 5:6 An alternator with an internal impedance of $Z_{41} = 0.2 + j1.0$ is connected to the parallel circuit shown in Fig. 5–17. The source current is $I_{41} = 10 + j10$. Find: E_{14}, I_{25}, I_{36}, V_{25}, and P_0. Draw the complete vector diagram.

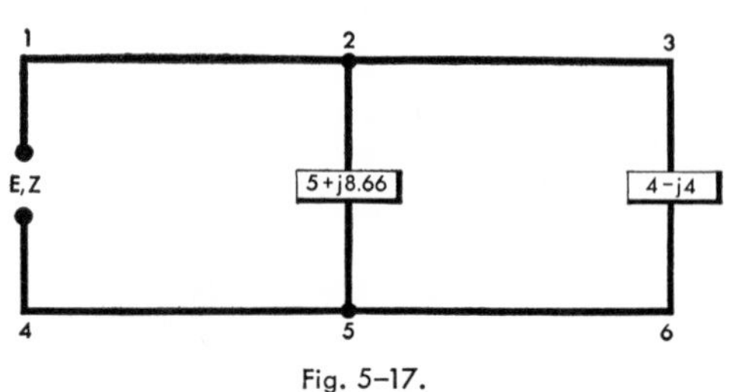

Fig. 5–17.

Solution The branch currents will be determined first. From equation 5–8, on rearranging,

$$I_{25} = I_{41}\frac{Z_p}{Z_{25}}$$

and the branch current may be determined if, in addition to the given data, Z_p is known. The equivalent impedance may be computed from equation 5–50 as

$$Z_p = \frac{10\epsilon^{j60}\sqrt{2}\,4\epsilon^{-j45}}{(5 + j8.66) + (4 - j4)} = \frac{\sqrt{2}\,40\epsilon^{j15}}{9 + j4.66} = \frac{\sqrt{2}\,40\epsilon^{j15}}{10.13\epsilon^{j27.4}}$$
$$= 5.58\epsilon^{-j12.4} = 5.45 - j1.20$$

The branch currents, therefore, will be

$$I_{25} = 14.14\epsilon^{j45}\frac{5.58\epsilon^{-j12.4}}{10\epsilon^{j60}} = 7.89\epsilon^{-j27.4} = 7.0 - j3.63$$

and

$$I_{36} = I_{41} + I_{52} = 3.00 + j13.63 = 13.95\epsilon^{j77.58}$$

The voltage across the load is

$$V_{36} = V_{25} = Z_{25}I_{25} = 10\epsilon^{j60}7.89\epsilon^{-j27.4} = 78.9\epsilon^{j32.6} = 66.47 + j42.5$$

The generator internal voltage follows from writing Kirchhoff's voltage law about the mesh 4–1–2–5. Thus, if V_{41}' represents the internal impedance voltage of the generator and E_{14} represents the generated voltage *assumed* as positive at 1,

$$E_{14} = V_{41}' + V_{25} = Z_{41}I_{41} + V_{25}$$

and

$$E_{14} = 1.02\epsilon^{j78.7}14.14\epsilon^{j45} + (66.46 + j42.5) = (0.2 + j1.0)(10 + j10) + 66.46 + j42.5$$
$$= -8 + j12 + 66.46 + j42.5 = 58.46 + j54.5 = 79.92\epsilon^{j43}$$

The total power may best be determined by means of the scalar product. The power losses are

$$P_{25} = V_{25} \cdot I_{25} = 7(66.46) - 3.63(42.5) = 311 \text{ watts}$$
$$P_{36} = V_{36} \cdot I_{36} = 3(66.46) + 13.63(42.5) = 779 \text{ watts}$$
$$P_{41} = V_{41}' \cdot I_{41} = -8(10) + 12(10) = 40 \text{ watts}$$

The total power supplied to the load is

$$P_L = P_{25} + P_{36} = 1090 \text{ watts}$$

and the internal loss in the generator is P_{41}. The total energy output of the generator is the sum of all the losses or

$$P_0 = P_{25} + P_{36} + P_{41} = 1130 \text{ watts}$$

The vector diagram is shown in Fig. 5–18.

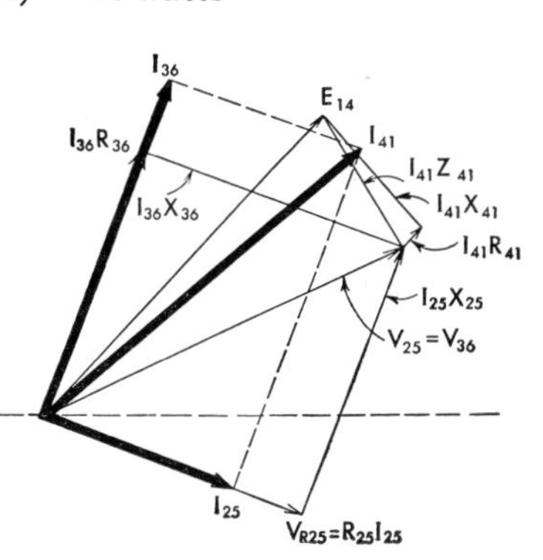

Fig. 5–18.

5.12 The Complex Form of the Expression for Apparent or Vector Power.

The parallel tuning circuit is used in communication systems almost entirely to produce minimum admittance. In power systems the parallel tuning circuit is used for power factor correction and voltage control.

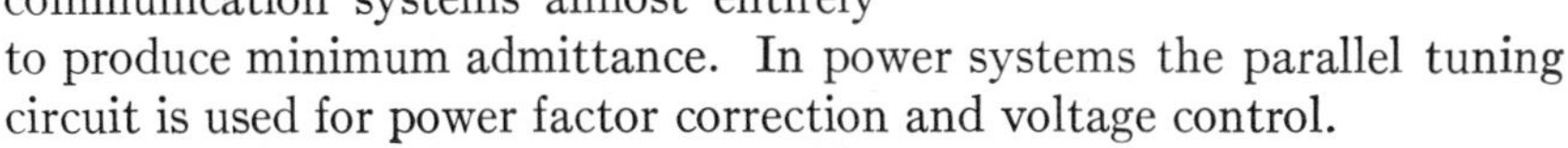

Power system loads are frequently highly reactive and of lagging power factor. The generators must, therefore, supply the load energy at a power factor lower than unity—sometimes very much so. Evidently such a condition requires a greater current than the same energy delivery at unity power factor. The load is for this reason often paralleled with a capacitor to produce a unity power factor or even a leading power factor combination. A static capacitor installation used for power factor correction is shown in Fig. 5–19*b*.

In addition to tuning a parallel circuit to produce power factor correction, power systems also employ this same circuit for voltage control. The synchronous capacitor shown in Fig. 5–19*a* shows one of many such installations. This rotating machine has the unusual property of being easily adjustable to operate at practically any leading or lagging power factor or at unity power factor. Viewed in terms of varying the circuit parameters, this machine is operated as a variable L or C at a constant frequency. As the solution of Problem 5–43 shows, a leading power factor load current will cause the voltage at the load end of a power transmission line to be greater than at the generator end, and a lagging power factor load current will lower the voltage of the load. It is possible, therefore, if the load is paralleled with a capacitor or inductor of sufficient size, to make the combination operate in such a manner that the load voltage is kept practically constant. Regulating devices are used with synchronous capacitors to keep the voltage constant by automatically making the machine operate as a capacitor or inductor of the proper size to keep the voltage at the end of the line constant.

The solution of the important problem of the rating of the capacitor to be used in parallel with a load for power factor correction is ordinarily accomplished by means of the complex number expression for apparent power. The basic concepts of complex number apparent power expression will, therefore, now be developed.

Because of the two expressions already developed, namely,

$$P = |V|\,|I| \cos \theta$$
$$Q = |V|\,|I| \sin \theta$$

it seems logical to express the vector power in the form

$$\begin{aligned} U &= P + jQ = |V|\,|I| \cos \theta + j|V|\,|I| \sin \theta \\ &= |V|\,|I|\epsilon^{j\theta} = |U|\epsilon^{j\theta} \end{aligned} \tag{5–54}$$

If this expression is multiplied and divided by $\epsilon^{j\phi}$,

$$U = |V|\,|I|\epsilon^{j\theta}\frac{\epsilon^{j\phi}}{\epsilon^{j\phi}} = |V|\epsilon^{-j\phi}|I|\epsilon^{j(\phi+\theta)} \tag{5–55}$$

Fig. 5–19a. Synchronous capacitor, 12,500/6250 kva, 4160 volt, 900 rpm, 60 cycle/sec. (Courtesy, Allis-Chalmers Mfg. Co.)

Fig. 5–19b. Static capacitor installation. (Courtesy, Cornell-Dubilier Electric Corp.)

But $|V|\epsilon^{-j\phi}$ represents the conjugate of V (Art. 2–4) and $|I|\epsilon^{j(\phi+\theta)}$ represents the current in an impedance of angle σ, or power factor angle $\theta = -\sigma$ with $|V|\epsilon^{j\phi}$ across its terminals. Therefore, equation 5–55 can be written as

$$U = P + jQ = \hat{V}I \tag{5-56}$$

Several relations of interest may be deduced from this equation. Thus

$$I = \frac{U}{\hat{V}} \tag{5-57}$$

and since, from this equation, $\hat{V} = \dfrac{U}{I}$,

$$V = \frac{\hat{U}}{\hat{I}} \tag{5-58}$$

Furthermore, since $V = ZI$, solving for Z and substituting for V from this last equation give

$$Z = \frac{V}{I} = \frac{\hat{U}}{\hat{I}I} = \frac{\hat{U}}{|I|^2} \tag{5-59}$$

The last relation follows from the fact that the product of a complex number and its conjugate is the square of the magnitude of the complex number.

Likewise, from equation 5–58 and the definition of the admittance,

$$Y = \frac{I}{V} = \frac{I\hat{I}}{\hat{U}} = \frac{|I|^2}{\hat{U}} \tag{5-60}$$

or, if I is substituted from equation 5–57,

$$Y = \frac{I}{V} = \frac{U}{V\hat{V}} = \frac{U}{|V|^2} \tag{5-61}$$

The impedance, from the last two equations, is

$$Z = \frac{1}{Y} = \frac{|V|^2}{U} = \frac{\hat{U}}{|I|^2} \tag{5-62}$$

These last relations rearranged give

$$U = I\hat{V} = YV\hat{V} = Y|V|^2 = (G + jB)|V|^2 = P + jQ \tag{5-63}$$

and

$$U = I\hat{V} = I\hat{I}\hat{Z} = \hat{Z}|I|^2 = (R - jX)|I|^2 = P + jQ \tag{5-64}$$

From these last two equations, it follows immediately that

$$P = G|V|^2 = R|I|^2 \tag{5-65}$$

and

$$Q = B|V|^2 = -X|I|^2 \tag{5-66}$$

where

$$X = X_L + X_C, \text{ and } B = \frac{-(X_L + X_C)}{R^2 + (X_L + X_C)^2}$$

as defined in Chap. 4.

Also note that, from equations 5–63 and 5–64,

$$|U| = |Z|\,|I|^2 = |Y|\,|V|^2 \tag{5-67}$$

and that the sign of the j-term of U, i.e., of Q, also indicates whether the power factor is lead or lag. Thus, if

$$\begin{aligned} Q > 0,&\ I \text{ leads } V \\ Q < 0,&\ I \text{ lags } V \end{aligned} \tag{5-68}$$

From the meaning of the magnitude of a complex number, evidently

$$|U| = \sqrt{P^2 + Q^2} \tag{5-69}$$

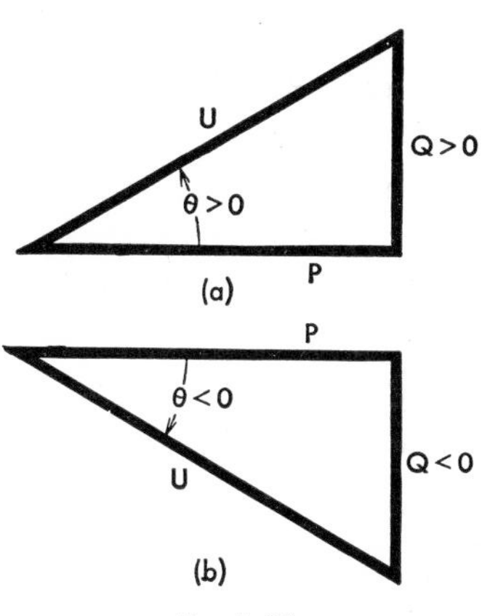

Fig. 5–20.

A pictorial representation of this relation is given in Fig. 5–20. Note that the apparent power diagram is not a *vector* diagram in the sense that a current and voltage diagram is a vector diagram. A circuit direction is not assigned to apparent power or reactive volt-amperes. The apparent power diagram is very useful, however, and is widely used.

It may be well to recall that the average power and reactive volt-amperes can also be computed from two simple measurements or values from the instantaneous power curve. This fact was demonstrated in equations 1–38 and 1–39, where the magnitudes of the positive and negative maxima were shown to determine P and $|Q|$. Note that only the magnitude of Q can be so determined.

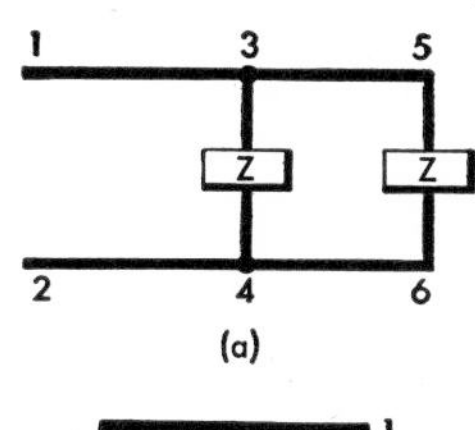

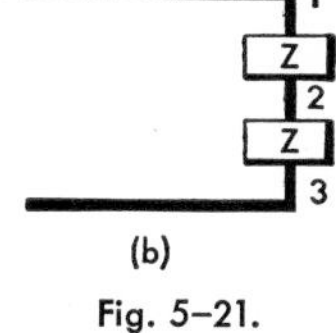

Fig. 5–21.

The complex expression for apparent power has the further property of adding for either series or parallel circuits. For (Fig. 5–21a)

$$\begin{aligned} U_{34} &= \hat{V}_{34} I_{34} \\ U_{56} &= \hat{V}_{34} I_{56} \\ U_{56} + U_{34} &= \hat{V}_{34}(I_{34} + I_{56}) = \hat{V}_{12} I_{13} = U_0 \end{aligned} \tag{5-70}$$

which is the total volt-amperes of the parallel circuit.

Furthermore (Fig. 5–21b), for a series circuit,

$$\begin{aligned} U_{12} &= \hat{V}_{12} I_{12} \\ U_{23} &= \hat{V}_{23} I_{12} \end{aligned}$$

and

$$U_{12} + U_{23} = (\hat{V}_{12} + \hat{V}_{23}) I_{12} = \hat{V}_{13} I_{12} = U_0 \tag{5-71}$$

which shows that vector powers *add* to produce the total vector power for a *series* circuit.

The following example shows the use of the vector power diagram and gives an example of power factor correction.

Example 5:7 A 1000-kva induction motor load operates at 0.8 power factor lag. Because of a favorable rate for leading power factor loads, it will pay to install parallel capacitance to correct the power factor on the line to 0.9 lead. What is the kva rating of the parallel capacitance required to make the power factor correction?

Solution (*a*) The apparent power for the induction motor load shown in Fig. 5–22*a* is $U_m = 800 - j600$. If static capacitors are used, it may be assumed

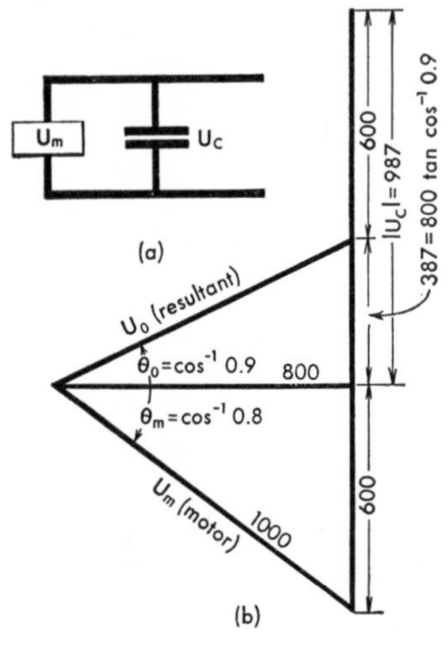

Fig. 5–22.

that the losses are negligible; hence the capacitor adds only reactive volt-amperes to the system. According to equation 5–70, the total volt-amperes, or kva, on the line is the sum of the two branch kvas U_m and U_C. Therefore, since the final line kva is to be 0.9 leading, with no change in the delivered energy, the resultant, or sum, of the motor and capacitor volt-amperes must be (see Fig. 5–22*b*)

$$U_0 = 800 + j800 \tan (\cos^{-1} 0.9)$$
$$U_0 = 800 + j387$$

But this total kva is also

$$U_0 = U_m + U_C$$

and, since

$$U_m = 800 - j600$$

as already indicated, and the capacitor kva has the complex form

$$U_C = 0 + j|U_C|$$

then

$$800 + j387 = 800 - j600 + 0 + j|U_C|$$

and

$$|U_C| = 987$$

is the kva in capacitors required.

Alternatively, this result may be immediately deduced from inspection of Fig. 5–22*b*.

(*b*) Suppose now that the capacitors used to correct the power factor of the motor load are not assumed 100 per cent efficient but rather that the losses amount to k per cent of the kva rating of the capacitors. What is the capacitor rating to correct the power factor?

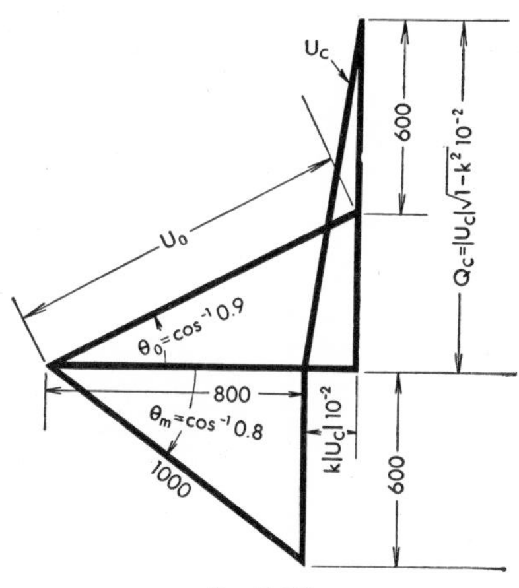

Fig. 5–23.

The simplest way to solve this problem is by means of the apparent power diagram. This diagram is shown in Fig. 5–23. The total energy taken from the source has now been increased by the capacitor loss $k|U_C|10^{-2}$ as shown. The reactive volt-amperes of the capacitor, taken from Fig. 5–23, are given by

$$|Q_C| = \sqrt{|U_C|^2 - [0.01k|U_C|]^2} = |U_C|\sqrt{1 - k^2 10^{-4}}$$

Also from the diagram

$$\tan(\cos^{-1} 0.9) = \frac{|U_C|\sqrt{1 - k^2 10^{-4}} - 600}{800 + |U_C|k10^{-2}} \qquad (5\text{–}72)$$

If a loss of 3 per cent (which is actually too high) is assumed in the capacitors and this equation is solved for $|U_C|$, the result is

$$|U_C| = 1003 \text{ kva}$$

only a slightly higher rating than was found in part (*a*).

Sometimes synchronous motors are used in parallel with other loads to correct the line power factor. The motor may be used to carry some load or not as desired. The synchronous motor power factor will be so adjusted that the desired power factor correction is obtained. The power load carried by the synchronous motor will, of course, be added directly to the power of the load of which the power factor is being corrected. There is no essential difference between the solution to this problem and part (*b*) above.

PROBLEMS

5-1 Three loads in one city block are connected in parallel to two wires on one side of a three-wire distribution system. These loads have impedances of $Z_1 = 4 + j3$, $Z_2 = 6 + j8$, $Z_3 = 2 - j7$. The connected terminal voltage is $v(t) = 200 \sin(\omega t - 30°)$. Find I_0, I_1, I_2, I_3, $i_0(t)$, $I_0(t)$, $i_1(t)$, $I_1(t)$, $i_2(t)$, $I_2(t)$, $i_3(t)$, $I_3(t)$, P_0, pf_0, rf_0. Draw a complete vector diagram.

5-2 Determine Z_1 of Fig. 5-24 so that removing Z_2 will reduce the current I_0 to 0.4 of its value with the two impedances in place. The phase position of I_0 is not to be changed.

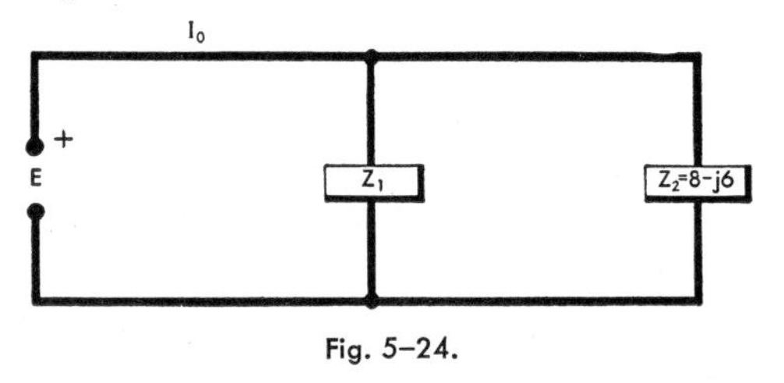

Fig. 5-24.

5-3 Repeat Problem 5-2, determining Z_1 so that the line current in addition to decreasing to 0.4 of its former value is shifted 30 degrees ahead of its position when the two impedances are in parallel.

5-4 The circuit of Fig. 5-25 has a current $I_{13} = 2 - j2$ flowing through the source. Find: I_{34}, $i_{34}(t)$, I_{56}, $i_{56}(t)$, V_{34}, $v_{34}(t)$, P_0. Draw the complete vector diagram.

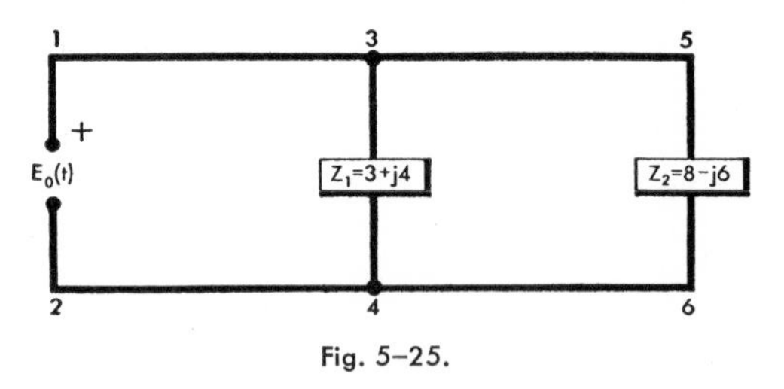

Fig. 5-25.

5-5 Derive the expression for the equivalent impedance of a three-branch parallel circuit. Repeat for an n-branch parallel circuit. Assume no mutual induction.

5-6 The input current in the radio tuning circuit shown in Fig. 5-26 is $i_0(t) = 0.1414 \sin(2\pi 10^6 t + 30°)$ milliamperes, $Q_{34} = 80$, $R_{34} = 1$ ohm. Find:

I_1, I_2, $i_1(t)$, $i_2(t)$, $v_0(t)$, V_0, U_0, P_0, Q_0(vars), Z_0, Y_0, G_0, B_0. Draw a complete vector diagram. $V_{m0} = 2\sqrt{2} + j0$ millivolts.

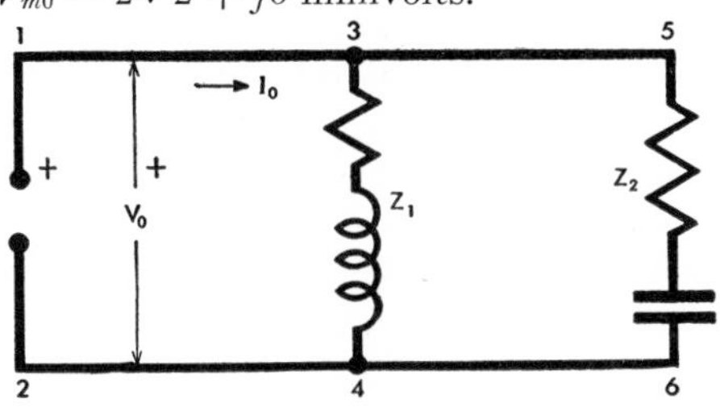

Fig. 5–26.

5–7 Assume a three-branch parallel circuit in which each branch is connected magnetically to the others. Solve for the three-branch currents of this system and express them in the admittance form. Can you predict the general form for the admittance of a parallel circuit if mutual induction is included? Try for a two-branch circuit and check.

5–8 What is the theoretical maximum value for M_{AB} of the circuit of Fig. 5–5 and Example 5–2 if the self-impedances remain as given and $f = 1000$ cps? Of Z_{AB}? Why? What is the coefficient of coupling for the circuit of Example 5–2? Prove that $1 > (|Z_{AB}|/\sqrt{|Z_{25}||Z_{36}|})$.

5–9 The voltage across the parallel branches of Fig. 5–16 is $V_{25} = 100 + j0$. The voltage $|V_{12}|$ is 20 volts and $3R_{12} = |X_{12}|$. Find the two values of Z_{12} and V_{14} which satisfy these relations if $Z_{25} = 3 + j4$ and $Z_{36} = 8 - j6$.

5–10 The alternator of Fig. 5–25 has an internal impedance of $1 + j1$. The generated voltage is $E_{12} = 200 + j0$, where $E_{12} = Z_{21}I_{21} + V_{34}$. Find: Z_0, I_{13}, I_{34}, I_{56}, $i_{56}(t)$, $I_{56}(t)$, P_0. Draw the vector diagram.

5–11 The circuit of Fig. 5–25 has an impedance $Z_{13} = 1 + j5$ ohms and $V_{34} = 100 + j0$ volts. Find: V_{21}, I_{21}, $i_{21}(t)$, $I_{21}(t)$, P_0, $|U_0|$, and U_0. Draw the vector diagram.

5–12 The current in branch 1–3 of Fig. 5–27 is $i(t)_{13} = 14.14 \sin (377t - 60)$. Find $v_{21}(t)$, $V_{21}(t)$, V_{21}, V_{13}, V_{34}, I_{34}, I_{56}, U, P_0, Q_0(vars). Draw the vector diagram. Use $Z_{13} = 1 + j1$.

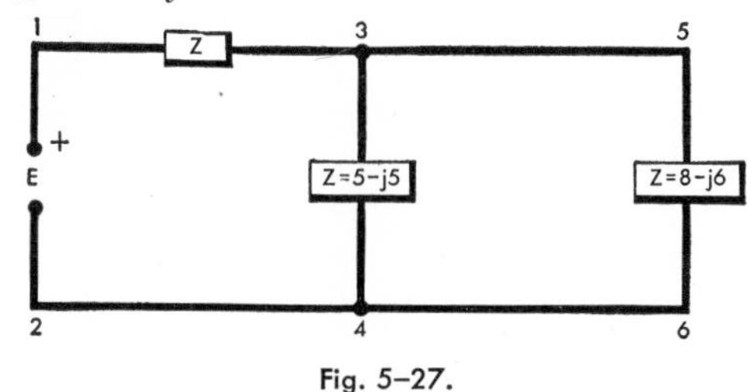

Fig. 5–27.

5–13 Derive the rectangular coordinate equation for the current in an R_C, C series circuit. Sketch the resulting locus diagram. Why is only a semicircle used?

5.3

5–14 Solve equation 5–18 for each of the variables in terms of the other four. Discuss each of the equations derived as to imaginary and real values, single and double values, infinite or zero values, or indeterminate forms. What is the significance of the indeterminate form of the frequency equation when $R_L^2 = R_C^2 = L/C$?

5.5

5–15 A vector *ed* of Fig. 5–9*c* represents the current in the inductor branch of Fig. 5–7 as R_L is varied until $|I_0|$ is a maximum. From Fig. 5–9 establish a formula for $I_L = ed$ for maximum $|I_0|$, divide $|V| + j0$ by this current, and compare the real part of the resulting Z with equation 5–21. The result should be the same.

5.5

5–16 Prove by the method suggested in the text that equation 5–21 gives the value of R_L to make $|I_0|$ a maximum. Show that the plus sign before the radical is required to make R_{LM} positive.

5.5

5–17 (*a*) Draw a locus diagram for R_L as the parallel tuning circuit variable but assume that $R_C = 0$. Discuss the properties of such a circuit. What about a maximum or minimum $|I_0|$? What of resonance? (*b*) Repeat for $X_C = 0$ rather than R_C.

5.6

5–18 Draw a typical set of locus diagrams for the parallel tuning circuit total input current as a function of R_C and show that the relations 5–30 are valid.

5.6

5–19 Use the tabular forms given by 5–27 and 5–30 on the circuits of Fig. 5–25, the two parallel branches of Fig. 5–27 with $Z_{56} = 8 + j6$, and the parallel part of the circuit of Fig. 5–29 to determine the nature of the curves of $|Y_0|$ vs. R_L and R_C for each. Assume that 1000 cps for Fig. 5–25, 60 cps for Fig. 5–27, and 10,000 cps for Fig. 5–29 were used to calculate the given reactances. Find the R_L and R_C to produce resonance and maximum admittance in each case.

5.6

5–20 Show that as R_C varies, the R_C to produce a maximum total current in a parallel tuning circuit is given by equation 5–28. Justify the plus sign before the radical.

5.7

5–21 Using the circuits of Problem 5–19, the tabular form given in 5–36, and L as the independent variable, determine L_m for minimum $|Y_0|$, L_{r2} and L_{r1}, and draw roughly the $|Y_0|$ vs. θ curves. Draw the locus diagram to scale.

5–22 Derive equation 5–34 and show that the other solution obtained in the process cannot be used, and explain why.

5.7

5–23 Show that $|Z_C|^2 > 2|X_C|R_L$, for a circuit of two resonance points as L is varied, is the same as the requirement that the radius of the locus semicircle of Fig. 5–11 be greater than the imaginary component of I_C. Also show that $|Z_C|^2 = 2|X_C|R_L$ is the same as requiring the equality of the radius of the locus semicircle and the imaginary component of I_C.

5.8

5–24 Plot the locus diagram for the parallel tuning circuit with C as the variable, for R_C equal to zero. Discuss this locus as to maximum, minimum, and resonance values for I_0.

5.8

5–25 Draw a locus diagram for the parallel tuning circuit I_0 as a function of C. Label this locus completely as in Fig. 5–11. Also verify equations 5–37, 5–38, and 5–39.

5.9

5–26 Design a parallel tuning circuit for varying frequency so that resonance and minimum admittance occur at 1,000,000 cps. A 100-μh coil of $Q =$ 70 should be used. Determine the minimum admittance.

5–27 Using the circuits of Problem 5–19, tabulation 5–49, and assuming frequency as the variable, classify each circuit as to type of $|Y_0|$ vs. f curve. Determine maximum or minimum and resonant values of f if they exist. Sketch roughly the $|Y_0|$ vs. f curves for each circuit from the information obtainable from 5–49. Use $Z_{56} = 8 + j6$ for Fig. 5–27.

5–28 Show that $|Y_0| = \sqrt{C/L}$ if $R_L^2 = R_C^2 = L/C$, for the parallel tuning circuit. Also show that the circuit is resonant at all frequencies under these conditions.

5–29 Suppose R_L is varied widely in the 60-cps circuit of Fig. 5–25. Determine the maximum value of the total admittance, $|Y_0|$; the value of R_L at which the smallest value of $|Y_0|$ occurs; the smallest value of $|Y_0|$; and the value of L to make maximum $|Y_0|$ and resonance occur at the same value of R_L.

5–30 Repeat Problem 5–29 if R_C is varied.

5–31 Vary L in the 60-cps circuit of Fig. 5–25. Determine the value of maximum and minimum $|Y_0|$. How many resonant points are there? Find the value of R_L or R_C or C, whichever will do it, to give only one resonant value of L. What is this value of L?

5–32 Repeat Problem 5–31 if C is varied.

5–33 Vary the frequency on the circuit of Fig. 5–25. The impedances of this figure were computed at 60 cps. What is the form of the $|Y_0|$vs. f curve? By changing the parameter L, make the circuit so that, if possible, it has a $|Y_0|$ vs. f variation of all the types shown in Fig. 5–15. Specify the value of L for each circuit. Find the value of f to give the maximum and minimum $|Y_0|$ for each case.

5–34 Show that if the two resistances of the circuit of Fig. 5–7 are zero, the total current is also zero at resonance.

5–35 A two-branch parallel circuit, each branch of which contains R, L, and C in series, has the parameter values: $R_1 = 2$ ohms, $L_1 = 0.1$ henry, $C_1 = 2\mu$f; $R_2 = 10$ ohms, $L_2 = 0.2$ henry, $C_2 = 10\mu$f. Plot vs. frequency the magnitude of the current into this circuit if 100 volts is maintained across the terminals. How many maximum and minimum points are there for this circuit? Are these points unity power factor conditions, i.e., resonant points?

5–36 (*a*) What is the meaning of the product $V\hat{I}$. What does the sign before Q now indicate? (*b*) If $U = 800 + j600$ and $I = 10$ amp, find Z and Y by the method of Art. 5–12.

5–37 If $U = 800 - j600$ and $I = 5 - j5$, find: V, Z, Y, $V_0(t)$. Use the method of Art. 5–12.

5–38 The voltage across an impedance is $V = 120 + j80$, and the current through this impedance is $I = 20 + j20$. Find: U, P, Q(vars), power factor, and reactive factor.

5–39 Three loads are connected in parallel across $2300 + j0$ volts. $I_1 = 50 + j50$, $I_2 = 100 + j50$, $I_3 = 75 - j200$. Find: U_0, pf_0, I_0, Z_0, Y_0.

5–40 Two loads $U_1 = 1000 + j1000$ and $U_2 = 1000 - j1732$ kva are connected in parallel. Find the capacitor kva required to correct the line power factor to unity. If the voltage is 4000 volts, find Z_0 and I_0.

5–41 Two loads $U_1 = 2000 + j0$ kva and $U_2 = 800 - j600$ kva are connected in parallel across 2300 volts. What must be the input rating of a synchronous motor required to carry 500 kw and correct the power factor to 0.8 lead? Assume that the motor losses are 4 per cent of the kva input rating.

5–42 Derive a formula for the resonant frequency of a two-branch parallel circuit. Each branch contains R, L, and C.

5–43 The "T" network of Fig. 5–28 has very nearly the same electrical characteristics as a two-wire power transmission line, and is often used to determine the behavior of a transmission line. Determine the voltage across the load terminals 5–6 for loads of: (*a*) 580 ohms at unity power factor;

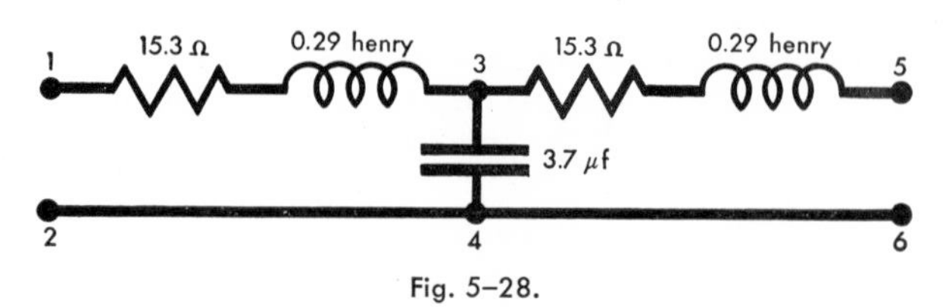

Fig. 5–28.

(*b*) 580 ohms at 0.6 power factor lead; and (*c*) 580 ohms at 0.6 power factor lag. The voltage at the generator terminals 1–2 is regulated at 165,500 volts. Draw vector diagrams. Also make a statement regarding the effect on the load voltages of a leading, lagging, or unity power factor load.

5–44 Determine the kva rating of the synchronous capacitor which will maintain a constant voltage of 160,000 volts at the load end of the transmission line represented by the "T" structure of Fig. 5–28. Assume the total variation of load as the two extremes of Problem 5–43. The manufacturer's bulletins should be consulted for ratings and properties of synchronous capacitors. Consider the losses of the synchronous capacitor in determining the rating.

5–45 The semicircular locus diagrams of R and L and R and C series circuits are derived in Chap. 4. The circuit of Fig. 5–29 is made up of such circuit elements. It would seem that the proper combination of straight line

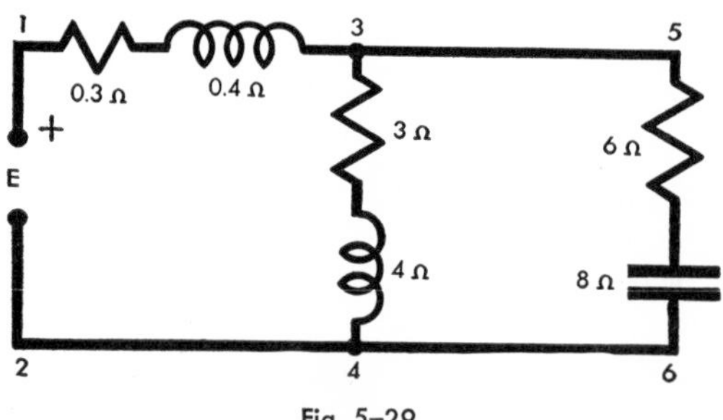

Fig. 5–29.

and semicircular loci would represent the locus of the generator current. Discuss this situation for: (*a*) constant $V_{12} = 100$ volts, (*b*) constant $V_{34} = 100$ volts. Assume any *one* of the elements of the circuit varies.

5–46 The ordinary static capacitor has practically zero resistive effect. Suppose such a capacitor is connected in the circuit of Fig. 5–7, thus making R_C equal to zero. It is possible to adjust the value of L for any particular capacitor and frequency, and constant value of V_{14} so that the current I_{12} is the same in *magnitude* for all possible values of R_L—0 to ∞. Use a locus diagram to show that such a result is possible. Also use the locus to show that $X_C = 2X_L$ is the circuit condition required. *Hint.* The center of the semicircular locus of I_{12} placed at the origin makes $|I_{12}|$ constant.

A laboratory demonstration of the foregoing circuit behavior is interesting and fairly simple.

5-47 Consider the capacitor of the preceding problem as the variable for fixed coil resistance and inductance. If a family of curves is plotted of $|I_{12}|$ vs. C, each curve corresponding to a particular value of coil resistance, the curves will intersect at a common point. Explain why from locus diagrams, and specify the circuit conditions to produce this intersecting point.

CHAPTER 6

Non-Sine Waves—Fourier Series

The representation of a particular alternating current or voltage by a sine wave or its equivalent vector or complex number may or may not be seriously in error. For example, in considering the usual current or voltage of power distribution networks the sine wave approximation is usually sufficiently accurate, whereas in radio or telephone circuits, or in electron tube circuits in general, the sine wave assumption is only occasionally permissible. The electrical impulses of voice or music transmission are not even approximately sinusoidal. There is, therefore, a serious limitation to the process of circuit analysis if only pure sine wave or the vector and complex number equivalent is available.

Fortunately the French mathematician Fourier developed a method, known as the Fourier series, of representing repeating functions or non-sine waves by means of a *series* or *sum* of many *pure* sine waves. Hence, if the connected voltage of a series circuit is not a sine wave, it is possible to consider it as a *sum of sine waves*. Then, as is shown in the following, the current for each sine wave component of voltage in a circuit of *constant* elements may be computed as though that voltage were the only one connected and all the so-determined currents added to give the total current. A similar process is possible for the more complex circuits, considered in later chapters, thus fully justifying both the consideration of the sine wave idealization as basic and the detailed study of this idealized form which is the basis of this book.

The importance of a certain concept in science can often be judged by the prevalence of a particular measuring device, as, for example, the integrating watthour meter found at every building wired for electricity; or, as in the case of non-sine waves, by the time and effort which is expended in building a particular measuring device, such as the oscillograph —a device for showing or photographing the wave form of voltages, currents, and instantaneous power. No laboratory—college or commercial—is complete today without one or more oscillographs.

Two kinds of oscillographs are in widespread use, namely, the electro-

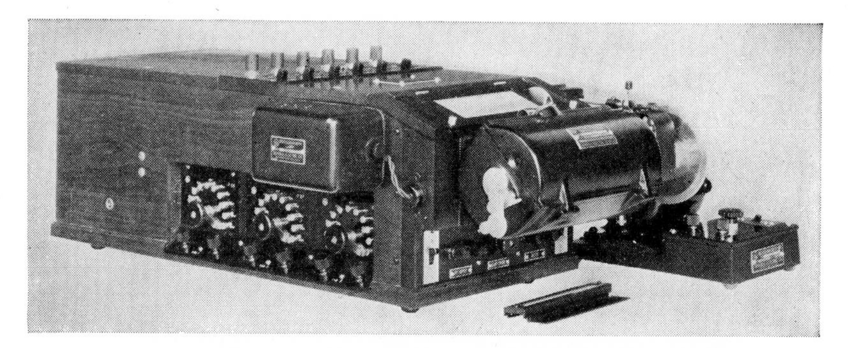

Fig. 6–1a. Electromagnetic oscillograph. (Courtesy, General Electric Co.)

magnetic one shown in Fig. 6–1 and the cathode ray one shown in Fig. 6–2. Both these oscillographs are basically simple, but physically complex and, in certain instances at least, very expensive.

The electromagnetic oscillograph is essentially a set—three or six usually—of D'Arsonval meter elements (Fig. 6–1*b*) which deflect a small mirror instead of a scale pointer. A light beam reflected from the mirror

Fig. 6–1b. Galvanometer of an electromagnetic oscillograph showing small mirror and suspension wires. (Courtesy, Westinghouse Electric & Mfg. Co.)

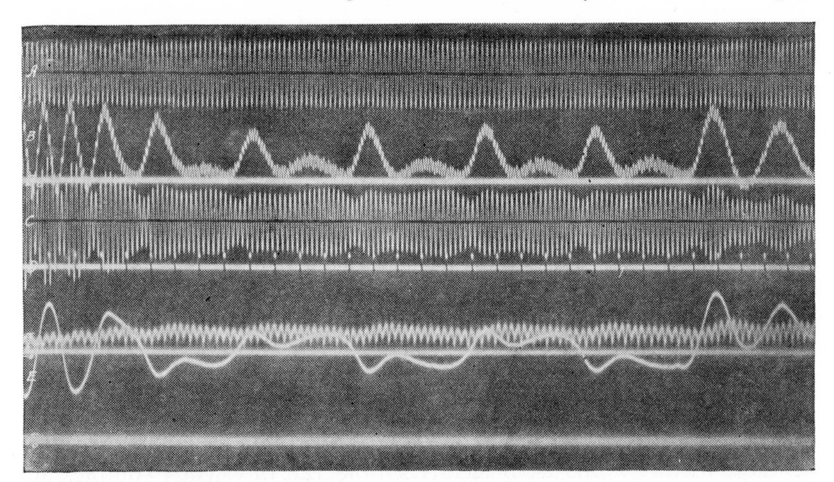

Fig. 6–1c. Record taken on an electromagnetic oscillograph. (Courtesy, General Electric Co.)

moves in proportion to the mirror deflection, i.e., in proportion to the current, voltage, or power. A sensitive film is moved at right angles to the plane of motion of the reflected light beam, and the result on the film is the time variation of current voltage or power. Vibrating or rotating

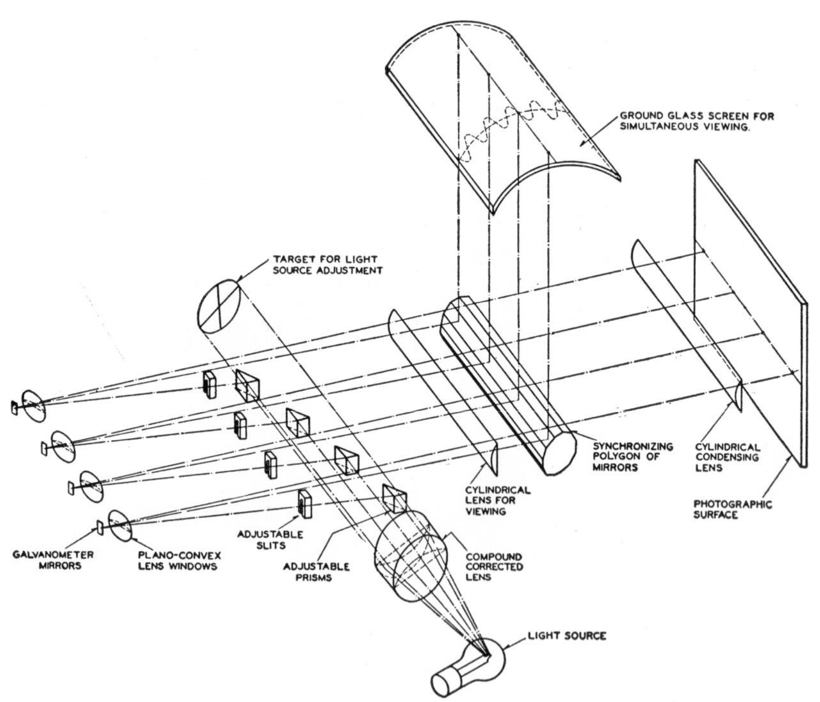

Fig. 6–1d. Diagrammatic sketch of the optical system of an electromagnetic oscillograph. (Courtesy, Westinghouse Electric & Mfg. Co.)

Fig. 6–2a. Cathode ray oscillograph. (Courtesy, Westinghouse Electric & Mfg. Co.)

mirrors are also sometimes used instead of sensitive film to delineate the vibrations of the light beam for observation.

The cathode ray oscillograph is essentially an evacuated tube in which a beam of high-speed electrons strikes a surface which glows wherever the electron beam strikes. The electron beam is deflected by two sets of two parallel plates or coils at right angles to each other (Fig. 6–2*d*). One pair of plates or coils deflects the beam according to the impulse to be observed, and the other pair of plates sweeps the beam across the screen in proportion to time. The result is a glowing trace on the screen of the time variation of the impulse under observation (Fig. 6–2*c*).

Fig. 6–2b. Cathode ray oscillograph. (Courtesy, General Electric Co.)

The electromagnetic oscillograph is limited in the frequency of impulses it will show on a screen, mirror, or film by the fact that any mechanical device, no matter how light in construction, cannot be caused to vibrate above a certain maximum determined by the characteristics of each device. The cathode ray oscillograph was developed for the observation of impulses with frequencies beyond the possibilities of any mechanical system. The electron beam, or cathode ray, is without inertia for all practical purposes so that it may be caused to vibrate at very high frequencies—millions of times per second is common.

As will be shown in the following, the frequencies, amplitudes, and relative phase positions of each of the Fourier series pure sine waves—harmonics—can be determined from the oscillographic wave trace.

There is today little question of the importance of viewing a non-sine wave impulse as a sum of pure sine wave impulses of different frequencies. The whole field of communication—wire and wireless—is based squarely on this concept. The power engineer is also grateful for the Fourier series view of the harmonic content of non-sine waves. In several instances in the past, power equipment troubles were seemingly inexplicable. When the electrical connections were analyzed with Fourier series, the cause of the difficulty was immediately evident.

The material of this chapter is largely the mathematical development and justification of the Fourier series analysis.

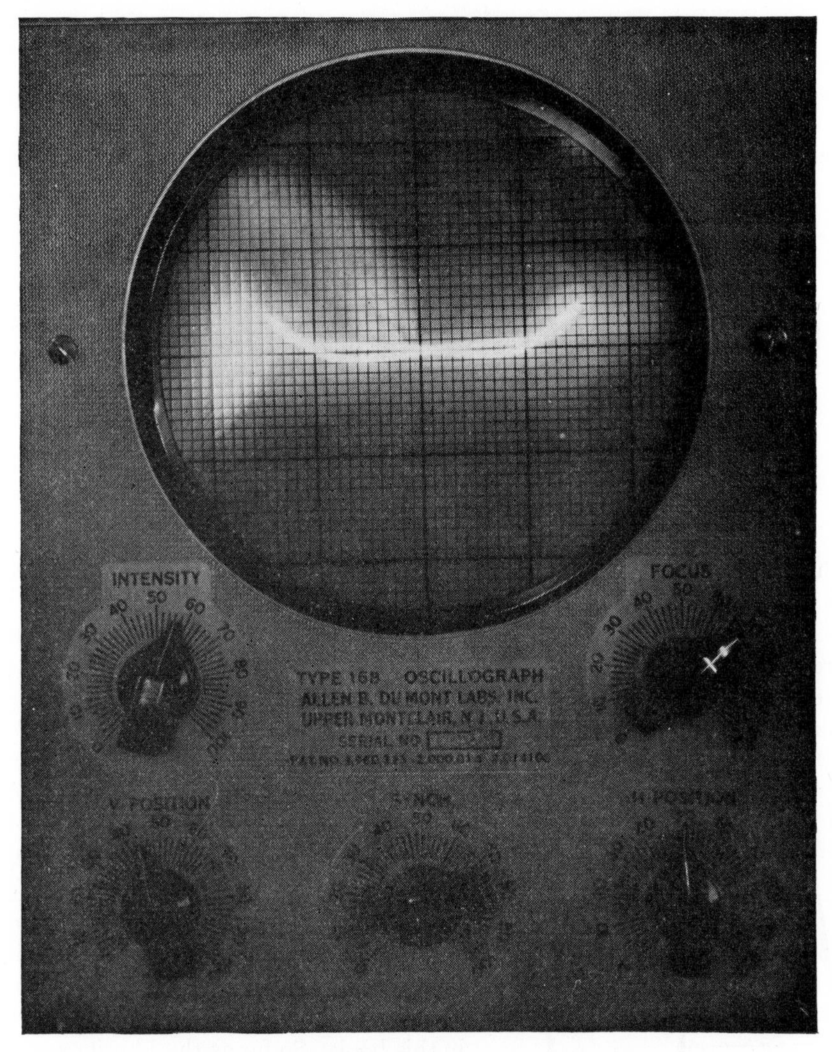

Fig. 6–2c. Cathode ray oscillograph with wave on screen.
(Courtesy, Westinghouse Electric & Mfg. Co.)

6.1 Non-Sine Waves—Synthesis.

The mathematical proof of the validity of the Fourier series is difficult and requires the training of a professional mathematician for complete understanding. It is possible, however, to demonstrate the effect of adding sinusoids of different frequencies and to introduce some of the nomenclature necessary for the development of the method. By showing that the addition of sine waves of different frequencies produces non-sine waves, the reader should at least be prepared to accept, without formal proof, the conclusions of mathematicians regarding the infinite Fourier series.

Consider first the two sine waves shown in Fig. 6–3. The sine wave marked 1 is the lowest frequency wave and is usually called the *fundamental*. The sine wave marked 2 is of higher frequency, in fact its frequency is three times that of the fundamental, and it is called a *harmonic* of the fundamental—in this case the *third harmonic*. The sum of

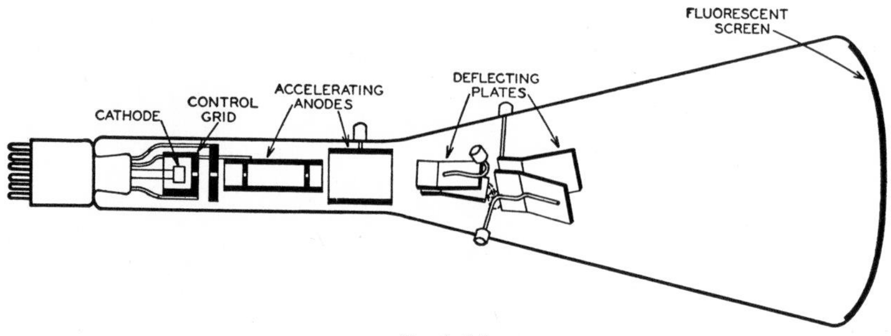

Fig. 6–2*d*.

the two sine waves is shown by the curve marked 3. Note that this wave is *not* sinusoidal and that it has the frequency of the fundamental.

Occasionally a circuit which as a whole operates at some particular frequency will develop harmonics of *lower* frequencies than the operating frequency. Since it is usually desirable to consider the operating frequency as the fundamental, these lower harmonics are spoken of as *subharmonics*—the first subharmonic having one-half the frequency of the fundamental, etc. The wave forms of Fig. 6–4 may be considered in this light. If curve 2 is considered as the fundamental, curve 1 is then a subharmonic with one-third the frequency of the fundamental. This approach is seldom used and so subharmonics will not be considered further in this book. So far as the Fourier series analysis considered here is concerned, the lowest frequency will be considered as the fundamental and the analysis will be carried out on this assumption.

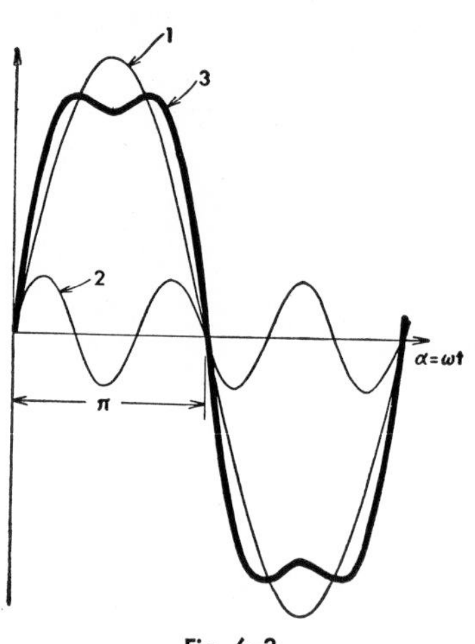

Fig. 6–3.

The lowest or fundamental frequency may generally be determined by an inspection of the curve to be considered. For example, the curve of Fig. 6–4 goes through a certain variation in the interval a–b, and repeats this variation, except that it is negative, in the interval b–c. The variation on a–c will be exactly repeated in the next and succeeding equal intervals. This wave would be treated on the assumption that from a

to c is one cycle of the fundamental. The non-sine wave of Fig. 6–5a shows a similar variation, and the interval a–c would be taken as the period of the fundamental. The curve of Fig. 6–5b, on the other hand, shows no

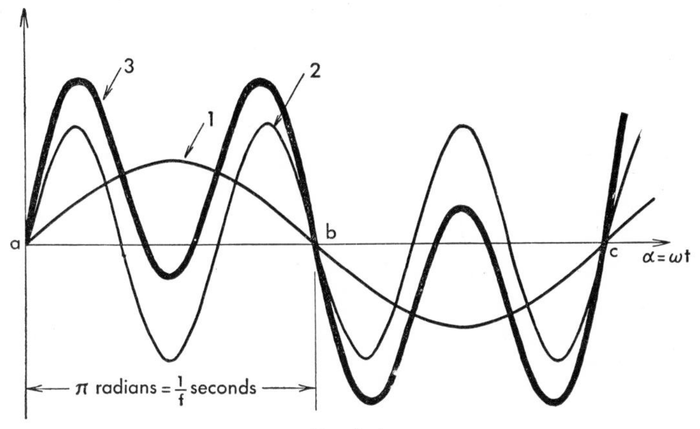

Fig. 6–4.

positive and negative symmetry, but it does show a repetition on the interval b–c which is exactly the variation on the interval a–b. A cycle on the fundamental of this wave is, therefore, the interval a–b. Note that in all these illustrations, the interval assumed as a fundamental cycle is

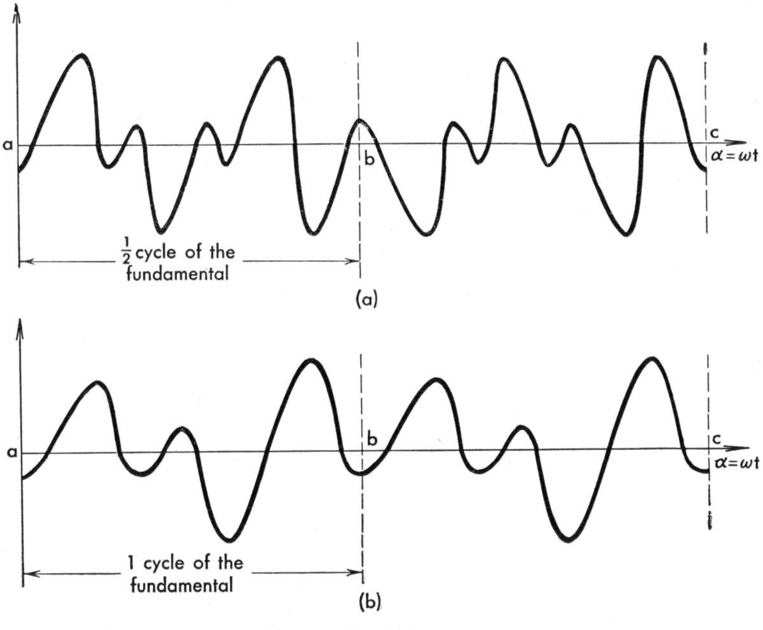

Fig. 6–5.

the interval on the abscissa over which the wave goes through a complete variation, and equal intervals thereafter show exactly the same curve.

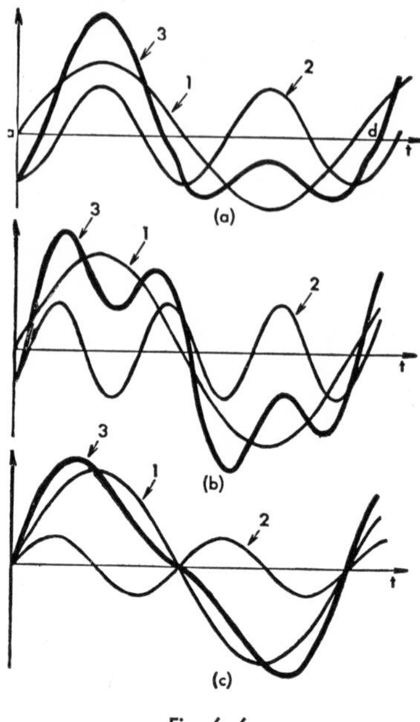

Fig. 6–6.

Many electric impulses must be represented by waves which *never* repeat over any interval, as, for example, a telephone conversation or radio broadcast. By experience, however, it has been found that even such waves may be effectively approximated by using the concepts of harmonics as they are developed in this chapter.

The triple or third harmonics shown in Figs. 6–3 and 6–4 may be defined as in phase. The term *in phase* obviously does not have the same meaning for sinusoids of different frequencies that it does for sine waves of the same frequency. But the term is useful in the consideration of harmonic analysis. Two harmonics will be considered out of phase by ψ degrees if the separation between the two *nearest* zero points at which the sinusoids are increasing positively is ψ degrees *on the scale of the higher frequency harmonic*. Thus in Fig. 6–6*a* curve 2 lags curve 1 by 90 degrees, in Fig. 6–6*b* curve 2 lags curve 1 by less than 90 degrees, and in Fig. 6–6*c* all curves are in phase.

6.2 Equivalent Forms of the Fourier Series.

The Fourier series can be expressed in several different mathematical forms. Three of these possible expressions are used here.

One of the most common Fourier series expressions is

$$\begin{aligned} v(\alpha) = v_{c0} &+ v_{c1}\cos\alpha + v_{c2}\cos 2\alpha + v_{c3}\cos 3\alpha + \cdots \\ &+ v_{s1}\sin\alpha + v_{s2}\sin 2\alpha + v_{s3}\sin 3\alpha + \cdots \end{aligned} \tag{6–1}$$

Note that v_{c0} may be positive or negative and represents the d-c component. The coefficients v_{c1}, v_{c2}, $\cdots v_{s1}$, v_{s2}, $\cdots$ are maximum-value constants which may be positive or negative. Note furthermore that there are no phase angles in this form of the Fourier series. The expression of equation 6–1 is rather lengthy and may be symbolically shortened by using the summation sign, so that

$$v(\alpha) = v_{c0} + \sum_{k=1}^{\infty} (v_{ck}\cos k\alpha + v_{sk}\sin k\alpha) \tag{6–2}$$

It is possible to make this expression still more compact by summing from zero to infinity, or

$$v(\alpha) = \sum_{k=0}^{\infty} (v_{ck} \cos k\alpha + v_{sk} \sin k\alpha) \tag{6–3}$$

because if k is replaced by zero in this last expression, v_{c0} results, since $\sin 0 = 0$.

Attention has already been drawn to the fact that any sine and cosine wave of a particular frequency can be represented by a sine wave of the same frequency with a phase shift depending on the original sine and cosine coefficients (Art. 1–9). Therefore, if it is agreed that $v_{s0} = 0$, equation 6–3 can be expressed as

$$v(\alpha) = \sum_{k=0}^{\infty} |V_{mk}| \sin (k\alpha + \phi_k) \tag{6–4}$$

where

$$|V_{mk}| = \sqrt{v_{ck}{}^2 + v_{sk}{}^2} \tag{6–5}$$

$$\phi_k = \tan^{-1} \frac{v_{ck}}{v_{sk}} \tag{6–6}$$

According to this expression, for $k = 0$, $\phi_0 = \pm \dfrac{\pi}{2}$, depending on the sign of v_{c0}, and the term of equation 6–4 for $k = 0$ once more gives v_{c0}.

In equations 6–5 and 6–6, the values of $|V_{mk}|$ and ϕ_k were given in terms of v_{ck} and v_{sk}. The values of v_{ck} and v_{sk}, in terms of $|V_{mk}|$ and ϕ_k, may be found by expanding equation 6–4. Thus

$$v(\alpha) = \sum_{k=0}^{\infty} [(|V_{mk}| \cos \phi_k) \sin k\alpha + (|V_{mk}| \sin \phi_k) \cos k\alpha] \tag{6–7}$$

and when this equation is compared with equation 6–3, evidently

$$\begin{aligned} v_{ck} &= |V_{mk}| \sin \phi_k \\ v_{sk} &= |V_{mk}| \cos \phi_k \end{aligned} \tag{6–8}$$

A third form of the Fourier series is useful, namely, the rotating vector equivalent to the sine wave. Since these two types of expressions are equivalent *but not equal*, a different symbol, $V(\alpha)$, to correspond with the symbolism already used in this book, is used to designate the rotating vector equivalent. Since the rotating vector and sine equivalence can be expressed as

$$|V_{mk}| \sin (k\alpha + \phi_k) \approx |V_{mk}|\epsilon^{j\phi_k}\epsilon^{jk\alpha} = V_{mk}\epsilon^{jk\alpha} \tag{6–9}$$

the Fourier series rotating vector expression is

$$V(\alpha) = \sum_{k=0}^{\infty} |V_{mk}|\epsilon^{j\phi_k}\epsilon^{jk\alpha} = \sum_{k=0}^{\infty} V_{mk}\epsilon^{jk\alpha} \tag{6–10}$$

But this expression, by using the rectangular equivalent to the exponential, is

$$V(\alpha) = \sum_{k=0}^{\infty} [|V_{mk}| \cos \phi_k + j|V_{mk}| \sin \phi_k]\epsilon^{jk\alpha} \tag{6–11}$$

which, from equations 6–8, becomes

$$V(\alpha) = \sum_{k=0}^{\infty} (v_{sk} + jv_{ck})\epsilon^{jk\alpha} = \sum_{k=0}^{\infty} V_{mk}\epsilon^{jk\alpha} \tag{6–12}$$

A particularly interesting feature of this last expression is that for $k = 0$

$$V_{m0} = 0 + jv_{c0} \tag{6–13}$$

This result is actually to be expected, of course, because it is the vertical or j-component of the rotating vector system that represents the actual voltage.

Example 6:1 (*a*) A Fourier series is given in the form

$$v(\alpha) = -10 + 100 \cos \alpha - 60 \cos 2\alpha + 20 \cos 3\alpha + 8.66 \cos 4\alpha + 100 \sin \alpha + 80 \sin 2\alpha + 34.64 \sin 3\alpha + 5 \sin 4\alpha$$

Express this series as a sum of sine waves and as an equivalent rotating vector sum.

(*b*) If the formulas

$$V_{mh} = j20\left[\frac{\epsilon^{jh\pi} - 1}{1 - h} + j\,\frac{\epsilon^{-jh\pi} + 1}{1 + h}\right],\ h \neq 1$$
$$V_{m1} = 50 + j50$$
$$V_{m0} = j5$$

represent the complex number coefficients of the rotating vector Fourier series, determine the Fourier series as a sum of sine and cosine terms, and in the form of sine waves only.

Solution (*a*) From equations 6–4, 6–5, and 6–6,

$$v(\alpha) = -10 + 141.4 \sin (\alpha + 45°) + 100 \sin (2\alpha - 36.9°) + 40 \sin (3\alpha + 30°) + 10 \sin (4\alpha + 60°)$$

The rotating vector Fourier series, from equations 6–12 and 6–3, is

$$V(\alpha) = -j10 + (100 + j100)\epsilon^{j\alpha} + (80 - j60)\epsilon^{j2\alpha} + (34.64 + j20)\epsilon^{j3\alpha} + (5 + j8.66)\epsilon^{j4\alpha}$$
$$= -j10 + 141.4\epsilon^{j(\alpha+45)} + 100\epsilon^{j(2\alpha-36.9)} + 40\epsilon^{j(3\alpha+30)} + 10\epsilon^{j(4\alpha+60)}$$

(*b*) Substituting values of h from unity on, and using the given values for V_{m0} and V_{m1}, gives

$$V_{m0} = 0 + j5 \qquad V_{m4} = -\tfrac{40}{5} + j0$$
$$V_{m1} = 50 + j50 \qquad V_{m5} = 0 + j\tfrac{40}{4} = 0 + j10$$
$$V_{m2} = -\tfrac{40}{3} + j0 \qquad V_{m6} = -\tfrac{40}{7} + j0$$
$$V_{m3} = 0 + j\tfrac{40}{2} = 0 + j20 \qquad V_{m7} = 0 + j\tfrac{40}{6} \text{ etc.}$$

The rotating vector equivalent to the sine wave Fourier series is then (equation 6–12)

$$V(\alpha) = (0 + j5) + (50 + j50)\epsilon^{j\alpha} + (-\tfrac{40}{3} + j0)\epsilon^{j2\alpha} + (0 + j20)\epsilon^{j3\alpha} + (-8 + j0)\epsilon^{j4\alpha} + (0 + j10)\epsilon^{j5\alpha} + (-\tfrac{40}{7} + j0)\epsilon^{j6\alpha} + (0 + j\tfrac{40}{6})\epsilon^{j7\alpha} + \cdots$$

$$= j5 + 70.7\epsilon^{j(\alpha+45)} - \tfrac{40}{3}\epsilon^{j2\alpha} + 20\epsilon^{j(3\alpha+90)} - 8\epsilon^{j4\alpha} + 10\epsilon^{j(5\alpha+90)} - \tfrac{40}{7}\epsilon^{j6\alpha} + \tfrac{40}{6}\epsilon^{j(7\alpha+90)} + \cdots$$

The sine wave expression can be taken directly from this result as (j-component)

$$v(\alpha) = 5 + 70.7 \sin(\alpha + 45^\circ) - \tfrac{40}{3} \sin 2\alpha + 20 \sin(3\alpha + 90^\circ) - 8 \sin 4\alpha + 10 \sin(5\alpha + 90^\circ) - \tfrac{40}{7} \sin 6\alpha + \tfrac{40}{6} \sin(7\alpha + 90^\circ) + \cdots$$

Finally the sine and cosine series—equations 6–1 and 6–8—

$$v(\alpha) = 5 + 50 \cos \alpha + 20 \cos 3\alpha + 10 \cos 5\alpha + \tfrac{40}{6} \cos 7\alpha + \cdots + 50 \sin \alpha - \tfrac{40}{3} \sin 2\alpha - 8 \sin 4\alpha - \tfrac{40}{7} \sin 6\alpha + \cdots$$

6.3 Symmetric and Non-Symmetric Waves.

A comparison of the resultant waves given in Fig. 6–6*b* and *c* shows the difference between waves which are defined as symmetric and non-symmetric. Curve 3 of Fig. 6–6*b* is symmetric and curve 3 of Fig. 6–6*c* is non-symmetric. Both these curves are symmetric in the sense that the positive and negative lobes are similar. However, the curve of Fig. 6–6*b* is *defined* as symmetric because this type of symmetry occurs oftener than any other. This particular curve is characterized by definition, as are symmetric waves in general, by the fact that *ordinates separated by one-half cycle on the scale of the fundamental are numerically equal but of opposite sign.* By this definition the resultant curves of Figs. 6–3, 6–4, 6–5*a*, and 6–6*b* are symmetric, and the resultant curves of Figs. 6–5*b*, 6–6*a*, and 6–6*c* are non-symmetric. The curve of Fig. 6–6*a* is non-symmetric over a fundamental cycle by any criterion for symmetry. Note in connection with this curve that the time interval of the positive part of the curve is shorter than the interval of the negative part.

Examination of the symmetric waves of Figs. 6–3, 6–4, and 6–6 shows that the harmonic is in each case of third order, but, what is more important, note that this is an *odd*-numbered harmonic. Furthermore, the harmonic of the non-symmetric resultant of Figs. 6–6*a* and *c* is of second order, i.e., *even* numbered. In general, a combination of *odd*-numbered harmonics forms a symmetric wave, and of *even*-numbered harmonics a non-symmetric wave. A resultant wave consisting of the sum of fundamental, even harmonics and odd harmonics will always be non-symmetric. These conclusions may be proved in the following manner.

In order to apply the definition of symmetry of a non-sine wave, ordinates separated by 180 degrees, or π radians, on the scale of the fundamental must be compared. These ordinates are given by $v(\alpha)$ and

$v(\alpha + 180°)$. Equation 6–4 gives $v(\alpha)$, and from this expression $v(\alpha + 180°)$ may also be obtained by substituting $\alpha + 180°$ for α. Thus

$$v(\alpha + 180°) = \sum_{k=0}^{\infty} |V_{mk}| \sin [k(\alpha + 180°) + \phi_k]$$
$$= \sum_{k=0}^{\infty} |V_{mk}| \sin [(k\alpha + \phi_k) + k180°] \tag{6–14}$$

But

$$\sin [(k\alpha + \phi_k) + k180°] = \begin{bmatrix} -\sin (k\alpha + \phi_k) \text{ if } k \text{ is odd} \\ +\sin (k\alpha + \phi_k) \text{ if } k \text{ is even} \end{bmatrix} \tag{6–15}$$

Therefore, if for the moment the symbolism

$$v(\alpha) = v(\alpha)_{\text{even}} + v(\alpha)_{\text{odd}} \tag{6–16}$$

is used, equation 6–15 shows that

$$v(\alpha + 180°) = v(\alpha)_{\text{even}} - v(\alpha)_{\text{odd}} \tag{6–17}$$

Consequently *if only odd harmonics are present*—no d-c component or even harmonics, i.e., $v(\alpha)_{\text{even}} = 0$—this last equation shows that

$$v(\alpha) = -v(\alpha + 180°), \text{ for } k \text{ odd} \tag{6–18}$$

which is just the definition of symmetry. So non-sine waves consisting of *fundamental and odd harmonics only* are always symmetric. Also if equation 6–18 is satisfied, equations 6–16 and 6–17 show that $v(\alpha)_{\text{even}} = 0$ and a symmetric wave can contain only odd harmonics. Therefore, a symmetric wave can contain only odd harmonics, and a sum of odd harmonics only is always symmetric.

Alternating current generators which supply the energy to power networks deliver *symmetric* waves of voltage, and, therefore, only odd harmonics, because both the north and south poles of the machines are alike. As these poles move past the machine conductors they inevitably generate voltages which have exactly the same time sequence magnitudes but are of opposite polarity in the conductors when generated by north or south poles. On the other hand, electron tube circuits usually deliver non-symmetric waves containing both odd and even harmonics.

6.4 Fourier Series—Determination of Coefficients.

The treatment in the foregoing articles of this chapter is simply a demonstration, by the synthesizing process, of forming irregular waves by adding sine waves of different frequencies, magnitudes, and phase positions. Suppose next that the irregular—non-sine—wave is known and the Fourier series coefficients, $|V_{mk}|$ and phase angles ϕ_k are to be determined. The problem is now somewhat different from the foregoing one.

First it must be known that the function of α of the irregular, or non-sine, wave which is to be represented by a Fourier series can be so represented. Actually, much more general functions than *can ever be obtained* as a voltage or current variation in an electric circuit can be represented as a Fourier series. For example, functions which have any finite number of finite discontinuities, or "jumps," over the period of the fundamental can be represented by a Fourier series. The wave shown in heavy lines in Fig. 6–7*a* has two such jumps in the period of the fundamental, and this function can be represented by a Fourier series. Also the function shown in Fig. 6–7*b* can be represented by a Fourier series. This function

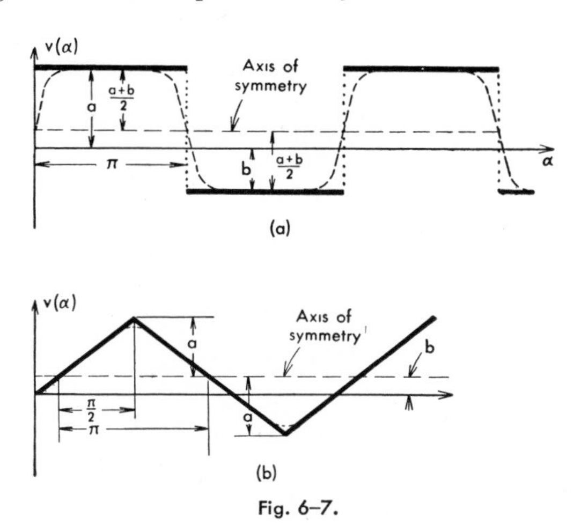

Fig. 6–7.

has no discontinuities but it has no derivative at the vertices. Neither of the curves of Fig. 6–7 could actually be obtained from an electric circuit as a current or voltage variation. Current and voltage variations are always such that "jumps," or the non-existence of a derivative, rarely occur more than once for any particular wave. If either of the curves of Fig. 6–7 were approximated in an electric circuit, the abrupt changes would not appear, but the variation would be somewhat as shown by the dashed line. If, therefore, the function under consideration has at most occasional jumps or discontinuities, and if its derivative exists at all but one or two points, a Fourier series representation is always possible. Thus repeating current and voltage variations in an electric circuit are always representable by a Fourier series.

In order to represent any particular non-sine wave by a Fourier series, the coefficients $|V_{mk}|$ and the phase angles ϕ_k must be determinable from the particular wave $v(\alpha)$. Once having determined $|V_{mk}|$ and ϕ_k for any particular $v(\alpha)$, the Fourier series representing $v(\alpha)$ can be written by substituting these amplitudes and angles in equation 6–4.

Many mechanical devices have been developed for determining the

Fig. 6–8. Mechanical harmonic analyzer. (Courtesy, S. L. Brown, University of Texas)

coefficients $|V_{mk}|$ and ϕ_k for any given non-sine wave. One such device is shown in Fig. 6–8. A pointer of this machine is used to trace the non-sine wave already drawn on paper. The motion of the pointer actuates the harmonic analyzer mechanism so that, after one cycle on the fundamental scale has been traversed, an indicator on the machine shows the magnitude of one of the coefficients of equation 6–1. The curve must be traced

Fig. 6–9. Electrical harmonic analyzer; measures amplitude and frequency of the harmonics. (Courtesy, General Radio Co.)

twice for each harmonic. The Fourier series of equation 6–1 can be written as soon as the harmonic coefficients are determined. Needless to say, an oscillographic trace of the non-sine wave to be analyzed must be available if a mechanical analyzer is to be used.

An electrical harmonic analyzer which determines the Fourier series coefficients directly from the electrical impulse without graphical intermediaries is shown in Fig. 6–9. This apparatus operates on the basis of tuning a circuit to resonate at the frequencies of the fundamental and harmonics.

Because occasions arise in which the harmonic content of a non-sine wave is required and no analyzer is available so that the coefficients must be obtained mathematically, and because the mathematical expressions for the Fourier series coefficients lead to a further understanding of the whole subject, equations for these coefficients are developed next. A complex variable method is used since it is simpler and gives a more compact and more easily evaluated result. Also, both $|V_{mk}|$ and ϕ_k can be evaluated by one integration rather than the two which are required for the real variable computation usually employed.

Because a rotating vector and a sinusoid are equivalent only through the mathematical processes of differentiation, integration, addition, subtraction, and multiplication or division by a real variable or constant, and because multiplication by an exponential is required in the following derivation, the rotating vector equivalent Fourier series of equation 6–10 cannot be used. Instead, the Fourier series of equation 6–4 is used, and the sine is replaced by its exponential equivalent (equation 2–34) to give

$$v(\alpha) = \sum_{k=0}^{\infty} |V_{mk}| \frac{\epsilon^{j(k\alpha+\phi_k)} - \epsilon^{-j(k\alpha+\phi_k)}}{2j} \tag{6–19}$$

which by means of the conjugate concept (Art. 2–4) can be immediately transformed into

$$v(\alpha) = \sum_{k=0}^{\infty} \frac{V_{mk}\epsilon^{jk\alpha} - \hat{V}_{mk}\epsilon^{-jk\alpha}}{2j} \tag{6–20}$$

Note that $v(\alpha)$ as used here is still the exact real variable sinusoid since the real parts on the right cancel. The problem now is to determine V_{mk} in terms of $v(\alpha)$. Since equation 6–20 contains infinitely many unknowns the prospects at first do not seem hopeful of finding all these unknowns from one equation. However, it is possible to determine the complex coefficients V_{mk}, which include both $|V_{mk}|$ and ϕ_k, from this last equation. Multiply both sides of the equation by $\epsilon^{-jh\alpha}$, where h is some *particular* value of k, and integrate over a period of the fundamental, i.e., over the interval 0 to 2π. Then

$$2\int_0^{2\pi} jv(\alpha)\epsilon^{-jh\alpha}\, d\alpha = \int_0^{2\pi} \sum_{k=0}^{\infty} [V_{mk}\epsilon^{j(k-h)\alpha} - \hat{V}_{mk}\epsilon^{-j(k+h)\alpha}]\, d\alpha$$

and because the integral of a sum is the sum of the integrals

$$2\int_0^{2\pi} jv(\alpha)\epsilon^{-jh\alpha}\, d\alpha = \sum_{k=0}^{\infty} \int_0^{2\pi} [V_{mk}\epsilon^{j(k-h)\alpha} - \hat{V}_{mk}\epsilon^{-j(k+h)\alpha}]\, d\alpha \tag{6–21}$$

If use is made of the relation

$$\int_0^{2\pi} \epsilon^{\pm jk\alpha}\, d\alpha = \frac{\epsilon^{\pm jk2\pi} - 1}{\pm jk} = 0 \text{ (k any integer)} \tag{6–22}$$

all the infinitely many terms on the right of equation 6–21 for which $h \neq k$ are zero since $h \pm k$ then will be an integer. Consequently only two of the infinitely many terms on the right of equation 6–21 remain to be investigated, namely, the ones for which $h = k \neq 0$ and $h = k = 0$.

If these two terms are considered separately, $h = k \neq 0$ is substituted into the right-hand side of equation 6–21, and equation 6–22 is used once more,

$$2\int_0^{2\pi} jv(\alpha)\epsilon^{-jh\alpha}\, d\alpha = \int_0^{2\pi} (V_{mh} - \hat{V}_{mh}\epsilon^{-j2h\alpha})\, d\alpha = 2\pi V_{mh} \quad (6\text{–}23)$$

from which

$$V_{mh} = v_{sh} + jv_{ch} = \frac{1}{\pi}\int_0^{2\pi} jv(\alpha)\epsilon^{-jh\alpha}\, d\alpha \; (h \neq 0) \quad (6\text{–}24)$$

This relation gives a formula by which all the Fourier series coefficients V_{mh} except the d-c component can be calculated from a known non-sine wave of voltage $v(\alpha)$. It is necessary merely to set h equal to the number of the harmonic desired and then to integrate. Note once more that V_{mh} includes both $|V_{mh}|$ and ϕ_h since the result given by equation 6–24 is complex.

Consider next the determination of the formula for the d-c component. This result must of necessity arise from the one remaining term of the right-hand side of equation 6–21, i.e., the one for which $h = k = 0$. Substituting $h = k = 0$ into equation 6–21 produces

$$2\int_0^{2\pi} jv(\alpha)\, d\alpha = \int_0^{2\pi} (V_{m0} - \hat{V}_{m0})\, d\alpha \quad (6\text{–}25)$$

But, since from equation 6–13, $V_{m0} = 0 + jv_{c0}$

$$V_{m0} - \hat{V}_{m0} = (0 + jv_{c0}) - (0 - jv_{c0}) = 0 + j2v_{c0} = 2V_{m0}$$

Equation 6–25 is, therefore,

$$2\int_0^{2\pi} jv(\alpha)\, d\alpha = 2\int_0^{2\pi} V_{m0}\, d\alpha \quad (6\text{–}26)$$

The right-hand integral can be evaluated immediately since V_{m0} is not a function of α. The resulting expression for the d-c component of the Fourier series is

$$V_{m0} = 0 + jv_{c0} = \frac{j}{2\pi}\int_0^{2\pi} v(\alpha)\, d\alpha \quad (6\text{–}27)$$

This last equation and equation 6–24 completely determine the Fourier series coefficients for any given function $v(\alpha)$. The values obtained from these equations (6–27 and 6–24) can be substituted directly into equation 6–10 to establish the rotating vector Fourier series. From this result equations 6–3 and 6–4 can be established immediately.

The following example illustrates the process of determining the Fourier series for a particular $v(\alpha)$.

Example 6:2 The Fourier series coefficients of the wave shown in Fig. 6–10 are to be determined. Such a wave would not likely be obtained in practice, but it is mathematically relatively simple and so does not divert attention from the main point of studying the evaluation of the Fourier series coefficients.

Solution This wave is *not* symmetric, hence both odd and even harmonics may be present. Furthermore, since the areas under the positive and negative lobes are not equal, the area integral of equation 6–27 will not be zero, and so a d-c component will also be present. This component will be computed first.

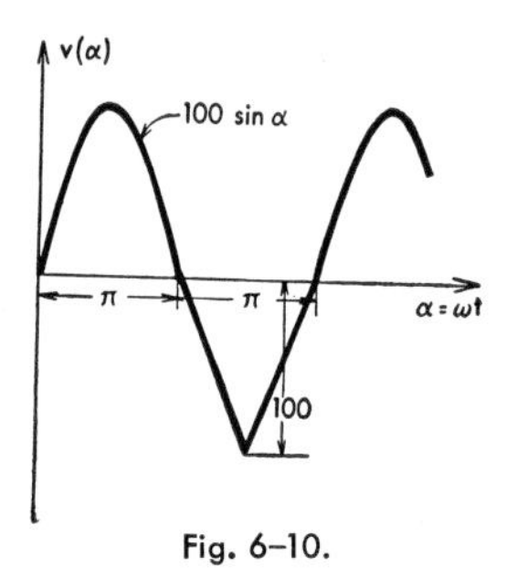

Fig. 6–10.

Before applying the formulas for the Fourier series coefficients, the mathematical form of $v(\alpha)$ must be written. The following relations give $v(\alpha)$ from 0 to 2π:

$$v(\alpha) = 100 \sin \alpha, \qquad 0 \leqslant \alpha \leqslant \pi$$

$$v(\alpha) = \frac{-200}{\pi}\alpha + 200, \qquad \pi \leqslant \alpha \leqslant \frac{3\pi}{2}$$

$$v(\alpha) = \frac{200}{\pi}\alpha - 400, \qquad \frac{3\pi}{2} \leqslant \alpha \leqslant 2\pi$$

The d-c component of the irregular wave being considered is then (equation 6–27)

$$V_{m0} = \frac{j}{2\pi}\left[\int_0^{\pi} 100 \sin \alpha \, d\alpha + \int_{\pi}^{3\pi/2}\left(\frac{-200}{\pi}\alpha + 200\right) d\alpha + \int_{3\pi/2}^{2\pi}\left(\frac{200}{\pi}\alpha - 400\right) d\alpha\right]$$

Integrating gives

$$V_{m0} = \frac{j100}{2\pi}\left[-\cos \alpha \Big|_0^{\pi} + \left(-\frac{\alpha^2}{\pi} + 2\alpha\right)\Big|_{\pi}^{3\pi/2} + \left(\frac{\alpha^2}{\pi} - 4\alpha\right)\Big|_{3\pi/2}^{2\pi}\right]$$

Substituting the limits and combining establishes the relation

$$V_{m0} = \frac{j100}{2\pi}\left[2 - \frac{\pi}{4} - \frac{\pi}{4}\right] = j\left[\frac{100}{\pi} - 25\right] = 0 + j6.8$$

Note that the d-c component is a pure imaginary, as it must be, since the *imaginary components* of the *complex variables* have been defined in this work as the actual circuit voltages and currents.

The sine coefficients will be (equation 6–24)

$$V_{mh} = \frac{1}{\pi}\int_0^{\pi} j100 \sin \alpha \epsilon^{-jh\alpha} \, d\alpha + \frac{1}{\pi}\int_{\pi}^{3\pi/2} j\left(\frac{-200}{\pi}\alpha + 200\right)\epsilon^{-jh\alpha} \, d\alpha + \frac{1}{\pi}\int_{3\pi/2}^{2\pi} j\left(\frac{200}{\pi}\alpha - 400\right)\epsilon^{-jh\alpha} \, d\alpha$$

Carrying out the indicated integration (in the first integral making use of equation 2–34 and the fact that $\epsilon^{j\pi} = \epsilon^{-j\pi} = -1$), substituting the limits, and combining gives

$$V_{mh} = \frac{j100}{\pi}\left[\frac{1+\epsilon^{-jh\pi}}{1-h^2} + \left(\frac{1}{jh} - \frac{2}{\pi h^2}\right)\epsilon^{-jh3\pi/2} + \frac{2}{\pi h^2}\epsilon^{-jh\pi} + \frac{2}{\pi h^2} - \left(\frac{1}{jh} + \frac{2}{\pi h^2}\right)\epsilon^{-jh3\pi/2}\right]$$

$$= \frac{j100}{\pi}\left[\frac{1+\epsilon^{-jh\pi}}{1-h^2} - \frac{4}{\pi h^2}\epsilon^{-jh3\pi/2} + \frac{2}{\pi h^2}\epsilon^{-jh\pi} + \frac{2}{\pi h^2}\right]$$

as the general form of coefficients of the Fourier series. This formula gives the particular results for $h = 1, 2, 3, 4, \cdots$, successively,

$$V_{m1} = 50 + \frac{400}{\pi^2} = 90.5 + j0 = 90.5\epsilon^{j0}$$

$$V_{m2} = j\left(-\frac{200}{3\pi} + \frac{200}{\pi^2}\right) = 0 - j0.96 = 0.96\epsilon^{-j\pi/2}$$

$$V_{m3} = \frac{-400}{9\pi^2} = -4.5 + j0 = 4.5\epsilon^{j\pi}$$

$$V_{m4} = 0 - \frac{j40}{3\pi} = 0 - j4.24 = 4.24\epsilon^{-j\pi/2}$$

$$V_{m5} = \frac{16}{\pi^2} + j0 = 1.62 + j0 = 1.62\epsilon^{j0}$$

Note that in determining V_{m1} the first term of the general expression for V_{mh} is indeterminate and of the form $0/0$. This general expression, therefore, cannot be used to evaluate V_{m1}. It is necessary to use the original integral definition of V_{mh} (equation 6–24) with $h = 1$. Integration then gives the value of V_{m1} shown.

The first five terms of the Fourier series (rotating vector) are, from the values just calculated and equation 6–10,

$$V(\alpha) = 6.8\epsilon^{j(\pi/2)} + 90.5\epsilon^{j0}\epsilon^{j\alpha} + 0.96\epsilon^{-j(\pi/2)}\epsilon^{j2\alpha} + 4.5\epsilon^{j\pi}\epsilon^{j3\alpha} + 4.24\epsilon^{-j(\pi/2)}\epsilon^{j4\alpha} + 1.62\epsilon^{j0}\epsilon^{j5\alpha}\cdots$$

which as a sum of sine waves, from the j-component of these terms, is

$$v(\alpha) = 6.8 + 90.5\sin\alpha - 4.5\sin 3\alpha + 1.62\sin 5\alpha \cdots - 0.96\cos 2\alpha - 4.24\cos 4\alpha \cdots$$

The d-c component and sine and cosine harmonics given by this equation are shown plotted in Fig. 6–11. Their sum is also shown. Many more harmonics must be added before the sum reproduces the original function of Fig. 6–10.

An examination of the foregoing example, or of the symbolic treatment preceding, shows that if the $t = 0$ or $\alpha = 0$ point is taken at different abscissa points on a curve, the resulting mathematical expressions will differ. Thus, if the $\alpha = 0$ point had been taken at the maximum point of the sine wave instead of the zero point of Fig. 6–10, all the Fourier series coefficients, except the d-c one, would have differed from the ones computed in Example 6–2. However, the difference is found to occur only in the *angles* of the complex number coefficients. The magnitudes are always the same. Note, however, that *all* the coefficients of the sine and cosine expressions given in the last equation of Example 6–2 except the d-c one

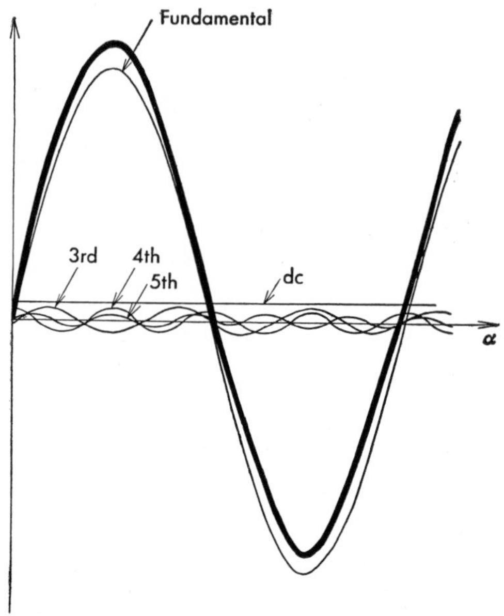

Fig. 6–11.

differ for each possible different $\alpha = 0$ point. Thus the sine and cosine harmonics differ for each $\alpha = 0$ point. The important point, though, is that any starting point for the determination of the Fourier series coefficients leads to the same number of harmonics with the same maximum values, but with different phase position angles corresponding to the shifting of the origin of coordinates.

A specialization of the formula for V_{mh} which is sometimes useful will now be developed. If a non-sine wave is symmetric, i.e., consists of only odd harmonics—no even harmonics or d-c component—equation 6–24 can be expressed as an integral over one-half a fundamental period rather than over the whole fundamental period. To show this fact, equation 6–24 may be expressed by two integrals as

$$\begin{aligned} V_{mh} &= \frac{1}{\pi}\int_0^{2\pi} jv(\alpha)\epsilon^{-jh\alpha}\,d\alpha \\ &= \frac{1}{\pi}\int_0^{\pi} jv(\alpha)\epsilon^{-jh\alpha}\,d\alpha + \frac{1}{\pi}\int_\pi^{2\pi} jv(\alpha)\epsilon^{-jh\alpha}\,d\alpha \end{aligned} \qquad (6\text{–}28)$$

The last integral on the right may be transformed in the following way. Substitute in this integral for the variable α the new variable $\alpha' + \pi$. Then

$$\begin{aligned} v(\alpha) &= v(\alpha' + \pi) \\ d\alpha &= d\alpha' \\ \epsilon^{-jh\alpha} &= \epsilon^{-jh\alpha'}\epsilon^{-jh\pi} \\ \alpha' &= 0, \text{ when } \alpha = \pi \\ \alpha' &= \pi, \text{ when } \alpha = 2\pi \end{aligned} \tag{6–29}$$

which gives

$$\frac{1}{\pi}\int_{\pi}^{2\pi} jv(\alpha)\epsilon^{-jh\alpha}\,d\alpha = \frac{\epsilon^{-jh\pi}}{\pi}\int_0^{\pi} jv(\alpha' + \pi)\epsilon^{-jh\alpha'}\,d\alpha' \tag{6–30}$$

Furthermore, on substituting the symmetry requirement $v(\alpha') = -v(\alpha' + \pi)$ into this relation (on the right),

$$\frac{1}{\pi}\int_{\pi}^{2\pi} jv(\alpha)\epsilon^{-jh\alpha}\,d\alpha = \frac{-\epsilon^{-jh\pi}}{\pi}\int_0^{\pi} jv(\alpha')\epsilon^{-jh\alpha'}\,d\alpha'$$

But the variable of integration of a definite integral may be indicated by any variable whatsoever; hence the primes may be dropped for this last equation, giving

$$\frac{1}{\pi}\int_{\pi}^{2\pi} jv(\alpha)\epsilon^{-jh\alpha}\,d\alpha = \frac{-\epsilon^{-jh\pi}}{\pi}\int_0^{\pi} jv(\alpha)\epsilon^{-jh\alpha}\,d\alpha \tag{6–31}$$

This result may now be substituted into equation 6–28 so that for $v(\alpha) = -v(\alpha + \pi)$,

$$V_{mh} = \frac{(1 - \epsilon^{-jh\pi})}{\pi}\int_0^{\pi} jv(\alpha)\epsilon^{-jh\alpha}\,d\alpha \tag{6–32}$$

But because $\epsilon^{-jh\pi} = \pm 1$, depending on whether h is even or odd, the coefficient of this last integral is zero or 2. Therefore,

$$\begin{aligned} V_{mh} &= \frac{2}{\pi}\int_0^{\pi} jv(\alpha)\epsilon^{-jh\alpha}\,d\alpha \left[\begin{matrix} v(\alpha) \text{ symmetric,} \\ \text{i.e., } h \text{ odd} \end{matrix}\right] \\ V_{mh} &= 0\ [h \text{ even}] \end{aligned} \tag{6–33}$$

gives the expression for the Fourier series coefficients for *symmetrical* waves (odd harmonics—no d-c component or even harmonics).

If the Fourier series coefficients must be determined from an oscillographic record by graphical means (see the next chapter) the saving in labor possible by the use of equation 6–33 is very appreciable. For then only the interval from 0 to π need be considered rather than twice that interval, 0 to 2π.

A fact of further interest is evident on assuming $v(\alpha) = v(\alpha + \pi)$. The coefficient of the integral of equation 6–32 is then $(1 + \epsilon^{-jh\pi})/\pi$ and equation 6–33 applies for *even* values of h. Therefore, if $v(\alpha) = v(\alpha + \pi)$

—e.g., Fig. 6–16—equation 6–33 can be used to determine these *even* harmonics by integrating over half the 0 to 2π interval. The odd harmonics are all zero. Note that for $v(\alpha) = v(\alpha + \pi)$, $v(\alpha)$ has a period of π.

6.5 Average Value of a Non-Sine Wave.

The average value of a non-sine wave is not very definite. For example, assigning an average value to the irregular wave of Fig. 6–5 is not easy. Of course, the $|V_{m0}|$ coefficient is an average value, and this average value can always be determined. Ordinarily when determining the average value of an alternating current, however, only part of a cycle is averaged (see Art. 1–5), and in Figs. 6–5*a* and 6–5*b* the part of a cycle to be averaged is not evident. In fact, an average over part of a cycle of such wave forms is more or less meaningless. If the wave is not so irregular, however,—for example, the resultant waves of Figs. 6–3 and 6–6—a meaning can be assigned to an average value as the average of the positive lobe of a cycle, or perhaps the negative lobe, or both.

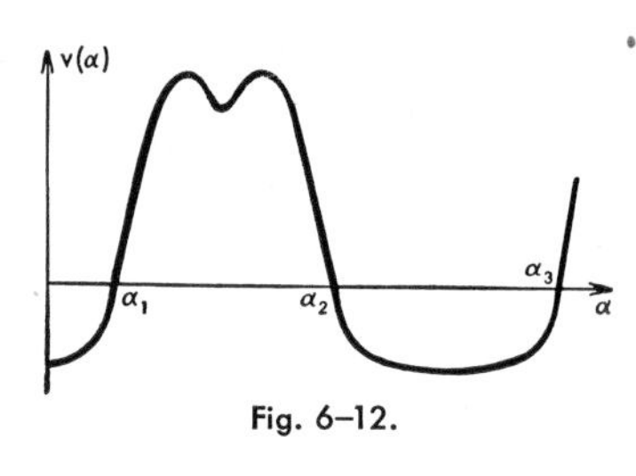

Fig. 6–12.

Mathematically, the average value, where it has meaning, may be defined from Fig. 6–12 as

$$|V_{\text{av}}| = \frac{1}{\alpha_2 - \alpha_1} \int_{\alpha_1}^{\alpha_2} v(\alpha)\, d\alpha \tag{6–34}$$

where α_1 and α_2 are the values of α at the *crossing points* of the positive lobe. A second average value may be determined from the α_2, α_3 interval or the negative half-cycle lobe of this figure. The positive and negative lobe average values need not be equal.

Such average values are not often used except in some aspects of the treatment of low-frequency or power systems. In such systems, as has already been indicated, the non-sine waves are symmetrical so that the positive and negative half-lobe averages are equal and this value is considered as *the* average. The average value of a symmetric wave may thus be expressed as

$$|V_{\text{av}}| = \frac{1}{\pi} \int_0^{\pi} v(\alpha)\, d\alpha \tag{6–35}$$

provided $v(\alpha)$ *has the values*

$$v(0) = 0, \quad v(\pi) = 0$$

i.e., *provided the equation of* $v(\alpha)$ *is written so that the zero values of the resultant wave occur at* 0 *and* π.

A particular formula for the average value of a symmetric non-sine wave *which crosses the α-axis at* 0 *and* π may be obtained by substituting equation 6–4 into equation 6–35 and integrating. The result is

$$|V_{\text{av}}| = \sum_{k=0}^{\infty} \frac{2|V_{mk}|}{k\pi} \cos \phi_k (k \text{ odd}) \tag{6–36}$$

where ϕ_k = the phase angle of the kth harmonic *measured from the crossing point of the resultant wave*, and on the scale of the kth harmonic. The derivation of equation 6–36 and the proof of the statement following are left as an exercise for the reader (see Problem 6–9).

6.6 Effective Value of a Non-Sine Wave.

The average and effective values of non-sine waves can be determined directly from a graph of these waves by graphical means (see Chap. 7), but for theoretical considerations, or a study of the properties of circuits with non-sine waves of voltage and current, the effective values in terms of the Fourier series coefficients are very useful.

Equation 1–18 or 1–14 expresses the effective value of any voltage or current by the same general mathematical formula. In terms of voltage

$$|V| = \sqrt{\frac{1}{T_p}\int_0^{T_p} v^2(t)\, dt} \tag{6–37}$$

This equation may be expressed in terms of a more convenient variable α rather than t by making a change in variable through the relation $\alpha = \omega t$. Thus if

$$\omega t = 2\pi f t = \alpha$$

then

$$dt = \frac{d\alpha}{\omega}$$

and

$$\text{when } t = 0,\ \alpha = 0$$
$$\text{when } t = T_p = \frac{1}{f},\ \alpha = 2\pi \tag{6–38}$$

Substituting these relations into equation 6–37 gives

$$|V| = \sqrt{\frac{1}{\frac{1}{f}}\int_0^{2\pi} v^2(\alpha)\frac{d\alpha}{\omega}} = \sqrt{\frac{1}{2\pi}\int_0^{2\pi} v^2(\alpha)\, d\alpha} \tag{6–39}$$

where $v(t)$ becomes $v(\alpha)$ on making the substitution, because t always occurs multiplied by ω in the Fourier series expansion, as is shown by

$$V(\omega t) = V(t) = \sum_{k=0}^{\infty} V_{mk}\epsilon^{jk\omega t} \tag{6–40}$$

or instantaneously

$$v(\omega t) = v(t) = \sum_{k=(}^{\infty} |V_{mk}| \sin (k\omega t + \phi_k) \tag{6-41}$$

Using the variable α slightly shortens the symbolism required and also expresses the Fourier series in terms of angular measure, both of which are often helpful.

To return now to an evaluation of the rms value of a non-sine wave, substituting equation 6–20 into equation 6–39 gives

$$|V| = \sqrt{\frac{1}{2\pi} \int_0^{2\pi} \left[\sum_{k=0}^{\infty} \frac{V_{mk}\epsilon^{jk\alpha} - \hat{V}_{mk}\epsilon^{-jk\alpha}}{2j} \right]^2 d\alpha} \tag{6-42}$$

The square of an infinite series is another infinite series, which may be expressed as follows. Suppose, to shorten the symbolism, it is assumed that the infinite series is written as

$$v(\alpha) = \sum_{k=0}^{\infty} A_k = \sum_{k=0}^{\infty} \frac{V_{mk}\epsilon^{jk\alpha} - \hat{V}_{mk}\epsilon^{-jk\alpha}}{2j} \tag{6-43}$$

Then

$$[v(\alpha)]^2 = \left[\sum_{k=0}^{\infty} A_k \right]^2$$

$$\begin{aligned} = A_0^2 &+ A_0A_1 + A_0A_2 + A_0A_3 + \cdots \\ &+ A_0A_1 + A_1^2 + A_1A_2 + A_1A_3 + \cdots \\ &+ A_0A_2 + A_1A_2 + A_2^2 + A_2A_3 + \cdots \\ &+ A_0A_3 + A_1A_3 + A_2A_3 + A_3^2 + \cdots \\ &\cdot \quad \cdot \quad \cdot \quad \cdot \quad \cdot \quad \cdot \quad \cdot \quad \cdot \quad \cdot \quad \cdot \quad \cdot \end{aligned}$$

or

$$[v(\alpha)]^2 = \sum_{k=0}^{\infty} A_k^2 + \sum_{\substack{h=0 \\ k=0}}^{\infty} A_hA_k (h \neq k) \tag{6-44}$$

It would, of course, be impossible to integrate all the terms of the infinite series, but it is possible to consider *typical* types of the only two general terms of this last equation and integrate them. Thus, since

$$A_k = \frac{V_{mk}\epsilon^{jk\alpha} - \hat{V}_{mk}\epsilon^{-jk\alpha}}{2j}$$

the typical terms become

$$A_k^2 = \frac{V_{mk}V_{mk}\epsilon^{j2k\alpha} - 2V_{mk}\hat{V}_{mk} + \hat{V}_{mk}\hat{V}_{mk}\epsilon^{-2jk\alpha}}{-4} \tag{6-45}$$

and

$$A_kA_h = \frac{V_{mk}V_{mh}\epsilon^{j(h+k)\alpha} - V_{mh}\hat{V}_{mk}\epsilon^{j(h-k)\alpha} - V_{mk}\hat{V}_{mh}\epsilon^{-j(h-k)\alpha} + \hat{V}_{mk}\hat{V}_{mh}\epsilon^{-j(h+k)\alpha}}{-4} \tag{6-46}$$

As may be easily shown, see equation 6–22,

$$\int_0^{2\pi} \epsilon^{\pm jm\alpha}\, d\alpha = 0, \quad \text{for } m \text{ any integer, } m \neq 0$$

and because $h + k$ is an integer, being the sum or difference of two integers, the terms like those of equation 6–46 will *all become zero* if integrated over the interval 0 to 2π. Therefore, all the infinitely many terms in equation 6–42 of the form of equation 6–46 will integrate to zero. The remaining infinite set of terms of equation 6–42 which are represented typically by equation 6–45 must be considered in two steps. First, if $k \neq 0$, equation 6–45 on integrating becomes

$$\frac{1}{2\pi}\int_0^{2\pi} A_k^{\,2}\, d\alpha = \frac{V_{mk}\hat{V}_{mk}}{2} = \frac{|V_{mk}|^2}{2}, \; k \neq 0 \tag{6–47}$$

Second, if $k = 0$, equation 6–45, on integration, becomes

$$\frac{1}{2\pi}\int_0^{2\pi} \frac{(V_{m0} - \hat{V}_{m0})^2}{-4}\, d\alpha = \frac{(V_{m0} - \hat{V}_{m0})^2}{-4}$$

Recalling that

$$V_{m0} = |V_{m0}|\epsilon^{\pm j\pi/2} = 0 \pm j|V_{m0}| = 0 + jv_{c0}$$

then

$$\frac{(V_{m0} - \hat{V}_{m0})^2}{-4} = \frac{(2jv_{c0})^2}{-4} = v_{c0}^{\,2} = |V_{m0}|^2 \tag{6–48}$$

Therefore, on integrating equation 6–42, all the terms become zero except the term given by equation 6–48 and infinitely many terms like the one given in equation 6–47 (one for each value of k except the zero value), and the square root of the sum of all these terms gives the rms value of a non-sine wave.

It has now been shown that the effective value of a non-sine wave in terms of the Fourier series coefficients is

$$|V| = \sqrt{|V_{m0}|^2 + \frac{|V_{m1}|^2}{2} + \frac{|V_{m2}|^2}{2} + \frac{|V_{m3}|^2}{2} + \cdots}$$
$$= \sqrt{|V_{m0}|^2 + \sum_{k=1}^{\infty}\frac{|V_{mk}|^2}{2}} \tag{6–49}$$

If effective values are used throughout, the final expression for the effective value of *any* periodic non-sine wave, in terms of the *effective values* of the *harmonics* of the non-sine wave, is

$$|V| = \sqrt{|V_0|^2 + \sum_{k=1}^{\infty}|V_k|^2} = \sqrt{\sum_{k=0}^{\infty}|V_k|^2} \tag{6–50}$$

Whether equation 6–50 is of more than theoretical usefulness for any particular problem depends on whether the infinite sum of this equation can be evaluated. If, as for most practical problems, the sum is finite, the effective value may be determined very readily from equation 6–50 if the Fourier coefficients are known. On the other hand, the determination of the Fourier series coefficients from an oscillographic record entails a certain amount of work so that computing the effective value by means of these coefficients will generally not be the simplest method. The graphical method given in Chap. 7 when applied directly to the non-sine wave is probably the most direct method of getting the effective value of a non-sine wave.

The usefulness of equation 6–50 is not confined entirely to determining numerically the effective value of a non-sine wave, but this effective value formula will facilitate the understanding of non-sine wave phenomena. Equation 6–50 shows immediately one fact of considerable importance, namely, that *the effective value of a sum of sine waves of different frequencies is not affected by the phase positions of the waves, but is determined entirely from the effective values of the harmonics.* Notice the difference, if the sinusoids are of the *same frequency*. Then the phase positions of the waves is one of the major factors in determining the effective value of the sum. This distinction is important and should be kept in mind (see Problem 6–11).

Example 6:3 Determine the effective value of the non-sinusoidal voltage represented by the Fourier series expression

$$v(\alpha) = -10 + 150 \sin(\alpha + 30^\circ) - 25 \sin(2\alpha - 10^\circ) + 5 \sin(3\alpha + 20^\circ) \\ -5 \sin 4\alpha - 3 \sin(5\alpha - 50^\circ)$$

Solution Determining the effective value of a Fourier series expression is merely a matter of substituting into the formula (equation 6–49)

$$|V| = \sqrt{|V_{m0}|^2 + \sum_{k=1}^{\infty} \frac{|V_{mk}|^2}{2}}$$

$$= \sqrt{10^2 + \frac{150^2}{2} + \frac{25^2}{2} + \frac{5^2}{2} + \frac{5^2}{2} + \frac{3^2}{2}}$$

$$|V| = \sqrt{11{,}692} = 108.1 \text{ volts}$$

6.7 Power in a Circuit of Non-Sine Waves of Current and Voltage.

The instantaneous power is given by the product of the instantaneous expressions for the current and voltage

$$p(t) = v(t)i(t)$$

This expression may also be written as a function of α as

$$p(\alpha) = v(\alpha)i(\alpha) \tag{6–51}$$

through the change in variable $\alpha = \omega t$. Furthermore, through this same change of variable (see equations 6–38) the average power formula of equation 1–27 may be expressed as a function of α by

$$P = \frac{1}{2\pi}\int_0^{2\pi} p(\alpha)\, d\alpha = \frac{1}{2\pi}\int_0^{2\pi} v(\alpha)i(\alpha)\, d\alpha \tag{6–52}$$

Recalling the existence of the power factor angle θ_k, this equation in terms of the Fourier series expansions for $v(\alpha)$ and $i(\alpha)$ is

$$P = \frac{1}{2\pi}\int_0^{2\pi}\left[\sum_{k=0}^{\infty}|V_{mk}|\sin(k\alpha+\phi_k)\right]\left[\sum_{k=0}^{\infty}|I_{mk}|\sin(k\alpha+\phi_k+\theta_k)\right]d\alpha \tag{6–53}$$

The evaluation of this equation may be carried out either by integrating the product of the infinite series of sine waves or by converting the sines to their equivalent exponential form as was done for equation 6–42 by means of equation 6–20. Since the exponentials make the integration process much simpler, they will be used. The rotating vector equivalent, of course, cannot be used in this process.

Therefore, average power, from equations 6–53 and 6–20, is

$$P = \frac{1}{2\pi}\int_0^{2\pi}\left[\sum_{k=0}^{\infty}\frac{(V_{mk}\epsilon^{jk\alpha} - \hat{V}_{mk}\epsilon^{-jk\alpha})}{2j}\sum_{h=0}^{\infty}\frac{(I_{mh}\epsilon^{jh\alpha} - \hat{I}_{mh}\epsilon^{-jh\alpha})}{2j}\right]d\alpha \tag{6–54}$$

where

$$V_{mk} = |V_{mk}|\epsilon^{j\phi_k}$$
$$I_{mh} = |I_{mh}|\epsilon^{j(\phi_h+\theta_h)}$$

If, for convenience, the integrand of this equation is symbolized in a briefer form, the product may be expressed as

$$\sum_{k=0}^{\infty}A_k\sum_{h=0}^{\infty}B_h = \sum_{k=0}^{\infty}A_kB_k + \sum_{\substack{k=0\\h=0}}^{\infty}A_kB_h(k \neq h) \tag{6–55}$$

Typical terms of this expression are

$$A_kB_k = \frac{V_{mk}I_{mk}\epsilon^{j2k\alpha} - I_{mk}\hat{V}_{mk} - \hat{I}_{mk}V_{mk} + \hat{V}_{mk}\hat{I}_{mk}\epsilon^{-j2k\alpha}}{-4} \tag{6–56}$$

and

$$A_kB_h = \frac{V_{mk}I_{mh}\epsilon^{j(k+h)\alpha} - \hat{V}_{mk}I_{mh}\epsilon^{j(h-k)\alpha} - V_{mk}\hat{I}_{mh}\epsilon^{j(k-h)\alpha} + \hat{V}_{mk}\hat{I}_{mh}\epsilon^{-j(h+k)\alpha}}{-4} \tag{6–57}$$

As in preceding discussions in this chapter, it is necessary to consider as a special case $h = k = 0$. This condition can fit only into equation 6–56, with the result

$$
\begin{aligned}
A_0B_0 &= \frac{V_{m0}I_{m0} - I_{m0}\hat{V}_{m0} - \hat{I}_{m0}V_{m0} + \hat{V}_{m0}\hat{I}_{m0}}{-4} \\
&= \frac{(V_{m0} - \hat{V}_{m0})(I_{m0} - \hat{I}_{m0})}{-4} \\
&= \frac{V_{m0}I_{m0}}{j^2} = \frac{V_0I_0}{j^2} = \frac{(0 + jv_{c0})(0 + ji_{c0})}{j^2} \\
&= v_{c0}i_{c0}
\end{aligned}
\tag{6-58}
$$

If a power factor angle θ_0 is defined as 0 or 180 degrees, depending on whether v_{c0} and i_{c0} have the same or different signs, equation 6–58 can be expressed to fit into the usual power formula as

$$
A_0B_0 = |V_0|\,|I_0| \cos \theta_0 \tag{6-59}
$$

To turn next to the further consideration of equations 6–56 and 6–57, since $h + k$ and $h - k$ are both integers if $h \neq k$, the integral from 0 to 2π of all the exponential terms of these expressions will vanish for $h \neq k$. All terms of the type represented by equation 6–57, therefore, vanish, and equation 6–56 gives

$$
\begin{aligned}
\frac{1}{2\pi}\int_0^{2\pi} A_kB_k\,d\alpha &= \frac{1}{2\pi}\int_0^{2\pi} \frac{I_{mk}\hat{V}_{mk} + \hat{I}_{mk}V_{mk}}{4}\,d\alpha (k \neq 0) \\
&= \frac{I_{mk}\hat{V}_{mk} + \hat{I}_{mk}V_{mk}}{4} \\
&= \frac{|I_{mk}|\,|V_{mk}|}{2}\left[\frac{\epsilon^{j(\phi_k + \theta_k - \phi_k)} + \epsilon^{-j(\phi_k + \theta_k - \phi_k)}}{2}\right] \\
&= \frac{|I_{mk}|\,|V_{mk}|}{2} \cos \theta_k = |I_k|\,|V_k| \cos \theta_k (k \neq 0)
\end{aligned}
\tag{6-60}
$$

There are as many terms of this kind as there are values of $k \neq 0$ and $h \neq 0$ common to both sums of equation 6–54. There is also a similar term for the d-c components as given in equation 6–59. The sum of all such possible terms represents the average power.

Accordingly, the average power formula of equation 6–52 when expressed in terms of Fourier series coefficients and angles is

$$
P = \sum_{k=0}^{\infty} |I_k|\,|V_k| \cos \theta_k \tag{6-61}
$$

where, by definition, $\theta_0 = 0°$ or $180°$, depending on whether i_{c0} and v_{c0} have the same or different signs.

This equation may also be expressed in terms of the dot or scalar product of Art. 2–8 as

$$
P = \sum_{k=0}^{\infty} V_k \cdot I_k \tag{6-62}
$$

Corresponding to the average power definition of equation 6–61, the reactive volt-amperes are defined by

$$Q = \sum_{k=0}^{\infty} |V_k|\, |I_k| \sin \theta_k \tag{6–63}$$

The particular point of interest of equation 6–61 is that, *on the average, power is supplied only to a circuit by currents and voltages of like frequencies.* For example, if a sinusoidal voltage connected to a circuit gives rise to a current which has a fundamental and third harmonic, the average power is supplied by the fundamental only, the triple harmonic contributing nothing on the average. *Instantaneously*, of course, the harmonics of the current or voltage, respectively, which do not have a corresponding harmonic of voltage or current, respectively, represent some energy transfer or power. On the average, however, these harmonics return to the system the energy they take from it, just as does an inductor or a capacitor.

Example 6:4 Determine the average power absorbed by an impedance which has the following non-sinusoidal current and voltage through and across its terminals:

$$\begin{aligned} i(\alpha) &= 1.0 + 10 \sin \alpha - 4 \sin (2\alpha + 30°) - 2 \sin (3\alpha + 45°) \\ v(\alpha) &= 100 \sin (\alpha - 15°) + 30 \sin (2\alpha + 150°) \end{aligned}$$

Solution The average power may be determined from equation 6–61. The result is

$$\begin{aligned} P &= \frac{10 \cdot 100}{2} \cos 15° + \frac{4 \cdot 30}{2} \cos 60° \\ &= 500 \times 0.966 + 60 \times 0.5 = 513 \text{ watts} \end{aligned}$$

The d-c component and third harmonic of current do not produce power on the average because there is no corresponding harmonic in the voltage.

6.8 Form Factor, Peak Factor, Equivalent Sine Wave, and Equivalent Power Factor.

(*a*) The form factor has already been defined in Art. 1–5, and was given there as

$$\text{form factor} \equiv \frac{\text{effective value}}{\text{average value}} \equiv \frac{|I|}{|I_{\text{av}}|} \tag{6–64}$$

(*b*) Peak or crest factor is defined as the ratio

$$\text{crest factor} \equiv \frac{\text{maximum value}}{\text{effective value}} \equiv \frac{|I_m|}{|I|} \tag{6–65}$$

(*c*) An equivalent sine wave is one which has the same effective value as the non-sine wave.

(*d*) The equivalent power factor may be determined readily from the general definition of the power factor, namely, by

$$\text{power factor} \equiv \frac{\text{average power}}{\text{volt-amperes}} \equiv \frac{P}{|V|\,|I|} \tag{6–66}$$

6.9 A Non-Sine Wave of Voltage Connected to a Series Circuit.

Suppose that the series circuit of Fig. 6–13 has a non-sine wave of voltage connected to it, and that the current response is desired. Since all our theoretical knowledge of circuits comes directly or indirectly from Kirchhoff's laws, the basic equation for this circuit, which is the voltage

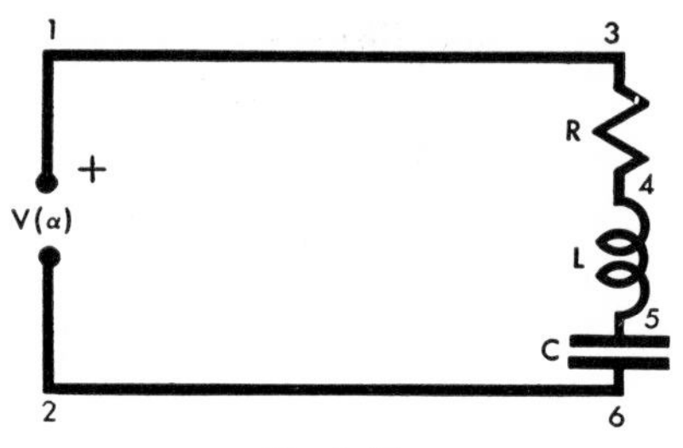

Fig. 6–13.

equation, may be expected to furnish the information desired. The rotating vector equivalent can be used to represent the Fourier series of the source voltage because the Kirchhoff voltage equation for this circuit does not require the product of the rotating vector and another complex number. Accordingly, if the complex variable expression for the Fourier series of the connected voltage and the variable $Q(t)$, where $I(\alpha) = I(\omega t) = \dot{Q}(\omega t)$, are used, the voltage equation for the series circuit is

$$V(\omega t) = \sum_{k=0}^{\infty} V_{mk}\epsilon^{jk\omega t} = \sum_{k=1}^{\infty} V_{mk}\epsilon^{jk\omega t} + V_{m0}$$
$$= L\dot{Q}(\omega t) + R\ddot{Q}(\omega t) + \frac{Q(\omega t)}{C} + V_C(0) \tag{6–67}$$

The current response to this non-sinusoidal voltage across the R, L, C series circuit may be obtained by following the method of Art. 4–1. Assume that

$$Q(\omega t) = \sum_{k=0}^{\infty} |Q_{mk}|\epsilon^{j(k\omega t + \phi_k + \theta_k)} = \sum_{k=0}^{\infty} Q_{mk}\epsilon^{jk\omega t} \equiv \sum_{k=1}^{\infty} Q_{mk}\epsilon^{jk\omega t} + Q_{m0} \tag{6–68}$$

and so

$$I(\omega t) = \dot{Q}(\omega t) = \sum_{k=1}^{\infty} j\omega k Q_{mk}\epsilon^{jk\omega t} = \sum_{k=1}^{\infty} I_{mk}\epsilon^{jk\omega t} \tag{6–69}$$

and substitute in equation 6–67 to determine $|Q_{mk}|$, $|I_{mk}|$, and θ_k, or Q_{mk} and $I_{mk} = j\omega k Q_{mk}$. The angle ϕ_k is, of course, given with the voltage coefficient V_{mk}. Equation 6–67, on substituting equations 6–68 and 6–69 and replacing the variable t by α, where $\omega t = \alpha$, becomes

$$\sum_{k=1}^{\infty} V_{mk}\epsilon^{jk\alpha} + V_{m0} - V_C(0)$$

$$= \sum_{k=1}^{\infty}\left(R + jk\omega L + \frac{1}{jk\omega C}\right) jk\omega Q_{mk}\epsilon^{jk\alpha} + \frac{Q_{m0}}{C} \qquad (6\text{–}70)$$

$$= \sum_{k=1}^{\infty} Z_k jk\omega Q_{mk}\epsilon^{jk\alpha} + \frac{Q_{m0}}{C} = \sum_{k=1}^{\infty} Z_k I_{mk}\epsilon^{jk\alpha} + \frac{Q_{m0}}{C} \qquad (6\text{–}71)$$

where

$$Z_k = R + jk\omega L + \frac{1}{jk\omega C} = R + j(X_{Lk} + X_{Ck}) = R + jX_{0k} \qquad (6\text{–}72)$$

Note that the resistance R has been assumed to be the same for all the harmonics. Actually it would not be, owing to an increase in resistance of a conductor with increase in frequency caused by the so-called skin effect, proximity effect, and shape. Skin effect is, briefly, a name applied to the concentration of current toward the surface of a conductor and away from the center as the frequency increases. The reason for this change in the current distribution is the increase, with increase in the frequency of magnetic field variation, in the self-induction voltage in the conductor. The self-induction voltage is larger at the center of the conductor because more magnetic field is about the center than the surface. At low frequencies—power systems of 60 cps—the skin effect is seldom large enough to require consideration. At higher frequencies, the skin effect is appreciable but generally small compared to the reactance change. Formulas have been worked out for skin effect, and recognition of its existence is evident in the hollow tubing used as conductor in radio stations and even in power stations.

To return once more to a consideration of equation 6–71, a slight rearrangement leads to

$$\sum_{k=1}^{\infty} (V_{mk} - Z_k I_{mk})\epsilon^{jk\alpha} + \left(V_{m0} - V_C(0) - \frac{Q_{m0}}{C}\right) = 0 \qquad (6\text{–}73)$$

But since this relation must be true for *every* value of α, the terms in parentheses must be equal to zero, i.e., *term by term* the infinite series of equation 6–73 must be equal to zero; hence

$$V_{mk} = Z_k I_{mk}, \text{ for each } k \neq 0;\ Q_{m0} = C[V_{m0} - V_C(0)] \qquad (6\text{–}74)$$

or

$$I_{mk} = \frac{V_{mk}}{Z_k} \quad \text{and} \quad I_k = \frac{V_k}{Z_k},\ k \neq 0 \qquad (6\text{–}75)$$

The Fourier series for the current may now be written by substituting this current value into equation 6–69.

The rotating vector current is, therefore,

$$I(\alpha) = \sum_{k=1}^{\infty} I_{mk}\epsilon^{jk\alpha} = \sum_{k=1}^{\infty} \frac{V_{mk}}{Z_k}\epsilon^{jk\alpha} = \sum_{k=1}^{\infty} \frac{|V_{mk}|}{|Z_k|}\epsilon^{j(k\alpha+\phi_k+\theta_k)} \quad (6\text{–}76)$$

The very important conclusion to be deduced from this last equation is that exactly the same relation is valid for the kth harmonic as that deduced for a single sinusoid of connected voltage. Hence the relations already deduced concerning the interrelations of current, voltage, impedance, power factor angle, etc., for a sine wave of voltage connected to the R, L, and C series circuit may be deduced also from equation 6–76 for the kth harmonic. Since the relations for the kth harmonic and for a single sine wave voltage are identical except for a subscript k, they will not be repeated here.

In spite of the similarity of the single sine wave equation and the kth harmonic equation there are some points which need mentioning. Note first that each component, or harmonic, of the voltage acts separately on the circuit and that (equation 6–76) each *harmonic of current can be calculated from the corresponding voltage harmonic alone.* The problem of treating a series circuit to which a non-sine voltage is connected becomes, therefore, a problem of treating each harmonic alone by the method of Chap. 4 and then adding the results in a Fourier series as given in equation 6–76. Further proof of the fact that the harmonics of the voltage act independently of each other may be deduced by considering the power expression of equation 6–61. For since $\cos\theta_k = R/|Z_k|$

$$P = \sum_{k=0}^{\infty} |V_k|\,|I_k|\frac{R}{|Z_k|} = \sum_{k=0}^{\infty} R|I_k|^2 \quad (6\text{–}77)$$

and the total power loss formula is the sum of all $|I|^2R$ power losses due to each harmonic.

Another point of particular importance may be seen from equation 6–72. Note that the *inductive reactance increases directly with the frequency of the harmonic and that the capacitor reactance varies inversely with the frequency of the harmonic.* This fact accounts for the short-circuiting effect of capacitors at high frequencies and the very high impedance or blocking effect of inductors at high frequencies. More will be said of these points in later discussions of non-sine wave applications.

The apparent impedance or, perhaps better, the equivalent impedance of a series circuit is given, from *definition*, by

$$|Z_e| = \frac{\sqrt{\sum_{k=0}^{\infty} |V_k|^2}}{\sqrt{\sum_{k=0}^{\infty} |I_k|^2}} = \frac{|V|}{|I|} \quad (6\text{–}78)$$

i.e., it is the ratio of the effective voltage to the effective current. Notice that the equivalent impedance is *not a constant* for a particular circuit as is the impedance of a particular harmonic, but that the total impedance is now a *function of wave form of the connected voltage.*

Although a complex number for the equivalent impedance is seldom useful, such a number may be expressed through the equivalent sine wave relations, i.e., in complex form the equivalent impedance Z_e is

$$Z_e = \frac{\sqrt{\sum_{k=0}^{\infty} |V_k|^2}}{\sqrt{\sum_{k=0}^{\infty} |I_k|^2}} (\cos \theta_e + j \sin \theta_e) = \frac{|V|}{|I|} (pf_e + jrf_e) \qquad (6\text{–}79)$$

where

$$\theta_e = \cos^{-1} \frac{P}{|V|\,|I|} = \cos^{-1} pf_e$$

The reader should not fail to keep in mind that the relations just deduced for a series circuit with a non-sine source voltage are valid *only* if R, L, and C are *independent of current, voltage, and frequency.* Many applications permit this assumption, and where R, L, and C cannot be considered constant with sufficient accuracy it is often possible to gain some key to the circuit behavior by assuming them so at appropriate average values.

Example 6:5 Suppose the output voltage under load of a high-power vacuum tube may be represented in complex variable by

$$V(\alpha) = 10\epsilon^{j90} + 200\epsilon^{j(\alpha+30)} + 25\epsilon^{j(2\alpha+60)} + 10\epsilon^{j(3\alpha+45)} \text{ volts}$$

This voltage is connected to a series tuning circuit of $R = 10$ ohms, $L = 1$ mh, and $C = 0.1$ μf. The fundamental frequency is 6000 cps. (*a*) Find the complex and real variable expression for the current. (*b*) Find the total average power loss. (*c*) Find the equivalent impedance of the circuit. (*d*) Find the equivalent power factor.

Solution (*a*) In order to find the current expression, each harmonic will be treated separately, as the foregoing development suggests.

(1) For the d-c component, because $f = 0$,

$$Z_0 = R + j(X_{kL} + X_{kC}) = 10 + j\infty$$

and, of course, there is no direct current.

(2) For the fundamental, since $2\pi 6000 = 37{,}700$,

$$Z_1 = 10 + j(37.7 - 265.3) = 10 - j227.6 = 227.8\epsilon^{-j87.5}$$

$$I_{m1} = \frac{V_{m1}}{Z_1} = \frac{200\epsilon^{j30}}{227.8\epsilon^{-j87.5}} = 0.878\epsilon^{j117.5} = -0.405 + j0.78$$

(3) For the second harmonic,

$$Z_2 = 10 + j(75.4 - 132.6) = 10 - j57.2 = 58.1\epsilon^{-j80.1}$$

$$I_{m2} = \frac{V_{m2}}{Z_2} = \frac{25\epsilon^{j60}}{58.6\epsilon^{-j80.1}} = 0.43\epsilon^{j140.1} = -0.330 + j0.276$$

(4) For the third harmonic,

$$Z_3 = 10 + j(113 - 88.4) = 10 + j24.7 = 26.6\epsilon^{j67.9}$$

$$I_{m3} = \frac{V_{m3}}{Z_3} = \frac{10\epsilon^{j45}}{26.6\epsilon^{j67.2}} = 0.376\epsilon^{-j22.9} = 0.346 - j0.147$$

The complex variable representation of the current is, therefore, the sum of the harmonics

$$I(\alpha) = 0.878\epsilon^{j(\alpha+117.5)} + 0.43\epsilon^{j(2\alpha+140.1)} + 0.376\epsilon^{j(3\alpha-22.9)}$$

or the sine wave expression is

$$i(\alpha) = 0.878 \sin (\alpha + 117.5) + 0.43 \sin (2\alpha + 140.1) + 0.376 \sin (3\alpha - 22.9)$$

(*b*) Any one of the formulas given by equations 6–61, 6–62, or 6–77 may be used to determine the power. Suppose equation 6–62 is used. In order to use this equation the complex equation for the voltage harmonics must be determined. These equations are

$$V_{m1} = 200(\cos 30° + j \sin 30°) = 173.2 + j100$$
$$V_{m2} = 25(\cos 60° + j \sin 60°) = 12.5 + j21.6$$
$$V_{m3} = 10(\cos 45° + j \sin 45°) = 7.07 + j7.07$$

The total power is, then,

$$P = \sum_{k=1}^{3} \frac{V_{mk} \cdot I_{mk}}{2}$$
$$= \tfrac{1}{2} [(-0.405 \times 173.2 + 0.779 \times 100) + (-0.330 \times 12.5 + 0.276 \times 21.6) + (0.346 \times 7.07 - 0.147 \times 7.07)] = 5.48 \text{ watts}$$

As a check, taking $|I|$ from part (*c*) below,

$$P = R|I^2| = 10 \times (0.74)^2 = 5.48 \text{ watts}$$

(*c*) Since the equivalent impedance is the ratio of the effective values of the voltage and current, these values must first be computed. From equation 6–49,

$$|V| = \sqrt{10^2 + \frac{200^2 + 25^2 + 10^2}{2}} = 143 \text{ volts}$$

$$|I| = \sqrt{\frac{0.878^2 + 0.432^2 + 0.376^2}{2}} = 0.74 \text{ amp}$$

The equivalent impedance is

$$|Z_e| = \frac{143}{0.74} = 193 \text{ ohms}$$

(*d*) The equivalent power factor, or simply the power factor, is

$$pf_e = \frac{P}{|V||I|} = \frac{5.48}{143 \times 0.74} = 0.05$$

6.10 Resonance in a Series Circuit with a Non-Sine Wave of Connected Voltage.

As already shown—last of equations 4–26—there is a certain frequency at which any R, L, and C series circuit is in resonance, i.e., a frequency for which the total reactance X_0 is equal to zero. If a non-sine wave of voltage is connected to a series circuit of R, L, and C, the circuit may be in resonance with one of the voltage harmonics, and the corresponding harmonic current may be large. Equation 6–72 indicates that the condition for resonance for the kth harmonic—the impedance to the kth harmonic becoming a non-reactive resistance—is $X_{0k} = 0$, i.e.,

$$\omega_k L - \frac{1}{\omega_k C} = 0$$

from which

$$f_{kr} = \frac{1}{2\pi\sqrt{LC}} \tag{6–80}$$

The right side of this equation is fixed in value for any particular circuit and k is always an integer—the zero value of k has no meaning in resonance considerations. Whether a series circuit will be in resonance for one of the harmonics of the source voltage may be determined from this equation by evaluating the right-hand side and noting whether the result is near one of the harmonic frequencies. The effect of a circuit being in resonance or near resonance with a harmonic of the source voltage may best be shown by an example.

Example 6:6 Consider a series circuit of $R = 1$ ohm, $L = 0.1$ mh, and $C = 0.0028$ μf. The connected voltage is

$$V(\alpha) = 150\epsilon^{j\alpha} + 50\epsilon^{j(2\alpha+30)} - 25\epsilon^{j(3\alpha-45)} + 10\epsilon^{j5\alpha} \text{ volts}$$

and the fundamental frequency is 60,000 cps. Determine the magnitudes of the current harmonics and show the effects of resonance.

Solution Since current magnitudes only are needed, impedance magnitudes only will be computed.

$$|Z_1| = \sqrt{1 + (37.7 - 947)^2} = 909 \text{ ohms}$$
$$|Z_2| = \sqrt{1 + (75.4 - 473.6)^2} = 398 \text{ ohms}$$
$$|Z_3| = \sqrt{1 + (113 - 315.7)^2} = 203 \text{ ohms}$$
$$|Z_5| = \sqrt{1 + (188.5 - 189.5)^2} = 1.41 \text{ ohms}$$

The effective values of the currents are

$$|I_1| = \frac{150}{909\sqrt{2}} = 0.117 \text{ amp}$$

$$|I_2| = \frac{50}{398\sqrt{2}} = 0.088 \text{ amp}$$

$$|I_3| = \frac{25}{203\sqrt{2}} = 0.087 \text{ amp}$$

$$|I_5| = \frac{10}{1.41\sqrt{2}} = 5 \text{ amp}$$

A comparison of these current magnitudes shows that, even though the fifth harmonic voltage is smallest, the fifth harmonic current is very much larger than any of the others. The expression for the impedance to the fifth harmonic shows that the circuit is practically in resonance at five times the fundamental frequency—300,000 cps. Hence, instead of a current of a little over 0.1 amp as should be expected on the basis of the fundamental impedance, a current of over 5 amp flows. If the circuit is designed to handle the fundamental current satisfactorily, connecting the voltage of this example may burn out the circuit. Thus connecting a non-sine voltage to a circuit may produce a current out of all proportion with that expected on the basis of the fundamental impedance.

As is usual in resonant circuits, the voltage across the capacitor and inductor are excessive. In this case a resonant fifth harmonic voltage of $X_{L5}|I_5| =$

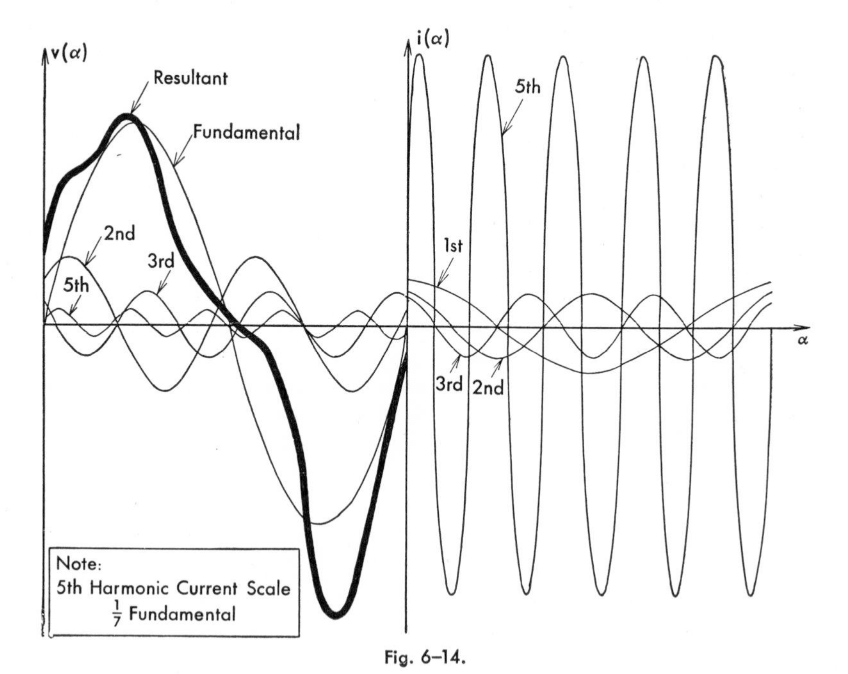

Fig. 6–14.

$|X_{c5}|\,|I_5| \simeq 945$ volts will appear across each of these elements, very likely destroying both.

The voltage and the current response for the circuit of this example are shown in Fig. 6–14. Note the very great difference in the wave form of the voltage and the current even though the impedance is linear for any particular harmonic. These results serve to emphasize strongly that the impedance of a circuit, even though linear, is a function of the voltage connected to the circuit if the circuit is other than a pure resistor. The possible distorting effect of even a very simple circuit for non-sine wave source voltages is evident from Fig. 6–14.

6.11 A Non-Sine Wave of Voltage Connected to a Parallel Circuit.

The fact that the currents in the branches of a parallel circuit like the one shown in Fig. 6–15 are independent of each other, provided the generator terminal voltage is kept constant and the connecting lead impedance is kept small, permits a direct application of the results deduced in Art. 6–9 for a non-sine wave source voltage. The branch currents may be immediately expressed as a Fourier series by

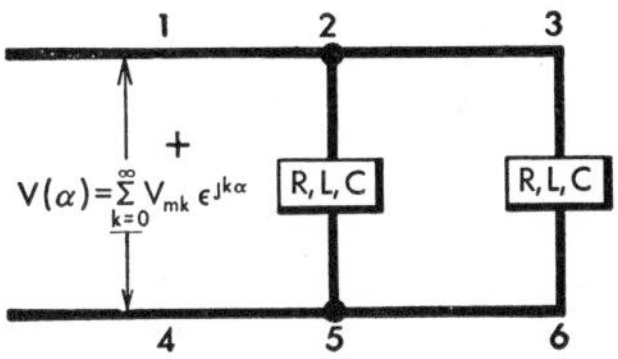

$$I(\alpha)_{25} = \sum_{k=0}^{\infty} I_{m25k}\epsilon^{jk\alpha} = \sum_{k=0}^{\infty} \frac{V_{m14k}}{Z_{25k}}\epsilon^{jk\alpha} \quad (6\text{–}81)$$

$$I(\alpha)_{36} = \sum_{k=0}^{\infty} I_{m36k}\epsilon^{jk\alpha} = \sum_{k=0}^{\infty} \frac{V_{m14k}}{Z_{36k}}\epsilon^{jk\alpha} \quad (6\text{–}82)$$

Fig. 6–15.

The total current is the sum of these currents and is

$$I(\alpha)_{12} = \sum_{k=0}^{\infty} I_{m12k}\epsilon^{jk\alpha} = \sum_{k=0}^{\infty} V_{m14k}\left(\frac{1}{Z_{25k}} + \frac{1}{Z_{36k}}\right)\epsilon^{jk\alpha}$$

$$= \sum_{k=0}^{\infty} V_{m14k}Y_{41k}\epsilon^{jk\alpha} \quad (6\text{–}83)$$

where

$$Y_{41k} = \frac{1}{Z_{25k}} + \frac{1}{Z_{36k}}$$

the total admittance to the kth harmonic.

Since two Fourier series, to be equal for all values of time, must be equal term by term, from equation 6–83,

$$I_{m12k} = V_{m14k}Y_{41k} = \frac{V_{m14k}}{Z_{41k}} \quad (6\text{–}84)$$

or

$$V_{m14k} = Z_{41k}I_{m41k} \quad (6\text{–}85)$$

where Z_{41k} is the equivalent impedance of the parallel circuit at the kth harmonic.

The total generator terminal voltage is the sum of its harmonics so that

$$V(\alpha)_{14} = \sum_{k=0}^{\infty} V_{m14k}\epsilon^{jk\alpha} = \sum_{k=0}^{\infty} Z_{41k}I_{m12k}\epsilon^{jk\alpha} \tag{6–86}$$

Equations 6–83 and 6–86 show that for *linear*—constant parameter—parallel circuits, as for linear series circuits, each harmonic may be treated separately and the results added.

PROBLEMS

6–1 Sketch the following sine wave combinations and add. Note the effect of odd and even harmonics and of phase shift on the resultant wave.

(1) Fundamental and third, 30 degrees lagging—maximum value of the fundamental three times the harmonic maximum.

(2) Fundamental and second as in (1).

(3) Parts (1) and (2) combined, except that the second harmonic is 60 degrees leading and has a maximum one-tenth the fundamental maximum.

(4) Same as (1), except that fundamental and harmonic maximum values are equal.

6–2 If

$$v(\alpha) = -10 + 100 \cos \alpha - 50 \cos 2\alpha + 20 \cos 3\alpha - 50 \sin \alpha - 30 \sin 2\alpha + 5 \sin 3\alpha$$

(*a*) Express $v(\alpha)$ as in equation 6–4.

(*b*) Express $v(\alpha)$ in the rotating vector equivalent form of equation 6–12.

6–3 If

$$V_{mh} = j\frac{a}{\pi^2 h^2}[\epsilon^{-jh\pi}(jh\pi + 1) - 1]\ (h \neq 0)$$

$$V_{m0} = 0 + j0$$

express the corresponding Fourier series as in the three equations 6–1, 6–4, and 6–12.

6–4 If

$$V_{m0} = 0 + j6$$

$$V_{mh} = \frac{1}{2h+1} + j\frac{(-1)^h}{h+1}$$

write the three Fourier series represented by equations 6–1, 6–4, and 6–12.

Indicate whether the resultant wave is symmetric or not and why.

6–5 Determine the Fourier series coefficient v_{ck} and v_{sk} from equation 6–2. *Hint.* Multiply equation 6–3 by cos $(h\alpha)$ and integrate from 0 to $2\pi (h \neq 0)$ to derive a formula for v_{ch}. The results should be:

$$v_{c0} = \frac{1}{2\pi}\int_0^{2\pi} v(\alpha)\,d\alpha$$

$$v_{ch} = \frac{1}{\pi}\int_0^{2\pi} v(\alpha)\cos(h\alpha)\,d\alpha$$

$$v_{sh} = \frac{1}{\pi}\int_0^{2\pi} v(\alpha)\sin(h\alpha)\,d\alpha$$

Apply the formulas developed to the non-sine wave of Fig. 6–10, and from these results compute $|V_{mk}|$ and ϕ_k. Write the Fourier series for $v(\alpha)$ of Fig. 6–10 and compare with the result in Example 6–2. Compare the method of this problem with the complex variable method given on Art. 6–4 and Example 6–2.

6–6 Determine the Fourier series sine and cosine coefficients of the rectangular wave given in Fig. 6–7*a*. Use the heavy-line curve. Find $|V_{mk}|$ and ϕ_k and write out five terms of the expansion in the three equivalent forms given in Art. 6–2. The square topped wave of this problem is rapidly assuming an increasingly important role in electrical engineering. Special generating equipment is used to produce a square-topped wave, and this wave is used to test the response of a circuit to *all* odd frequencies. The square-top wave is useful because a distortion of it is easy to detect, and because it contains all odd frequencies and so covers the whole frequency spectrum.

6–7 Repeat Problem 6–6 for a non-sine wave as shown in Fig. 6–16. This wave is the approximate output of a full wave rectifier, a device widely used to convert alternating current to pulsating direct current. Each of the loops is a half sine wave.

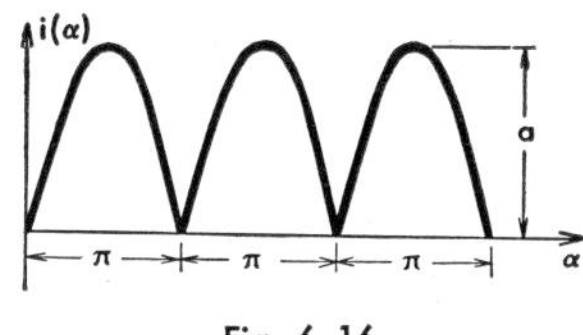

Fig. 6–16.

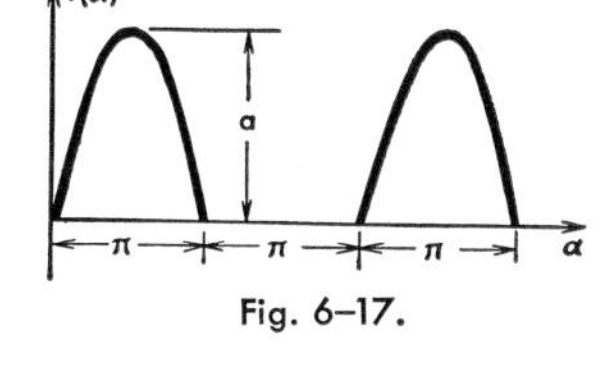

Fig. 6–17.

6–8 Repeat Problem 6–7 for the half wave rectifier result given in Fig. 6–17. Assume the loops are sinusoidal. Half wave rectifiers are in common use, and consist essentially of a device which conducts in only one direction. Alternating voltages applied to this device will, therefore, cause a current only half the time, as shown in Fig. 6–17.

6–9 Derive equation 6–36 and show that ϕ_k must be measured from, and that α must be, zero at the crossing point of the resultant wave.

6–10 Find the average value of the non-sine wave

$$v(\alpha) = 200 \sin (\alpha + 30°) + 25 \sin (3\alpha - 60°) + 10 \sin (5\alpha + 45°) \text{ volts}$$

Note that it will be necessary, before using equation 6–36, to locate the crossing point of $v(\alpha)$ and then to rewrite the equation for $v(\alpha)$ with the crossing point so determined as the $\alpha = 0$ point.

6–11 Compare the effective value of the sum of two sine waves of different frequencies with the effective value of the sum of two sine waves of the same frequency. For what phase difference of the like frequency waves will the effective value of their sum equal the effective value of the non-sine wave sum? For what phase difference will it be less? Greater? What is the effect on the foregoing answers if one of the different frequency components is direct current?

6–12 Plot the instantaneous power wave for a fundamental voltage and a third harmonic current. Hence show that the instantaneous power is not zero; but, by comparing areas above and below the axis, that the average power is zero.

6–13 Non-sine waves of voltage and current are given by—$\alpha = 377t$—

$$v(\alpha) = 150 \sin(\alpha + 45°) - 30 \sin(2\alpha - 20°) + 10 \sin(3\alpha - 60°) \text{ volts}$$
$$i(\alpha) = 10 \sin(\alpha + 15°) + 5 \sin(3\alpha + 30°) + 3 \sin(5\alpha + 10°) \text{ amperes}$$

(*a*) Compute the effective value of current and voltage. (*b*) Express the current and voltage in rotating vector form. (*c*) Calculate the average power and equivalent power factor. (*d*) Calculate the crest factor of the current and voltage.

6–14 A voltage represented by

$$V(\alpha) = 3\epsilon^{j90} + 10\epsilon^{j(\alpha-10°)} - 2\epsilon^{j(2\alpha+30°)} + \epsilon^{j3\alpha} \text{ volts}$$

is connected to a series circuit of $R = 100$ ohms and $L = 0.01$ henry. The fundamental frequency is 1000 cps. (*a*) Find the current equation in complex variable and sine wave form. (*b*) Find the total power loss. (*c*) Find the equivalent impedance of the circuit. (*d*) Find the equivalent power factor.

6–15 Repeat Problem 6–14 for L replaced by a capacitor of $C = 2\mu$f.

6–16 The current and voltage equations for a series circuit are

$$V(\alpha) = 100\epsilon^{j\alpha} + 60\epsilon^{j(2\alpha-60)} - 10\epsilon^{j(4\alpha+45)} \text{ volts}$$

and

$$I(\alpha) = 10\epsilon^{j(\alpha-30)} + 25\epsilon^{j(3\alpha+20)} + 2\epsilon^{j(4\alpha-15)} \text{ amperes}$$

Determine: (*a*) the equivalent impedance of the circuit; (*b*) the equivalent power factor; (*c*) the total power loss; and (*d*) the complex equivalent impedance.

6–17 A voltage

$$V(\alpha) = 30\epsilon^{j\alpha} + 10\epsilon^{j(3\alpha-15)} + 5\epsilon^{j(4\alpha+30)} - 2\epsilon^{j5\alpha} \text{ volts}$$

is connected to a series circuit of $R = 1$ ohm, $L = 0.5$ henry, and $C = 5\mu$f. Determine the fundamental frequency so that this circuit is in resonance with the fourth harmonic. Determine the current equation, fourth harmonic V_L, and V_C, total power loss, and the equivalent impedance of the circuit.

6–18 Methods of harmonic analysis are given in handbooks. Look up such a method, state its restrictions carefully, and use the method on a wave form plotted from

$$e(\alpha) = 10 \sin(\alpha + 30°) - 3 \sin(3\alpha - 60°) + 0.8 \sin 9\alpha$$

Compare the results obtained with the known coefficients of this equation.

6–19 The non-sine voltage

$$v(t) = 10 + 100 \sin 2000\pi t - 20 \sin(4000\pi t - 30°)$$

is connected to a two-branch parallel circuit consisting of the elements: $R_1 = 10$ ohms, $L_1 = 0.1$ henry, $C_1 = 10\ \mu$f, $R_2 = 20$ ohms, $L_2 = 0.4$ henry. Determine the rms value of the voltage across each element of the circuit, and the rms value of the total current and of each branch current.

6–20 (*a*) Show that if $v(\alpha) = v(-\alpha)$, V_{mh} is pure imaginary so that the Fourier series will consist of pure cosine terms only.

(*b*) Show that if $v(\alpha) = -v(-\alpha)$, V_{mh} is pure real so that the Fourier series will consist of pure sine terms only.

CHAPTER 7

Graphical Methods of Computation

Certain of the computations and mathematical manipulations carried out in foregoing parts of this book may be impossible if the currents and voltages are obtained from laboratory observations. The equations for such currents and voltages ordinarily cannot be expressed mathematically except through the medium of Fourier series, and the Fourier series coefficients cannot be obtained by any of the methods thus far indicated. In this chapter, certain techniques are given which permit a current or voltage relation determined in the laboratory to be expressed and studied mathematically with a degree of accuracy which will satisfy practical applications.

7.1 Graphical Differentiation.

Since differentiation is one of the commonest mathematical processes used in engineering, a method of carrying out this process graphically is useful. By such a method, the voltage of self-induction or mutual induction may be determined for any current variation.

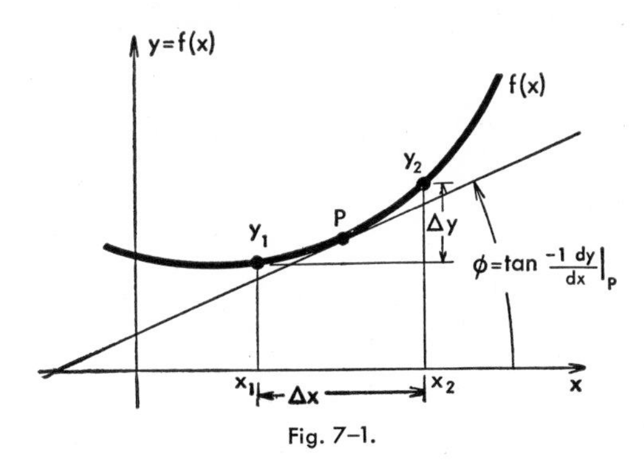

Fig. 7–1.

Suppose that a curve, which is to be the derivative of the curve $f(x)$, shown in Fig. 7–1, is to be established. The actual theory and basis of graphical differentiation follow immediately from the fact that the derivative at any point on a curve is the tangent of the angle which a tangent line at the point makes with the axis of the abscissa. This statement is illustrated in Fig. 7–1, where tan ϕ (ϕ the angle of the tangent line at P) is equal to the derivative of $f(x)$ with respect to x *evaluated at the point* P. A good approximation to the value of the derivative at P is

$$\frac{\Delta y}{\Delta x} = \frac{y_2 - y_1}{x_2 - x_1} \tag{7-1}$$

if Δx is short enough so that $f(x)$ is substantially a straight line between x_1 and x_2. This approximation evidently can be made as good as desired for any $f(x)$ by making Δx short enough. Determining the curve which is the derivative of a given curve is simply a matter of applying equation 7–1 successively at points along the original curve.

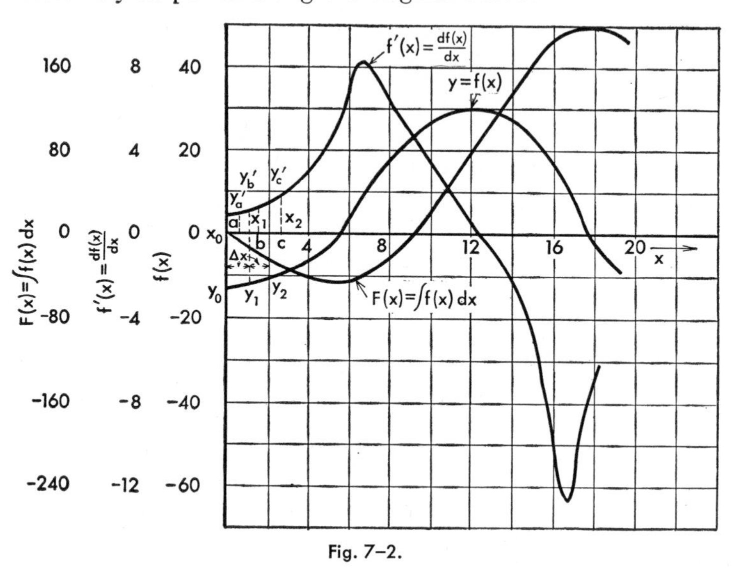

Fig. 7–2.

The actual process of determining the derivative curve can be simplified by choosing a particular value of Δx which can be used throughout the graphical differentiation. The reader should not forget that such an assumption is ***not necessary***, merely convenient. Choosing Δx to have one value throughout the process requires that the value chosen be small enough so that $f(x)$ is substantially a straight line over Δx, *no matter where along the curve the* Δx *is taken.*

To proceed now to the application of equation 7–1, consider on Fig. 7–2 the curve for $f(x)$. If a uniform abscissa interval Δx, is assumed, the value of the derivative at a, (the midpoint of the first Δx interval) is

$$f'(a) = \left.\frac{dy}{dx}\right|_a = y_a' \simeq \frac{y_1 - y_0}{x_1 - x_0} = \frac{y_1 - y_0}{\Delta x} \tag{7-2}$$

and at point b the approximate derivative value is

$$f'(b) = \left.\frac{dy}{dx}\right|_b = y_b' \simeq \frac{y_2 - y_1}{x_2 - x_1} = \frac{y_2 - y_1}{\Delta x} \qquad (7\text{–}3)$$

and so on for each of the midpoints of the Δx intervals. If the derivative values so obtained are plotted, the curve joining these points will be the curve which is everywhere the approximate derivative of $f(x)$ (see the $f'(x)$ curve of Fig. 7–2).

When actually carrying out a numerical computation for a derivative curve, a tabulation of the computational process is of considerable assistance. Such a tabulation, which in the light of the foregoing discussion should be practically self-explanatory, is given below. The symbols of the tabulation should, of course, be replaced in any problem by the appropriate numbers.

TABLE 7–1

x	Δx	$y = f(x)$	$\Delta y = \Delta f(x)$	$f'(x) \simeq \frac{\Delta y}{\Delta x}$
x_0		y_0		
$x_a = \frac{x_1 + x_0}{2}$	$x_1 - x_0$		$y_1 - y_0$	$\frac{y_1 - y_0}{x_1 - x_0}$
x_1		y_1		
$x_b = \frac{x_2 + x_1}{2}$	$x_2 - x_1$		$y_2 - y_1$	$\frac{y_2 - y_1}{x_2 - x_1}$
x_2		y_2		
$x_c = \frac{x_3 + x_2}{2}$	$x_3 - x_2$	.	$y_3 - y_2$	$\frac{y_3 - y_2}{x_3 - x_2}$
x_3	.	.	.	
.	.	.	.	.
.	.	.	.	.
.	.	.	.	.

This tabulation has been formulated in general terms. If, as suggested in the foregoing, a uniform Δx is used, all the x-differences of the second column may be omitted. The meaning of the remainder of the table should be evident. The last column when plotted against the midpoint values in the first column will give the derivative curve.

Example 7:1 A curve representing the derivative of $f(x)$ of Fig. 7–2 is to be obtained by graphical differentiation.

Solution An examination of $f(x)$ shows that a uniform $\Delta x = 1$ will make the curve practically a straight line over any such Δx. Then, by substituting in Table 7–1:

x	Δx	$y = f(x)$	$\Delta y = \Delta f(x)$	$f'(x) \simeq \dfrac{\Delta f(x)}{\Delta x}$
0.0		−13		
0.5	1		0.9	0.9
1.0		−12.1		
1.5	1		1.2	1.2
2.0		−10.9		
2.5	1		1.9	1.9
3.0		−9.0		
3.5	1		2.5	2.5
4.0		−6.5		
4.5	1		3.7	3.7
5.0		−2.8		
5.5	1		5.6	5.6
6.0		2.8		
6.5	1		8.2	8.2
7.0		11.0		
7.5	1		6.9	6.9
8.0		17.9		
8.5	1		5.1	5.1
9.0		23.0		
9.5	1		4.0	4.0
10.0		27.0		
10.5	1		2.5	2.5
11.0		29.5		
11.5	1		0.7	0.7
12.0		30.2		
12.5	1		−0.2	−0.2
13.0		30.0		
13.5	1		−1.6	−1.6
14.0		28.4		
14.5	1		−3.4	−3.4
15.0		25.0		
15.5	1		−7.5	−7.5
16.0		17.5		
16.5	1		−12.0	−12.0
17.0		5.5		
17.5	1		−8.5	−8.5
18.0		−3.0		
18.5	1		−5.3	−5.3
19.0		−8.3		

The last column of this tabulation is shown plotted as $f'(x)$ in Fig. 7–2.

7.2 Graphical Integration.

A second mathematical process which is of major importance in engineering is integration. A graphical process for forming a curve which at every point is very nearly the integral of another curve may be established from the area interpretation of an integral.

Four different ways of approximating the area under a curve are shown by the broken lines in Fig. 7–3. The integral of the curve, i.e., the area between the curve and the coordinate axes, can be obtained approximately by adding the areas of the trapezoids or rectangles. The accuracy of the result depends on the width of the Δx intervals. If Δx is short so that the curve is very nearly a straight line over Δx, the results obtained from

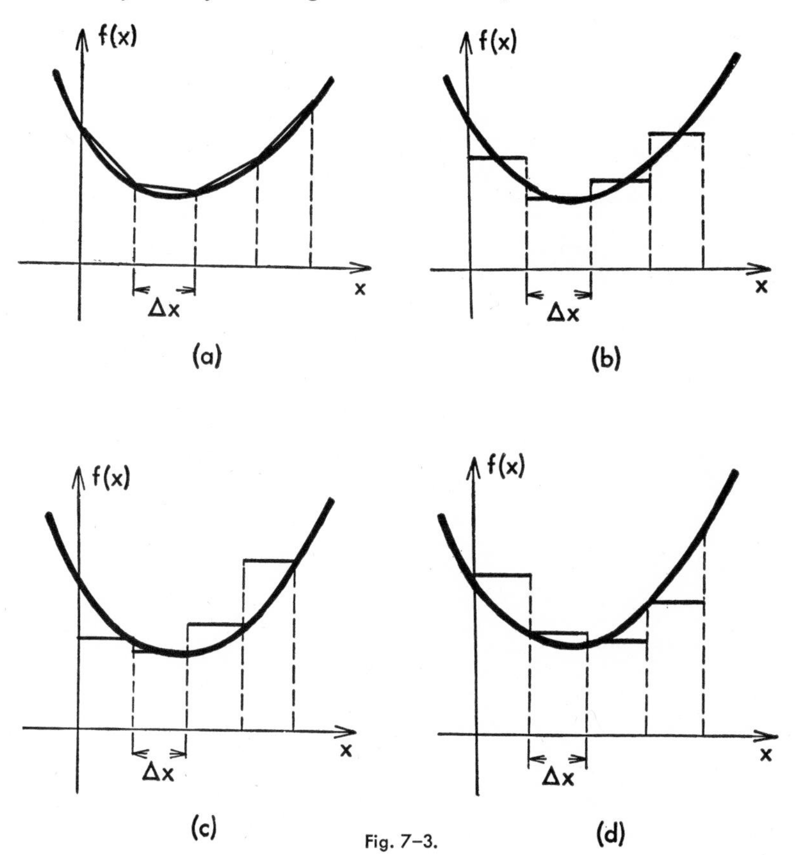

Fig. 7–3.

Fig. 7–3*a* and 7–3*b* will be good. Furthermore, these two results will be very nearly identical. They would be exactly the same if the curve were straight over the Δx intervals. The results obtainable by employing approximations given by Figs. 7–3*c* and 7–3*d* are not so good as for Fig. 7–3*a* or 7–3*b*, although for small Δx intervals they are satisfactory. The fact that Fig. 7–3*b* is probably the simplest to use accounts for its use here.

The diagram of Fig. 7–4 is a more detailed sketch of the approximation method of Fig. 7–3*b*. The area of the first rectangle on the left, in terms of the midordinate of the Δx_1 interval, is

$$A_1 = \Delta A_1 = y_{m1}\,\Delta x_1 \tag{7–4}$$

The area of any of the other rectangles may be computed similarly. That such area computations represent the areas under the curve is evident from the figure, as is also the fact that the shorter the Δx intervals the greater the accuracy.

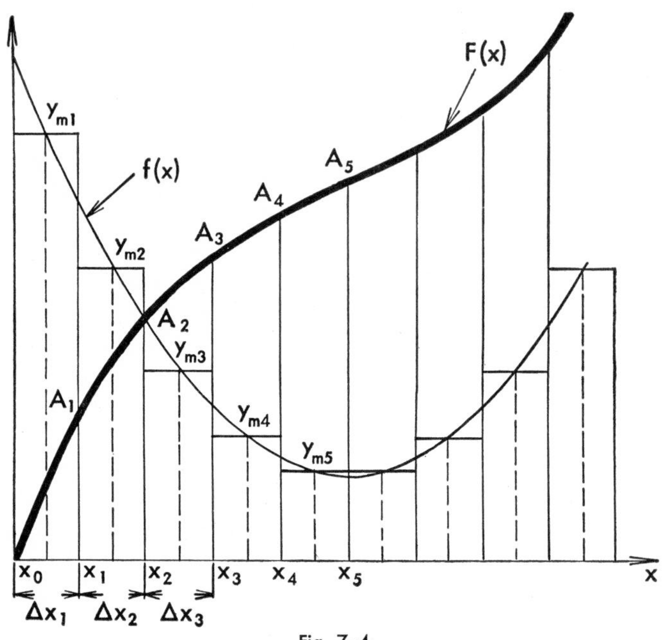

Fig. 7–4.

To compute the integral of $f(x)$, therefore, requires only that these areas be computed and added in accordance with

$$\begin{aligned} A_1 &= y_{m1}\,\Delta x_1 \\ A_2 &= y_{m1}\,\Delta x_1 + y_{m2}\,\Delta x_2 \\ A_3 &= y_{m1}\,\Delta x_1 + y_{m2}\,\Delta x_2 + y_{m3}\,\Delta x_3 \\ &\cdots\cdots\cdots\cdots \end{aligned} \tag{7–5}$$

If these area numbers are plotted *at the ends of the* Δx *intervals,* the line drawn through the points so plotted represents the integral of $f(x)$.

Usually to simplify calculations a uniform Δx is chosen. This Δx interval is taken small enough so that $f(x)$ is practically a straight line over any Δx interval. Equations 7–5 then take on the form

$$\begin{aligned} A_1 &= y_{m1}\,\Delta x \\ A_2 &= y_{m1}\,\Delta x + y_{m2}\,\Delta x = (y_{m1} + y_{m2})\,\Delta x \\ A_3 &= (y_{m1} + y_{m2} + y_{m3})\,\Delta x \\ &\cdots\cdots\cdots\cdots \\ A_n &= \sum_{k=1}^{n} y_{mk}\,\Delta x \end{aligned} \tag{7–6}$$

The rectangular areas computed from $f(x)$ between any two points on $f(x)$, when added, represent the definite integral between these points. Accordingly, a simple approximate form for a definite integral is

$$\int_{x_0}^{x_n} f(x)\, dx \simeq \sum_{k=1}^{n} y_{mk}\, \Delta x \tag{7-7}$$

A curve $f(x)$ and its integral curve are shown in Fig. 7–2. Note that $f(x)$ here starts at zero as it will always do, and that $f(x)$ continues to increase as long as the area under $f(x)$ is positive.

A tabulation is the most convenient way to carry out a graphical integration. Such a tabulation is:

TABLE 7-2

x	Δx	y_{mk}	ΔA_k	$F(x)$
x_0				0
x_{m1}		y_{m1}		
x_1	$x_1 - x_0$		$\Delta A_1 = y_{m1}(x_1 - x_0) = y_{m1}\,\Delta x_1$	$F(x_1) = \Delta A_1 = y_{m1}\,\Delta x_1$
x_{m2}		y_{m2}		
x_2	$x_2 - x_1$		$\Delta A_2 = y_{m2}(x_2 - x_1) = y_{m2}\,\Delta x_2$	$F(x_2) = F(x_1) + \Delta A_2$
x_{m3}	.	y_{m3}	.	.
.	.	.	.	.
.	.	.	.	.
.	.	.	.	.

If Δx is taken as the uniform abscissa increment, the second column of this tabulation can be omitted. Plotting the values obtained in the last column for $F(x)$ vs the values of x in the first column gives the integral curve.

Example 7:2 A curve representing the definite integral of $f(x)$ of Fig. 7–2 is to be determined, starting at the $x = 0$ point.

Solution As in Example 7–1, the uniform abscissa interval $\Delta x = 1$ will lead to practically linear variation of $f(x)$ over any interval. The tabulation of Table 7–2 may, therefore, be filled out as follows:

x	y_{mk}	$\Delta A_k = y_{mk}\,\Delta x$	$F(x) \simeq \Sigma\, \Delta A_k$
0.0			0.0
0.5	−12.6		
1.0		−12.6	−12.6
1.5	−11.5		
2.0		−11.5	−24.1
2.5	−9.9		
3.0		−9.9	−34.0
3.5	−7.8		
4.0		−7.8	−41.8
4.5	−4.7		

x	y_{mk}	$\Delta A_k = y_{mk}\,\Delta x$	$F(x) \simeq \Sigma\,\Delta A_k$
5.0		−4.7	−46.5
5.5	0.0		
6.0		0.0	−46.5
6.5	6.9		
7.0		6.9	−39.6
7.5	14.5		
8.0		14.5	−25.1
8.5	20.6		
9.0		20.6	−4.5
9.5	25.2		
10.0		25.2	20.7
10.5	28.3		
11.0		28.3	49.0
11.5	29.9		
12.0		29.9	78.9
12.5	30.1		
13.0		30.1	109.0
13.5	29.2		
14.0		29.2	138.2
14.5	26.7		
15.0		26.7	164.9
15.5	21.3		
16.0		21.3	186.2
16.5	11.4		
17.0		11.4	197.6
17.5	1.1		
18.0		1.1	198.7
18.5	−5.7		
19.0		−5.7	193.0

The integral of $f(x)$ shown plotted in Fig. 7–2 as $F(x)$ was taken from the last column of this tabulation.

7.3 Graphical Determination of Fourier Series Coefficients by Integration.

The determination of the Fourier series coefficients of a wave obtained from the laboratory or field can be determined and a mathematical expression for the wave can be written if the Fourier coefficients are known. These coefficients, according to the results of Chap. 6, are defined in terms of definite integrals so that graphical integration may be employed in their calculation.

The function to be integrated for the determination of the Fourier series coefficients (equation 6–24) is a product of two functions. If this product is plotted, the method of graphical integration already formulated can be used. However, a method which does not require the plotting of additional curves would be better since less time and effort would be required. Such a method is easily established.

The curves of Fig. 7–5 represent: (1) a function $v(\alpha)$, (2) the function $\sin \alpha$, and (3) the product of these two functions. The rectangular approximations to each of the curves are shown. The representation is exact at the midpoints of the Δx intervals.

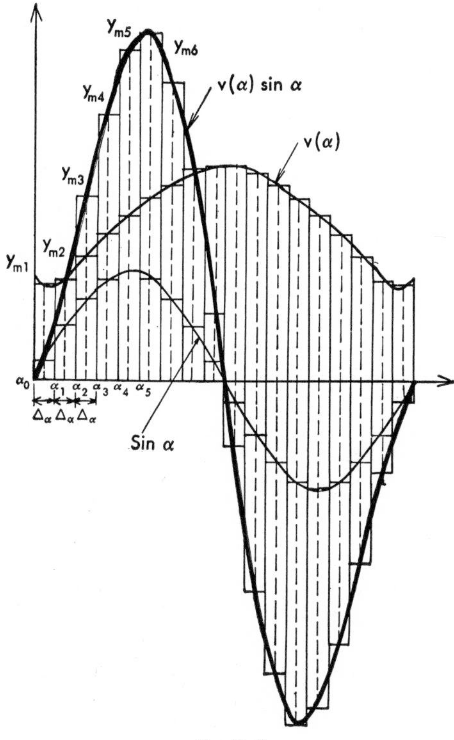

Fig. 7–5.

To proceed then to the evaluation of the Fourier series coefficients, the areas of the rectangles formed on the product curve are

$$\Delta A_1 = \left(y_{m1} \sin \frac{\Delta\alpha}{2}\right) \Delta\alpha = \left[v\left(\alpha_0 + \frac{\Delta\alpha}{2}\right) \sin\left(\alpha_0 + \frac{\Delta\alpha}{2}\right)\right] \Delta\alpha$$

$$\Delta A_2 = \left(y_{m2} \sin \frac{3\Delta\alpha}{2}\right) \Delta\alpha = \left[v\left(\alpha_1 + \frac{\Delta\alpha}{2}\right) \sin\left(\alpha_1 + \frac{\Delta\alpha}{2}\right)\right] \Delta\alpha \qquad (7\text{–}8)$$

$$\Delta A_3 = \left(y_{m3} \sin \frac{5\Delta\alpha}{2}\right) \Delta\alpha = \left[v\left(\alpha_2 + \frac{\Delta\alpha}{2}\right) \sin\left(\alpha_2 + \frac{\Delta\alpha}{2}\right)\right] \Delta\alpha$$

. . . .

$$\Delta A_k = \left(y_{mk} \sin \frac{2k-1}{2} \Delta\alpha\right) \Delta\alpha = \left[v\left(\alpha_{k-1} + \frac{\Delta\alpha}{2}\right) \sin\left(\alpha_{k-1} + \frac{\Delta\alpha}{2}\right)\right] \Delta\alpha$$

The definite integral of the product function is then approximately the sum

$$\int_0^{2\pi} v(\alpha) \sin \alpha \, d\alpha \simeq \sum_{k=0}^{n-1} \left[v\left(\alpha_k + \frac{\Delta\alpha}{2}\right) \sin\left(\alpha_k + \frac{\Delta\alpha}{2}\right) \right] \Delta\alpha \quad (7\text{–}9)$$

where n is the number of $\Delta\alpha$ intervals on a 2π range of α. A tabulation will make the computation of this result possible without requiring a plotting of the curve.

It should be noted that the choice of the length of a uniform $\Delta\alpha$ depends on the curve which varies most rapidly. For example, suppose $\sin 5\alpha$ is one member of the product. A 10-degree interval for $\Delta\alpha$ corresponds to $5 \times 10 = 50$ degrees on the fifth harmonic. Obviously 50 degrees is too wide an interval over which to assume $\sin 5\alpha$ can be represented accurately by a straight line. However, a 15-degree interval on any sine or cosine wave is often small enough so that the sine or cosine can be approximated by straight lines over this interval. Then, if the fifth harmonic is a member of the product to be integrated a $\Delta\alpha = 15/5 = 3$ degrees must be used to obtain the same accuracy as $\Delta\alpha = 15$ degrees on $\sin \alpha$.

Consider next the approximate evaluation of the Fourier series coefficients from a known curve of current or voltage. The integral expression for all these coefficients except the d-c component in terms of a known $v(\alpha)$ is, from Chap. 6,

$$V_{mh} = \frac{1}{\pi} \int_0^{2\pi} jv(\alpha) \epsilon^{-jh\alpha} \, d\alpha \; (h \neq 0)$$

On the basis of the approximation given by equation 7–9, for n intervals of width $\Delta\alpha = 2\pi/n$ on 2π, an approximate value of V_{mh} is

$$V_{mh} \simeq \frac{1}{\pi} \sum_{k=0}^{n-1} jv\left(\alpha_k + \frac{\Delta\alpha}{2}\right) \epsilon^{-jh(\alpha_k + \Delta\alpha/2)} \, \Delta\alpha \; (h \neq 0) \quad (7\text{–}10)$$

which, since $(n/2) \, \Delta\alpha = \pi$, is

$$V_{mh} \simeq \frac{2}{n} \sum_{k=0}^{n-1} jv\left(\alpha_k + \frac{\Delta\alpha}{2}\right) \epsilon^{-jh(\alpha_k + \Delta\alpha/2)} \; (h \neq 0) \quad (7\text{–}11)$$

Also the formula for the approximate value of the d-c component (equation 6–27) of a non-sine wave is, for n intervals of $\Delta\alpha$ width on 2π,

$$V_{m0} \simeq \frac{j}{2\pi} \sum_{k=0}^{n-1} v\left(\alpha_k + \frac{\Delta\alpha}{2}\right) \Delta\alpha \quad (7\text{–}12)$$

and once more because $n \, \Delta\alpha = 2\pi$

$$V_{m0} \simeq \frac{j}{n} \sum_{k=0}^{n-1} v\left(\alpha_k + \frac{\Delta\alpha}{2}\right) \quad (7\text{–}13)$$

Equations 7–11 and 7–13 can be evaluated with the least effort and least chance of error by using a tabulation such as the following for equation 7–11:

TABLE 7–3

FOR n UNIFORM INTERVALS $\Delta\alpha$ ON A 2π RANGE OF α

α_k	$h\left(\alpha_k + \frac{\Delta\alpha}{2}\right)$	$v\left(\alpha_k + \frac{\Delta\alpha}{2}\right)$	$\epsilon^{-jh(\alpha_k+\Delta\alpha/2)}$	$v\left(\alpha_k + \frac{\Delta\alpha}{2}\right)\epsilon^{-jh(\alpha_k+\Delta\alpha/2)}$
α_0				
	$h\left(\alpha_0 + \frac{\Delta\alpha}{2}\right)$	$v\left(\alpha_0 + \frac{\Delta\alpha}{2}\right)$	$\epsilon^{-jh(\alpha_0+\Delta\alpha/2)}$	$v\left(\alpha_0 + \frac{\Delta\alpha}{2}\right)\epsilon^{-jh(\alpha_0+\Delta\alpha/2)}$
α_1				
	$h\left(\alpha_1 + \frac{\Delta\alpha}{2}\right)$	$v\left(\alpha_1 + \frac{\Delta\alpha}{2}\right)$	$\epsilon^{-jh(\alpha_1+\Delta\alpha/2)}$	$v\left(\alpha_1 + \frac{\Delta\alpha}{2}\right)\epsilon^{-jh(\alpha_1+\Delta\alpha/2)}$
α_2				
	$h\left(\alpha_2 + \frac{\Delta\alpha}{2}\right)$	$v\left(\alpha_2 + \frac{\Delta\alpha}{2}\right)$	$\epsilon^{-jh(\alpha_2+\Delta\alpha/2)}$	$v\left(\alpha_2 + \frac{\Delta\alpha}{2}\right)\epsilon^{-jh(\alpha_2+\Delta\alpha/2)}$
	⋮	⋮	⋮	⋮

The sum of the last column of Table 7–3 multiplied by $2j/n$ gives the approximate value of V_{mh} in accordance with equation 7–11.

An important shortening of the foregoing tabulation can be used if the wave to be analyzed is symmetric. It was proved in Chap. 6 (equation 6–33) that the integration to determine the Fourier series coefficient need be carried out only over one-half cycle for symmetric waves. A tabulation over one-half cycle of a symmetric non-sine wave is, therefore, all that is required. Thus instead of, say, thirty-six 10-degree intervals and so 36

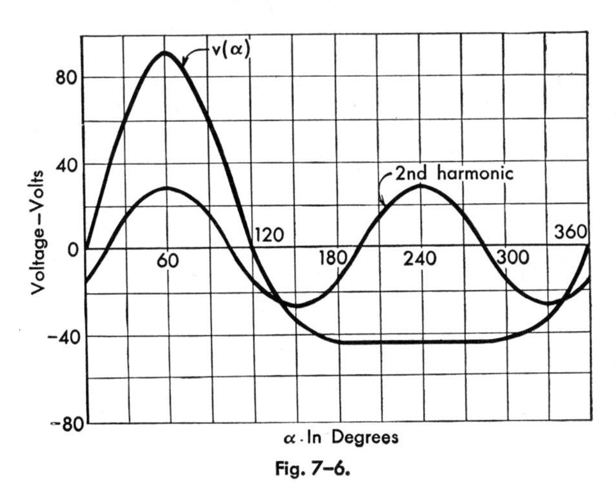

Fig. 7–6.

α_k	$2\left(\alpha_k+\dfrac{\Delta\alpha}{2}\right)$	$\epsilon^{-j2(\alpha_k+\Delta\alpha/2)}$	$v\left(\alpha_k+\dfrac{\Delta\alpha}{2}\right)$	$v\left(\alpha_k+\dfrac{\Delta\alpha}{2}\right)\epsilon^{-j2(\alpha_k+\Delta\alpha/2)}$
0				
	15	ϵ^{-j15}	17.5	$17.5\epsilon^{-j15} = 16.9 - j4.53$
15				
	45	ϵ^{-j45}	49.0	$49.0\epsilon^{-j45} = 34.7 - j34.7$
30				
	75	ϵ^{-j75}	72.5	$72.5\epsilon^{-j75} = 18.8 - j70.0$
45				
	105	ϵ^{-j105}	87.0	$87.0\epsilon^{-j105} = -22.5 - j84.0$
60				
	135	ϵ^{-j135}	87.0	$87.0\epsilon^{-j135} = -61.5 - j61.5$
75				
	165	ϵ^{-j165}	72.5	$72.5\epsilon^{-j165} = -70.1 - j18.8$
90				
	195	ϵ^{-j195}	49.0	$49.0\epsilon^{-j195} = -47.3 + j12.7$
105				
	225	ϵ^{-j225}	17.5	$17.5\epsilon^{-j225} = -12.4 + j12.4$
120				
	255	ϵ^{-j255}	−11.5	$-11.5\epsilon^{-j255} = 3.0 - j11.1$
135				
	285	ϵ^{-j285}	−29.5	$-29.5\epsilon^{-j285} = -7.6 - j28.5$
150				
	315	ϵ^{-j315}	−38.0	$-38.0\epsilon^{-j315} = -26.8 - j26.8$
165				
	345	ϵ^{-j345}	−41.0	$-41.0\epsilon^{-j345} = -39.6 - j10.6$
180				
	375	ϵ^{-j375}	−42.2	$-42.2\epsilon^{-j375} = -40.8 + j10.9$
195				
	405	ϵ^{-j405}	−42.7	$-42.7\epsilon^{-j405} = -30.2 + j30.2$
210				
	435	ϵ^{-j435}	−43.4	$-43.4\epsilon^{-j435} = -11.2 + j41.9$
225				
	465	ϵ^{-j465}	−43.9	$-43.9\epsilon^{-j465} = 11.4 + j42.4$
240				
	495	ϵ^{-j495}	−44.0	$-44.0\epsilon^{-j495} = 31.1 + j31.1$
255				
	525	ϵ^{-j525}	−43.9	$-43.9\epsilon^{-j525} = 42.4 + j11.4$
270				
	555	ϵ^{-j555}	−43.7	$-43.7\epsilon^{-j555} = 42.2 - j11.3$
285				
	585	ϵ^{-j585}	−42.9	$-42.9\epsilon^{-j585} = 30.3 - j30.3$
300				
	615	ϵ^{-j615}	−41.0	$-41.0\epsilon^{-j615} = 10.6 - j39.6$
315				
	645	ϵ^{-j645}	−37.3	$-37.3\epsilon^{-j645} = -9.7 - j36.1$
330				
	675	ϵ^{-j675}	−28.9	$-28.9\epsilon^{-j675} = -20.4 - j20.4$
345				
	705	ϵ^{-j705}	−11.5	$-11.5\epsilon^{-j705} = -11.1 - j3.0$
360				
				$-169.8 - j298.3$

entries in Table 7–3, a symmetric wave can be analyzed with only 18 entries in the table.

A tabulation of the form of Table 7–3 will be required for *each harmonic* to be determined. The following example illustrates the method of procedure for determining one of the harmonics of a non-symmetric wave. This particular tabulation must be carried out to cover the full 360-degree range of the curve to be analyzed because of its lack of symmetry (Fig. 7–6).

Example 7:3 Suppose that the second harmonic content of $v(\alpha)$ of Fig. 7–6 is desired.

Solution The tabulation of Table 7–3 with $h = 2$ will determine the second harmonic. Examination of the curve of Fig. 7–6 will show that a $\Delta\alpha =$ 15 degrees will be satisfactory over the whole curve except near the positive maximum, and even here the error will be slight. Also a 15-degree interval on the scale of $v(\alpha)$ corresponds to a 30-degree interval on the second harmonic scale. A smaller interval would, of course, be more accurate, but $\Delta\alpha =$ 15 degrees will be sufficiently accurate.

The numerical tabulation on page 236 shows the details of the computational process.

From equation 7–11 and the sum of the last column of the foregoing tabulation,

$$V_{m2} = \frac{2j}{24}(-169.8 - j298.3) = 24.9 - j14.2 = 28.7\epsilon^{-j29.7}$$

Accordingly, the second harmonic of the voltage curve of Fig. 7–6 has a maximum value of 28.7 volts and is located as shown in the figure, -29.7 degrees from the origin on the scale of the second harmonic.

7.4 Fischer-Hinnen Method of Determining the Fourier-Series Coefficients.

Several methods of graphically determining the Fourier series coefficients have been developed which are usually much less laborious than the method of straight integration. One of these, the Fischer-Hinnen method, is presented here.

The basic concept of the Fischer-Hinnen method of analysis may be obtained from Fig. 7–7. The *cosine* waves of Fig. 7–7*a* and the *sine* waves of Fig. 7–7*b* are the harmonics of the curve of Fig. 7–7*c* in correspondence with the Fourier series given in equation 6–3. Consider first the value of $i(\alpha)$ at zero, i.e., at the first maximum of the fundamental cosine. From Fig. 7–7 it is evident that $i(0)$ consists entirely of the sum of the maximum values of all the *cosine* harmonics because *all sine* harmonics are always zero at $\alpha = 0$. Also because the non-sine waves being expressed as a Fourier series are periodic on a 2π interval $i(0) = i(2\pi)$. Therefore,

$$\begin{aligned} i(0) = i(2\pi) &= i_{c0} + i_{c1} + i_{c2} + i_{c3} + \cdots \\ &= \sum_{k=0}^{\infty} i_{ck} \end{aligned} \qquad (7\text{–}14)$$

Equation 6–3 shows this same result immediately since

$$\cos n0 = \cos n2\pi = 1$$
$$\sin n0 = \sin n2\pi = 0$$

Consider next the $\alpha = \pi/2$ position which is at the first maximum of the fundamental sine. From Fig. 7–7 and equation 6–3, the value of $i(\alpha)$ at $\pi/2$ is

$$i\left(\frac{\pi}{2}\right) = i_{c0} + i_{s1} - i_{c2} - i_{s3} + i_{c4} + i_{s5} \cdots$$
$$= \sum_{k=0}^{\infty} [i_{c2k} + i_{s(2k+1)}](-1)^k \qquad (7\text{–}15)$$

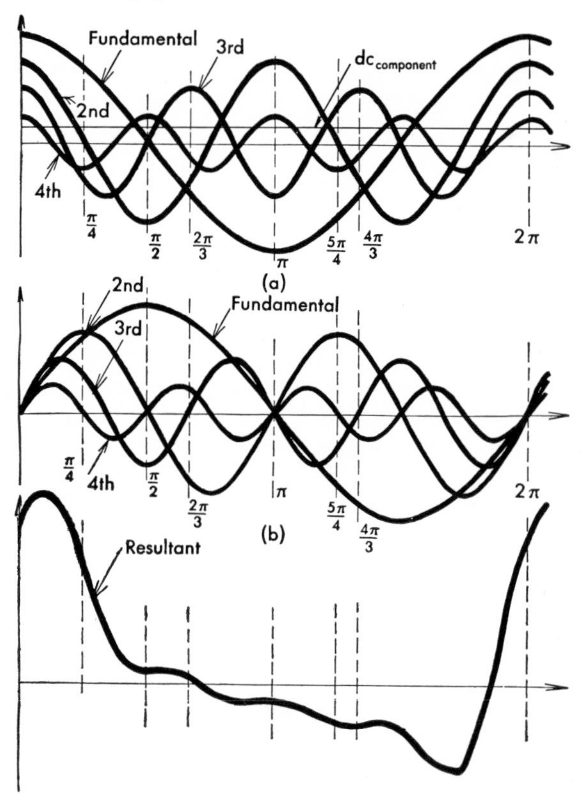

Fig. 7–7.

Both equations 7–14 and 7–15 are expressed in terms of the *maximum* values of the various harmonics without any multiplying sine and cosine functions. These results suggest that if more equations of the same kind can be determined, a set of very simple equations can be obtained from which the maximum values of the sine and cosine harmonics can be determined. The fact that each equation represents an infinite sum is not the serious handicap it at first glance seems. For any actual wave all the harmonics past a certain point are zero or practically so, which means that equations 7–14 and 7–15 need not be expressed as infinite sums but may be correctly represented by finite sums. Therefore, establishing more equations of the type shown in 7–14 and 7–15 leads to a finite set of linear equations which may be solved simultaneously for the Fourier series coefficients of any particular known wave.

These simultaneous equations can be expressed in many ways. *Any set* of ordinates equated to corresponding values of equation 6–3 will serve. Actually unless the equations are formed from specially located values of $i(\alpha)$, the resulting equations may present a formidable computing job to obtain a solution. Thus, if the ordinates are chosen indiscriminately for a non-sine wave consisting of d-c component, fundamental, and eight other harmonics, a set of nineteen simultaneous equations without any symmetry will arise. The job of solving such a set of equations is not to be lightly undertaken. On the other hand, as will be shown, by the proper choice of the values of α for which equations are established, nineteen equations still are required. They can be made so simple, however, that the solution may be obtained in a few minutes of calculations.

A hint as to how other equations in terms of maximum values of the harmonics may be obtained was given when the values of $i(\alpha)$ of equations 7–14 and 7–15 were chosen at the first maxima of the fundamental sine and cosine. Consider the second harmonic in the same light. On Fig. 7–7 the second harmonic cosine has *two* positive maxima located at $\alpha = 0$ and $\alpha = \pi$, and the second harmonic sine has positive maxima at $\alpha = \pi/4$ and $5\pi/4$. Consider the cosine harmonics first. Since $i(0)$ has already been computed, $i(\pi)$ will be investigated. From Fig. 7–7*a* or equation 6–3,

$$i(\pi) = i_{c0} - i_{c1} + i_{c2} - i_{c3} + i_{c4} \cdots$$
$$= \sum_{k=0}^{\infty} i_{ck}(-1)^k \qquad (7\text{–}16)$$

Equations 7–14 and 7–16 form two independent equations which may be taken as part of a set of independent equations. But notice that if $i(0)$ and $i(\pi)$ are added, certain cancellations result in

$$i(0) + i(\pi) = 2i_{c0} + 2i_{c2} + 2i_{c4} + \cdots$$
$$= \sum_{k=0}^{\infty} 2i_{c2k} \qquad (7\text{–}17)$$

This equation, together with equation 7–14, is a simpler pair than equations 7–16 and 7–17 because of the absence of many terms in equation 7–17. Equation 7–17 will, therefore, be taken as a member of the set of equations now being formed.

Next, if the ordinates at the positive maxima of the second harmonic sine are computed from equation 6–3 or Fig. 7–7b,

$$i\left(\frac{\pi}{4}\right) = i_{c0} + \frac{1}{\sqrt{2}}i_{c1} + \frac{1}{\sqrt{2}}i_{s1} + i_{s2} - \frac{1}{\sqrt{2}}i_{c3} + \frac{1}{\sqrt{2}}i_{s3}$$
$$- i_{c4} - \frac{1}{\sqrt{2}}i_{c5} - \frac{1}{\sqrt{2}}i_{s5} - i_{s6} \cdots \tag{7–18}$$

$$i\left(\frac{5\pi}{4}\right) = i_{c0} - \frac{1}{\sqrt{2}}i_{c1} - \frac{1}{\sqrt{2}}i_{s1} + i_{s2} + \frac{1}{\sqrt{2}}i_{c3} - \frac{1}{\sqrt{2}}i_{s3}$$
$$- i_{c4} + \frac{1}{\sqrt{2}}i_{c5} + \frac{1}{\sqrt{2}}i_{s5} - i_{s6} \cdots \tag{7–19}$$

The sum of these equations gives

$$i\left(\frac{\pi}{4}\right) + i\left(\frac{5\pi}{4}\right) = 2i_{c0} + 2i_{s2} - 2i_{c4} - 2i_{s6} + 2i_{c8} + \cdots$$
$$= \sum_{k=0}^{\infty} 2[i_{c4k} + i_{s2(2k+1)}](-1)^k \tag{7–20}$$

in which, once more, many of the possible terms are absent.

Adding the ordinates at the *three* positive maxima of the third harmonics—sine and cosine—gives two more equations in which many of the Fourier coefficients are absent and all multiplying coefficients are integers. Similar results arise for each harmonic. In general for the nth harmonic, n ordinates spaced $2\pi/n$ degrees apart may be equated to a certain sum of the harmonic maximum values. The problem now is to determine, if possible, the general form of the sum of maximum value coefficients which is to be equated to the sum of ordinates taken from the known $i(\alpha)$.

The process of forming the required set of equations as described in the foregoing can be expressed in two formulas. These formulas can be derived from elementary trigonometric considerations, but only after lengthy manipulation. Consequently, only the results will be given. They are

$$\sum_{h=1}^{n} i\left(\frac{2\pi}{n}h\right) = \sum_{p=0}^{\infty} n i_{c(pn)} \tag{7–21}$$

$$\sum_{h=1}^{n} i\left[\frac{\pi}{2n}(4h-3)\right] = \sum_{p=0}^{\infty} n(-1)^p[i_{c(2np)} + i_{s(2p+1)n}] \tag{7–22}$$

Expanding these sums to the extent which any particular problem demands will establish a set of simultaneous linear equations from which the Fourier series coefficients may be determined.

The following example illustrates the method of procedure for a particular case.

Example 7:4 Suppose, as seems reasonable from its regular appearance, that the non-sine wave of Fig. 7–6 has no harmonics past the fourth. Determine the value of all the Fourier series coefficients on this assumption.

Solution Using equations 7–21 and 7–22 for $n = 1, 2, 3,$ and 4

$$\sum_{1}^{1} v\left(\frac{2\pi}{1}h\right) = v_{c0} + v_{c1} + v_{c2} + v_{c3} + v_{c4}$$

$$\sum_{1}^{1} v\left(\frac{\pi}{2}[4h - 3]\right) = v_{c0} + v_{s1} - v_{c2} - v_{s3} + v_{c4}$$

$$\sum_{1}^{2} v\left(\frac{2\pi}{2}h\right) = 2v_{c0} + 2v_{c2} + 2v_{c4}$$

$$\sum_{1}^{2} v\left(\frac{\pi}{4}[4h - 3]\right) = 2v_{c0} + 2v_{s2} - 2v_{c4}$$

$$\sum_{1}^{3} v\left(\frac{2\pi}{3}h\right) = 3v_{c0} + 3v_{c3}$$

$$\sum_{1}^{3} v\left(\frac{\pi}{6}[4h - 3]\right) = 3v_{c0} + 3v_{s3}$$

$$\sum_{1}^{4} v\left(\frac{2\pi}{4}h\right) = 4v_{c0} + 4v_{c4}$$

$$\sum_{1}^{4} v\left(\frac{\pi}{8}[4h - 3]\right) = 4v_{c0} + 4v_{s4}$$

When the left-hand sums are evaluated, this set of equations gives eight equations in nine unknowns. Using any of the equations beyond the first eight gives an expression in terms of the d-c component only because all harmonics higher than the fourth are supposed as zero. This equation may be

$$\sum_{h=1}^{5} v\left(\frac{2\pi}{5}h\right) = 5v_{c0}$$

Nine equations in nine unknowns are thus made available.

Evaluating the sums on the left of these equations from Fig. 7–6 gives

$$\sum_{h=1}^{1} v\left(\frac{2\pi}{1}h\right) = v(2\pi) = 0$$

$$\sum_{h=1}^{1} v\left(\frac{\pi}{2}[4h - 3]\right) = v\left(\frac{\pi}{2}\right) = 62$$

$$\sum_{h=1}^{2} v\left(\frac{2\pi}{2}h\right) = v(\pi) + v(2\pi) = -42 + 0 = -42$$

$$\sum_{h=1}^{2} v\left(\frac{\pi}{4}[4h - 3]\right) = v\left(\frac{\pi}{4}\right) + v\left(\frac{5\pi}{4}\right) = 82 - 43 = 39$$

$$\sum_{h=1}^{3} v\left(\frac{2\pi}{3}h\right) = v\left(\frac{2\pi}{3}\right) + v\left(\frac{4\pi}{3}\right) + v(2\pi) = 0 - 44 + 0 = -44$$

$$\sum_{h=1}^{3} v\left(\frac{\pi}{6}[4h-3]\right) = v\left(\frac{\pi}{6}\right) + v\left(\frac{5\pi}{6}\right) + v\left(\frac{3\pi}{2}\right) = 63 - 36 - 44 = -17$$

$$\sum_{h=1}^{4} v\left(\frac{2\pi}{4}h\right) = v\left(\frac{\pi}{2}\right) + v(\pi) + v\left(\frac{3\pi}{2}\right) + v(2\pi) = 62 - 42 - 44 = -24$$

$$\sum_{h=1}^{4} v\left(\frac{\pi}{8}[4h-3]\right) = v\left(\frac{\pi}{8}\right) + v\left(\frac{5\pi}{8}\right) + v\left(\frac{9\pi}{8}\right) + v\left(\frac{13\pi}{8}\right) = 49 + 17 - 43 - 43 = -20$$

$$\sum_{h=1}^{5} v\left(\frac{2\pi}{5}h\right) = v\left(\frac{2\pi}{5}\right) + v\left(\frac{4\pi}{5}\right) + v\left(\frac{6\pi}{5}\right) + v\left(\frac{8\pi}{5}\right) + v(2\pi) = 85 - 32 - 43 - 43 + 0 = -33$$

Placing these numerical results at the left of the set of linear equations to be solved gives

$$\begin{aligned}
0 &= v_{c0} + v_{c1} + v_{c2} + v_{c3} + v_{c4} \\
62 &= v_{c0} + v_{s1} - v_{c2} - v_{s3} + v_{c4} \\
-42 &= 2v_{c0} + 2v_{c2} + 2v_{c4} \\
39 &= 2v_{c0} + 2v_{s2} - 2v_{c4} \\
-44 &= 3v_{c0} + 3v_{c3} \\
-17 &= 3v_{c0} + 3v_{s3} \\
-24 &= 4v_{c0} + 4v_{c4} \\
-20 &= 4v_{c0} + 4v_{s4} \\
-33 &= 5v_{c0}
\end{aligned}$$

The solution of this set of equations may be determined by starting with the last equation, which gives a value for v_{c0} immediately, and using the results obtained to substitute successively in the preceding equations. Thus

$$v_{c0} = \frac{-33}{5} = -6.6$$

$$v_{s4} = \frac{-20 - 4v_{c0}}{4} = 1.6$$

$$v_{c4} = \frac{-24 - 4v_{c0}}{4} = 0.6$$

$$v_{s3} = \frac{-17 - 3v_{c0}}{3} = 0.9$$

$$v_{c3} = \frac{-44 - 3v_{c0}}{3} = -8.1$$

$$v_{s2} = \frac{39 - 2v_{c0} + 2v_{c4}}{2} = 26.7$$

$$v_{c2} = \frac{-42 - 2v_{c0} - 2v_{c4}}{2} = -15.0$$

$$v_{s1} = 62 - v_{c0} + v_{c2} + v_{s3} - v_{c4} = 53.9$$

$$v_{c1} = 0 - v_{c0} - v_{c2} - v_{c3} - v_{c4} = 29.1$$

As a comparison of the Fischer-Hinnen method and the Fourier series method, the second harmonic from this last computation is

$$|V_{m2}| = \sqrt{v_{c2}^2 + v_{s2}^2} = \sqrt{(26.7)^2 + (15.0)^2} = 30.6$$

$$\phi_2 = \tan^{-1} \frac{v_{c2}}{v_{s2}} = \tan^{-1} \frac{-15.0}{26.7} = -29.4°$$

Reference to Example 7–3 shows that the two methods compare favorably as to results even though the Fischer-Hinnen method was used to carry the analysis only through the fourth harmonic. Starting with the sixth harmonic would have led to more accurate results. Note also that with the Fischer-Hinnen method *all the harmonics* through the fourth have been obtained with less work than was required to evaluate one harmonic by the regular Fourier series equation.

The determination of the point in the harmonic range beyond which all harmonics may be neglected may not be easy. Experience will serve as a guide, of course. Also determining the d-c component for different higher order sets of ordinates sums will show, when the values so obtained are equal, that the higher harmonics probably may be neglected.

The Fischer-Hinnen method of analysis of this article and the Fourier series method of analysis of the preceding article have certain particular merits which may make one or the other more effective for a specific problem. The Fourier method, for example, permits the computation of any particular harmonic coefficient and phase angle without regard to the existence of any other harmonic and is thus the most effective method to use if knowledge of a particular harmonic is desired. If, however, the total harmonic content of a non-sine wave is desired, the Fischer-Hinnen method requires very much less computation and time. For accuracy, the Fischer-Hinnen method must be carried to the point where all harmonics of higher order than the highest computed are negligible.

7.5 Graphical Determination of the Effective Value of a Non-Sine Wave.

According to the general definition of the effective value, or characteristic number of an alternating current or voltage, given by equation 1–5, graphical integration is required to determine the effective value of a wave form obtained from physical equipment. The equation for the effective value is

$$|V| = \sqrt{\frac{1}{T}\int_0^T v^2(t)\,dt} = \sqrt{\frac{1}{2\pi}\int_0^{2\pi} v^2(\alpha)\,d\alpha}$$

or, in a form for graphical integration,

$$|V| \simeq \sqrt{\frac{1}{n}\sum_{k=1}^{n} v^2(t_k)} = \sqrt{\frac{1}{n}\sum_{k=1}^{n} v^2(\alpha_k)} \qquad (7\text{–}23)$$

where the ordinates $v(t_k)$ or $v(\alpha_k)$ are *mid*ordinates of the Δt or $\Delta\alpha$ intervals.

7.6 Graphical Determination of the Average Value of a Non-Sine Wave.

The definition of average value, as given by Art. 1–5, indicates that graphical integration is required to determine the average value of a graphical wave form. A tabulation for computing the average value of a wave is very simple and should need no explanation.

PROBLEMS

7–1 A function $f(t)$ is given in the following tabulation:

t	$f(t)$	t	$f(t)$	t	$f(t)$
0.00	1.00	0.07	−0.30	0.14	0.20
0.01	0.50	0.08	−0.10	0.15	0.50
0.02	0.25	0.09	0.00	0.16	0.60
0.03	0.00	0.10	−0.20	0.17	0.85
0.04	−0.10	0.11	−0.40	0.18	1.10
0.05	−0.20	0.12	−0.30	0.19	1.05
0.06	−0.40	0.13	0.00	0.20	1.00

Plot this curve, choose the proper uniform value of Δt, and plot the derivative curve.

7–2 (*a*) Plot the integral curve, $F(t)$, for the function $f(t)$, given in the preceding problem. (*b*) Differentiate graphically the result, $F(t)$, obtained in part (*a*) and plot. Compare the result with the original $f(t)$.

7–3 Make up a tabulation for graphically integrating a curve on the basis of Fig. 7–3*a*. Plot the curve which represents the integral of the curve given in Problem 7–1 by the method devised.

7–4 Determine, by graphical integration, the Fourier series coefficients for the periodic wave of Problem 7–1. Write the complex and real variable forms of this periodic function through the fifth harmonic. Determine the coefficients v_{sh} and v_{ch} of equation 6–3.

7–5 Assume no harmonics higher than the third exist in the non-sine wave of Fig. 7–6. Find all the remaining harmonics and compare with the results of Example 7–4.

7–6 Determine all harmonic coefficients up to and including the sixth for the non-sine wave of Fig. 7–6 by the Fischer-Hinnen method. Compare with the results of Example 7–4.

7–7 Use the Fischer-Hinnen method to determine the harmonic content of the function given in Problem 7–1.

(*a*) Assume the fourth harmonic is the highest order harmonic existing.

(*b*) Repeat part (*a*) for the sixth harmonic as the highest and compare results with part (*a*).

7–8 Erect a sufficient number of equally spaced ordinates on the non-sine wave of Fig. 7–6 to form a set of nine simultaneous equations. Write these equations in terms of the d-c component and the sine and cosine coefficients up to and including the fourth harmonic. If all harmonics past the fourth are negligible, use this system of equations to determine the second harmonic sine and cosine coefficients and compare with the result obtained in Examples 7–3 and 7–4.

7–9 Determine the effective value of the periodic wave of Problem 7–1.

7–10 Determine the two average values for the wave of Problem 7–1. Consider one of the part cycles as the wave portion between $t = 0.03$ and $t = 0.13$ sec.

CHAPTER 8

Transients—Alternating-Current Source Voltages

The current, voltage, power, and energy relations which have already been established in the earlier chapters of this book are classed as steady state relations. These and all steady state circuit relations are characterized by a stable existence which may continue indefinitely in the circuit. In fact, the stability of the steady state condition of an electrical network is so marked that no matter what the original circuit condition or how the circuit is finally established its steady state behavior is always the same. A change in an electric circuit, however, necessarily establishes conditions which require another steady state; and because a circuit cannot change instantaneously from one steady state to another, an adjustment or transient period arises. This transient period is of short duration, frequently measured in microseconds and rarely in more than seconds. It may seem that such extremely short duration phenomena could be ignored, but practical usage has demonstrated not only that transients cannot be ignored, but also that they must be studied in detail. Very large currents or high voltages which exist even momentarily may be dangerous, and their values must be investigated.

Power system operators have found that the transient behavior of their systems sometimes has devastating effects. For example, transformers have been blasted, as though with dynamite, by the immense transient current surging into the equipment as it is connected to the system. Alternators have been and still are being melted down, or having their internal conductors distorted by the terrific surges of current which occur during the first moments of short circuit. The short duration of some transients, in particular of a lightning discharge, is shown in the oscillographic record of Fig. 8–1, taken on a cathode ray oscillograph. The extremely short duration of such surges is shown by the time scale of this picture.

Transient conditions are not always to be avoided because of their destructive characteristics, as the foregoing might seem to indicate. Engineers make use of *all* the properties of the physical systems with

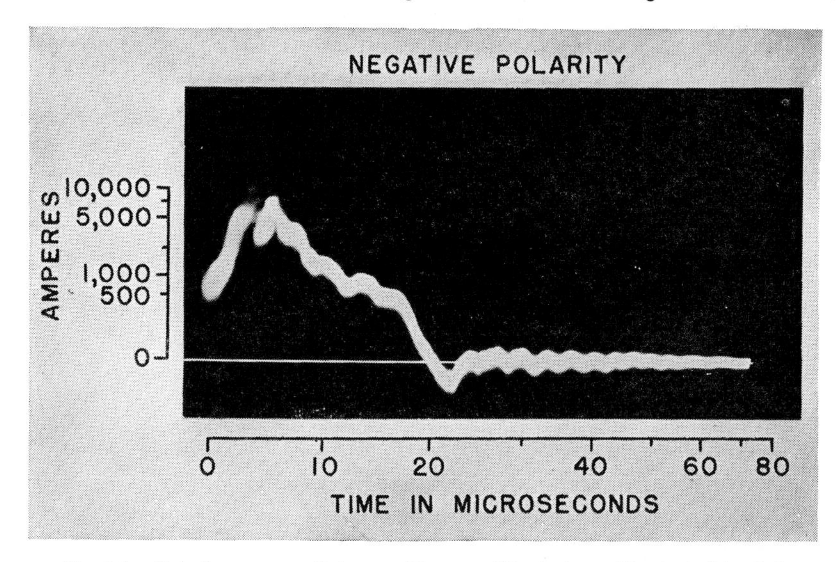

Fig. 8–1. Lightning arrester discharge. (Courtesy, Westinghouse Electric & Mfg. Co.)

which they deal, and transient phenomena are no exception. The surge generator being used to develop artificial lightning is an example of the ingenuity of engineers in turning the forces of nature into means of studying and controlling these same forces. Surge generators are shown in Figs. 8–2*a* and *b*. This device, by charging capacitors in parallel and discharging them in series, sets up a transient surge of energy which is

Fig. 8–2*a*. High-ampere surge generator. (Courtesy, General Electric Co.)

Fig. 8–2*b*. High-voltage surge generator. (Courtesy, Westinghouse Electric & Mfg. Co.)

immensely powerful and which simulates a lightning discharge with sufficient accuracy to permit a controlled study of lightning phenomena.

The ignition system of all gasoline engines operates entirely on transients. The low d-c battery voltage is turned into a high a-c voltage at the spark plugs by the rapid make and break of the inductive distributor circuit.

Transients are used in many other applications, a typical example of which is the production of the delineation or sweep voltage required on the plates of a cathode ray oscillographic tube. The circuit—sweep circuit—is required to produce a linear voltage increase with time as shown in Fig. 8–3. This voltage is applied to one pair of the cathode ray tube electrodes and has the effect of sweeping the electron beam repeatedly across the tube screen at the desired constant velocity in one direction and almost instantly back to the starting point.

All communication transmission—radio, telephone, television—is in a sense transient and is being increasingly studied as such.

In the light of the preceding discussion, there seems little doubt that some knowledge of transient behavior is a necessity for all electrical engineers. The basic essentials of transient behavior are presented in this chapter as they occur in simple series circuits of combinations of R, L, and C. From these results the transient behavior of circuits in general can be understood, although further study is required to acquire techniques for calculating complicated circuits. In particular, the method of Laplace transform,* which changes differential equations into algebraic equations, is being widely used for the advanced theoretical study of electric transients, as well as for particular computations.

Fig. 8–3. Sweep circuit voltage.

8.1 The Fundamental Cause of Transients.

It has already been stated that transients arise as a result of an electric circuit change which alters the stable steady state requirement of the circuit. However, the existence of a transient is not required solely because of a change in the steady state current and voltage requirements of a circuit. If all the currents and voltages of a circuit could change abruptly, a change from one steady state condition to another could be accomplished instantaneously and no transient would arise. It actually happens, though, that for a large class of network problems the *current in an inductor and the voltage across a capacitor do not change instantaneously*. Therefore, for such problems, changing instantaneously from one steady state condition to another, which to be satisfied requires an abrupt change in inductor current or capacitor voltage, is impossible. Instead a certain time lapse is required during which the circuit adjusts from one steady state condition to the one required by the changed circuit. Because the characteristics of inductor currents and capacitor voltages are the sole cause, for this class of problems, of the existence of transients, a brief discussion of these two circuit quantities is presented next.

In the first place, experimental evidence long ago seemed to indicate that the current in an inductor cannot change abruptly. The flaming arcs which appear across the terminals of a switch used to open an inductor circuit, as well as oscillographic observations on inductors, attest to the reluctance of an inductor current to make abrupt changes. Similarly,

---

* E. J. Scott, *Transform Calculus, with an Introduction to Complex Variables,* Harper & Brothers, 1955.

the fact that a capacitor retains a voltage across its terminals for some time after its removal from an electrical system, as well as oscillographic observations on capacitors, suggested that capacitor voltages are continuous. Evidence now exists that there are certain situations of practical importance for which jumps, i.e., discontinuities, in capacitor voltages and inductor currents exist. However, neither of these situations is considered here. Thus for this discussion, for inductor currents

$$i_L(0-) = i_L(0+) \tag{8–1}$$

and for capacitor voltages

$$v_C(0-) = v_C(0+) \tag{8–2}$$

where 0− indicates the left-hand and 0+ the right-hand value at $t = 0$.

8.2 Solution of Linear, Constant Coefficient Differential Equations.

A differential equation may be characterized broadly as any equation in which derivatives appear. Because inductor voltages are proportional to the rate of change of current and capacitor currents are proportional to the rate of change of capacitor voltages, differential equations must inevitably arise in formulating electric circuit behavior.

There are many kinds of differential equations, only one of which is of interest here. In particular, the differential equation, known as linear,

$$a\frac{d^3i(t)}{dt^3} + b\frac{d^2i(t)}{dt^2} + c\frac{di(t)}{dt} + ei(t) = f(t) \tag{8–3}$$

is the type of greatest interest in electric circuit theory. For linear circuits, a, b, c, and e are constant, and the equation is called linear with constant coefficients.

Equations of the type shown in equation 8–3 appear widely in all branches of science. They have been studied extensively by mathematicians, and many methods of obtaining a solution, i.e., the function $i(t)$ which reduces the equation to an identity, have been worked out. The method used here is based on the fact, proved by mathematicians, that any analytical function satisfying a linear differential equation and the initial conditions is the *only solution* of that differential equation which satisfies the initial conditions. The importance of this uniqueness property of the solution of a differential equation cannot be overestimated. It assures that the differential equation can be solved by *any scheme whatsoever* and that solution will be the *only one* to be obtained by *any* method. Therefore, guessing at the solution, and trying it for validity, is as good as any other method and many times easier than any other technique. At first, guessing at the solution of a differential equation will probably seem like a crude technique, but a little practice makes the method very effective. As a guide, which is frequently, although not always, useful, the known function, as on the right of equation 8–3, should be differentiated successively until the result no longer differs from preceding derivatives. The assumed solution should then be the sum of all the different expressions obtained by differentiation, with each one multiplied by a different constant. For example, suppose that $f(t)$ of equation 8–3 is

$$f(t) = |V_m| \sin \omega t \tag{8–4}$$

Differentiating once produces a cosine function, and a second time brings the result back to a sine function. Accordingly,

$$i(t) = K_1 \sin \omega t + K_2 \cos \omega t \tag{8–5}$$

should be used as the assumed solution. This solution should be substituted into the differential equation and a value for K_1 and K_2 obtained by equating coefficients.

Or again, suppose $f(t)$ of equation 8–3 is a complex number (rotating vector) function, say

$$f(t) = V_m \epsilon^{j\omega t} \tag{8–6}$$

Differentiating does not alter the time function; hence the solution

$$i(t) = K\epsilon^{j\omega t} \tag{8–7}$$

should be assumed, substituted into the differential equation, and K determined by equating coefficients.

It may happen that not all the terms placed in an assumed solution are required, or that more or different terms are required. If such is the case, the fact will be evident because substituting the assumed solution into the differential equation will lead to impossible relations when the equating of coefficients is carried out.

Example 8:1 Determine the function $i(t)$ which will satisfy the differential equation

$$\frac{di(t)}{dt} + 2i(t) = t^3$$

Solution Differentiating t^3 until no further change results suggests that

$$i(t) = K_1t^3 + K_2t^2 + K_3t + K_4$$

may serve as a first guess at the solution. Substituting this assumed solution into the differential equation results in

$$(3K_1t^2 + 2K_2t + K_3) + 2(K_1t^3 + K_2t^2 + K_3t + K_4) = t^3$$

For this relation to be true for all values of t, coefficients of the same degree terms must be equal; hence equating coefficients of t^3, t^2, t, and constant terms

$$\begin{aligned} 2K_1 &= 1 \\ 3K_1 + 2K_2 &= 0 \\ 2K_2 + 2K_3 &= 0 \\ K_3 + 2K_4 &= 0 \end{aligned}$$

Solving these relations for the K's gives

$$\begin{aligned} K_1 &= \tfrac{1}{2} \\ K_2 &= -\tfrac{3}{4} \\ K_3 &= \tfrac{3}{4} \\ K_4 &= -\tfrac{3}{8} \end{aligned}$$

The function $i(t)$ which satisfies the differential equation is, therefore, on substituting these values for the K's,

$$i(t) = \frac{t^3}{2} - \tfrac{3}{4}t^2 + \tfrac{3}{4}t - \tfrac{3}{8}$$

A solution for a linear differential equation which reduces the equation to an identity would seem to be all that may be expected or required in a solution. Experience and experiment have both shown conclusively, however, that the solution known as the particular integral, obtained as in the foregoing example, is not the whole story. Situations arise in which this particular integral, or steady state solution, does not represent the current behavior of a circuit. What may be done about the impasse is not immediately evident. However, one thing is certain. The current behavior in an electric circuit must satisfy the fundamental differential equation obtained from Kirchhoff's voltage equation. If argued from this fact, it is soon apparent that only one possibility is available for altering the solution. Certainly if in equation 8–3 a function $i(t)$ is determined which reduces the left-hand side of the equation to the same $f(t)$ as is given on the right, the equation is satisfied. Only one possible alteration can be made: zero can be added to the left side of the equation. This may seem like a trivial statement conducive only to trivial results. It actually is the key to obtaining the complete solution. If a solution of

$$a\frac{d^3i(t)}{dt^3} + b\frac{d^2i(t)}{dt^2} + c\frac{di(t)}{dt} + ei(t) = 0 \qquad (8\text{–}8)$$

is added to the solution of equation 8–3, the sum is a solution of equation 8–3 which satisfies the original differential equation since the solution of 8–8 reduces the left side of equation 8–3 to zero.

It has been found that

$$i(t) = A\epsilon^{mt} \qquad (8\text{–}9)$$

is a solution of any homogeneous, linear, constant coefficient differential equation where A and m are constants to be determined from the particular differential equation to be solved. Thus, substituting equation 8–9 into equation 8–8 leads to

$$(m^3a + m^2b + mc + e)A\epsilon^{mt} = 0 \qquad (8\text{–}10)$$

Since $A \neq 0$ or equation 8–9 is a trivial solution, and since ϵ^{mt} is not zero for any finite value of m or t, the polynomial in m must be zero in order to satisfy this last equation, i.e.,

$$m^3a + m^2b + mc + e = 0 \tag{8-11}$$

This equation determines the value of m, in fact several values of m—three in the present case—, which make equation 8–9 a solution of the homogeneous differential equation 8–8. Once more, since a sum of solutions is a solution of a linear differential equation, the solution of equation 8–8 may be written as

$$i(t) = A_1\epsilon^{m_1t} + A_2\epsilon^{m_2t} + A_3\epsilon^{m_3t} \tag{8-12}$$

where m_1, m_2, and m_3 are the roots of the m-polynomial of equation 8–11.

The constants A_1, A_2, and A_3 of this last equation are undetermined but arbitrary, i.e., they may have any value whatsoever, and equation 8–12 is still a solution of the homogeneous differential equation. That these constants are arbitrary is evident from equation 8–10. For no matter what the non-zero value of A in this equation, it is still satisfied if equation 8–11 is satisfied. The particular values these arbitrary constants take on for a particular problem are determined from the initial or boundary conditions, which are the values the function $i(t)$ (the *complete* solution of the original differential equation) and its derivatives must have at $t = 0$.

The solution of 8–12 takes on several forms, depending on the nature of the values of m_1, m_2, and m_3. For example, suppose all the roots of equation 8–11 are real and distinct; then m_1, m_2, and m_3 are real and distinct, and equation 8–12 represents the solution desired. But suppose a pair of roots are complex conjugates, say $m_2 = a_2 + jb_2$ and $m_3 = a_2 - jb_2$. The solution is then

$$i(t) = A_1\epsilon^{m_1t} + A_2\epsilon^{a_2t}\epsilon^{jb_2t} + A_3\epsilon^{a_2t}\epsilon^{-jb_2t} \tag{8-13}$$

$$= A_1\epsilon^{m_1t} + \epsilon^{a_2t}(B_1 \cos b_2t + B_2 \sin b_2t) \tag{8-14}$$

The equivalence of these last two equations is of very great importance. It indicates that, *because complex roots always occur* in conjugate pairs, if any of the roots of the m-polynomial are complex the solution is *oscillatory*. In electric circuits, such a result means an alternating current.

There is one other possibility in the form of the roots of the m-polynomial, i.e., some or all of them may be real and equal. The solution then takes on a slightly different form from equation 8–12. Mathematicians have shown that, if two roots are equal, the solution should be

$$i(t) = A_1\epsilon^{m_1t} + A_2\epsilon^{m_2t} + tA_3\epsilon^{m_2t} \tag{8-15}$$

or, if all of them are equal,

$$i(t) = A_1\epsilon^{m_1t} + tA_2\epsilon^{m_1t} + t^2A_3\epsilon^{m_1t} \tag{8-16}$$

and so on.

As already indicated, the complete solution of a linear differential equation is the sum of the solution of the type obtained in Example 8-1 and the solution in the form of equation 8-12 or its modification.

Example 8:2 Determine the complete solution of the differential equation

$$\frac{d^3Q(t)}{dt^3} + 14\frac{d^2Q(t)}{dt^2} + 48\frac{dQ(t)}{dt} + 80Q(t) = 200\epsilon^{j(100t+45)}$$

subject to the conditions that $Q(0) = 0 + j0$, $Q'(0) = 0 - j10$, $Q''(0) = 0 + j5$.

Solution Since the particular integral, or steady state solution, of this equation will be an exponential, assume that the steady state solution is

$$Q_s(t) = K\epsilon^{j100t}$$

Substituting this assumed solution into the differential equation results in

$$[(j100)^3 + 14(j100)^2 + 48(j100) + 80]K\epsilon^{j100t} = 200\epsilon^{j45}\epsilon^{j100t}$$

But because this equation must be valid for all values of t, the coefficients of the time-varying exponentials must be equal; therefore

$$K = \frac{200\epsilon^{j45}}{-14(100)^2 + 80 + j[4800 - (100)^3]} = \frac{200\epsilon^{j45}}{-139{,}920 - j995{,}200}$$

Accordingly, the steady state solution is

$$Q_s(t) = \frac{200\epsilon^{j(100t+45)}}{-139{,}920 - j995{,}200}$$

The transient solution is to be obtained from assuming a solution

$$Q_t(t) = A\epsilon^{mt}$$

and substituting into

$$\frac{d^3Q(t)}{dt^3} + 14\frac{d^2Q(t)}{dt^2} + 48\frac{dQ(t)}{dt} + 80Q(t) = 0$$

The result of such a substitution is

$$(m^3 + 14m^2 + 48m + 80)A\epsilon^{mt} = 0$$

from which the m-polynomial is

$$m^3 + 14m^2 + 48m + 80 = 0$$

The roots of this equation are

$$m_1 = -10, \quad m_2 = -2 + j2, \quad m_3 = -2 - j2$$

and the transient solution is

$$Q_t(t) = A_1\epsilon^{-10t} + A_2\epsilon^{(-2+j2)t} + A_3\epsilon^{(-2-j2)t}$$

The complete solution, which is the sum of the transient and steady state solutions, is

$$Q(t) = \frac{200\epsilon^{j(100t+45)}}{-139{,}920 - j995{,}200} + A_1\epsilon^{-10t} + A_2\epsilon^{(-2+j2)t} + A_3\epsilon^{(-2-j2)t}$$

The arbitrary constants of this solution must be determined so that the initial ($t = 0$) conditions on the function $Q(t)$ and its first and second derivatives are satisfied. So

$$Q(0) = 0 + j0 = \frac{200\epsilon^{j45}}{-139{,}920 - j995{,}200} + A_1 + A_2 + A_3$$

$$Q'(0) = 0 - j10 = \frac{(j100)200\epsilon^{j45}}{-139{,}920 - j995{,}200} - 10A_1 + (-2+j2)A_2 + (-2-j2)A_3$$

$$Q''(0) = 0 + j5 = \frac{(j100)^2 200\epsilon^{j45}}{-139{,}920 - j995{,}200} + 100A_1 - j8A_2 + j8A_3$$

The simultaneous solution of this set of three equations for the constants A_1, A_2, and A_3 gives

$$A_1 = -0.0225 - j0.4961$$
$$A_2 = -3.4771 + j0.2899$$
$$A_3 = 3.4997 + j0.2061$$

Substituting these values of the constants into the complete solution establishes the fully determined complete solution as

$$Q(t) = \frac{200\epsilon^{j(100t+45)}}{-139{,}920 - j995{,}200} + (-0.0225 - j0.4961)\epsilon^{-10t}$$
$$+ (-3.4771 + j0.2899)\epsilon^{(-2+j2)t} + (3.4997 + j0.2061)\epsilon^{(-2-j2)t}$$

The method of solving linear, constant coefficient differential equations given here might be called the classical method. This method is used here because it requires the least mathematical training for its understanding and use and also because separating the solution into determining the transient and the steady state solutions serves to emphasize their distinction.

With these preliminaries as background, the solution of the few differential equations which arise from possible variations of a series circuit should offer no difficulty. Accordingly, attention will now be turned to some electric circuits and their differential equations.

Some knowledge of the transient behavior of series circuits with a d-c source voltage will be assumed, as well as some knowledge of the meaning of time constant and decrement factor as interpreted for a d-c circuit.*

* W. H. Timbie and V. Bush, *Principles of Electrical Engineering*, John Wiley & Sons, 1930; E. B. Kurtz and G. F. Corcoran, *Introduction to Electric Transients*, Wiley, 1935; H. H. Skilling, *Transient Electric Currents*, McGraw-Hill Book Co., 1937; M. B. Reed, *The Fundamentals of Electrical Engineering*, International Textbook Co., 1938.

8.3 Alternating-Current Source Voltage Connected to a Non-Reactive Resistor.

The equation for the instantaneous voltage in the circuit of a non-reactive resistance load (Fig. 8–4) is, in terms of the generator terminal voltage,

$$v(t) = Ri(t) \tag{8–17}$$

This equation may be solved for the current simply by dividing both sides of the equation by the constant R. Hence, for a sinusoidal voltage at the terminals of a resistor R,

$$i(t) = \frac{v(t)}{R} = \frac{|V_m|}{R} \sin(\omega t + \phi) = |I_m| \sin(\omega t + \phi) \tag{8–18}$$

So for an a-c source voltage, just as for a d-c source voltage, there is no transient period for a circuit of purely non-reactive resistance. The current starts at the value required by the steady state condition, whatever it is, and continues at steady state condition. Actually, there is no such thing as an absolutely non-reactive circuit. However, such a circuit can be approximated very closely.

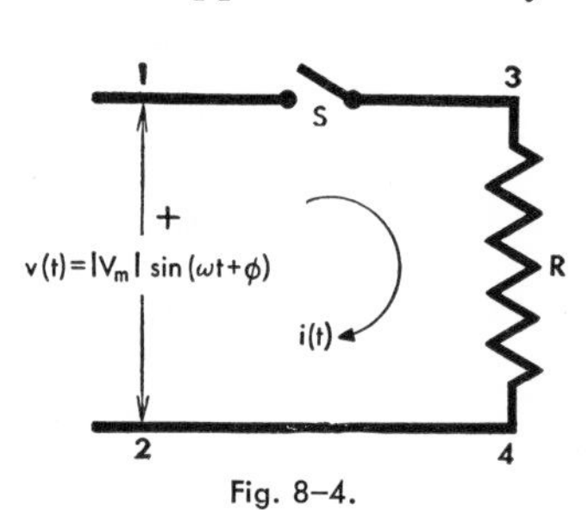

Fig. 8–4.

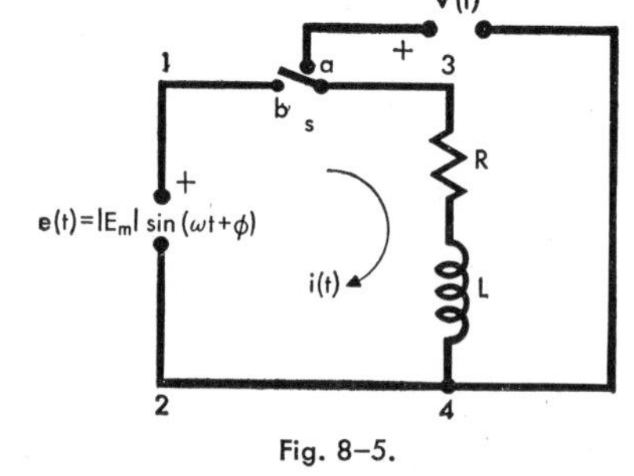

Fig. 8–5.

8.4 Transient in an Inductive Resistor—Alternating-Current Source Voltage.

Since the instantaneous voltage equation gives, at least potentially, all the information about series circuits, as in the preceding article the voltage differential equation for the circuit of Fig. 8–5, with the switch closed in the b-position, serves as a starting point. This equation is, for zero internal impedance of the generator, or a specified terminal voltage

$$e(t) = v(t) = v(t)_R + v(t)_L = Ri(t) + L\frac{di(t)}{dt} \tag{8–19}$$

Substituting for the generated voltage $e(t)$, or better for the generator terminal voltage $v(t)$, since no consideration then need be given to the internal impedance of the generator, gives

$$|V_m| \sin(\omega t + \phi) = Ri(t) + L\frac{di(t)}{dt} \tag{8–20}$$

Since this equation is linear, the complex variable or rotating vector representation of a sine wave

$$V(t) = V_m\epsilon^{j\omega t} = |V_m|\epsilon^{j(\omega t+\phi)} \tag{8-21}$$

can be used to replace the sinusoid and so to simplify obtaining the solution of the differential equation 8–20. This equation in complex variable form becomes

$$V_m\epsilon^{j\omega t} = RI(t) + L\frac{dI(t)}{dt} \tag{8-22}$$

which represents the rotating vector, current-voltage relation of a R and L series circuit at any instant. It specifies the voltage directly, but the current is given only implicitly. The explicit form of current as a rotating vector function of time is to be determined, i.e., the solution of equation 8–22 is sought as a value for $I(t)$ which reduces the equation to an identity.

The solution of equation 8–22 is obtained by *assuming* that the current may be expressed by

$$I(t) = I_m\epsilon^{j\omega t} \tag{8-23}$$

in accordance with the method discussed in Art. 8–2. Substituting this assumed current solution into the differential equation 8–22 gives

$$V_m\epsilon^{j\omega t} = RI_m\epsilon^{j\omega t} + j\omega LI_m\epsilon^{j\omega t}$$

Canceling the common exponential which can never be zero

$$V_m = (R + j\omega L)I_m \tag{8-24}$$

from which the unknown constant of the assumed solution is

$$I_m = \frac{V_m}{R + j\omega L} = \frac{V_m}{R + jX_L} = \frac{V_m}{Z} \tag{8-25}$$

If this result is substituted back into equation 8–23, the solution of equation 8–22 is $(\sigma = -\theta)$

$$I(t) = \frac{V_m}{Z}\epsilon^{j\omega t} = \frac{|V_m|\epsilon^{j\phi}}{|Z|\epsilon^{j\sigma}}\epsilon^{j\omega t} = \frac{|V_m|}{|Z|}\epsilon^{j(\omega t+\phi+\theta)} \tag{8-26}$$

which is the particular integral, or steady state, rotating vector current already considered in detail in preceding chapters.

The transient solution is obtained by solving the *homogeneous* differential equation

$$RI(t) + L\frac{dI(t)}{dt} = 0 \tag{8-27}$$

for $I(t)$. Assume the current takes the form

$$I(t) = I'\epsilon^{mt} \tag{8-28}$$

Substituting this assumption into equation 8–27 gives, on canceling the common, not zero, I'

$$R + mL = 0$$

and a value of m which satisfies equations 8–28 and 8–27 is

$$m = -\frac{R}{L} \tag{8–29}$$

Substituting this result back into equation 8–28 gives

$$I(t) = I'\epsilon^{-(R/L)t} \tag{8–30}$$

as a solution of the homogeneous equation. As may be seen by substitution, *this solution satisfies the homogeneous equation* for *any* value of I'; hence I' is *arbitrary*. Since equation 8–27 has a first-order derivative only and, therefore, should require *one* integration to solve, the arbitrary symbol I' is considered the arbitrary constant of integration which will be given a particular value by means of the initial condition of the current in the circuit.

Adding equation 8–30 to equation 8–26 gives the complete current equation as

$$I(t) = \frac{V_m}{Z}\epsilon^{j\omega t} + I'\epsilon^{-(R/L)t} \tag{8–31}$$

In order to complete the solution, i.e., determine the proper value of the integration constant I', a condition in the dependent variable, $I(t)$, at some value of the independent variable, t, must be known.

When the switch s of Fig. 8–5 is in position a, a current will be present in the inductive resistor. Then, since the current in an inductor cannot change instantly, if at $t = 0$ the switch is changed to position b, the current at $t = 0$ is

$$I(0) = 0 + ji(0) \tag{8–32}$$

where $i(0)$ is the current in amperes in the inductor at the instant the switch is changed. Because it is the imaginary component of $I(t)$ which is the instantaneous value of $i(t)$, the real component of $I(0)$ may be made anything desired without affecting the instantaneous value, or imaginary component, and zero is the most convenient value to give it.

Substituting the initial condition thus established into equation 8–31 and solving for the constant I' produces

$$I' = I(0) - \frac{V_m}{Z} \tag{8–33}$$

and substituting this result back into equation 8–31 gives the complete solution of equation 8–22 as

$$I(t) = \frac{V_m}{Z}\epsilon^{j\omega t} + \left[I(0) - \frac{V_m}{Z}\right]\epsilon^{-(R/L)t}$$

or

$$I(t) = \frac{|V_m|}{|Z|} \epsilon^{j(\omega t+\phi+\theta)} + \left[I(0) - \frac{|V_m|}{|Z|} \epsilon^{j(\phi+\theta)} \right] \epsilon^{-(R/L)t} \qquad (8\text{–}34)$$

where $\theta = -\tan^{-1} X_L/R$, as was defined in Chap. 4, and

ϕ = the voltage phase angle which specifies the value of the source voltage at the instant of closing the switch.

The instantaneous value of the current may be taken directly from this last equation by simply writing the j-component of the expression. Thus, from inspection,

$$i(t) = \frac{|V_m|}{|Z|} \sin(\omega t + \phi + \theta) + \left[i(0) - \frac{|V_m|}{|Z|} \sin(\phi + \theta) \right] \epsilon^{-(R/L)t} \qquad (8\text{–}35)$$

From this equation for the instantaneous current, it is possible to write the equations for the voltage across the resistor and the voltage across the inductor. Thus

$$v_R(t) = Ri(t) = R\frac{|V_m|}{|Z|} \sin(\omega t+\phi+\theta) + R\left[i(0) - \frac{|V_m|}{|Z|} \sin(\phi+\theta) \right] \epsilon^{-(R/L)t} \qquad (8\text{–}36)$$

$$v_L(t) = L\frac{di(t)}{dt} = \omega L\frac{|V_m|}{|Z|} \cos(\omega t+\phi+\theta) - R\left[i(0) - \frac{|V_m|}{|Z|} \sin(\phi+\theta) \right] \epsilon^{-(R/L)t} \qquad (8\text{–}37)$$

With the complete solution established for the current and voltages in an R and L series circuit with sinusoidal source voltage, attention is turned to the interpretation of these equations.

Consider first the transient term as a function of time. Since R, L, and t are all positive for any electric circuit, the transient dies out as time increases. The ratio L/R, known as the time constant, determines how rapidly the transient decreases—the larger L/R, the longer it takes for the transient to decrease to a particular amount. According to the equation, the transient never becomes zero. For practical purposes, however, the transient is usually zero in a fraction of a second.

Consider next the coefficient of the transient exponential given in equations 8–33 and 8–34. It is evident that the maximum, or $t = 0$, value of the transient is given by the j-component of I'. Furthermore, the transient will be zero if the j-component of I' is zero. Already, in Art. 8–1, it has been indicated that, if the incoming steady state current of an inductor matches (is the same in magnitude and direction) the actual current in the inductor at the instant of making the circuit change, no transient will result. The mathematical results deduced in equation 8–35 corroborate this conclusion. For the $t = 0$ value of the transient taken from equation 8–35 is

$$i_d = i(0) - \frac{|V_m|}{|Z|} \sin(\phi + \theta) \qquad (8\text{–}38)$$

which is exactly the difference or discrepancy between the actual inductor current at $t = 0$, $i(0)$, and the $t = 0$ current value required by the incoming steady state. This difference is called the discrepancy factor i_d, or in complex number form $I' = I_d$ is the discrepancy factor. Evidently, if $i_d = 0$ or if the j-component of $I' = I_d$ is zero, *no transient* results.

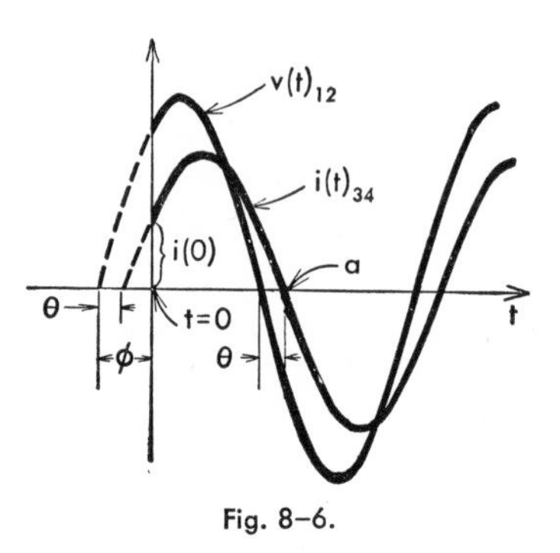

Fig. 8–6.

The condition for no transient is shown graphically in Fig. 8–6. The current already in the circuit is positive as shown by $i(0)$. This current, in turn, is just equal in magnitude and direction to the steady state current required at the instant of closing the switch as determined by ϕ.

The maximum transient possible for any particular $i(0)$ can also be established from equation 8–38. Evidently if i_d is a maximum the transient will be a maximum, which in turn means that if the actual $i(0)$ and the required incoming steady state differ as much as possible the transient will be a maximum. Thus in Fig. 8–7, if $i(0)$ is negative as shown, initiating a transient at such an instant that the required incoming steady state current is a *positive* maximum produces maximum transient of negative value as shown.

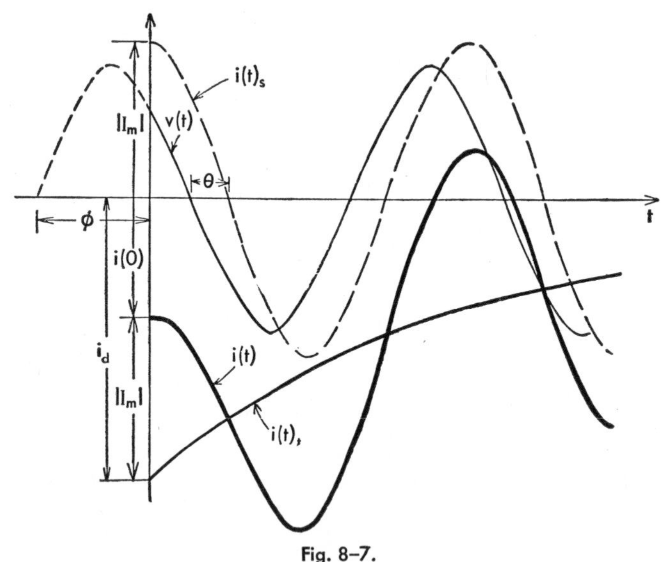

Fig. 8–7.

In general, for maximum transient, from equation 8–38 $\sin(\phi + \theta) = \pm 1$, the sign to be used being the opposite of the sign of $i(0)$.

It should be noted that the derivative (slope) of the current need not have the same value on each side of the $t = 0$ point for no transient, because $i_d = 0$ requires only a match of current magnitude and direction. The voltage across the inductor can change abruptly, therefore, since $v_L(t) = L\,di(t)/dt$.

It should also be noted that *the transient voltage across the inductor and across the resistor are always equal and opposite.* This relation follows immediately from an examination of equations 8–36 and 8–37, or from the fact that Kirchhoff's voltage law around the mesh is completely satisfied by the *steady state,* which requires that the transient voltages must add to zero. An immediate consequence of this conclusion is that if the current transient is a maximum, the resistor and inductor transient voltages will be a maximum because

$$Ri(t)_t = v_R(t)_t = -v_L(t)_t$$

Example 8:3 A series circuit of 10 ohms resistance and 0.01 henry inductance (Fig. 8–5) is connected to a regulated voltage source for which $\omega = 1000$ and the terminal voltage is 100 volts. The voltage $v'(t)_{4a}$ is direct current and constant at 20 volts. (*a*) Find the complete current equation if the switch is moved from the *a* to *b* position when $v(t)_{12}$ is half its positive maximum and increasing. (*b*) Determine the time of closing the switch to *b* to produce zero transient. (*c*) Determine the time of closing the switch to *b* to produce maximum transient. (*d*) Determine the initial voltage across the resistor and across the inductor for maximum transient.

Solution (*a*) If $t = 0$ at the time of closing the switch of Fig. 8–5 to *b*, the voltage is

$$v(t)_{12} = 100\sqrt{2}\sin(1000t + 30°)$$

since at $t = 0$ this voltage is half its maximum value and increasing. The initial current in the circuit, determined at the instant of moving the switch from *a* to *b* but with the switch in the *a*-position, is

$$i(0)_{43} = \frac{v'(0)_{4a}}{R} = \frac{20}{10} = 2 \text{ amp}$$

The differential equation to be solved should be written after the switch has been closed to *b*. Thus

$$100\sqrt{2}\epsilon^{j(1000t+30)} = 10I(t) + 0.01\frac{dI(t)}{dt}$$

which is of the same form as equation 8–22. Assuming $I(t) = I'\epsilon^{j1000t}$, and following the procedure used in solving equation 8–22, or substituting directly into equation 8–35 the values: $i(0) = -2$ amp, $|V_m| = 100\sqrt{2}$, $Z = 10 + j1000 \times 0.01 = 10\sqrt{2}\epsilon^{j45}$, $|Z| = 10\sqrt{2}$, $\theta = -45°$, $\phi = 30°$, $R = 10$ ohms, and $L = 0.01$ henry, gives the current solution as (instantaneous)

$$i(t) = \frac{100\sqrt{2}}{10\sqrt{2}}\sin(1000t + 30° - 45°) + \left[-2 - \frac{100\sqrt{2}}{10\sqrt{2}}\sin(30° - 45°)\right]\epsilon^{-(10/0.01)t}$$

or

$$i(t) = 10 \sin(1000t - 15°) + [-2 - 10 \sin(-15°)]\epsilon^{-10^3 t}$$
$$= 10 \sin(1000t - 15°) + 0.59\epsilon^{-1000t}$$

The steady state current is thus

$$i(t)_s = 10 \sin(1000t - 15°)$$

and the maximum, or $t = 0$, value of the transient, i.e., the discrepancy factor, is

$$i_d = 0.59 \text{ amp}$$

(*b*) Zero transient will result if the switch is closed to the *b*-position when the discrepancy factor is zero, or when the required steady state current is equal to the initial current, which is 2 amp, from 4 to 3. Therefore, the angle on the current wave at which the steady state current $i(t)_{34} = -2$ amp may be calculated from equating the steady state current equation to -2. Thus

$$-2 = 10 \sin \alpha$$

where α is referred to a different origin from the current equation of part (*a*), namely, the zero increasing point on the incoming steady-state *current curve*. From this equation

$$\alpha = \sin^{-1}(-0.2) = -11.6° \quad \text{or} \quad 191.6°$$

Accordingly, if the switch is closed to the *b*-position 11.6 degrees before the required steady state current is zero and increasing, as at *a* of Fig. 8–8, or 11.6 degrees after the steady state current is zero and decreasing (191.6 degrees

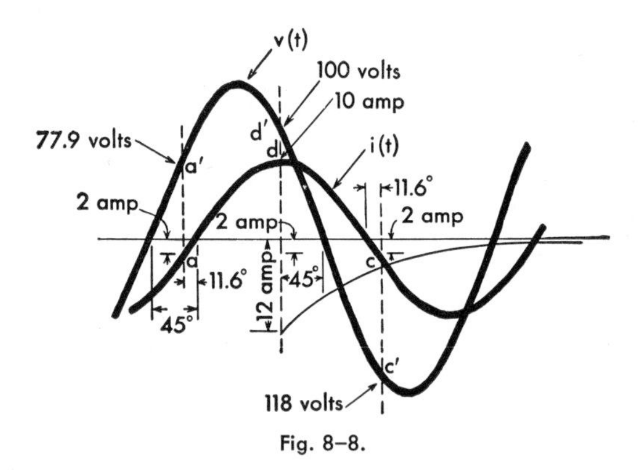

Fig. 8–8.

after the current is zero and increasing) as at *c* of Fig. 8–8, no transient will result. Since the steady state current lags the voltage by 45 degrees, from Fig. 8–8 or from $\alpha = -11.6°$ or $191.6°$, and $\alpha = \phi - 45°$, at once

$$\phi = 33.4° \quad \text{or} \quad 236.6°$$

and the angle on the source voltage curve for no transient is 33.4 degrees after a zero increasing point, as at a' in Fig. 8–8, or 56.6 degrees after a zero decreasing point, as at c' in Fig. 8–8.

(*c*) To produce a maximum transient, the switch should be closed to *b* of Fig. 8–5 when the current is a positive maximum, or (see Fig. 8–8) for $\phi =$ 135 degrees. This is the point *d* on Fig. 8–8, and the voltage is $100\sqrt{2} \sin 135° =$ 100 volts, and decreasing.

The maximum ($t = 0$) value of this maximum current transient is $-2 - 10 \sin 90° = -12$ amp. The sum of this transient and the positive maximum steady state current (10 amp) equals -2 amp, initial current. The maximum transient is shown by the exponential curve of Fig. 8–8.

(*d*) The equations for the voltage across the resistor and inductor may be written, from equations 8–36 and 8–37, as

$$v_R(t) = Ri(t) = 100 \sin (1000t + \phi - 45°) + 10[-2 - 10 \sin (\phi - 45°)]\epsilon^{-1000t}$$

$$v_L(t) = L\frac{di(t)}{dt} = 100 \cos (1000t + \phi - 45°) - 10[-2 - 10 \sin (\phi - 45°)]\epsilon^{-1000t}$$

In particular, for the maximum transient ($\phi = 135°$),

$$v_R(t) = 100 \sin (1000t + 90°) - 120\epsilon^{-1000t}$$
$$v_L(t) = 100 \cos (1000t + 90°) + 120\epsilon^{-1000t}$$

and the initial or $t = 0$ value of this voltage across the resistor is $Ri(0) = -20$ volts, and across the inductor is $v_L(t) = 120$ volts. Note that the inductor voltage changes abruptly from zero before closing the switch to *b* to 120 volts at the instant of closing the switch for the maximum transient. Note also that at the same time the $t = 0$ value of the transient voltage across the resistor is equal and opposite to the $t = 0$ value of the transient component of the inductor voltage.

8.5 Transient in an *R* and *C* Series Circuit—Alternating-Current Source Voltage.

A second simple but important circuit with transient reaction somewhat different from the *R* and *L* series circuit is the *R* and *C* series circuit. As a preliminary to writing the voltage equation for such a circuit, an examination of the fundamental relation of current, voltage, and charge will be undertaken.

Experimentally, the relation between the voltage across the terminals of a capacitor and the positive charge on one of the plates is

$$v_c(t) = \frac{q(t)}{C} + \frac{q_0}{C} \qquad (8\text{–}39)$$

where $q(t)$ = the positive charge on the capacitor plate due to the current, and

q_0 = the positive charge already on the capacitor.

The charge $q(t)$ due to current specifies the current by

$$i(t) = \frac{dq(t)}{dt} \qquad (8\text{–}40)$$

or the current specifies the charge due to current by

$$q(t) = \int_0^t i(t)\,dt \tag{8–41}$$

The value of this integral is *zero at* $t = 0$ from the definition of an integral with upper and lower limits zero. From a physical standpoint, at $t = 0$ *no current can have added charge to the capacitor.* Accordingly *the charge due to current has a zero initial value.*

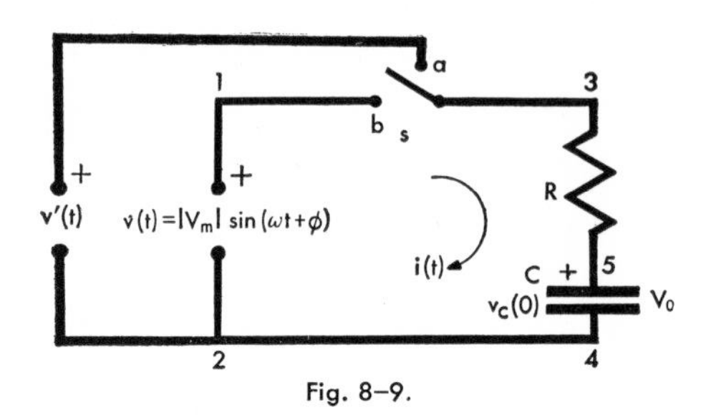

Fig. 8–9.

The differential equation for an R and C series circuit (Fig. 8–9), with switch closed to the b-position, may now be written *in terms of charge due to current* as

$$v(t) = R\frac{dq(t)}{dt} + \frac{q(t)}{C} + \frac{q_0}{C} \tag{8–42}$$

where q_0 = the charge on the capacitor at the instant of closing the switch.

The initial voltage across the capacitor is, of course,

$$v_c(0) = \frac{q_0}{C} \tag{8–43}$$

If a sinusoidal voltage is assumed at the terminals of the source of the R and C series circuit, the rotating vector voltage is the most convenient from which to obtain a solution. Equation 8–42 in rotating vector form will be used. This equation is

$$V(t) = V_m\epsilon^{j\omega t} = R\frac{dQ(t)}{dt} + \frac{Q(t)}{C} + V_0 \tag{8–44}$$

where

$$V_0 = 0 + jv_c(0) = 0 + j\frac{q_0}{C} \tag{8–45}$$

The first step in obtaining the solution of this differential equation is to rearrange it into

$$V_m\epsilon^{j\omega t} - V_0 = R\frac{dQ(t)}{dt} + \frac{Q(t)}{C} \tag{8–46}$$

The solution of this equation can be readily established in accordance with the method already discussed at some length in this chapter.

As suggested by the two terms on the left, the steady state solution of equation 8–46 will be assumed to be

$$Q(t)_s = Q_m\epsilon^{j\omega t} + K \tag{8–47}$$

Substituting this assumed solution into the differential equation, and equating the proper coefficients, gives

$$Q_m = \frac{V_m}{j\omega\left(R + \frac{1}{j\omega C}\right)} = \frac{V_m}{j\omega Z} \tag{8–48}$$

$$K = -CV_0 \tag{8–49}$$

The steady state solution for the charge due to current is, therefore,

$$Q(t)_s = \frac{V_m}{j\omega Z}\epsilon^{j\omega t} - CV_0 \tag{8–50}$$

The transient solution follows immediately from assuming that

$$Q(t)_t = A\epsilon^{mt} \tag{8–51}$$

is the solution of the homogeneous equation

$$R\frac{dQ(t)}{dt} + \frac{Q(t)}{C} = 0 \tag{8–52}$$

Substituting the assumed solution into this equation, canceling the arbitrary constant A and the exponential, leaves the m-polynomial

$$mR + \frac{1}{C} = 0 \tag{8–53}$$

from which

$$m = -\frac{1}{RC} \tag{8–54}$$

The transient solution is, therefore,

$$Q(t)_t = A\epsilon^{-(t/RC)} \tag{8–55}$$

and the complete solution is—sum of equations 8–50 and 8–55—

$$Q(t) = \frac{V_m}{j\omega Z}\epsilon^{j\omega t} - CV_0 + A\epsilon^{-(t/RC)} \tag{8–56}$$

The evaluation of the arbitrary constant A may now be accomplished by setting t equal to zero in this equation and substituting zero for the left-hand term because of the already observed fact that charge due to current is equal to zero at $t = 0$. The constant A so determined is

$$A = CV_0 - \frac{V_m}{j\omega Z} \tag{8–57}$$

and the final and complete solution for the charge due to current in Fig. 8–9, with switch closed to b-position, is

$$Q(t) = \frac{V_m}{j\omega Z}\,\epsilon^{j\omega t} - CV_0 + \left(CV_0 - \frac{V_m}{j\omega Z}\right)\epsilon^{-(t/RC)} \tag{8–58}$$

Because the charge on the capacitor at any instant is the sum of the charge due to current and the charge initially present, the rotating vector charge on the capacitor of Fig. 8–9 at any instant is

$$\begin{aligned} Q_C(t) &= Q(t) + CV_0 \\ &= \frac{V_m}{j\omega Z}\,\epsilon^{j\omega t} + \left(CV_0 - \frac{V_m}{j\omega Z}\right)\epsilon^{-(t/RC)} \end{aligned} \tag{8–59}$$

The j-component of this expression is the actual charge on the capacitor at any instant following the closing of the switch and is

$$q_C(t) = \frac{-|V_m|}{\omega|Z|}\cos(\omega t + \phi + \theta) + \left[Cv_C(0) + \frac{|V_m|}{\omega|Z|}\cos(\phi + \theta)\right]\epsilon^{-(t/RC)} \tag{8–60}$$

The rotating vector voltage across the capacitor is

$$V_C(t) = \frac{Q_C(t)}{C} = \frac{V_m}{j\omega CZ}\,\epsilon^{j\omega t} + \left(V_0 - \frac{V_m}{j\omega CZ}\right)\epsilon^{-(t/RC)} \tag{8–61}$$

and in instantaneous form (j-component of the last equation or equation 8–60 divided by C)

$$\begin{aligned} v_C(t) = \frac{q_C(t)}{C} &= \frac{X_C|V_m|}{|Z|}\cos(\omega t + \phi + \theta) \\ &\quad + \left[v_C(0) - \frac{X_C|V_m|}{|Z|}\cos(\phi + \theta)\right]\epsilon^{-(t/RC)} \end{aligned} \tag{8–62}$$

The rotating vector current is

$$\begin{aligned} I(t) &= \frac{dQ(t)}{dt} = \frac{dQ_C(t)}{dt} \\ &= \frac{V_m}{Z}\,\epsilon^{j\omega t} - \left(\frac{V_0}{R} - \frac{V_m}{j\omega CRZ}\right)\epsilon^{-(t/RC)} \end{aligned} \tag{8–63}$$

and instantaneously the current is represented by the j-component of this last expression or

$$i(t) = \frac{|V_m|}{|Z|}\sin(\omega t + \phi + \theta) - \frac{1}{R}\left[v_C(0) - \frac{X_C|V_m|}{|Z|}\cos(\phi + \theta)\right]\epsilon^{-(t/RC)} \tag{8–64}$$

Finally, the rotating vector expression for the voltage across the resistor is

$$V_R(t) = RI(t) = \frac{RV_m}{Z}\epsilon^{j\omega t} - \left(V_0 - \frac{V_m}{j\omega CZ}\right)\epsilon^{-(t/RC)} \qquad (8\text{–}65)$$

and instantaneously

$$v_R(t) = Ri(t) = R\frac{|V_m|}{|Z|}\sin(\omega t + \phi + \theta) - \left[v_C(0) - \frac{X_C|V_m|}{|Z|}\cos(\phi + \theta)\right]\epsilon^{-(t/RC)} \qquad (8\text{–}66)$$

Certain immediately evident facts appear from an examination of the foregoing results. Corresponding to the similar term in the R and L series circuit solution, the coefficient of the transient exponential is a discrepancy factor, i.e., vectorially

$$V_d = V_0 - \frac{V_m}{j\omega CZ} \qquad (8\text{–}67)$$

or instantaneously

$$v_d = v_C(0) - \frac{X_C|V_m|}{|Z|}\cos(\phi + \theta) \qquad (8\text{–}68)$$

This discrepancy factor is the *difference between the initial voltage on the capacitor and the required steady state capacitor voltage at* t = 0 (see equation 8–62). If the required steady state capacitor voltage and the initial capacitor voltage are the same, no transient will result.

The curves of Fig. 8–10 show the condition for zero transient for a capacitor initially uncharged. Closing the switch on the source voltage

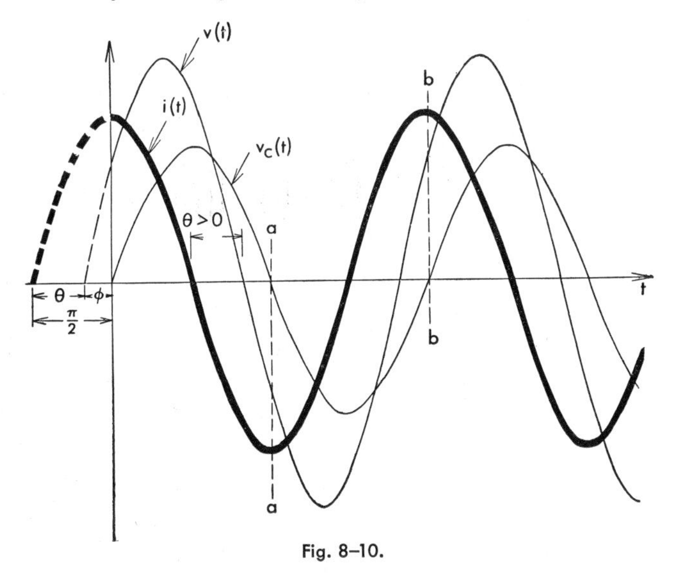

Fig. 8–10.

corresponding to the instants of zero value of steady state capacitor voltage, at *a–a* and *b–b* of this figure, would also give no transient.

The maximum transient for a particular initial voltage on the capacitor occurs when the required incoming steady state capacitor voltage differs most from the initial capacitor voltage; i.e., when the steady state capacitor voltage is numerically a maximum and opposite in sign to the initial capacitor voltage. The curves of Fig. 8–11 show a maximum transient

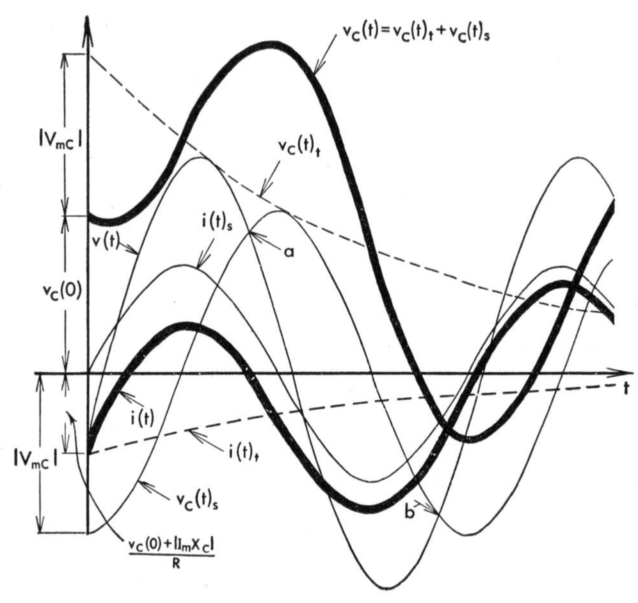

Fig. 8–11.

condition. The initial voltage across the capacitor is taken as positive as shown by $v_C(0)$. Closing the switch at such an instant that the required steady state capacitor voltage is a negative maximum produces the maximum transient.

Again an examination of the transient coefficient of equations 8–62 and 8–66 shows that, as for the R and L circuit, the *transient* voltages are equal and opposite.

The initial value of the current in the R and C series circuit is also of interest. Setting $t = 0$ in equation 8–63 gives

$$I(0) = \frac{V_m}{Z} + \frac{V_m}{j\omega CRZ} - \frac{V_0}{R}$$

which because

$$jX_C \equiv \frac{1}{j\omega C} \quad \text{and} \quad Z = R + jX_C$$

becomes

$$I(0) = \frac{V_m}{Z}\left(1 + j\frac{X_C}{R}\right) - \frac{V_0}{R}$$
$$= \frac{V_m - V_0}{R} \tag{8–69}$$

The j-component of this last expression is evidently

$$i(0) = \frac{|V_m| \sin \phi - v_C(0)}{R} \tag{8–70}$$

The numerator of this equation represents the sum of the $t = 0$ value of the source voltage and the initial voltage on the capacitor. The initial ($t = 0$) value of the current in an R-C series circuit, therefore, does not depend on a preceding current but only on the total active voltage in the circuit at $t = 0$ and on the resistance. The current can and usually does change abruptly in the R and C series circuit.

Example 8:4 A series circuit of 20 ohms resistance and 10 μf capacitance is arranged as shown in Fig. 8–9. The regulated source terminal voltages are

$$v(t) = 282.8 \sin (2000\pi t + \phi)$$

and

$$v'(t) = 100 \sin (2000\pi t + \phi')$$

and $v'(t)$ leads $v(t)$ by 60 degrees.

(*a*) Determine the equation for the current and the voltage across the capacitor in terms of ϕ and ϕ' following shifting the switch from the a-position to the b-position. Assume that steady state has been reached before the switch is moved.

(*b*) Determine the value of ϕ and ϕ' to produce zero transient on moving the switch from a to b.

(*c*) Determine the value of ϕ and ϕ' to cause maximum transient on moving the switch from a to b.

Solution (*a*) The current equation has already been established in 8–64 as

$$i(t) = |I_m| \sin (\omega t + \phi + \theta) - \left[\frac{v_C(0)}{R} - |I_m|\frac{X_C}{R} \cos (\phi + \theta)\right]\epsilon^{-(t/RC)}$$

All but one of the elements of this equation can be computed or taken directly from the given data. Thus:

$$X_C = \frac{-10^6}{2\pi fC} = \frac{-10^6}{2\pi 1000(10)} = -15.92 \text{ ohms}$$
$$|Z| = \sqrt{R^2 + X_C^2} = \sqrt{(20)^2 + (15.92)^2} = 25.56 \text{ ohms}$$
$$|I_m| = \frac{|V_m|}{|Z|} = \frac{282.8}{25.56} = 11.06 \text{ amp}$$
$$\theta = -\tan^{-1}\frac{X_C}{R} = -\tan^{-1}\frac{-15.92}{20} = 38.5°$$

The value of the initial voltage across the capacitor must be determined with the switch in the a-position. The steady state $t = 0$ value of the rotating vector representing the current is then

$$I_{m54} = \frac{V_m}{Z'} = \frac{100\epsilon^{j\phi'}}{20 - j15.92} = \frac{100\epsilon^{j\phi'}}{25.56\epsilon^{-j38.5}} = 3.92\epsilon^{j(\phi'+38.5)}$$

and the voltage across the capacitor is

$$V_{m54} = jX_C I_{m54} = (-j15.92)3.92\epsilon^{j(\phi'+38.5)} = 62.5\epsilon^{j(\phi'-51.5)}$$

The j-component of this voltage is the actual voltage on the capacitor at $t = 0$ if $t = 0$ is taken at ϕ' degrees from the zero and increasing point on the source voltage $v'(t)$. Consequently the initial voltage on the capacitor is

$$v_C(0) = v(0)_{54} = 62.5 \sin (\phi' - 51.5°)$$

The current equation is then

$$\begin{aligned} i(t) = {} & 11.06 \sin (2000\pi t + \phi + 38.5°) \\ & - [3.13 \sin (\phi' - 51.5°) + 8.8 \cos (\phi + 38.5°)]\epsilon^{-5000t} \end{aligned}$$

The equation for the voltage across the capacitor at every instant after the switch reaches the b-position is, on substituting into equation 8–62,

$$\begin{aligned} v_C(t) = {} & -176 \cos (2000\pi t + \phi + 38.5°) \\ & + [62.5 \sin (\phi' - 51.5°) + 176 \cos (\phi + 38.5°)]\epsilon^{-5000t} \end{aligned}$$

(b) In order that zero transient should result from moving the switch from a to b of Fig. 8–9, the coefficient of the exponential in the last equation must be equal to zero. This equation can be expressed in terms of one variable ϕ or ϕ' from the fact that

$$\phi' - \phi = 60°$$

as given in the problem statement. Therefore, zero transient occurs if ϕ is determined from

$$62.5 \sin (\phi' - 51.5°) + 176 \cos (\phi + 38.5°) = 0$$

which, on substituting for ϕ' and rearranging, becomes

$$-62.5 \sin (\phi + 60° - 51.5°) = 176 \cos (\phi + 38.5°)$$

Expanding these expressions and collecting coefficients of $\sin \phi$ and $\cos \phi$ leads to the result

$$\phi = \tan^{-1} 3.05 = 71.9°$$

from which

$$\phi' = \phi + 60° = 131.9°$$

(c) The value of ϕ to produce maximum transient can be determined by setting the derivative of the coefficient of the transient exponential with respect to ϕ or ϕ' equal to zero and solving the resulting equation for ϕ or ϕ'. Thus

$$\frac{d}{d\phi}[62.5 \sin (\phi + 8.5°) + 176 \cos (\phi + 38.5°)] = 0$$

becomes

$$62.5 \cos(\phi + 8.5°) - 176 \sin(\phi + 38.5°) = 0$$

from which

$$\phi = \tan^{-1}(-0.328) = -18.1°$$

and

$$\phi' = \phi + 60° = 41.9°$$

for maximum transient.

8.6 Transient in a Circuit of *R*, *L*, and *C* in Series — Alternating-Current Source Voltage.

The transient behavior of an *R*, *L*, and *C* series circuit has some of the characteristics of the *R-L* and *R-C* series circuits and in addition has some properties which do not appear in the simpler circuits. A study of this *R*, *L*, and *C* series circuit is necessary to complete the transient study of series circuits. Such a circuit is represented by Fig. 8–12. Because of the presence of a capacitor, the differential equation in terms of charge is most convenient. With the switch of Fig. 8–12 in the *a*-position,

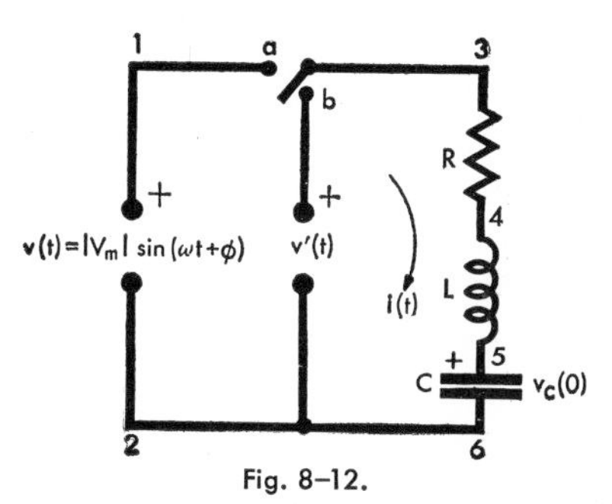

Fig. 8–12.

$$v(t) = R\frac{dq(t)}{dt} + L\frac{d^2q(t)}{dt^2} + \frac{q_C(t)}{C} \tag{8–71}$$

Since the capacitor charge at every instant is the sum of the charge due to current and the initial charge on the capacitor, i.e.,

$$q_C(t) = q(t) + q_C(0) \tag{8–72}$$

the voltage equation in terms of real variable cyclic charge is (set $S = 1/C$ for convenience)

$$v(t) = R\frac{dq(t)}{dt} + L\frac{d^2q(t)}{dt^2} + Sq(t) + Sq_C(0) \tag{8–73}$$

Expressed in complex variable form, this equation is

$$V_m\epsilon^{j\omega t} = R\frac{dQ(t)}{dt} + L\frac{d^2Q(t)}{dt^2} + SQ(t) + SQ_C(0) \tag{8–74}$$

Where $Q_C(0)$ is the complex number,

$$Q_C(0) = 0 + jq_C(0)$$

Equation 8–74 should be rearranged for solution into

$$L\frac{d^2Q(t)}{dt^2} + R\frac{dQ(t)}{dt} + SQ(t) = V_m\epsilon^{j\omega t} - SQ_C(0) \tag{8–75}$$

which is a differential equation of the same general type as equation 8–46, differing only in the fact that it is of second order, i.e., the highest derivative is of second order. This equation may be solved by the same substitutions as were used to solve equation 8–46. Hence, using the assumed solution given by equation 8–47, substituting into equation 8–75, and equating the coefficients leads to

$$Q_m = \frac{V_m}{j\omega\left[R + j\left(\omega L - \frac{1}{\omega C}\right)\right]} = \frac{V_m}{j\omega Z} \tag{8–76}$$

and

$$K = -Q_C(0)$$

If these results are substituted into the assumed solution (equation 8–47) the steady state charge due to current is

$$Q(t)_s = \frac{V_m}{j\omega Z}\,\epsilon^{j\omega t} - Q_C(0) \tag{8–77}$$

The steady state charge across the capacitor is

$$Q_C(t)_s = Q(t)_s + Q_C(0) \tag{8–78}$$

which, on substituting from equation 8–77 is

$$Q_C(t)_s = \frac{V_m}{j\omega Z}\,\epsilon^{j\omega t} \tag{8–79}$$

The transient may once more be determined from the homogeneous differential equation, which is the same as equation 8–75 except that the right-hand side is zero, namely,

$$L\frac{d^2Q(t)}{dt^2} + R\frac{dQ(t)}{dt} + SQ(t) = 0 \tag{8–80}$$

The same substitution as was used to solve the homogeneous equation in the preceding article may be used, i.e.,

$$Q(t) = A\epsilon^{mt}$$

Substituting this assumed solution into the homogeneous equation 8–80, canceling the constant and exponential, and rearranging, gives the m-polynomial as a quadratic equation, sometimes called the determinantal equation,

$$m^2 + \frac{R}{L}m + \frac{1}{LC} = 0 \tag{8–81}$$

The two roots of this equation are

$$m_1 = -\frac{R}{2L} + \frac{\sqrt{R^2 - 4LS}}{2L} = -\alpha + \beta' \tag{8–82}$$

and

$$m_2 = -\frac{R}{2L} - \frac{\sqrt{R^2 - 4LS}}{2L} = -\alpha - \beta' \tag{8-83}$$

where

$$\alpha \equiv \frac{R}{2L} \tag{8-84}$$

and

$$\beta' \equiv \frac{\sqrt{R^2 - 4LS}}{2L}, \text{ if } R^2 > 4LS \tag{8-85}$$

these latter substitutions being made simply as a matter of convenience. Note that, if $R^2 < 4LS$, the square-root terms of m_1 and m_2 are imaginary, i.e., they are the square roots of negative numbers. The different symbolism

$$\frac{\sqrt{R^2 - 4LS}}{2L} = \frac{\sqrt{-1}\sqrt{4LS - R^2}}{2L} \equiv j\beta, \; R^2 < 4LS \tag{8-86}$$

will then be used. Furthermore, note that m_1 and m_2 are equal if $R^2 = 4LS$. There are thus three sets of values for the m's and, anticipating the results of further discussion of the solution, they will be designated as

$$\text{non-oscillatory case: } R^2 > 4LS, \begin{bmatrix} m_1 = -\alpha + \beta' \\ m_2 = -\alpha - \beta' \end{bmatrix} \tag{8-87}$$

$$\text{critical case: } R^2 = 4LS, \; m_1 = m_2 = -\alpha \tag{8-88}$$

$$\text{oscillatory case: } R^2 < 4LS, \begin{bmatrix} m_1 = -\alpha + j\beta \\ m_2 = -\alpha - j\beta \end{bmatrix} \tag{8-89}$$

The occurrence of two values of m for the assumed transient solution raises the question as to what to do with them. Either one of these values of m satisfies the differential equation. But the sum of two solutions is also a solution, as direct substitution will show. Therefore, the following sums in terms of *two arbitrary integration constants*, corresponding to two integrations required to reduce the second-order derivative of equation 8–80, are solutions of the homogeneous differential equation:

$$Q(t)_t = A_1\epsilon^{(-\alpha+\beta')t} + A_2\epsilon^{(-\alpha-\beta')t} \text{—non-oscillatory} \tag{8-90}$$

$$Q(t)_t = A_1\epsilon^{-\alpha t} + tA_2\epsilon^{-\alpha t} \text{—critical} \tag{8-91}$$

$$Q(t)_t = A_1\epsilon^{(-\alpha+j\beta)t} + A_2\epsilon^{(-\alpha-j\beta)t} \text{—oscillatory} \tag{8-92}$$

Note that for the critical case given by equation 8–91, since there is only one value of m, two distinct constants of integration can be used only by resorting to some such modification as is used in this equation, namely, multiplying one of the terms by the independent variable, t. Otherwise the two terms could be combined into the exponential multiplied by the sum of two arbitrary constants, which, of course, is equivalent to only *one* arbitrary constant multiplied by the exponential. The required *two* integration constants would thus not be available.

Adding the steady state solution given by equation 8–79, which has the same form for any set of values for R, L, and C, to any one of the transient solutions, which differ for different R, L, and C values, gives the complete solution. In particular, the addition of equations 8–79 and 8–92 gives

$$Q_C(t) = \frac{V_m}{j\omega Z} \epsilon^{j\omega t} + A_1 \epsilon^{(-\alpha+j\beta)t} + A_2 \epsilon^{(-\alpha-j\beta)t} \tag{8–93}$$

as the complex variable equation for the charge at any instant on the capacitor, subject to the condition that $R^2 < 4LS$ (oscillatory case).

In order to evaluate two constants of integration, two equations must be available. These equations may be established from a known value of the dependent variable $Q(t)$, and its first derivative $I(t)$ at some value of the independent variable t. Since the capacitor may be initially charged and current may be initially in the circuit, and since as already noted in foregoing articles neither the charge nor the current can change instantly in the presence of both L and C, the initial conditions are:

$$Q(0) = 0 + j0 \quad \text{or} \quad Q_C(0) = 0 + jq_C(0) \tag{8–94}$$

and

$$I(0) = 0 + ji(0) \tag{8–95}$$

where $q_C(0)$ is the initial capacitor charge, and $i(0)$ is the current in the inductor at the instant of changing the circuit.

The two initial conditions given by equations 8–94 and 8–95 suffice to evaluate the constants of integration for any of the solutions—oscillatory, critical, or non-oscillatory. The oscillatory case (equation 8–93) will be considered first and in detail.

Substituting from equation 8–94 into 8–93, and from equation 8–95 into the first derivative of equation 8–93 gives the two independent equations

$$Q_C(0) - \frac{V_m}{j\omega Z} = [0 + jq_C(0)] - \frac{V_m}{j\omega Z} = A_1 + A_2 \tag{8–96}$$

$$I(0) - \frac{V_m}{Z} = 0 + ji(0) - \frac{V_m}{Z} = (-\alpha + j\beta)A_1 + (-\alpha - j\beta)A_2 \tag{8–97}$$

Note that the discrepancy between the initial conditions once more appears immediately the transient evaluation is undertaken. Now, however, owing to the presence of both L and C in the circuit, both inductor-current and capacitor-charge discrepancies appear. If I_d and Q_d are used to represent these discrepancies, i.e., if

$$I_d = I(0) - \frac{V_m}{Z} = [0 + ji(0)] - \frac{V_m}{Z} \tag{8–98}$$

and

$$Q_d = Q_C(0) - \frac{V_m}{j\omega Z} = [0 + jq_C(0)] - \frac{V_m}{j\omega Z} \tag{8–99}$$

equations 8–96 and 8–97 become

$$\begin{aligned} Q_d &= A_1 + A_2 \\ I_d &= (-\alpha + j\beta)A_1 + (-\alpha - j\beta)A_2 \end{aligned} \tag{8–100}$$

On solving for the arbitrary integration constants A_1 and A_2

$$\begin{aligned} A_1 &= \frac{(-\alpha - j\beta)Q_d - I_d}{-2j\beta} \\ A_2 &= \frac{(-\alpha + j\beta)Q_d - I_d}{2j\beta} \end{aligned} \tag{8–101}$$

Substituting these values for the integration constants into the general solution (equation 8–93) gives the complete solution, in complex form, for the charge on plate 5 of the capacitor of Fig. 8–12, as

$$\begin{aligned} Q_C(t) = \frac{V_m}{j\omega Z}\epsilon^{j\omega t} &+ \frac{(-\alpha - j\beta)Q_d - I_d}{-2j\beta}\epsilon^{-\alpha t}\epsilon^{j\beta t} \\ &+ \frac{(-\alpha + j\beta)Q_d - I_d}{2j\beta}\epsilon^{-\alpha t}\epsilon^{-j\beta t},\ (R^2 < 4LS) \end{aligned} \tag{8–102}$$

This equation may be simplified further by making certain combinations, and by using the relations given in equations 2–34 and 2–35. Thus

$$Q_C(t) = \frac{V_m}{j\omega Z}\epsilon^{j\omega t} + \frac{\epsilon^{-\alpha t}}{\beta}[(\alpha Q_d + I_d)\sin \beta t + \beta Q_d \cos \beta t] \tag{8–103}$$

Preparatory to expressing this solution in real variable—instantaneous—rather than complex variable—rotating vector—form, the following rectangular and exponential equivalents should be noted:

$$\frac{V_m}{j\omega Z}\epsilon^{j\omega t} = \frac{|V_m|}{\omega|Z|}\epsilon^{j(\omega t + \phi + \theta - \pi/2)} \tag{8–104}$$

From equation 8–99,

$$Q_d = q_d' + jq_d = q_C(0)\epsilon^{j(\pi/2)} - \frac{|V_m|}{\omega|Z|}\epsilon^{j(\phi + \theta - \pi/2)} \tag{8–105}$$

where

$$q_d = q_C(0) + \frac{|V_m|}{\omega|Z|}\cos(\phi + \theta) \tag{8–106}$$

and, from equation 8–98,

$$I_d = i_d' + ji_d = i(0)\epsilon^{j(\pi/2)} - \frac{|V_m|}{|Z|}\epsilon^{j(\phi + \theta)} \tag{8–107}$$

where

$$i_d = i(0) - \frac{|V_m|}{|Z|}\sin(\phi + \theta) \tag{8–108}$$

Now recall the significance of the rotating vector so far as instantaneous values are concerned, namely, that the vertical projection of the rotating vector at every instant, or simply the factor which is multiplied by j, is the instantaneous value. The charge on the plate 5 of the capacitor of Fig. 8–12, from equations 8–103 to 8–108, inclusive, is

$$q_C(t) = -\frac{|V_m|}{\omega|Z|}\cos(\omega t + \phi + \theta) + \frac{\epsilon^{-\alpha t}}{\beta}[(\alpha q_d + i_d)\sin\beta t + \beta q_d \cos\beta t] \quad (8\text{–}109)$$

The two terms of the transient may be combined into a single term by the method given in Art. 1–9 so that finally the complete charge solution in its simplest form is

$$q_C(t) = \frac{-|V_m|}{\omega|Z|}\cos(\omega t + \phi + \theta) + |Q_t|\epsilon^{-\alpha t}\sin(\beta t + \eta) \quad (8\text{–}110)$$

where

$$|Q_t| = \sqrt{\left[\frac{\alpha q_d + i_d}{\beta}\right]^2 + q_d^2} \quad (8\text{–}111)$$

and

$$\eta = \tan^{-1}\frac{\beta q_d}{\alpha q_d + i_d} \quad (8\text{–}112)$$

Note that η and $|Q_t|$ are both constants for any particular circuit and time of closing the switch.

Equation 8–110 is now as compact as it can be made. The result shows clearly the nature of the complete solution—it is the usual steady state plus a damped sine wave. Before going further with the interpretation of the oscillatory transient equation, the equations for the current in the circuit and the voltage across the capacitor will be written.

The current in the circuit follows immediately as the time derivative of equation 8–110 and is, after combining a sine and cosine term,

$$i(t) = \frac{dq_C(t)}{dt} = \frac{|V_m|}{|Z|}\sin(\omega t + \phi + \theta) + \frac{|Q_t|}{\sqrt{LC}}\epsilon^{-\alpha t}\sin(\beta t + \eta + \psi) \quad (8\text{–}113)$$

where

$$\psi = \tan^{-1}\frac{\beta}{-\alpha} \quad (8\text{–}114)$$

The voltage across the capacitor follows immediately by dividing the equation for the charge on the capacitor by C or multiplying it by S. Thus

$$v_C(t) = X_C\frac{|V_m|}{|Z|}\cos(\omega t + \phi + \theta) + S|Q_t|\epsilon^{-\alpha t}\sin(\beta t + \eta) \quad (8\text{–}115)$$

The equations for the voltage across the resistor and across the inductor may be determined from the fundamental relations $v(t)_R = Ri(t)$, and $v(t)_L = L\, di(t)/dt$.

To turn now to the interpretation of these equations, one point which should be noted is that the phase angle between the transient current and the transient voltage across the inductor or capacitor is *not* restricted to being *smaller than* 90 degrees as for the steady state. This fact may be shown by considering the transient terms of equations 8–113 and 8–115. The phase angle of the current transient from equation 8–113 is

$$\phi_i = \beta t + \eta + \psi \qquad (8\text{–}116)$$

and of the capacitor-voltage transient from equation 8–115 is

$$\phi_v = \beta t + \eta \qquad (8\text{–}117)$$

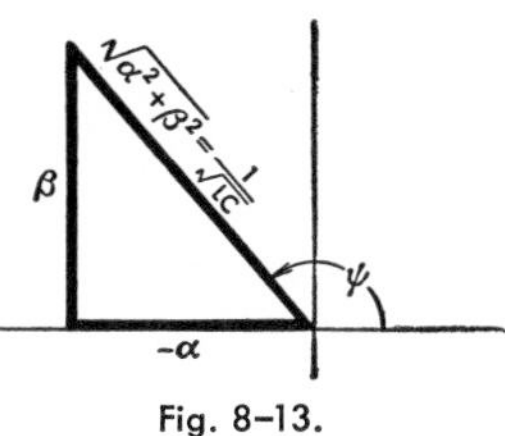

Fig. 8–13.

The difference

$$\theta_t = \phi_i - \phi_v = \psi \qquad (8\text{–}118)$$

is the angle by which the current transient *leads* the capacitor-voltage transient. From the definition of ψ (equation 8–114 or Fig. 8–13),

$$90° < \psi < 180°$$

hence from this result and equation 8–118,

$$90° < \theta_t < 180° \qquad (8\text{–}119)$$

and the transient current *always leads* the transient capacitor-voltage by *more than* 90 degrees. A similar relation holds for the inductor, as the reader should show (Problem 8–31).

Further properties of the R, L, and C series circuit are derived by considering the following questions:

(1) What is the frequency of oscillation of the transient term?

(2) What is the difference between the resonant frequency of an R, L, and C series circuit and the natural frequency (frequency of transient)?

(3) Is it possible to close the switch at such an instant that no transient occurs?

(4) What is the effect of connecting a voltage to a circuit which has the same frequency as the natural frequency of the circuit? What if the circuit is in resonance at the connected voltage frequency?

(5) In what way does the transient, for a-c connected to the circuit, differ from the d-c transient—oscillatory case?

To consider these questions in turn: (1) The combination of R, L, and C introduces the phenomena of self-oscillation which did not occur in the R-L or R-C series circuit. Under the proper set of parameter conditions—$R^2 < 4LS$—the transient term oscillates at a frequency which may be determined from β. To compare the angle of the steady state sinusoid with that of the transient sinusoid of equation 8–113 evidently β and ω are terms of the same kind, and since $\omega = 2\pi f_s$ for the steady state, for the transient

$$\beta = 2\pi f_t$$

from which, by means of equation 8–86,

$$f_t = \frac{\sqrt{4LS - R^2}}{4\pi L} \tag{8–120}$$

The value of frequency which may be computed from this equation is known as the *natural frequency*, and the reciprocal of $1/f_t$ is known as the *natural period* of the circuit. This *natural period* is, of course, the time, in seconds, of a cycle of the damped sinusoid of the transient.

The current at the frequency of the connected voltage is considered to be due to the *forced* oscillation of the circuit.

(2) In stating that the frequency of oscillation of the transient is the natural frequency of the circuit, the question arises as to the relation, if any, between this natural frequency as defined by equation 8–120 and the *resonant* frequency as defined by equation 4–26. Taking the ratio f_t/f_r of these two equations shows that the *natural frequency*, f_t, or frequency of the transient, is related to the *resonant frequency*, f_r, by

$$f_t = \left[\frac{\sqrt{4LS - R^2}}{2}\sqrt{\frac{1}{LS}}\right] f_r = f_r \sqrt{1 - \frac{R^2}{4LS}} \tag{8–121}$$

This relation shows that the *natural* and *resonant* frequencies are equal only if the resistance, R, is zero, the inductance, L, is infinite, or the capacitance, C, is zero. All these conditions are only theoretically possible, hence the *natural and resonant frequencies can never be equal*. Furthermore, since $R^2 < 4LS$, for a natural frequency to exist, i.e., for the transient to be oscillatory,

$$0 < 1 - \frac{R^2}{4LS} < 1 \tag{8–122}$$

hence, according to equation 8–121,

$$f_t < f_r \tag{8–123}$$

and the natural or transient term frequency is *always less than* the resonant frequency of the R, L, and C series circuit.

(3) Next consider the possibility of closing the switch on such a circuit condition that no transient occurs. The simplest way to derive the no-transient condition is to use equations 8–110 and 8–111. These equations indicate immediately that if the initial capacitor charge and initial current have the values required for steady state operation at the instant of

initiating the transient, i.e., if the charge and current discrepancies q_d and i_d are each zero, then $|Q_t|$ of equations 8–110 and 8–111 is zero and no transient results.

The conclusion just reached for the R, L, and C series circuit in connection with the corresponding conclusions for the R and L and R and C series circuits shows that, *if a series circuit is, at the instant of closing the switch on an a-c voltage, in a condition corresponding to the incoming steady state at the instant of closing the switch, no transient will result.* As may be expected, this rule applies for any circuit,

(4) Next consider the effect of connecting a voltage to the R, L, and C series circuit which has the same frequency as the natural frequency of the circuit. The resultant current is, from equation 8–113, by substituting ω for β,

$$i(t) = \frac{|V_m|}{|Z|} \sin(\omega t + \phi + \theta) + \frac{|Q_t|}{\sqrt{LC}} \sin(\omega t + \eta + \psi)\epsilon^{-\alpha t} \quad (8\text{–}124)$$

The two terms cannot be combined further, even though they are of the same frequency, because of the exponential multiplier of the transient term; and for the same reason the sum of the two terms will not be a sine wave.

Because the transient and steady state terms are of the same frequency, if the source voltage operates at the natural frequency of the circuit, the transient and steady state may be in phase or in phase opposition. The transient and steady state terms will be in phase provided (equation 8–124)

$$\phi + \theta = \eta + \psi \quad \text{or} \quad \phi = \eta + \psi - \theta \quad (8\text{–}125)$$

or in phase opposition provided

$$\phi = \eta + \psi - \theta + 180° \quad (8\text{–}126)$$

The maximum value of the total current, if the steady state and transient currents are in phase or phase opposition, is

$$|I_{\max}| = \frac{|V_m|}{|Z|} \pm \left|\frac{Q_t}{\sqrt{LC}}\right| \epsilon^{-\alpha \frac{\pi/2 - \phi - \theta}{\omega}} \quad (8\text{–}127)$$

The plus sign applies to the in-phase condition.

If the series circuit is in resonance at the frequency of the source voltage

$$\omega = 2\pi f_r > 2\pi f_t \quad \text{and} \quad \theta = 0$$

These relations result in a simpler form for $|Q_t|$ and, of course, unity power factor for the steady state term. Otherwise nothing of significance results from such a condition beyond what has already been noted in Chap. 4 concerning the conditions for and results of steady state resonance.

From the fact that the natural, or transient, frequency of an R, L, and C series circuit is always less than the resonant frequency, obviously a circuit cannot resonate at the natural frequency. As the resistance is lowered the natural and resonant frequencies approach each other and the current becomes increasingly great. This result is not new, however, since the reduction of the resistance in a circuit at resonance will certainly cause an increase in current to dangerous values if the resistance is reduced sufficiently.

(5) As a final consideration of an R, L, and C series circuit transient, the transient—oscillatory case—for a d-c source voltage and an a-c source voltage will be compared. The homogeneous form of the differential equation is always used to determine the transient so there could be no possible fundamental difference between the transient for d-c or a-c source voltages. The integration *constants* will be different in appearance, but they are still constants and so not essentially different.

The following example serves to illustrate some of the relations considered in the foregoing discussion.

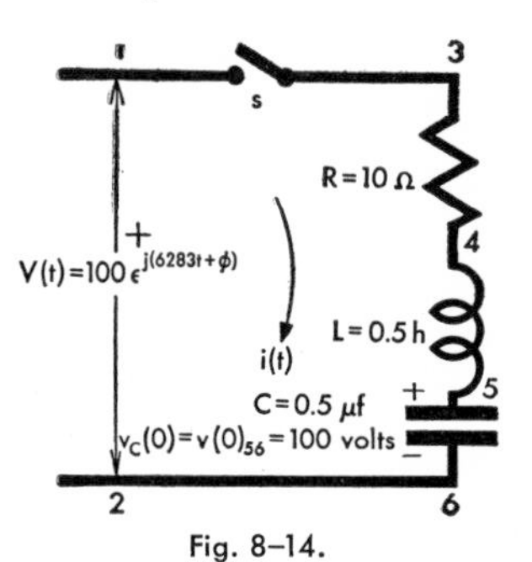

Fig. 8–14.

Example 8:5 The circuit shown in Fig. 8–14 will be considered:

(*a*) What is the instantaneous equation for the current and the voltages $v_R(t)$, $v_L(t)$, and $v_C(t)$? Plot these equations. Assume $\phi = 30$ degrees.

(*b*) What is the decrement factor, natural frequency, and resonant frequency?

(*c*) What is the value of ϕ and the charge on the capacitor to give no transient for zero initial current?

Solution The evaluation of the coefficients in the charge and current equations 8–110 and 8–113 will be carried out first:

$$\alpha = \frac{R}{2L} = \frac{10}{2 \times 0.5} = 10$$

$$\beta = \frac{\sqrt{4LS - R^2}}{2L} = \frac{\sqrt{4 \times 0.5 \times 2 \times 10^6 - 10^2}}{2 \times 0.5} = 2000$$

$$q_C(0) = Cv_C(0) = 0.5 \times 10^{-6} \times 100 = 5 \times 10^{-5} \text{ coulomb}$$

$$\sqrt{LC} = \sqrt{0.5 \times 0.5 \times 10^{-6}} = 5 \times 10^{-4}$$

$$|Z| = \sqrt{R^2 + X_0^2} = \sqrt{10^2 + \left[6283 \times 0.5 - \frac{10^6}{6283 \times 0.5}\right]^2} = 2823 \text{ ohms}$$

$$\frac{|V_m|}{|Z|} = \frac{100}{2823} = 0.0354 \text{ amp}$$

$$i(0) = 0$$

$$\frac{|V_m|}{\omega|Z|} = \frac{0.0354}{6283} = 0.563 \times 10^{-5} \text{ coulomb}$$

$$\theta = -\tan^{-1}\frac{X_0}{R} = -\tan^{-1}\tfrac{2823}{10} = -89.8^\circ$$

$$\cos(\phi+\theta) = \cos(-59.8^\circ) = 0.503$$

$$\sin(\phi+\theta) = \sin(-59.8^\circ) = -0.864$$

$$q_d = q_C(0) + \frac{|V_m|}{\omega|Z|}\cos(\phi+\theta) = 5\times10^{-5} + 0.563\times10^{-5}\times0.503$$

$$= 5.28\times10^{-5}\text{ coulomb}$$

$$i_d = i(0) - \frac{|V_m|}{|Z|}\sin(\phi+\theta) = 0 - 0.0354(-0.864) = 0.0306\text{ amp}$$

$$|Q_t| = \sqrt{\left[\frac{\alpha q_d + i_d}{\beta}\right]^2 + q_d^2} = \sqrt{\left[\frac{10\times5.28\times10^{-5}+0.0306}{2000}\right]^2 + (5.28\times10^{-5})^2}$$

$$= 5.5\times10^{-5}$$

$$\eta = \tan^{-1}\frac{\beta q_d}{\alpha q_d + i_d} = \tan^{-1}\frac{2000\times5.28\times10^{-5}}{10\times5.28\times10^{-5}+0.0306} = \tan^{-1}3.39$$

$$= 73.6^\circ$$

$$\psi = \tan^{-1}\frac{\beta}{-\alpha} = \tan^{-1}\frac{2000}{-10} = 90.3^\circ$$

$$\eta + \psi = 163.9^\circ$$

$$\frac{|Q_t|}{\sqrt{LC}} = \frac{5.5\times10^{-5}}{5\times10^{-4}} = 0.11$$

Substituting the numbers now computed into the charge and current expressions equations 8–110 and 8–113 gives

$$q_C(t) = -0.563\times10^{-5}\cos(6283t - 59.8^\circ) + 5.5\times10^{-5}\epsilon^{-10t}\sin(2000t + 73.6^\circ)\text{ (coulomb)}$$

and

$$i(t) = 0.0354\sin(6283t - 59.8^\circ) - 0.11\epsilon^{-10t}\sin(2000t - 16.1^\circ)\text{ (ampere)}$$

The voltage equations are

$$v_R(t) = Ri(t) = 0.354\sin(6283t - 59.8^\circ) - 1.1\epsilon^{-10t}\sin(2000t - 16.1^\circ)\text{ (volts)}$$

$$v_C(t) = \frac{q_C(t)}{C} = -11.26\cos(6283t - 59.8^\circ) + 110\epsilon^{-10t}\sin(2000t + 73.6^\circ)\text{ (volts)}$$

$$v_L(t) = L\frac{di(t)}{dt} = 111\cos(6283t - 59.8^\circ) + 110\epsilon^{-10t}\sin(2000t - 106.4^\circ)\text{ (volts)}$$

These equations are shown graphically in Fig. 8–15.

(*b*) The decrement factor is by definition the ratio of successive positive maxima of the transient. Worked out symbolically, for the present problem the decrement factor is

$$\frac{i_{m2t}}{i_{m1t}} = \Delta = \epsilon^{-(2\pi R)/\sqrt{4LS-R^2}}$$

where

i_{m1t} = first positive maximum of the transient,
i_{m2t} = second positive maximum of the transient.

Hence

$$\Delta = \epsilon^{-6283/2000} = \epsilon^{-3.1416} = 0.0432$$

shows that the transient in the circuit of Fig. 8–14 dies out very rapidly—the second positive maximum is reduced to 0.0432 times the first positive maximum. This reduction occurs in one cycle of the transient, or in 0.00363 second.

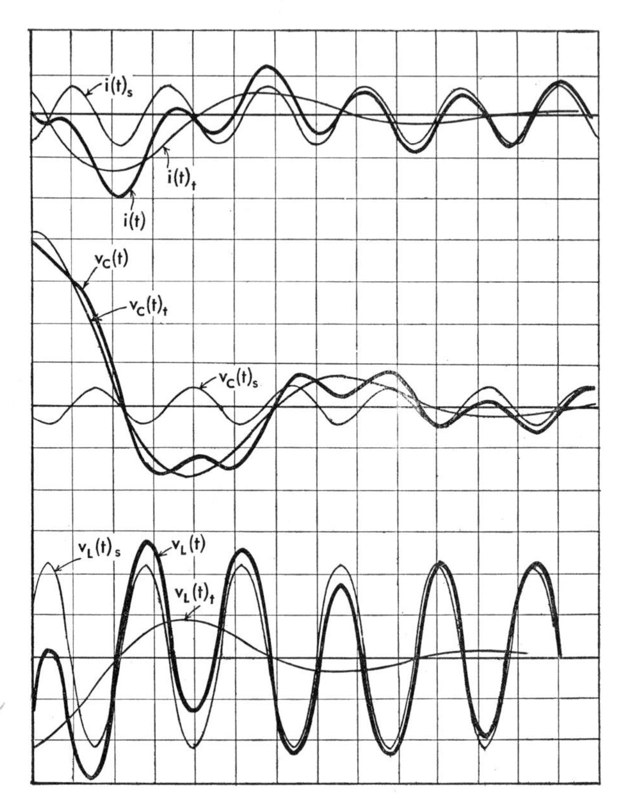

Fig. 8–15.

The natural frequency of the circuit is, from equation 8–120,

$$f_t = \frac{\sqrt{4LS - R^2}}{4\pi L} = \frac{\beta}{2\pi} = \frac{2000}{2\pi} = 318.3 \text{ cps}$$

and the resonant frequency of the circuit is

$$f_r = \frac{1}{2\pi\sqrt{LC}} = \frac{1}{2\pi \times 5 \times 10^{-4}} = 318.3 \text{ cps}$$

These two frequencies would be found to differ if the numerical computation were carried far enough. They are the same here since $R^2 \ll 4LS$. The frequency of forced oscillation, or the steady state, is 1000 cps.

(*c*) In order to determine the value of ϕ for no transient, i_d and q_d of equations 8–106 and 8–108 must each vanish for no transient. Because $i(0) = 0$, equation 8–108 requires that

$$\sin(\phi + \theta) = 0$$

so that

$$\phi + \theta = 0$$

and

$$\phi = -\theta = 89.8°$$

for $i_d = 0$. In addition q_d of equation 8–106 is zero for $\phi + \theta = 0$ if

$$q_C(0) = \frac{-|V_m|}{\omega|Z|}\cos(\phi + \theta) = -0.563 \times 10^{-5}$$

The given initial charge on the capacitor has been taken as 5×10^{-5} coulomb; hence a negative charge of 5.563×10^{-5} coulomb must be added to the capacitor to permit closing the switch for no transient.

A second value for ϕ and $q_C(0)$, to produce no transient, may be established by noting that, for $i(0) = 0$, i_d of equation 8–108 is also zero if

$$\phi + \theta = 180°$$

or

$$\phi = 180° - \theta = 180° + 89.8° = 269.8°$$

Then from equation 8–106 the required initial charge is

$$q_C(0) = \frac{-|V_m|}{\omega|Z|}\cos 180° = 0.563 \times 10^{-5}$$

and a negative charge of 4.437×10^{-5} coulomb should be added to the capacitor to reduce the given initial charge to the proper value.

The two possible initial charges correspond to the two zero values of current during a cycle. The first zero transient condition considered—$\phi + \theta = 0$—corresponds to a zero steady state current increasing positively, and the second zero transient condition—$\phi + \theta = 180°$—corresponds to zero steady state current increasing negatively.

The non-oscillatory and critical cases offer nothing essentially new in solving for the constants of integration. But, since the mathematical equations for these cases are somewhat different in appearance than for the oscillatory case, they will be discussed briefly.

The solution for the charge in the non-oscillatory case is similar to the solution for the oscillatory case of equation 8–109, being modified by replacing, in the transient term, sine and cosine by sinh and cosh and β by β'. Thus

$$q_C(t) = \frac{-|V_m|}{\omega|Z|} \cos(\omega t + \phi + \theta) + \frac{\epsilon^{-\alpha t}}{\beta'} [(\alpha q_d + i_d) \sinh \beta' t + \beta' q_d \cosh \beta' t] \quad (8\text{–}128)$$

where

$$\beta' = \frac{\sqrt{R^2 - 4LS}}{2L} \quad (8\text{–}129)$$

$$\alpha = \frac{R}{2L} \quad (8\text{–}130)$$

$$i_d = i(0) - \frac{|V_m|}{|Z|} \sin(\phi + \theta) \quad (8\text{–}131)$$

$$q_d = q_C(0) + \frac{|V_m|}{\omega|Z|} \cos(\phi + \theta) \quad (8\text{–}132)$$

Differentiating the charge equation gives the current for the non-oscillatory case as

$$i(t) = \frac{dq_C(t)}{dt} = \frac{|V_m|}{|Z|} \sin(\omega t + \phi + \theta) + \epsilon^{-\alpha t} \left[\frac{-\alpha i_d - \dfrac{1}{LC} q_d}{\beta'} \sinh \beta' t + i_d \cosh \beta' t \right] \quad (8\text{–}133)$$

It should be noted that it is possible to simplify equations 8–128 and 8–133 into a simpler form by combining the sinh and cosh terms as was done in combining the sine and cosine terms of equation 8–109 to give equation 8–110 (see Problem 2–24).

The graphical form of this current equation for the circuit of Fig. 8–14 of Example 8–5 is shown in Fig. 8–16*a*. The resistance has been changed from the 10 ohms of the oscillatory circuit to 3000 ohms. Note the difference in the appearance of the transient and of the total current in Figs. 8–15 and 8–16*a*.

The critical case, the transient of which is formulated by equation 8–91, on evaluating the integration constants, leads to the equation

$$q_C(t) = \frac{-|V_m|}{\omega|Z|} \cos(\omega t + \phi + \theta) + [(1 + \alpha t) q_d + i_d t]\, \epsilon^{-\alpha t} \quad (8\text{–}134)$$

and differentiating this expression gives the current as

$$i(t) = \frac{|V_m|}{|Z|} \sin(\omega t + \phi + \theta) + [(1 - \alpha t) i_d - \alpha^2 t q_d] \epsilon^{-\alpha t} \quad (8\text{–}135)$$

This current expression is shown graphically in Fig. 8–16*b* for the circuit of Fig. 8–14, and Example 8–5. While different in appearance mathematically, this critical case equation is graphically similar to the non-oscillatory case as shown in Fig. 8–16*a*. The critical resistance is the lowest value which will prevent the transient from oscillating. Note that, according to this equation, the transient in the critical case also *takes infinite time to die out.*

The reader should work through the details leading to equations 8–133 and 8–135. Other textbooks* give a more complete story of these

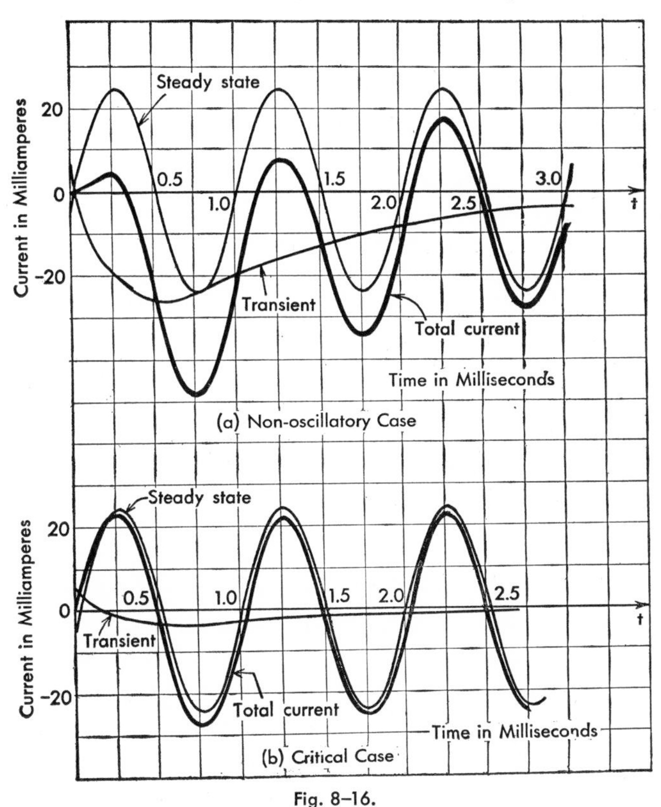

Fig. 8–16.

equations either pictorially or mathematically, and the reader may refer to them.

8.7 Transient Due to a Discharge of Capacitors.

Transients are often initiated by connecting a charged capacitor in a circuit. Many of the sweep circuits of cathode ray oscillographs are examples of such transient usage. Lightning strokes are all discharges of capacitors formed by clouds and earth or by two clouds. Surge generators also operate by discharging capacitors.

* E. B. Kurtz and G. F. Corcoran, *Introduction to Electrical Transients*, John Wiley & Sons, 1935; H. H. Skilling, *Transient Electric Currents*, McGraw-Hill Book Co., 1937; Myril B. and Georgia B. Reed, *Mathematical Methods in Electrical Engineering*, Harper & Brothers, 1951.

The transient of the discharge of a capacitor does not depend on whether the circuit energy has been supplied by alternating or direct current—mathematically because the source voltage is zero and the homogeneous equation is the only one to be considered; physically because the manner in which a circuit behaves *after* a voltage is disconnected can certainly depend only on the condition of the circuit at the instant the voltage is disconnected and not on the source voltage before.

Actually, the solution for a discharge transient is identical with the solution for the transient term when a voltage is connected to a circuit whether alternating or direct current, i.e., the discharge transient is determined from the homogeneous equation. In solving the homogeneous equation, it has already been seen that the important point is the initial value from which the discharge starts, which means mathematically that the important point is the determination of the constants of integration, for the particular initial conditions desired.

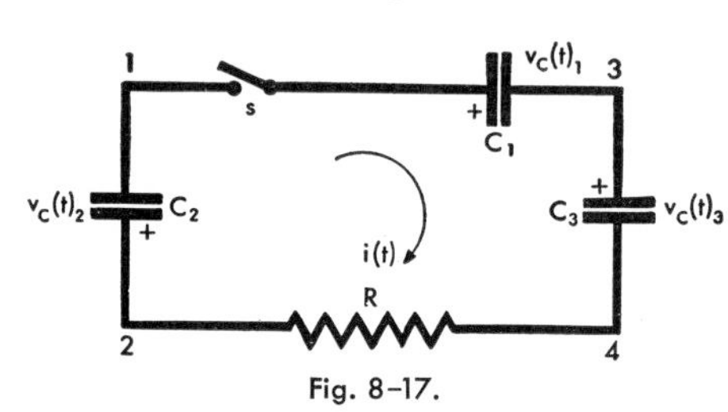

Fig. 8-17.

Consider the electric circuit symbolized by Fig. 8–17, which represents the electrical essentials of a surge generator on discharge. Suppose that each of the capacitors are charged and then placed in their respective positions and the switch closed. A current will appear until the *voltages across the capacitors add algebraically to zero.* In order to solve the equation for the current, the differential equation for the voltages in the circuit must be solved, as in the preceding discussions in this chapter. This equation is

$$v_C(t)_2 + v_C(t)_1 + v_C(t)_3 + v_R(t) = \frac{q_C(t)_2}{C_2} + \frac{q_C(t)_1}{C_1} + \frac{q_C(t)_3}{C_3} + R\frac{dq(t)}{dt} = 0 \tag{8–136}$$

If the significance of the charge symbols (equation 8–39 and the accompanying discussion) is recalled, this equation may be written as

$$\frac{q(t) + q_C(0)_2}{C_2} + \frac{q(t) + q_C(0)_1}{C_1} + \frac{q(t) + q_C(0)_3}{C_3} + R\frac{dq(t)}{dt} = 0 \tag{8–137}$$

which, on being rearranged, gives the differential equation, now *nonhomogeneous,* to be solved

$$q(t)\left(\frac{1}{C_2} + \frac{1}{C_1} + \frac{1}{C_3}\right) + R\frac{dq(t)}{dt} = -\frac{q_C(0)_2}{C_2} - \frac{q_C(0)_1}{C_1} - \frac{q_C(0)_3}{C_3} \tag{8–138}$$

If the equivalent capacitance of the three capacitors in series is symbolized as C_0,

$$\frac{1}{C_0} = \frac{1}{C_2} + \frac{1}{C_1} + \frac{1}{C_3} = \frac{C_1C_3 + C_2C_3 + C_2C_1}{C_2C_1C_3}$$

and equation 8–138 becomes

$$R\frac{dq(t)}{dt} + \frac{q(t)}{C_0} = \frac{-q_C(0)_2}{C_2} - \frac{q_C(0)_1}{C_1} - \frac{q_C(0)_3}{C_3} \tag{8–139}$$

In order to shorten the symbolism required to continue the solution of this equation, let

$$v_0 = \frac{q_C(0)_2}{C_2} + \frac{q_C(0)_1}{C_1} + \frac{q_C(0)_3}{C_3} = v_C(0)_2 + v_C(0)_1 + v_C(0)_3 \tag{8–140}$$

then equation 8–139 may be written as

$$R\frac{dq(t)}{dt} + \frac{q(t)}{C_0} = -v_0 \tag{8–141}$$

Because a sinusoidal voltage function does not appear in this equation it will not facilitate the solution to use complex variable, or rotating vector, expressions. Hence, the real variable equation of 8–141 will be solved just as it stands.

Essentially this same equation has been solved in Art. 8–5; hence only the outline of the method is given here. First, to solve for the particular integral—steady-state solution—assume that

$$q(t) = K = \text{constant} \tag{8–142}$$

Substituting this assumption into equation 8–141 and solving for K produces

$$K = -C_0v_0 \tag{8–143}$$

Note that this product C_0v_0 is the equivalent capacitance of the mesh multiplied by the effective source voltage active at $t = 0$.

The solution of the auxiliary homogeneous equation of equation 8–141 has already been established in equation 8–55. Therefore, the general solution of equation 8–141 is the sum

$$q(t) = -C_0v_0 + A\epsilon^{-(t/RC_0)} \tag{8–144}$$

The arbitrary constant A may be evaluated from the fact that the charge due to current is always initially zero, so that $q(0) = 0$. As a consequence, from equation 8–144,

$$A = C_0v_0$$

and the complete solution for the charge due to current is

$$q(t) = -C_0v_0(1 - \epsilon^{-(t/RC_0)}) \tag{8–145}$$

The charge on each of the capacitors at any instant is

$$q_C(t)_1 = q(t) + q_C(0)_1 = -C_0v_0(1 - \epsilon^{-(t/RC_0)}) + q_C(0)_1 \quad (8\text{–}146)$$
$$q_C(t)_3 = q(t) + q_C(0)_3 = -C_0v_0(1 - \epsilon^{-(t/RC_0)}) + q_C(0)_3 \quad (8\text{–}147)$$
$$q_C(t)_2 = q(t) + q_C(0)_2 = -C_0v_0(1 - \epsilon^{-(t/RC_0)}) + q_C(0)_2 \quad (8\text{–}148)$$

and the current is

$$i(t) = \frac{dq(t)}{dt} = \frac{-v_0}{R}\epsilon^{-(t/RC_0)} \quad (8\text{–}149)$$

Note that the initial current is equal to the algebraic sum of the capacitor voltages divided by the resistance of the circuit.

The final value of the charge on the capacitors of the circuit is of particular interest. Letting t become indefinitely large gives these final values of charge as

$$\begin{aligned} q_C(\infty)_1 &= -C_0v_0 + q_C(0)_1 \\ q_C(\infty)_3 &= -C_0v_0 + q_C(0)_3 \\ q_C(\infty)_2 &= -C_0v_0 + q_C(0)_2 \end{aligned} \quad (8\text{–}150)$$

Dividing these final charge expressions by the proper capacitance gives the final voltage across the capacitors. The sum of the resulting voltages must be zero (see Problem 8–27).

Equation 8–150 illustrates the "trapped" charge idea. If the initial charges on the capacitors of Fig. 8–17 are not equal, the final charges cannot be zero for any values of the C's. Thus charge is "trapped" in this circuit unless the capacitor charges are initially equal.

8.8 Transient Due to Insertion or Removal of Circuit Elements.

Switching operations and cases of trouble such as short circuits represent circuit changes in power systems which initiate transients. The changing of capacitance or resistance of microphone circuits is the most common example of transient initiation in communication systems by parameter changes. The full mathematical treatment of this latter type of circuit variation cannot be attempted here, but the relatively simple discussion to follow is a necessary preliminary to solving any of the problems of transient initiation by circuit changes. Since it is not feasible to attempt a consideration of all possible arrangements, the method of attack on removing or inserting a circuit element will be illustrated by two typical examples.

Consider first the circuit of Fig. 8–18. Suppose that this circuit is operating under steady state condition when the switch s is closed. The angle ϕ, as heretofore, designates the time of closing the switch. The differential equation for this problem must be written from the circuit *after* the change has been made. This fact seems obvious because the differential equation is to represent the circuit behavior *after* the closing of the switch.

The Kirchhoff voltage equation for Fig. 8–18, after the switch is closed, is

$$v(t) = R_1 i(t) + L\frac{di(t)}{dt} \tag{8–151}$$

or in terms of complex variable, i.e., rotating vector,

$$V(t) = V_m \epsilon^{j\omega t} = R_1 I(t) + L\frac{dI(t)}{dt} \tag{8–152}$$

The resistor voltage in line 1–3 is *not* included in this equation since this resistor is out of the circuit from the instant the switch *s* is closed, i.e., for the transient period being considered.

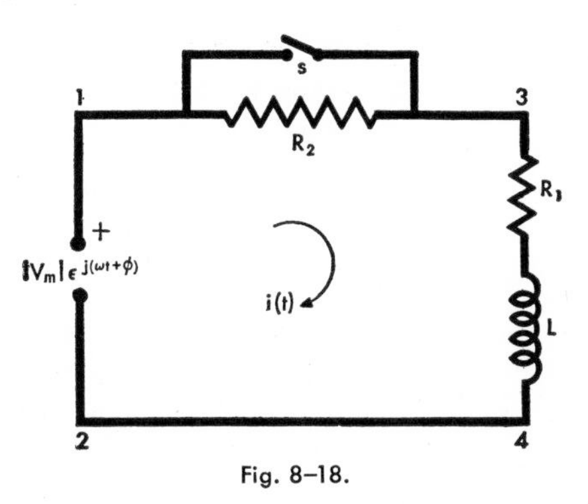

Fig. 8–18.

The solution of equation 8–152 is the same as that of equation 8–22 because the equations are alike. Equation 8–31 is, therefore, the solution of equation 8–152 also. So

$$I(t) = \frac{V_m}{Z_{34}}\,\epsilon^{j\omega t} + A\epsilon^{-(R_1/L)t} \tag{8–153}$$

The evaluation of the integration constant A requires a consideration of the initial condition of the circuit. Because of the presence of the inductor in the circuit, the current cannot change abruptly. Consequently the initial current must be determined from the circuit condition immediately preceding the closing of the switch. Therefore, from Fig. 8–18, at $t = 0$,

$$I(0) = \frac{V_m}{(R_1 + R_2) + j\omega L} = \frac{V_m}{Z_0} \tag{8–154}$$

Equating this current to the $t = 0$ value of equation 8–153 and solving for A gives

$$A = \frac{V_m}{Z_0} - \frac{V_m}{Z_{34}} \tag{8–155}$$

Substituting this result into equation 8–153 establishes the complete solution for the current as

$$I(t) = \frac{V_m}{Z_{34}} \epsilon^{j\omega t} + \left(\frac{V_m}{Z_0} - \frac{V_m}{Z_{34}}\right) \epsilon^{-(R_1/L)t} \tag{8–156}$$

which instantaneously is

$$i(t) = \frac{|V_m|}{|Z_{34}|} \sin (\omega t + \phi + \theta_{34}) + |V_m| \left[\frac{\sin (\phi + \theta_0)}{|Z_0|} - \frac{\sin (\phi + \theta_{34})}{|Z_{34}|}\right] \epsilon^{-(R_1/L)t} \tag{8–157}$$

Note that the initial magnitude of the transient is equal to the *difference between the current in the circuit at the instant of closing the switch and the steady state current required for the changed circuit at that particular instant,* i.e., it is the usual discrepancy factor. The condition for zero transient in equation 8–157 is evidently

$$|Z_{34}| \sin (\phi + \theta_0) = |Z_0| \sin (\phi + \theta_{34})$$

from which

$$\tan \phi = \frac{|Z_0| \sin \theta_{34} - |Z_{34}| \sin \theta_0}{|Z_{34}| \cos \theta_0 - |Z_0| \cos \theta_{34}} \tag{8–158}$$

If the factors $|Z_0|$, $|Z_{34}|$, θ_{34}, and θ_0 are known, as they must be for a solution of the voltage equation to be possible, the angle ϕ can be determined.

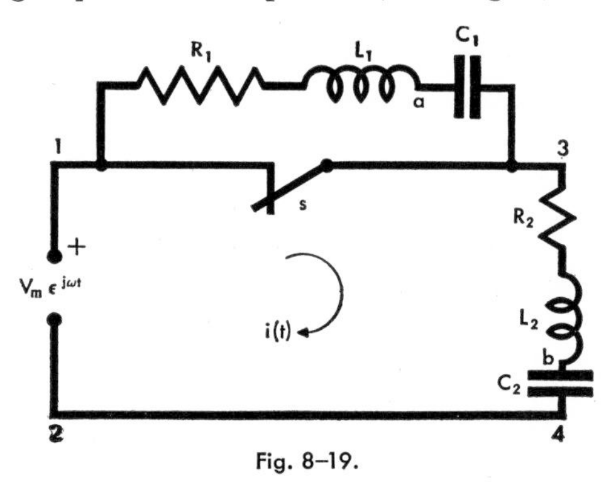

Fig. 8–19.

In order to illustrate still further the method of solving equations resulting from changes in a circuit, one more circuit will be considered—the one shown in Fig. 8–19. Suppose that a switch *s* is *opened* at an instant represented by the phase angle ϕ. The differential equation to be solved for this circuit must be written from the circuit with the switch open, i.e., with both sets of circuit elements in series. This equation is

$$v(t) = (R_1 + R_2) \frac{dq(t)}{dt} + (L_1 + L_2) \frac{d^2q(t)}{dt^2} + \frac{q_C(t)_1}{C_1} + \frac{q_C(t)_2}{C_2} \tag{8–159}$$

which is similar to equation 8–73 and the solution is as given by equation 8–91, or an equivalent form, depending on whether the oscillatory, critical, or non-oscillatory case must be considered. The determination of the constants of integration is, just as before, carried out by establishing two initial conditions of the circuit in order to derive two equations from which the constants can be determined.

Since the initial conditions once more are easier to state in terms of charge and its first derivative, current, than in terms of current and its first derivative, consider the initial conditions in terms of charge and current.

Because, before the opening of the switch, the circuit is operating at a steady state with only the set of circuit elements in branch 3–4 in series, the initial value of the current in the circuit is the $t = 0$ value of the current through the impedance Z_{34}, or

$$I(0) = \frac{V_m}{Z_{34}} = \frac{|V_m|}{|Z_{34}|} \epsilon^{j(\phi+\theta)} \tag{8–160}$$

The initial value of the cyclic charge is, as always, zero.

Using equation 8–90, 8–91, or 8–92 and its first derivative with the foregoing initial conditions, the two constants of integration can be evaluated. The solution is thereby completed.

Some circuits which are subject to rapid changes—thyraton inverters in which the resistance of the tubes changes abruptly and often, or cathode ray oscillograph sweep circuits which operate from one transient state to another—never really reach a steady state. The initial conditions for the circuit solution must, therefore, be determined from the value of the preceding transient at the instant of interrupting the first transient to form a second one. Since there is nothing essentially new in such a process, the details are left for the reader (Problem 8–36).

PROBLEMS

8–1 Determine the complete solution of the differential equation

$$10^{-4}\frac{d^2q(t)}{dt^2} + 3 \times 10^{-2}\frac{dq(t)}{dt} + 2q(t) = 100 \sin 300t$$

if $q(0) = 4$ and $i(0) = -2$. Substitute the complete solution into the differential equation and show that it satisfies this equation.

8–2 Repeat Problem 8–1 for the differential equation

$$2 \times 10^{-4}\frac{d^2Q(t)}{dt^2} + 2 \times 10^{-2}\frac{dQ(t)}{dt} + 2\,Q(t) = 10\epsilon^{j100t}$$

$$Q(0) = 0 + j4;\ I(0) = 0 - j450$$

8–3 Repeat Problem 8–1 for the differential equation

$$10^{-4}\frac{d^2Q(t)}{dt^2} + 2 \times 10^{-2}\frac{dQ(t)}{dt} + Q(t) = (8 + j6)10^2\epsilon^{j200t}$$

Assume that all initial conditions are zero.

8–4 Show that equation 8–14 is equivalent to equation 8–13 as stated. Use $\epsilon^{j\theta} = \cos\theta + j\sin\theta$ to demonstrate the equivalence.

8–5 Determine, by guessing, the value of $i(t)$ which will reduce the following equations to identities, i.e., find the solution of:

$$(a)\quad \frac{di(t)}{dt} + 4i(t) = t^3$$

$$(b)\quad \frac{d^2i(t)}{dt^2} + i(t) = 10\sin t$$

$$(c)\quad \frac{d^2i(t)}{dt^2} + 2\frac{di(t)}{dt} + i(t) = \epsilon^{-t}$$

Note that the scheme suggested in the text does not work for (*b*) or (*c*). Try $t\epsilon^{-t}$, $t^2\epsilon^{-t}$, or $t^3\epsilon^{-t}$ for (*c*).

8–6 Derive the expression for the current in a pure inductor if a battery of 6 volts is connected to the coil of 0.1 henry at $t = 0$. Assume that as the battery is connected the coil is removed from another circuit so that the current in the coil is 10 amp directed toward the positive terminal of the battery. Plot the current curve. Determine the expression for the energy supplied to the coil at any instant. What is happening to this energy?

8–7 Derive the transient equation for the current in a pure inductor if the voltage $v(t) = |V_m| \sin(\omega t + \phi)$ volts is connected at $t = 0$. What is the condition for no transient and for maximum transient? Is the transient alternating or direct? Sketch the transient, steady state, and the total current.

8–8 Assume no resistance in the circuit of Fig. 8–5. The voltage $v'(t) = 100 \sin 1000t$, $v(t) = 200 \sin(1000t + 60°)$, and $L = 0.025$ henry. (*a*) If the switch is moved from position *a* to position *b* at $t = 0$, determine the current from $t = 0$ on. What is the transient? (*b*) Determine the instant of closing the switch to produce no transient. What is the value of $v(t)$ at this instant and its phase angle ϕ? (*c*) What are the values at $t = 0$ of $v(t)$ and $v'(t)$ and their phase positions for maximum transient?

8–9 A voltage of $150\epsilon^{j1000t}$ is connected to a coil of $R = 10$ ohms and $L = 20$ mh at $t = 0$. (*a*) Determine the current, resistance voltage, and inductance voltage equations. (*b*) Find the power being supplied to the circuit as a whole, to the resistor, and to the inductor at the end of 0.002 sec. (*c*) What is the total energy supplied to the circuit during the first 0.002 sec? (*d*) At what point on the voltage should the switch be closed to produce zero transient? (*e*) To produce maximum transient? (*f*) What are the maximum values of maximum transients of current and inductance voltage?

8–10 Some small remote-controlled three-phase power plants are paralleled with the system by simply bringing the machine up to speed and closing the oil switch. No attention is paid to voltage relations. At worst, double voltage will thereby be connected in series with the internal impedance of the incoming machine. Because the resulting current surge would be large enough to be a serious hazard, reactors are placed in the connecting lines to prevent excessive current. Suppose a 9000-kva, 3-phase machine is so installed and that double the phase voltage of 3000 becomes connected in series with the impedance $2 + j12$ ohms. (*a*) What is the value of the voltage at the instant the switch should be closed for no transient? (*b*) Determine the time constant for this circuit. (*c*) What is the value of ϕ to give maximum current transient? (*d*) What is the approximate maximum of the total current during the transient period—$\phi = 60°$. Sketch the transient and steady state and their sum.

8–11 An initially unexcited $R = 10$ ohms and $L = 0.01$ henry series circuit is connected to a battery of 120 volts. (*a*) What is the voltage across the inductor at $t = 0$. Why? What is di/dt? (*b*) What is the maximum value of the transient current? (*c*) Assume this circuit has been in operation 0.001 sec when the battery is removed and a sine wave of voltage of $|V_m| = 100$ volts, $\omega = 1000$ is connected to the circuit. The alternating voltage is connected when it is positive at 0.5 maximum and decreasing. Without solving for the second transient formally, find the initial value of the second transient of current, and the transient of voltage across the inductor.

8–12 A voltmeter of 12,000 ohms resistance is connected across and an ammeter in series with a coil of $R = 5$ ohms and $L = 10$ henrys. This coil and meter combination is connected through a switch to a 125-volt d-c generator. Before the switch is opened at $t = 0$ the circuit is operating at steady state. (*a*) Find the energy stored in the coil when the switch is opened. (*b*) Find the voltmeter indication in magnitude and direction at the instant of opening the switch. Will the meter be damaged? What is the voltage across the inductor? (*c*) Find the magnitude and direction of the ammeter indication when the switch is opened. Will the meter be damaged? (*d*) Repeat if a 5.0-ohm field discharge resistor is automatically connected in parallel with the voltmeter and coil when the switch is opened.

8–13 In the circuit of Fig. 8–12 $|V_m| = 100$, $|V_m'| = 200$, $\omega = 1000$, $v(t)$ lags $v'(t)$ by 60 degrees, $R = 10$ ohms, $L = 0.01$ henry, $C = \infty$. (*a*) Specify ϕ and ϕ' so that no transient results on changing the switch from *a* to *b*. (*b*) Specify ϕ and ϕ' for maximum transient on changing the switch from the *a* to *b* position. (*c*) Determine the expression for the current in the coil if the switch is changed from *a* to *b* position when ϕ' is -30 degrees. (*d*) Repeat (*a*), (*b*), and (*c*) for changing the switch from *b* to *a*.

8–14 Repeat Problem 8–13 for $v'(t) = 50$ volts.

8–15 A voltage $v(t) = 200 \sin (377t + \phi)$ is connected across a coil of $R = 10$ ohms, $L = 1$ henry at $t = 0$. Find $I(t)$, $i(t)$, and ϕ for zero transient and for maximum transient if: (*a*) $i(0) = 2|I_m|$; (*b*) $i(0) = |I_m|$; (*c*) $i(0) = |I_m|/2$.

8–16 Compute the energy dissipated in heat in the inductive resistor of Problem 8–10, over the first 1000 cycles for zero initial current: (*a*) for the transient alone; (*b*) for the steady state current alone; (*c*) for the combined current. How does the sum of the values of (*a*) and (*b*) compare with the correct result of (*c*)? Assume $\phi = 30$ degrees.

8–17 Show, for an *R* and *C* series circuit, that the transient voltage across the initially uncharged capacitor for $\phi + \theta = 0$ has a maximum value equal to the maximum steady state voltage across the capacitor.

8–18 The switch is closed on a circuit connecting a 150-volt, 1000 cps sine voltage to an R and C series circuit (Fig. 8–9) at such a time that the generated voltage is $0.866|V_m|$ and increasing. The resistance is 20 ohms and the capacitor is 20 μf. The capacitor is initially charged to $v(0)_{54} = 200$ volts. (*a*) Determine the current, resistance voltage, and capacitance voltage equations. (*b*) How much energy is supplied to the circuit for the first two seconds? (*c*) What is the power being supplied to the circuit as a whole, to the resistor, and to the capacitor, at the end of 2 sec? (*d*) At what point on the voltage should the switch be closed to produce the greatest possible transient of current and capacitor voltage? What is the maximum value of the transient?

8–19 An R and C series circuit of $R = 10$ ohms, $C = 0.001$ μf has 50 volts connected to its terminals at $t = 0$. The capacitor is initially charged to 15 volts. Find the initial voltage across the resistor and the initial current. Find the resistor voltage, the capacitor voltage, and the current at 0.01 sec after closing the switch (two answers).

8–20 In the circuit of Fig. 8–12, $R = 10$ ohms, $X_C = -10$, $L = 0$, $\omega = 10^6$, $|V_m'| = 200$, $|V_m| = 100$, and $v'(t)_{b2}$ lags $v(t)_{12}$ by 45 degrees. (*a*) Find $I(t)$, $i(t)$, $v_C(t)$ if $\phi = 0$ degrees as switch is moved from a to b. (*b*) Find ϕ to give zero transient as switch is changed from a to b. (*c*) Find ϕ to give maximum transient as switch is changed from a to b.

8–21 Suppose $v'(t)_{b2}$ of Fig. 8–12 and Problem 8–20 is 100 direct volts. Repeat Problem 8–20.

8–22 Before closing the switch of Fig. 8–17, $v(0)_{12} = 200$ volts, $C_{12} = 2$ μf, $v(0)_{13} = 50$ volts, $C_{13} = 4$ μf, $v(0)_{34} = 100$ volts, $C_{34} = 5$ μf, and $R = 10$ ohms. (*a*) Find the expression for the charge on each capacitor at every instant after closing the switch. (*b*) Find the final voltage on each capacitor.

8–23 Determine the transient current equation for a circuit of L and C in series for a sine voltage connected. Determine the equation for voltage across the capacitor and the inductor. Assume that the capacitor is initially charged. What are the initial conditions to give no transient? Use the cyclic-charge complex variable differential equation.

8–24 (*a*) Solve the R, L, and C series circuit equation for the non-oscillatory case. Use the cyclic-charge complex variable differential equation. Assume the capacitor initially charged. Determine the expressions for $q(t)$, $i(t)$, $v_C(t)$, and $v_L(t)$. (*b*) Plot the transient current, steady state current, and the sum for a series circuit of $R = 200$ ohms, $L = 0.1$ henry, and $C = 20$ μf. The maximum value of the 1000 cps connected voltage is 200 volts, and the switch is closed so that $\phi = 30°$. The initial capacitor charge is $q_{56} = -4 \times 10^{-3}$ coulomb (Fig. 8–12).

8–25 Repeat Problem 8–24 for the critical case. In part (*b*) change R to the correct value to give the critical case.

8–26 Solve for the current in the circuit shown in Fig. 8–20 from the instant of closing the switch. The capacitors are initially charged as shown.

8–27 Show symbolically, by dividing equations 8–150 by the proper capacities and adding, that the sum of the voltages across the capacitors is zero in the steady state or at the end of the transient period.

8–28 Split the resistor into equal parts in branch 1–2 of Fig. 8–20 and insert a capacitor of $C = 2$ μf charged initially to 50 volts. Connect the positive terminal of this capacitor toward 2 of the figure. (*a*) Determine the equations for the charge on each capacitor and for the current. (*b*) Find the final charge on each capacitor. Can you assign any meaning to the final charge distribution? What determines which capacitor or capacitors will end up with reversed polarity? (*c*) What is the total energy dissipated in the resistors during the total transient time?

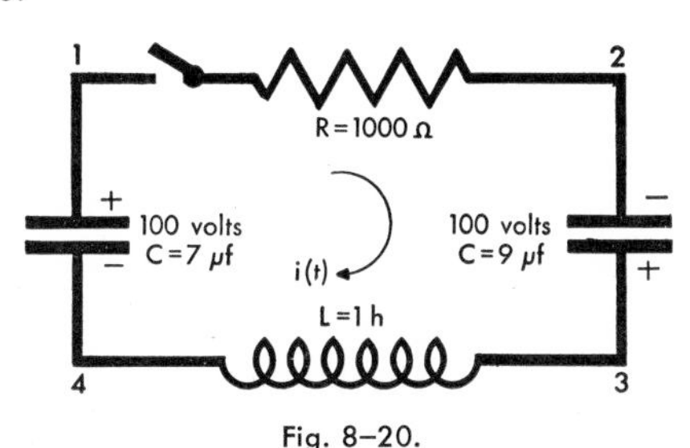

Fig. 8–20.

8–29 Determine the following for the series circuit which has constants as given in Problem 8–24*b* except $R = 100$ ohms. (*a*) Frequency of oscillation of the transient. (*b*) Value of the capacitor charge and voltage and angle ϕ for no transient. (*c*) If a voltage, which has the same frequency as the natural frequency of the system, is connected to the circuit being considered, determine the equation for the current in the circuit. What are the conditions for the transient and steady state term to be in phase? (*d*) What is the total energy supplied to the resistor, inductor, and capacitor in 4 cycles of the source voltage after closing the switch in part (*c*)?

8–30 Show that the magnitudes of the transient voltages of an R, L, and C series circuit, $v_R(t)_t$, $v_C(t)_t$, and $v_L(t)_t$, are equal if $R = \sqrt{LS}$. Determine the phase angles between the current transient and the capacitor and inductor voltage transients.

8–31 Determine whether or not the phase angle between the transients of current and inductor voltage in an R, L, and C series circuit is always more than 90 degrees—$R^2 < 4LS$.

8–32 If, in Fig. 8–21, the source voltage has a maximum value of 10 volts at 796 cps, determine the expression for the current after closing the switch at the positive increasing 45 degree point on the source voltage. Plot the current for one cycle before and after closing the switch.

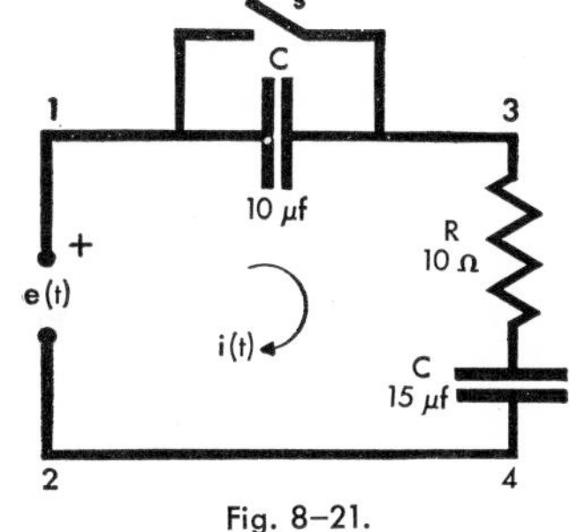

Fig. 8–21.

8–33 Suppose the capacitor in branch 1–3 of Fig. 8–21 is replaced by $R = 5$ ohms and $L = 0.1$ henry in series. Repeat Problem 8–32.

8–34 Evaluate the constants of integration for the circuit of Fig. 8–19 from the initial conditions. Write the equations for the charge on the capacitors C_{13} and C_{34}, and also the equation for the current from the instant of closing the switch.

8–35 Suppose that the circuit of Fig. 8–22 has been in operation long enough so that the steady state has been reached. The switch is closed when $\phi = 45°$. The frequency of the source voltage is 1 megacycle per second and the maximum value of this voltage is 0.5 volt. Determine the discharge transient current, voltage across the capacitor, and the voltage across the inductor. Express the results in micro- or milliamperes, volts, etc.

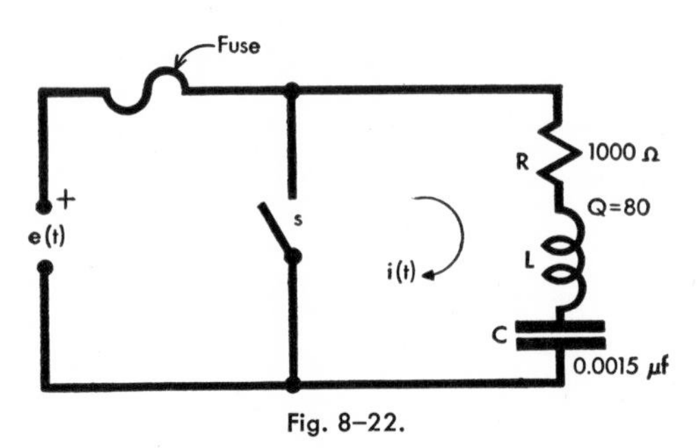

Fig. 8–22.

8–36 The switch s of Fig. 8–18 is closed on the steady state at $\phi = 45°$. When the transient thus formed has reached 50 per cent of its initial value the switch is opened. Determine the equations which give the total current at each instant from closing the switch. $R_{13} = 10$ ohms, $R_{34} = 5$ ohms, and $Q = 4$ at 1000 cps.

8–37 A typical lightning stroke can be represented by the discharge of an R, L, and C series circuit of $R = 400$ ohms, $C = 0.5$ μf, and $L = 15$ mh with an initial charge on the cloud of 5 coulombs. Determine the current equation. What is the maximum current? Determine the power expression and find the maximum power of the capacitor. Calculate the total energy of the lightning stroke in kilowatthours. How long would this energy operate a 100-watt lamp at 3 hours per day?

8–38 A one million volt surge generator is constructed of 10 capacitors each rated at 100 kvolts, 0.25 μf, each in series with $R = 3.5$ ohms. These capacitors are paralleled for charging to 100 kv, and then connected in series to deliver the one million volt surge. What is the equation of the current and total voltage discharge? What is the total energy of the surge? What is the maximum power delivered?

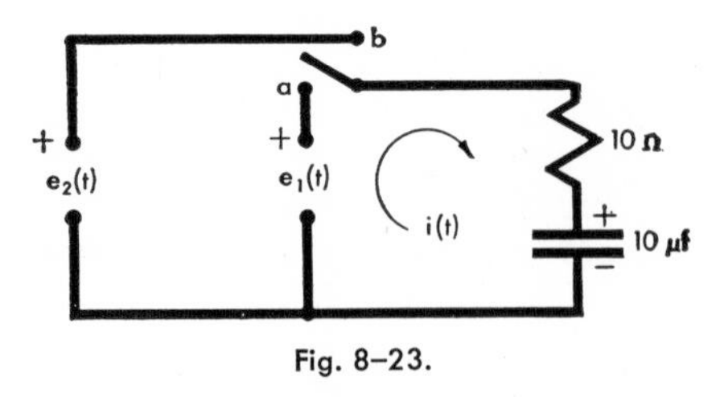

Fig. 8–23.

8–39 (*a*) Close the switch from a to b of Fig. 8–23, with $e_2(t) = 100$ direct volts, and $e_1(t) = 100 \sin 10^4 t$. Find $I(t)$, $i(t)$, $v_C(t)$. (*b*) Close the switch from b to a and repeat (*a*).

8–40 Given $e(t) = 200 \sin \dfrac{10^6}{6} t$ in Fig. 8–24. (*a*) Close the switch at $t = 0$. Find $I(t)$, $i(t)$. (*b*) Find the point on the voltage wave of closing the switch for zero transient. (*c*) Find the point on the voltage wave of closing the switch for maximum transient.

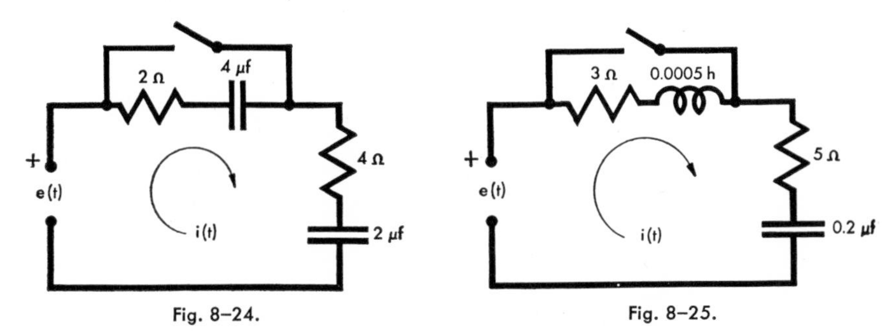

Fig. 8–24.

Fig. 8–25.

8–41 In Fig. 8–25, $e(t) = 10 \sin (10^5 t + 30°)$. Close the switch at $t = 0$. (*a*) Find $Q(t)$, $q(t)$, $I(t)$, and $i(t)$. (*b*) Find the point on the voltage wave of closing the switch for zero transient. (*c*) Find the point on the voltage wave of closing the switch for maximum transient.

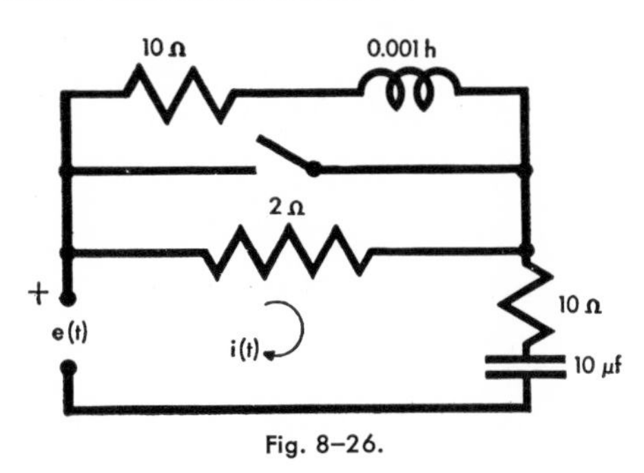

Fig. 8–26.

8–42 Assume $e(t) = 200 \sin (10{,}000t + 30°)$ in Fig. 8–26. Determine the current through and the voltage across the capacitor after the switch is closed at $t = 0$.

9.1-9.2

CHAPTER 9

Mesh and Node Systems of Network Equations

The basic material and ideas required for the analysis of linear networks have been presented in the preceding eight chapters. One-mesh networks only were used to develop these concepts in order to permit concentration upon the ideas as they were introduced. But relatively few electric circuits employed in practice are one mesh. The tremendously complex networks of the vast telephone and radio systems spread throughout the world, and the power network which is gradually spreading, to the far corners, particularly in the United States, must also be studied, maintained, and extended. A study of multimesh networks is, therefore, a necessity.

9.1 Some Remarks About Matrix Algebra.

The only essential difference in formulating the equations from which to determine the behavior of an n-mesh network and a one-mesh network is in the number of equations required. A one-mesh network requires only one equation—voltage. A two-mesh network requires at least two voltage equations; as, for example, two coils with magnetic field coupling but no electric connection or coupling (Fig. 3–13). If the two-mesh network has electrical connection between the meshes, as in Fig. 5–29, two voltage equations and one current equation are required to express the network behavior. The fact that *three* equations are required for such a circuit is immediately evident because, if all generated voltages and all impedances are known, *three* currents still remain to be evaluated. Furthermore, from the algebraic theory of linear equations, as many *independent* equations are required as there are unknowns to be determined. Physically, the currents of any linear electric circuit are completely established and unique for a particular set of generated voltages and impedances, *so that the number of independent equations required to express the behavior of a network is equal to the number of branch currents in the network.* The number of branches, or branch currents, can be counted on the circuit diagram.

The study of multimesh networks thus certainly requires the study of systems of equations. Mathematicians have worked out and published material (matrix algebra) which presents properties and methods of handling systems of equations. Happily, only a very small part of this matrix algebra is necessary to handle effectively many important aspects of the systems of equations of electrical network theory at the level presented in this book.

Essentially, matrix algebra symbolizes a system of equations as a single equation. All that is needed to convince anyone that some such method of formulating the manipulation of systems of equations is useful, is that a few such operations as substituting one set of equations in another be done. The details of the process are so great that it is virtually impossible to carry out the algebraic manipulation correctly. Furthermore, even after a few simple operations with systems of equations are completed, the result is so involved and extensive that it is not possible to interpret the results. But with matrix algebra these algebraic operations are simple and compact and the results are often obvious and useful.

The elementary aspects of matrix algebra needed for the treatment of the systems of equations of electrical networks are presented next.*

9.2 Definition and Multiplication of Matrices.

Consider a system of linear equations in terms of the variables x_1, x_2, x_3 and y_1, y_2, y_3 and constant coefficients a_{ij}

$$\begin{aligned} x_1 &= a_{11}y_1 + a_{12}y_2 + a_{13}y_3 \\ x_2 &= a_{21}y_1 + a_{22}y_2 + a_{23}y_3 \\ x_3 &= a_{31}y_1 + a_{32}y_2 + a_{33}y_3 \end{aligned} \tag{9-1}$$

These equations in matrix symbolism are represented by

$$\mathcal{X} = \mathcal{A}\mathcal{Y} \tag{9-2}$$

where

$$\mathcal{X} = \begin{bmatrix} x_1 \\ x_2 \\ x_3 \end{bmatrix} \tag{9-3}$$

$$\mathcal{A} = \begin{bmatrix} a_{11} & a_{12} & a_{13} \\ a_{21} & a_{22} & a_{23} \\ a_{31} & a_{32} & a_{33} \end{bmatrix} \tag{9-4}$$

$$\mathcal{Y} = \begin{bmatrix} y_1 \\ y_2 \\ y_3 \end{bmatrix} \tag{9-5}$$

* For more details on matrix algebra, see Myril B. and Georgia B. Reed, *Mathematical Methods in Electrical Engineering*, Harper & Brothers, 1951, Chap. 3.

The method of multiplying matrices is inherent in these symbolisms, for according to the indicated definitions

$$\mathfrak{X} = \begin{bmatrix} x_1 \\ x_2 \\ x_3 \end{bmatrix} = \mathfrak{A}\mathfrak{Y} = \begin{bmatrix} a_{11} & a_{12} & a_{13} \\ a_{21} & a_{22} & a_{23} \\ a_{31} & a_{32} & a_{33} \end{bmatrix} \begin{bmatrix} y_1 \\ y_2 \\ y_3 \end{bmatrix} = \begin{bmatrix} a_{11}y_1+a_{12}y_2+a_{13}y_3 \\ a_{21}y_1+a_{22}y_2+a_{23}y_3 \\ a_{31}y_1+a_{32}y_2+a_{33}y_3 \end{bmatrix} \quad (9\text{–}6)$$

and, therefore, elements in the ith row and jth column of a product matrix are formed by computing the *dot*, or *scalar*, product of the ith *row* of the left-hand member of the product and the jth *column* of the right-hand member of the matrix product. For example, the *first* row and *first* column element of the product $\mathfrak{A}\mathfrak{Y}$ is the dot product of the *first* row of $\mathfrak{A}$, and the *first* column of $\mathfrak{Y}$, i.e.,

$$[a_{11}, a_{12}, a_{13}] \begin{bmatrix} y_1 \\ y_2 \\ y_3 \end{bmatrix} = a_{11}y_1 + a_{12}y_2 + a_{13}y_3$$

Correspondingly, the *second* row and *first* column element of $\mathfrak{A}\mathfrak{Y}$ is the dot product of the *second* row of $\mathfrak{A}$ and *first* column of $\mathfrak{Y}$, i.e.,

$$[a_{21}, a_{22}, a_{23}] \begin{bmatrix} y_1 \\ y_2 \\ y_3 \end{bmatrix} = a_{21}y_1 + a_{22}y_2 + a_{23}y_3$$

There is no second column of $\mathfrak{Y}$ so there can be no second column in the product $\mathfrak{A}\mathfrak{Y}$. In fact, in general, the product matrix of any number of factor matrices, say $\mathfrak{A}\mathfrak{B}\mathfrak{C}\mathfrak{D}$, has the same number of *rows* as the first matrix on the left, $\mathfrak{A}$, and the same number of *columns* as the last matrix on the right, $\mathfrak{D}$.

The definition of the equality of matrices is also inherent in the requirement that equations 9–1 and 9–6 represent the same set of equations. The matrices $\mathfrak{X}$ and $\mathfrak{A}\mathfrak{Y}$ must be equal, *element by element*, for this equality to hold. Accordingly, matrices will be considered equal if and only if *all corresponding elements are equal.*

An interesting, useful, and important result may be obtained immediately from the foregoing definitions. Suppose that, in addition to the linear relations of equations 9–1 and 9–2, the similar relations

$$\begin{bmatrix} y_1 \\ y_2 \\ y_3 \end{bmatrix} = \begin{bmatrix} b_{11} & b_{12} & b_{13} \\ b_{21} & b_{22} & b_{23} \\ b_{31} & b_{32} & b_{33} \end{bmatrix} \begin{bmatrix} z_1 \\ z_2 \\ z_3 \end{bmatrix} \quad (9\text{–}7)$$

or

$$\mathfrak{Y} = \mathfrak{B}\mathfrak{Z} \quad (9\text{–}8)$$

are known to exist. Substituting from equation 9–8 into equations 9–2, ignoring for the moment the question of whether the process is valid, gives

$$\mathfrak{X} = \mathfrak{A}\mathfrak{Y} = \mathfrak{A}\mathfrak{B}\mathfrak{Z} = \mathfrak{C}\mathfrak{Z} \quad (9\text{–}9)$$

If such a substitution is valid, manipulating systems of equations by matrices is symbolically as easy as handling the simple relations of single equations. Verification of the validity of the substitution leading to equation 9–9 can be most easily effected by substituting into equations 9–1 the value of each y from equation 9–7. Combining the result into matrix form shows that $\mathcal{C} = \mathcal{A}\mathcal{B}$ is *exactly* the same as the product $\mathcal{A}\mathcal{B}$ already defined, namely,

$$\mathcal{A}\mathcal{B} = \begin{bmatrix} a_{11}b_{11}+a_{12}b_{21}+a_{13}b_{31} & a_{11}b_{12}+a_{12}b_{22}+a_{13}b_{32} & a_{11}b_{13}+a_{12}b_{23}+a_{13}b_{33} \\ a_{21}b_{11}+a_{22}b_{21}+a_{23}b_{31} & a_{21}b_{12}+a_{22}b_{22}+a_{23}b_{32} & a_{21}b_{13}+a_{22}b_{23}+a_{23}b_{33} \\ a_{31}b_{11}+a_{32}b_{21}+a_{33}b_{31} & a_{31}b_{12}+a_{32}b_{22}+a_{33}b_{32} & a_{31}b_{13}+a_{32}b_{23}+a_{33}b_{33} \end{bmatrix} \tag{9–10}$$

The solution of Problem 9–1 at the end of this chapter will demonstrate further the validity of the substitution leading to equation 9–9 and to the matrix multiplication process already defined. The following example also illustrates the multiplication process.

Example 9:1 Suppose that

$$\mathcal{A} = \begin{bmatrix} 2 & 0 & -3 \\ 4 & 1 & 1 \\ 0 & 6 & 2 \end{bmatrix} \quad \text{and } \mathcal{B} = \begin{bmatrix} -1 & 4 & 1 \\ 0 & 2 & 0 \\ 2 & 3 & 2 \end{bmatrix}$$

Evaluate the products $\mathcal{A}\mathcal{B}$ and $\mathcal{B}\mathcal{A}$.

Solution

$$\mathcal{A}\mathcal{B} = \begin{bmatrix} 2 & 0 & -3 \\ 4 & 1 & 1 \\ 0 & 6 & 2 \end{bmatrix} \begin{bmatrix} -1 & 4 & 1 \\ 0 & 2 & 0 \\ 2 & 3 & 2 \end{bmatrix}$$

$$= \begin{bmatrix} -2\times1+0\times0-3\times2 & 2\times4+0\times2-3\times3 & 2\times1+0\times0-3\times2 \\ -4\times1+1\times0+1\times2 & 4\times4+1\times2+1\times3 & 4\times1+1\times0+1\times2 \\ 0\times1+6\times0+2\times2 & 0\times4+6\times2+2\times3 & 0\times1+6\times0+2\times2 \end{bmatrix}$$

$$= \begin{bmatrix} -2+0-6 & 8+0-9 & 2+0-6 \\ -4+0+2 & 16+2+3 & 4+0+2 \\ 0+0+4 & 0+12+6 & 0+0+4 \end{bmatrix} = \begin{bmatrix} -8 & -1 & -4 \\ -2 & 21 & 6 \\ 4 & 18 & 4 \end{bmatrix}$$

The commuted product $\mathcal{B}\mathcal{A}$ is

$$\mathcal{B}\mathcal{A} = \begin{bmatrix} -1 & 4 & 1 \\ 0 & 2 & 0 \\ 2 & 3 & 2 \end{bmatrix} \begin{bmatrix} 2 & 0 & -3 \\ 4 & 1 & 1 \\ 0 & 6 & 2 \end{bmatrix} = \begin{bmatrix} 14 & 10 & 9 \\ 8 & 2 & 2 \\ 16 & 15 & 1 \end{bmatrix}$$

A very important implication of this example is that the product of matrices is in general *not commutative*, i.e., in general

$$\mathcal{A}\mathcal{B} \neq \mathcal{B}\mathcal{A} \tag{9–11}$$

9.3 Matrix Inverse.

The matrix manipulation corresponding to solving a set of equations is, of course, of major importance. This process can best be defined by an examination of the determinant solution of a system of equations.

Such a solution of the equations 9–1 is, if $|\mathcal{A}|$ is the determinant of these equations,

$$
\begin{aligned}
y_1 &= \frac{\begin{vmatrix} a_{22} & a_{23} \\ a_{32} & a_{33} \end{vmatrix}}{|\mathcal{A}|} x_1 + \frac{-\begin{vmatrix} a_{12} & a_{13} \\ a_{32} & a_{33} \end{vmatrix}}{|\mathcal{A}|} x_2 + \frac{\begin{vmatrix} a_{12} & a_{13} \\ a_{22} & a_{23} \end{vmatrix}}{|\mathcal{A}|} x_3 \\
y_2 &= \frac{-\begin{vmatrix} a_{21} & a_{23} \\ a_{31} & a_{33} \end{vmatrix}}{|\mathcal{A}|} x_1 + \frac{\begin{vmatrix} a_{11} & a_{13} \\ a_{31} & a_{33} \end{vmatrix}}{|\mathcal{A}|} x_2 + \frac{-\begin{vmatrix} a_{11} & a_{13} \\ a_{21} & a_{23} \end{vmatrix}}{|\mathcal{A}|} x_3 \qquad (9\text{–}12) \\
y_3 &= \frac{\begin{vmatrix} a_{21} & a_{22} \\ a_{31} & a_{32} \end{vmatrix}}{|\mathcal{A}|} x_1 + \frac{-\begin{vmatrix} a_{11} & a_{12} \\ a_{31} & a_{32} \end{vmatrix}}{|\mathcal{A}|} x_2 + \frac{\begin{vmatrix} a_{11} & a_{12} \\ a_{21} & a_{22} \end{vmatrix}}{|\mathcal{A}|} x_3
\end{aligned}
$$

In a briefer form, for convenience, these equations are written as

$$
\begin{aligned}
y_1 &= A_{11}x_1 + A_{12}x_2 + A_{13}x_3 \\
y_2 &= A_{21}x_1 + A_{22}x_2 + A_{23}x_3 \qquad (9\text{–}13) \\
y_3 &= A_{31}x_1 + A_{32}x_2 + A_{33}x_3
\end{aligned}
$$

and in matrix form

$$
\begin{bmatrix} y_1 \\ y_2 \\ y_3 \end{bmatrix} = \begin{bmatrix} A_{11} & A_{12} & A_{13} \\ A_{21} & A_{22} & A_{23} \\ A_{31} & A_{32} & A_{33} \end{bmatrix} \begin{bmatrix} x_1 \\ x_2 \\ x_3 \end{bmatrix}
$$

or

$$\mathcal{Y} = \mathcal{A}^{-1}\mathcal{X} \qquad (9\text{–}14)$$

where $\mathcal{A}^{-1}$ is called the *inverse* of $\mathcal{A}$.

Examination of equations 9–4, 9–12, 9–13, and 9–14 shows that the element in the ith row and jth column of the inverse, $\mathcal{A}^{-1}$, of $\mathcal{A}$ is

$$A_{ij} = \frac{\text{cofactor of } a_{ji}}{|\mathcal{A}|} \qquad (9\text{–}15)$$

Once more giving an example is probably the simplest and most effective way to explain further the calculation of an inverse.

Example 9:2 Find the inverse of

$$\mathcal{A} = \begin{bmatrix} 1 & 2 & 1 \\ 0 & 3 & 0 \\ 2 & 0 & 1 \end{bmatrix}$$

and the products $\mathcal{A}\mathcal{A}^{-1}$ and $\mathcal{A}^{-1}\mathcal{A}$.

Solution From equation 9–15, the element in the *first* row and *first* column of $\mathcal{A}^{-1}$ is

$$A_{11} = \frac{\text{cofactor } a_{11}}{|\mathcal{A}|} = \frac{\begin{vmatrix} 3 & 0 \\ 0 & 1 \end{vmatrix}}{\begin{vmatrix} 1 & 2 & 1 \\ 0 & 3 & 0 \\ 2 & 0 & 1 \end{vmatrix}} = \frac{3}{-3} = -1$$

The element in the *first* row and *second* column of $\mathcal{A}^{-1}$ is

$$A_{12} = \frac{\text{cofactor } a_{21}}{| \ |} = \frac{-\begin{vmatrix} 2 & 1 \\ 0 & 1 \end{vmatrix}}{-3} = \frac{-2}{-3} = \frac{2}{3}$$

The other element of $\mathcal{A}^{-1}$ may be computed similarly, giving the result

$$\mathcal{A}^{-1} = \begin{bmatrix} \frac{3}{-3} & \frac{-2}{-3} & \frac{-3}{-3} \\ \frac{0}{-3} & \frac{-1}{-3} & \frac{0}{-3} \\ \frac{-6}{-3} & \frac{4}{-3} & \frac{3}{-3} \end{bmatrix} = -\frac{1}{3}\begin{bmatrix} 3 & -2 & -3 \\ 0 & -1 & 0 \\ -6 & 4 & 3 \end{bmatrix}$$

Note that the factor $-\frac{1}{3}$, which appears in *each* element of $\mathcal{A}^{-1}$ has been factored out. It is always possible to factor any common factor from *every* element of a matrix. This result is markedly different from factoring common multipliers from determinants. It will be recalled that, if a multiplying factor appears in each element of a row or column of a determinant, the whole determinant should be multiplied by this factor once for each row or column from which it is removed. Thus the determinant of $\mathcal{A}^{-1}$ is

$$|\mathcal{A}^{-1}| = \left[-\frac{1}{3}\right]\begin{vmatrix} 3 & -2 & -3 \\ \frac{0}{3} & \frac{-1}{-3} & \frac{0}{-3} \\ \frac{-6}{-3} & \frac{4}{-3} & \frac{3}{-3} \end{vmatrix} = \left[-\frac{1}{3}\right]^2\begin{vmatrix} 3 & -2 & -3 \\ 0 & -1 & 0 \\ \frac{-6}{-3} & \frac{4}{-3} & \frac{3}{-3} \end{vmatrix}$$

$$= \left[-\frac{1}{3}\right]^3\begin{vmatrix} 3 & -2 & -3 \\ 0 & -1 & 0 \\ -6 & 4 & 3 \end{vmatrix}$$

The two products of $\mathcal{A}$ and its inverse are

$$\mathcal{A}\mathcal{A}^{-1} = \begin{bmatrix} 1 & 2 & 1 \\ 0 & 3 & 0 \\ 2 & 0 & 1 \end{bmatrix}\left[-\frac{1}{3}\right]\begin{bmatrix} 3 & -2 & -3 \\ 0 & -1 & 0 \\ -6 & 4 & 3 \end{bmatrix} = -\frac{1}{3}\begin{bmatrix} -3 & 0 & 0 \\ 0 & -3 & 0 \\ 0 & 0 & -3 \end{bmatrix} = \begin{bmatrix} 1 & 0 & 0 \\ 0 & 1 & 0 \\ 0 & 0 & 1 \end{bmatrix}$$

and

$$\mathcal{A}^{-1}\mathcal{A} = \left[-\frac{1}{3}\right]\begin{bmatrix} 3 & -2 & -3 \\ 0 & -1 & 0 \\ -6 & 4 & 3 \end{bmatrix}\begin{bmatrix} 1 & 2 & 1 \\ 0 & 3 & 0 \\ 2 & 0 & 1 \end{bmatrix} = -\frac{1}{3}\begin{bmatrix} -3 & 0 & 0 \\ 0 & -3 & 0 \\ 0 & 0 & -3 \end{bmatrix} = \begin{bmatrix} 1 & 0 & 0 \\ 0 & 1 & 0 \\ 0 & 0 & 1 \end{bmatrix}$$

so that

$$\mathcal{A}\mathcal{A}^{-1} = \mathcal{A}^{-1}\mathcal{A} = \mathcal{U} = \begin{bmatrix} 1 & 0 & 0 \\ 0 & 1 & 0 \\ 0 & 0 & 1 \end{bmatrix}$$

The result just derived, namely, that

$$\mathcal{A}\mathcal{A}^{-1} = \mathcal{A}^{-1}\mathcal{A} = \mathcal{U} \tag{9–16}$$

is a general property of matrices, subject to the condition that $\mathcal{A}^{-1}$ exists, which in turn requires that $|\mathcal{A}| \neq 0$. Such a requirement is to be expected since computing an inverse matrix is simply determining the solution of a system of equations, and the determinant of the equations must not be equal to zero for a unique solution to exist. A matrix which has a zero determinant is said to be *singular.*

The matrix $\mathcal{U}$ is known as the *unit* matrix and has the property that

$$\mathcal{U}\mathcal{A} = \mathcal{A}\mathcal{U} = \mathcal{A} \tag{9–17}$$

for any square matrix, $\mathcal{A}$, where $\mathcal{U}$ has the same number of rows and columns as $\mathcal{A}$.

The *symbolic* solution of the matrix equation 9–2 is now very simple. If both sides of this equation are multiplied on the left by $\mathcal{A}^{-1}$

$$\mathcal{A}^{-1}\mathcal{X} = \mathcal{A}^{-1}\mathcal{A}\mathcal{Y} = \mathcal{U}\mathcal{Y} = \mathcal{Y} \tag{9–18}$$

which is exactly the result given in equation 9–14.

9.4 The Sum and Difference and Distributive Law of Matrices.

The sum or difference of two matrices is defined as

$$\mathcal{A}\pm\mathcal{B}=\begin{bmatrix} a_{11} & a_{12} & a_{13} \\ a_{21} & a_{22} & a_{23} \\ a_{31} & a_{32} & a_{33} \end{bmatrix}\pm\begin{bmatrix} b_{11} & b_{12} & b_{13} \\ b_{21} & b_{22} & b_{23} \\ b_{31} & b_{32} & b_{33} \end{bmatrix}=\begin{bmatrix} a_{11}\pm b_{11} & a_{12}\pm b_{12} & a_{13}\pm b_{13} \\ a_{21}\pm b_{21} & a_{22}\pm b_{22} & a_{23}\pm b_{23} \\ a_{31}\pm b_{31} & a_{32}\pm b_{32} & a_{33}\pm b_{33} \end{bmatrix} \tag{9–19}$$

Then the distributive law which makes

$$\mathcal{A}(\mathcal{B} \pm \mathcal{C}) = \mathcal{A}\mathcal{B} \pm \mathcal{A}\mathcal{C} \tag{9–20}$$

may be demonstrated by evaluating the two sides of this expression separately and comparing.

9.5 Associative Law of Matrix Algebra.

The associative law for matrix multiplication is identical with the corresponding law of ordinary algebra.

$$\mathcal{A}\mathcal{B}\mathcal{C} = \mathcal{A}(\mathcal{B}\mathcal{C}) = (\mathcal{A}\mathcal{B})\mathcal{C} \tag{9–21}$$

i.e., the order in which the matrices of a product are multiplied is immaterial. Note particularly, however, that commuting elements of a product must be avoided, for in general

$$\mathcal{A}\mathcal{B}\mathcal{C} \neq \mathcal{A}(\mathcal{C}\mathcal{B}) \neq (\mathcal{C}\mathcal{A})\mathcal{B}$$

9.6 Matrix Transpose and Symmetry.

A simple but very useful operation with matrices, designated as *transposing*, is the interchanging of corresponding rows and columns. The transpose of a matrix $\mathcal{A}$ is indicated by $\mathcal{A}'$. Thus if

$$\mathcal{A} = \begin{bmatrix} 1 & 2 & 3 \\ 0 & -1 & 2 \\ 2 & 1 & 1 \end{bmatrix} \quad \text{then} \quad \mathcal{A}' = \begin{bmatrix} 1 & 0 & 2 \\ 2 & -1 & 1 \\ 3 & 2 & 1 \end{bmatrix}$$

and if

$$\mathfrak{B} = \begin{bmatrix} 2 & 1 \\ -1 & 0 \\ 2 & 2 \end{bmatrix} \qquad \text{then} \quad \mathfrak{B}' = \begin{bmatrix} 2 & -1 & 2 \\ 1 & 0 & 2 \end{bmatrix}$$

Evidently the transpose of the transpose of a matrix is the original matrix, i.e., $[\mathfrak{A}']' = \mathfrak{A}$.

A certain commutative pattern for matrix products may be expressed in terms of transposed matrices. Thus it can be proved that

$$[\mathfrak{A}\mathfrak{B}\mathfrak{C}\mathfrak{D}]' = \mathfrak{D}'\mathfrak{C}'\mathfrak{B}'\mathfrak{A}' \tag{9–22}$$

or by transposing both sides of this last equation

$$\mathfrak{A}\mathfrak{B}\mathfrak{C}\mathfrak{D} = [\mathfrak{D}'\mathfrak{C}'\mathfrak{B}'\mathfrak{A}']' \tag{9–23}$$

If corresponding rows and columns of a matrix are alike, the transpose of a matrix is the same as the matrix. Such a matrix is designated as *symmetric*. Thus if

$$\mathfrak{A} = \mathfrak{A}'$$

then $\mathfrak{A}$ is symmetric by definition.

9.7 Some Aspects of the Topology of Graphs.

The obvious necessity of studying ever larger electrical systems, and the growing size and availability of computers which may be used to facilitate this study, make an extensive and ordered study of the equations for such networks essential. It is possible to use these increasingly important aids to engineering (computers) only when the user has a thorough mathematical background for the computation. The problem for the computer cannot otherwise even be formulated. In addition to matrix algebra, therefore, some of the elementary aspects of a branch of mathematics known as topology are presented. These aspects of topology facilitate drawing some very important conclusions concerning the equations for electrical networks. A few definitions and some properties of graphs (electrical network diagrams) follow.

Element and Vertex The fundamental building blocks of graphs, called *elements*, are line segments terminated in vertices, as indicated in Fig. 9–1*a*. An element is shown in this figure with two possible ways of sensing the element, i.e., using an arrowhead or labeling the vertices differently.

E-Sensing The sensing of an element is here designated as *e-sensing*.

Graph Any set of elements associated in any way, as for example in Fig. 9–1*b*, is called a *graph*. The particular graph of this figure is said to be sensed since each element is e-sensed.

Subgraph A *subgraph* is any set of the elements of a graph, from all to any one. In contrast, a *proper subgraph* is some set of elements of a graph *less in number* than the total. Thus elements *abcf* form a proper subgraph of the graph in Fig. 9–1*b*.

Complement The *complement* of any *proper subgraph* is the set of elements of the graph not contained in the proper subgraph. Elements *efghi* are the complement of the proper subgraph *abcd* in Fig. 9–1*b*.

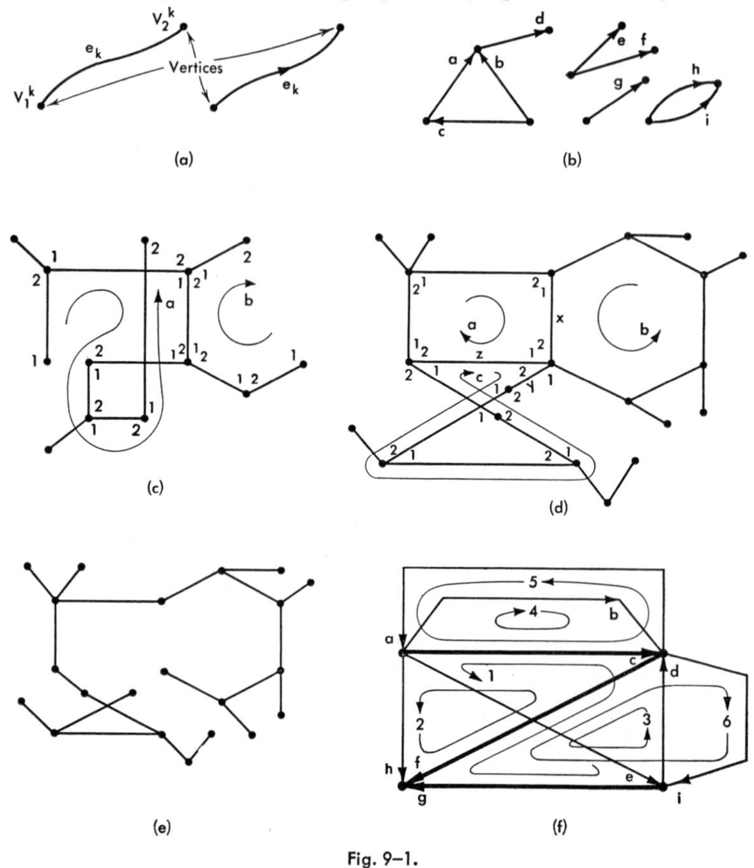

Fig. 9–1.

Path A path is a subgraph for which two of its vertices are each common to only one element and all other vertices are common to two elements. The subgraphs *ef*, *g* and *dac* in Fig. 9–1*b* are paths.

P-Sensing It is useful to define a sensing of a path, here designated as p-sensing, by arrows as in Fig. 9–1*c*. The arrows (*a* and *b*) are understood in all the discussion here to p-sense the elements of a path by sensing each element of the path in the ordered manner shown in Fig. 9–1*c*. Only the one arrow (*a* or *b*) need be used with this understanding. Reversing the arrow, of course, reverses all the element sensings. This p-sensing is understood to sense the elements of a path independently of the e-sensing of the elements.

Connected A graph is *connected* if there is a path between every pair of vertices of the graph. For example, the subgraphs made up of elements *abcd, ef, g, hi* in Fig. 9–1*b* and the graph in Fig. 9–1*c* are all connected. All electrical networks can be represented by connected graphs. Even the extreme of a multiwinding transformer can be considered as a connected system because making a common connection of only one point on each winding has no effect on the electrical performance of the transformer.

Circuit Another subgraph of particular importance, called a *circuit*, is one for which each vertex is common to two and only two elements of the subgraph. The proper subgraphs *abc* and *hi* in Fig. 9–1*b* are circuits.

C-Sensing Sensing of circuits is an essential aspect of the use of such subgraphs. A circuit is *c-sensed* if all of its elements are sensed in an ordered manner as are circuits *a* and *c* in Fig. 9–1*d*. The c-sensing is in addition to any e-sensing or p-sensing of these elements. An arrow is all that is required to c-sense a circuit—the circuit *b* in Fig. 9–1*d*—if it is understood that all the elements of the circuit are thereby sensed in proper order.

Tree Members of one of the most important classes of subgraphs are designated as trees. A *tree* of a *connected* graph, *G*, is a subgraph which contains all the vertices of *G*, is connected, and contains no circuits. The graph in Fig. 9–1*c* is its own tree, and the proper subgraph Fig. 9–1*e* is one of the many trees of the graph of Fig. 9–1*d*.

Branch The elements of trees are given the special name *branch*. The number of branches is always $v - 1$ for a connected graph of v-vertices.

Chords The elements of the complement of a tree are called *chords*. There are no chords in the graph (tree) of Fig. 9–1*c*, for example, and the elements *xyz* of Fig. 9–1*d* are chords if Fig. 9–1*e* is considered as a tree of Fig. 9–1*d*. The number of chords is always $e - v + 1$ for an e-element, v-vertex connected graph.

It is possible to prove that each tree has this property: *There is one and only one path in a tree between any two vertices of the tree.*

C-Circuits A set of circuits of considerable fundamental importance for the study of electrical networks can be determined from a tree and its chords. This set of circuits, called *c-circuits*, is determined from a tree and its chords in the following manner: Each circuit consists of one and only one chord and of one and only one tree path between the vertices of that chord. Since there are always $e - v + 1$ chords, there are always $e - v + 1$ c-circuits, one for each chord. The diagram in Fig. 9–1*f* shows a set of c-circuits for the tree of branches *cfg* and chords *abdehi*. Note that the sensing arrow for the c-circuits is such that the e-sensing and the c-sensing of the *chords* are the same. This last sensing pattern is considered as part of the definition of c-circuits.

9.8 Kirchhoff Vertex Equations; KVE (Kirchhoff Current Law).

If ammeters, which give instantaneous indications and have zero-center scales, are used in the elements connected to a vertex, as illustrated in Fig. 9–2*a*, heterogeneous orientations lead to heterogeneous results.

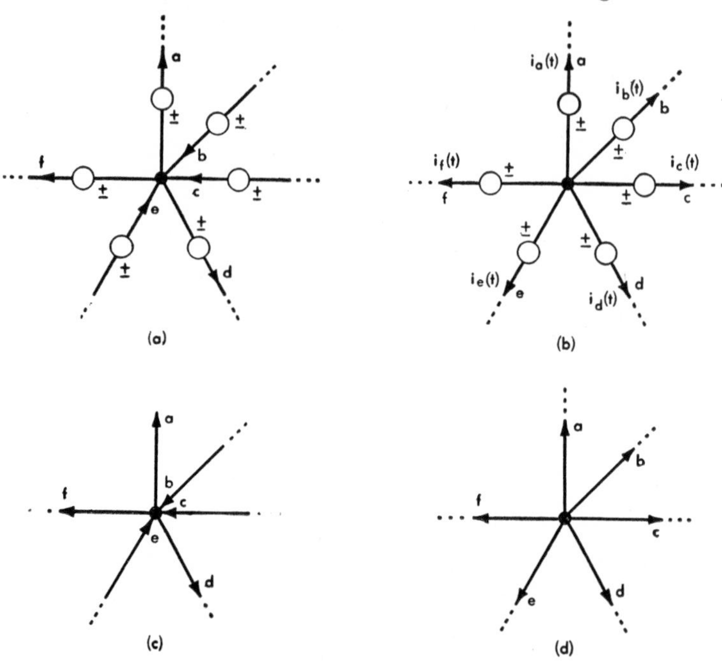

Fig. 9–2.

Suppose, however, that the ammeters are all aligned the same way with respect to a vertex, as illustrated for one of two possible situations in Fig. 9–2*b*. The sum of the numbers obtained from the meters which deflect in one direction (a-deflections) is then equal to the sum of the numbers obtained from the meters which deflect oppositely (b-deflections). The initial choice of the a-deflection direction is completely arbitrary. This pattern of deflections is the basis of the Kirchhoff current law. Indeed, the mathematical formulation of this ordered pattern of deflections and numbers *is* the Kirchhoff current law.

Suppose an a-deflection number is considered as a positive number and a b-deflection number as a negative number; the meter indications of Fig. 9–2*b* fit the pattern:

$$\text{sum of a-deflection numbers} + \text{sum of b-deflection numbers} = 0 \quad (9\text{–}24)$$

This last relation is observable in the laboratory for a particular case or many particular cases. Obviously, however, it cannot be observed for all cases; and, in any case, only after the physical network has been constructed can any observations be made on it. The problem then is to formulate equation 9–24 in mathematical form, i.e., in the form of an equation relating *mathematical symbols*, so that such equations may be used to describe the numerical pattern of equation 9–24 for an observed physical situation and to predict the numerical pattern to be expected on constructing a network.

If the symbols $i_a(t)$, $i_b(t)$, $i_c(t)$, etc., in Fig. 9–2*b* are to be replaced by a positive number for an a-deflection and a negative number for a b-deflection, equation 9–24 for this figure is

$$i_a(t) + i_b(t) + i_c(t) + i_d(t) + i_e(t) + i_f(t) = 0 \tag{9–25}$$

There is a simple correlation between (1) the signs of this last equation and (2) the relative orientation, with respect to a vertex, of the e-sensing arrows and of the instantaneous ammeters. See Problem 9–12.

A simpler designation for this orientation of the instantaneous meters is given by Figs. 9–2*c* and *d*. The arrowheads serve to indicate the manner of connecting the meters with respect to a vertex, provided the arrowhead implies the pattern of Figs. 9–2*a* and *b*. These arrowheads also serve to indicate the sign pattern of the equation at a vertex, i.e., the Kirchhoff vertex equation. Thus an element incident to a vertex and e-sensed away from the vertex (arrow pointing away from vertex) indicates, in the vertex equation, a plus sign preceding the variable $i(t)$ associated with the element. Of course, a reversal (toward the vertex) of the e-sensing arrowhead indicates a minus instead of a plus sign in the preceding scheme. Consequently, equation 9–25 is the vertex equation for Fig. 9–2*d*, and the vertex equation for Fig. 9–2*c* is

$$i_a(t) - i_b(t) - i_c(t) + i_d(t) - i_e(t) + i_f(t) = 0 \tag{9–26}$$

While the pattern of meter orientation, arrowhead, and a-deflection may be altered in several ways from that in the foregoing, the effect of considering such alterations is to complicate the discussion without in the least making the system more general. Therefore, for the discussion in this book:

(1) An e-sensing arrow on a diagram specifies the manner of locating the ammeter (instantaneous, not rms) in the corresponding physical element.

(2) An a-deflection may be taken as either deflection with complete arbitrariness but customarily is taken as the deflection direction which results from placing the meter in a standard situation so the meter deflection direction correlates in a known manner with the behavior of physical systems.

(3) An a-deflection number is considered as positive, and a positive number indicates an a-deflection.

(4) The e-sensing arrow, if directed from a vertex, indicates a plus sign preceding the corresponding $i_k(t)$ in the vertex equation (KVE) when of the form of equation 9–26.

The Kirchhoff vertex equations then are to be formed in accordance with the following instructions: At any vertex, the $i_k(t)$ associated with the elements connected to that vertex are to be made into an equation such that:

The sum of all the $i_k(t)$ associated with elements sensed away from the vertex = the sum of all the $i_k(t)$ associated with elements sensed toward the vertex; or, in terms of double subscripts,

The sum of all the $i_{jk}(t)$ with double subscript order j to k away from the vertex = the sum of all the $i_{jk}(t)$ with double subscript order j to k toward the vertex.

9.9 Incidence Matrix.

A Kirchhoff vertex equation is available for every vertex (junction) of a network. Consequently, a system of equations, rather than just one equation, is usually a part of studying a network. These equations, one for each vertex of the diagram, when considered as a system, are found not to be independent; see Problems 9–13 and 9–14. However, it can be demonstrated that any set of vertex equations, for any set of vertices, less than the total of v-equations for a v-vertex graph, are independent. The largest number of independent vertex equations possible is the most useful set for network analysis. This largest number is $v - 1$ equations from *any* $v - 1$ vertices of a v-vertex graph.

The matrix formulation of the vertex equations (KVE), $v - 1$ in number, is here expressed by

$$\mathcal{A}\mathcal{I}_e = 0 \tag{9–27}$$

where $\mathcal{A}$ is a $(v - 1) \times e$ matrix, called the *incidence* matrix, with entries of $+1$, -1, and 0 only, and $\mathcal{I}_e$ is an $e \times 1$ matrix consisting of I's of the network elements.

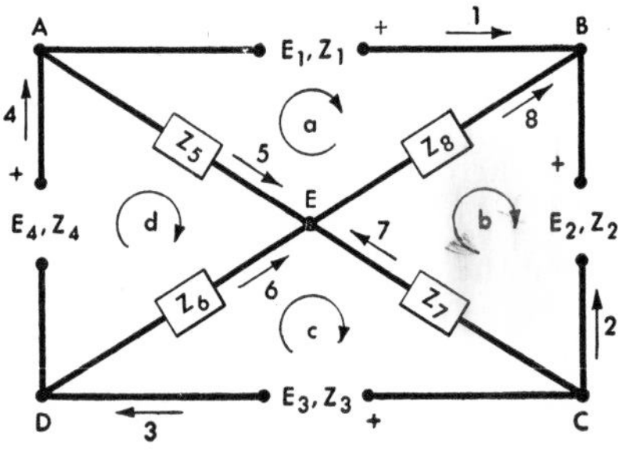

Fig. 9–3.

Example 9:3 Form the incidence matrix for the graph in Fig. 9–3. Omit the equation at vertex D.

Solution The KVE are

$$\begin{matrix} A \\ B \\ C \\ E \end{matrix}\begin{bmatrix} 1 & 0 & 0 & -1 & 1 & 0 & 0 & 0 \\ -1 & -1 & 0 & 0 & 0 & 0 & 0 & -1 \\ 0 & 1 & 1 & 0 & 0 & 0 & 1 & 0 \\ 0 & 0 & 0 & 0 & -1 & -1 & -1 & 1 \end{bmatrix}\begin{bmatrix} I_1 \\ I_2 \\ I_3 \\ I_4 \\ I_5 \\ I_6 \\ I_7 \\ I_8 \end{bmatrix} = \mathcal{A}\mathcal{I}_e = 0$$

The ordering of the variables in $\mathcal{I}_e$ and the ordering of the rows in $\mathcal{A}$ are both arbitrary, but both must be chosen before the incidence matrix can be written.

9.10 Kirchhoff Circuit Equations; KCE (Kirchhoff Voltage Law).

If voltmeters having zero-center scales and giving instantaneous indications are connected to elements of a network which form a circuit, as illustrated in Fig. 9–4*a*, heterogeneous orientations lead to heterogeneous

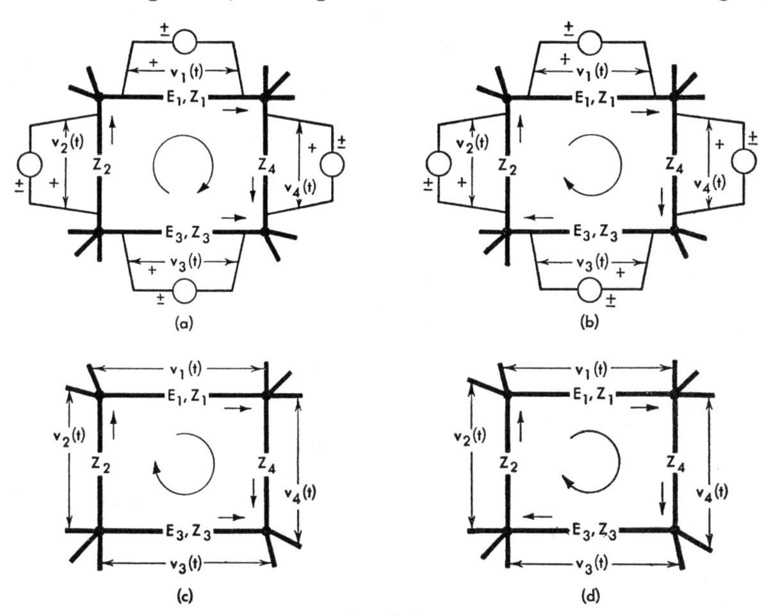

Fig. 9–4.

results. However, if the voltmeters are all aligned the same way with respect to a circuit (Fig. 9–4*b* shows one of two possible ways) the sum of the a-deflection meter indications is equal to the sum of the b-deflection meter indications. This experimental observation on the *terminal pairs* of the elements of a circuit is the basis of the postulation of the Kirchhoff voltage law.

As for the current law, correlation of the instrument indications with the real number system is the first essential. Suppose, as for the KVE, that an a-deflection (either one) is taken as a positive number and a b-deflection (opposite the arbitrarily chosen a-deflection) is taken as a negative number. The sum of the numbers, from the meters all oriented the same way with respect to a circuit as in Fig. 9–4*b*, fits the relation

$$\text{sum of the a-deflection numbers} + \text{sum of the b-deflection numbers} = 0 \qquad (9\text{–}28)$$

The mathematical formulation of this last relation is, for Fig. 9–4*b*.

$$v_1(t) + v_2(t) + v_3(t) + v_4(t) = 0 \qquad (9\text{–}29)$$

if these *terminal* voltage symbols represent positive or negative numbers depending on whether the $v_k(t)$ corresponds to an a-deflection or b-deflection respectively. Since reversing the connection of an instantaneous voltmeter reverses the instantaneous direction of deflection and so changes the sign of the deflection number, the Kirchhoff circuit equation for Fig. 9–4*a* is

$$v_1(t) + v_4(t) - v_3(t) + v_2(t) = 0 \tag{9–30}$$

If, in correspondence with the convention generally used in this book, the reference plus for voltages is at the tail of the reference, e-sensing arrow of a network element, and if the e-sensing arrow also indicates the orientation of a voltmeter, equation 9–29 holds for Fig. 9–4*d* and equation 9–30 for Fig. 9–4*c*. Thus the arrow associated with the network element serves to indicate the pattern of plus and minus signs of the Kirchhoff equation for a circuit as well as to indicate the way a voltmeter should be connected to the actual network so that the calculated and observed numbers are the same.

It should be evident from the foregoing that the only essential difference between forming a Kirchhoff vertex equation and a Kirchhoff circuit equation is, respectively, observation of the alignment of references (e-sensings) with respect to a vertex and with respect to a circuit. The word description of the formation details differs somewhat in the two cases, however. Hence to show this difference and to emphasize the pattern for forming Kirchhoff circuit equations of the Kirchhoff voltage law:

(1) an e-sensing arrow (or, whenever preferred, a plus mark) on a diagram specifies the manner of locating the voltmeter (instantaneous, not rms) in the corresponding physical element.

(2) an a-deflection may be taken as either deflection with complete arbitrariness, but customarily is taken as the deflection direction which results from placing the meter in a standard situation so the meter deflection direction indicates the polarity of voltage.

(3) an a-deflection number is considered as positive and a positive number indicates an a-deflection.

(4) the e-sensing arrow, if coincident with the c-sensing arrow, indicates a plus sign preceding the corresponding $v_k(t)$ in the circuit equations (KCE) when of the form of equation 9–30.

The Kirchhoff circuit equation, then, is to be formed according to the following: For any circuit, the $v_k(t)$ associated with the elements contained in that circuit are to be made into an equation in which:

The sum of all the $v_k(t)$ (terminal) associated with elements which have coincident e-sensing and c-sensing = the sum of all the $v_k(t)$ associated with elements which have non-coincident e-sensing and c-sensing; or, in terms of double subscripts:

The sum of all the $v_{jk}(t)$ with double subscript order j to k coincident with the c-sensing = the sum of all the $v_{jk}(t)$ with double subscript order j to k non-coincident with the c-sensing.

9.11 Circuit Matrix.

A Kirchhoff circuit equation is available for every circuit of an electrical network or its diagram. The simple evident pattern available for the vertices and hence the vertex equations is definitely lost in considering the pattern of circuits and hence the circuit equations. For example, in the diagram in Fig. 9–3 the following pattern of circuits is easily located:

Circuit Indicated by the Vertices	Number of Circuits of Given Type
ABCDA	1
ABEA, BCEB, CDEC, DAED	4
ABECDA, BCEDAB, CDEABC, DAEBCD	4
ABCEA, BCDEB, CDAEC, DABED	4

Suppose now that the KCE for this set of 13 circuits is considered as a simultaneous set. What of their independence? These equations are *not* independent, as, for example, addition of the set of four equations for the circuits specified by the second row shows. This sum is the first equation. What, then, of the independence character of the KCE of a network?

It can be shown by using more advanced topology than is presented in the foregoing* that, of the system of all possible circuit equations for a graph, only $e - v + 1$ of them are independent—e-elements and v-vertices in the graph. Even after this fact is established there remains the problem of which $e - v + 1$ of these equations are independent. This question can best be answered after the matrix formulation of the KCE is established.

In matrix form the Kirchhoff circuit equations are

$$\mathcal{B}\mathcal{V}_{et} = 0 \tag{9–31}$$

te

where $\mathcal{B}$ is an $(e - v + 1) \times e$ matrix, called the circuit matrix, with entries of $+1$, -1, and 0 only, and

$\mathcal{V}_{et}$ is an $e \times 1$ matrix consisting of the V_t(t for terminal) of the elements of the network.

Example 9:4 (*a*) Establish the circuit matrix for a set of c-circuits for Fig. 9–3. Consider the tree elements 5, 6, 7, and 8.

(*b*) Establish a second circuit matrix for the same figure so that the circuit equations are independent.

---

* Sundaram Seshu and Myril B. Reed, *On the Topology of Networks*, Proceedings of a Symposium on Circuit Analysis, Sponsored by the Division of University Extension of the University of Illinois and the P.G.C.T. of the I.R.E, May 16–18, 1955, Allerton Park, Monticello, Ill.

Solution (*a*) The circuits indicated by the curved arrows in Fig. 9–3 are the c-circuits for the tree elements 5, 6, 7, and 8. These c-circuit equations are

$$\begin{matrix} a \\ b \\ c \\ d \end{matrix}\begin{bmatrix} 1 & 0 & 0 & 0 & -1 & 0 & 0 & -1 \\ 0 & 1 & 0 & 0 & 0 & 0 & -1 & -1 \\ 0 & 0 & 1 & 0 & 0 & 1 & -1 & 0 \\ 0 & 0 & 0 & 1 & 1 & -1 & 0 & 0 \end{bmatrix}\begin{bmatrix} V_{t1} \\ V_{t2} \\ V_{t3} \\ V_{t4} \\ V_{t5} \\ V_{t6} \\ V_{t7} \\ V_{t8} \end{bmatrix} = 0$$

where the V_{tk} are for the *terminals* and so include the E's and ZI's.

Note that the set of $e - V + 1$ (four) c-circuit equations are independent since there is a fourth-order determinant in the matrix which is not zero. Also note particularly the appearance of the unit matrix in the first four columns. It is this unit matrix which makes it evident at once that this particular set of c-circuit equations are independent.

An $(e - v + 1) \times (e - v + 1)$ unit matrix always occurs in this leading position in the c-circuit matrix if the order of the rows—i.e., the circuits—and the order of the defining chord variables are the same. The c-circuit equations are therefore always independent.

(*b*) Consider the set of circuits in Fig. 9–3: *ABCDA*, *ADEBA*, *CEDC*, *AEDA*. These circuits can be characterized by the fact that each circuit in the order given incorporates an element in the circuit which has not been included in a preceding circuit. If the first four V_{tk} are ordered in $\mathcal{V}_{et}$ in correspondence with this element inclusion, the circuit equations take the form:

$$\begin{matrix} \text{Circuit} \\ ABCDA \\ ADEBA \\ CEDC \\ AEDA \end{matrix}\begin{bmatrix} 1 & 0 & 0 & 0 & -1 & 1 & 1 & 0 \\ -1 & 1 & 0 & 0 & 0 & 0 & -1 & 1 \\ 0 & -1 & 1 & 0 & 0 & -1 & 0 & 0 \\ 0 & -1 & 0 & 1 & 0 & 0 & 1 & 0 \end{bmatrix}\begin{bmatrix} V_{t1} \\ V_{t6} \\ V_{t7} \\ V_{t5} \\ V_{t2} \\ V_{t3} \\ V_{t4} \\ V_{t8} \end{bmatrix} = 0$$

Note that while a four-by-four unit matrix does not occur in the leading position of this circuit matrix, still this leading determinant is different from zero. These circuit equations are therefore independent.

A triangular matrix in the leading position is always possible and can be effected by ordering the equations and V_{tk} in correspondence with incorporating a "new" element in succeeding equations.

The foregoing example illustrates the following two criteria for establishing a system of circuit equations which are independent.

Criterion 1: The c-circuit equations are always $e - v + 1$ in number and are always independent. Ordering the equations and variables to locate an $(e - v + 1) \times (e - v + 1)$ unit matrix in the leading position is not essential although often desirable and always possible.

Criterion 2: Form the $e - v + 1$ circuits of a graph in such an order that an element not included in any preceding circuit is incorporated in each succeeding circuit. The order of writing the circuit equations is not important, although it is sometimes useful to locate a triangular $(e - v + 1) \times (e - v + 1)$ matrix in the leading position. In any event the $e - v + 1$ circuit equations established according to this criterion are always independent. Note also that the sensing of the circuits is immaterial, since reversing the c-sensing has the sole effect of changing all signs in the corresponding circuit equation.

One final comment on the $e - v + 1$ independent circuit equations formed according to either of the foregoing criteria should perhaps be made. Note that in the two cases in Example 9:4 each element of the graph is included at least once in some circuit; i.e., the graph is "covered." Either of these two criteria always establishes a set of circuits which places each element in at least one circuit. There is no need, therefore, for paying the slightest attention to including all elements in the system of circuits. Use of either criterion makes it impossible not to include all elements in the set of circuits.

9.12 Interrelations of the $\mathcal{V}_{et}$ and $\mathcal{I}_e$.

The KVE and KCE of Kirchhoff's current and voltage laws, as formulated by equations 9–27 and 9–31, are not sufficient to determine the currents or voltages because this total of e equations does not determine $2e$ variables—e variables in $\mathcal{I}_e$ and $\mathcal{V}_{et}$ each. The interrelations of the i- and v-functions, as formulated in Chap. 3, serve to supply an additional set of e relations, one for each network element. These interrelations can be formulated into a matrix pattern as follows.

Consider first the single network element representation in Fig. 9–5. The terminal voltage symbol, V_t, for the reference alignments shown, and with the agreement that the reference plus for ZI is at the tail of the I reference arrow, may be expressed as (use KCE)

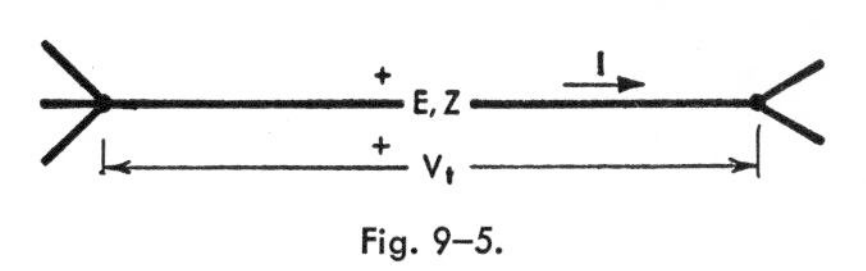

Fig. 9–5.

$$V_t = E + ZI \tag{9–32}$$

The matrix form of this last relation is symbolized by

$$\mathcal{V}_{et} = \mathcal{E}_e + \mathfrak{z}_e \mathcal{I}_e \tag{9–33}$$

which represents a system of e equations relating the functions of the elements of networks.

Example 9:5 Establish the detailed form of equation 9–33 for the diagram in Fig. 9–6.

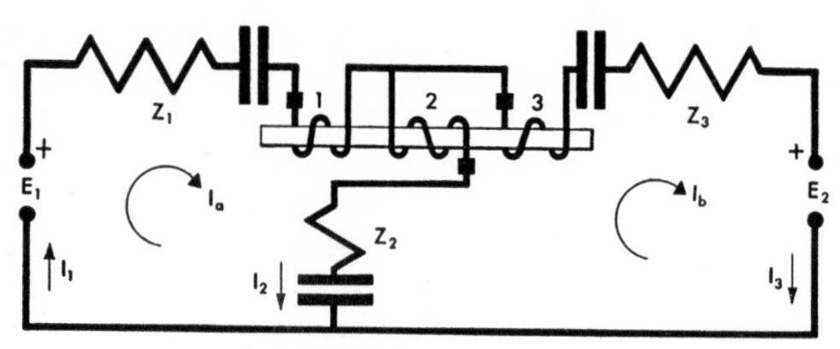

Fig. 9–6.

Solution The pattern of references established in Chap. 3 is used here. The reference plus for the terminal voltages and the ZI are all to be located at the tail of the e-sensing arrow. Also the mutual induction reference marks are located at the tails of the e-sensing arrows. The KCE of the Kirchhoff voltage law for element 1 of Fig. 9–6 is, then,

$$V_{1t} = -E_1 + Z_1I_1 + Z_{12}I_2 + Z_{13}I_3$$

This last equation, and the two other corresponding equations for elements 2 and 3, when expressed in the matrix form of equation 9–33, become

$$\mathcal{V}_{et} = \begin{bmatrix} V_{1t} \\ V_{2t} \\ V_{3t} \end{bmatrix} = \begin{bmatrix} -E_1 \\ 0 \\ E_2 \end{bmatrix} + \begin{bmatrix} Z_1 & Z_{12} & Z_{13} \\ Z_{21} & Z_2 & Z_{23} \\ Z_{31} & Z_{32} & Z_3 \end{bmatrix} \begin{bmatrix} I_1 \\ I_2 \\ I_3 \end{bmatrix} = \mathcal{E}_e + \mathfrak{Z}_e \mathcal{I}_e$$

where
$$\begin{aligned} Z_1 &= R_1 + j\omega L_1 + \frac{1}{j\omega C_1} \\ Z_2 &= R_2 + j\omega L_2 + \frac{1}{j\omega C_2} \\ Z_3 &= R_3 + j\omega L_3 + \frac{1}{j\omega C_3} \\ Z_{12} &= Z_{21} = j\omega M_{12},\ M_{12} < 0 \\ Z_{13} &= Z_{31} = j\omega M_{13},\ M_{13} > 0 \\ Z_{23} &= Z_{32} = j\omega M_{23},\ M_{23} < 0 \end{aligned}$$

The square matrix of impedance symbols is symmetric since $Z_{12} = Z_{21}$, $Z_{13} = Z_{31}$, and $Z_{23} = Z_{32}$. Notice a very important feature of this impedance matrix, $\mathfrak{Z}_e$, namely, that all signs are positive under the reference alignments used in this book—all reference pluses for all ZI, whether self or mutual, at the tail of the e-sensing arrow. This positive-sign characteristic of $\mathfrak{Z}_e$ is entirely a consequence of the reference alignments used here. The location of the entries in $\mathfrak{Z}_e$ is also relatively very simple and may be characterized by "a place for every Z and every Z in its place." In order further to illustrate this location of the Z's in the impedance matrix, $\mathfrak{Z}_e$, the following example is presented.

Example 9:6 Establish in detail the matrix equation 9–33 for Fig. 9–7. The coils A and B, as well as F and G, are on a common core. The two cores are *not* located in space as shown. However, the squares indicate the *actual* mutual induction marks.

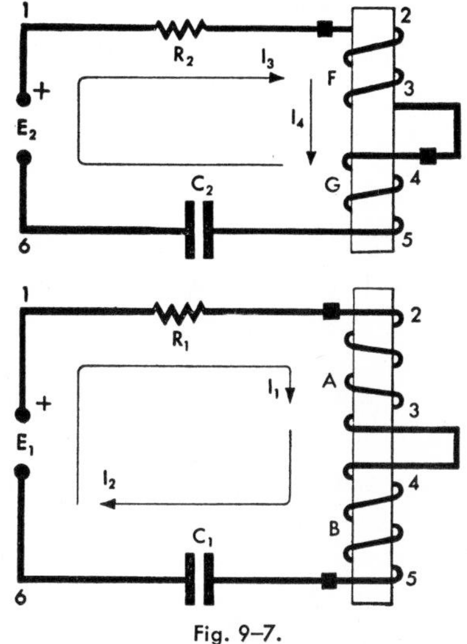

Fig. 9–7.

Solution The use of equation 9–33 requires that a network be considered as a combination of two-terminal elements. In such situations as Fig. 9–7, where a two-terminal element feature is not evident, each circuit should be considered as consisting of two elements. The portions of the circuit which are taken as the two elements are arbitrary. A particular choice is made for this example and others are suggested in the problems. For this example, consider the four elements as indicated by the e-sensing arrows. The matrix $\mathfrak{Z}_e$ is then 4×4. The equation for $\mathcal{V}_{et}$, with all voltage and mutual induction reference marks at the tail of e-sensing arrow except those for E_1 and E_2, is

$$\begin{bmatrix} V_{1t} \\ V_{2t} \\ V_{3t} \\ V_{4t} \end{bmatrix} = \begin{bmatrix} -E_1 \\ 0 \\ -E_2 \\ 0 \end{bmatrix} + \begin{bmatrix} Z_1 & Z_{AB} & 0 & Z_{AF} + Z_{AG} \\ Z_{AB} & Z_2 & 0 & Z_{BF} + Z_{BG} \\ 0 & 0 & Z_3 & 0 \\ Z_{AF} + Z_{AG} & Z_{BF} + Z_{BG} & 0 & Z_4 + 2Z_{FG} \end{bmatrix} \begin{bmatrix} I_1 \\ I_2 \\ I_3 \\ I_4 \end{bmatrix}$$

where

$$\begin{aligned} Z_1 &= R_1 + R_A + j\omega L_A \\ Z_2 &= R_B + \frac{1}{j\omega C_1} + j\omega L_B \\ Z_3 &= R_2 + \frac{1}{j\omega C_2} \\ Z_4 &= R_F + R_G + j\omega L_F + j\omega L_G \\ Z_{AB} &= Z_{BA} = j\omega M_{AB}, \ M_{AB} < 0 \\ Z_{AF} &= Z_{FA} = j\omega M_{AF}, \ M_{AF} > 0 \\ Z_{AG} &= Z_{GA} = j\omega M_{AG}, \ M_{AG} > 0 \\ Z_{BF} &= Z_{FB} = j\omega M_{BF}, \ M_{BF} < 0 \\ Z_{BG} &= Z_{GB} = j\omega M_{BG}, \ M_{BG} < 0 \\ Z_{FG} &= Z_{GF} = j\omega M_{FG}, \ M_{FG} > 0 \end{aligned}$$

A study of these last two examples in addition, perhaps, to a review of Chap. 3, should make the pattern of the $\mathcal{E}_e$, $\mathfrak{Z}_e$, $\mathcal{V}_{et}$ and $\mathcal{I}_e$ matrices evident. Further word descriptions are more likely to confuse than clarify the process of forming these matrices. As a general observation, it may be noted that the only problems are the ordering of the entries in the matrices and the inclusion of all the entries. There are no sign problems in the symbolic form. In the absence of mutual induction, $\mathfrak{Z}_e$ is always a diagonal matrix, i.e., a matrix with zero entries everywhere except on the main diagonal—upper left to lower right.

9.13 Mesh System of Network Equations—Matrix Method.

The combination of the Kirchhoff vertex and circuit equations—equations 9–27 and 9–31—and the interrelation of terminal voltage functions and current functions—equation 9–33—specifies

$$\mathcal{A}\mathcal{I}_e = 0$$
$$\mathcal{B}[\mathcal{E}_e + \mathfrak{Z}_e\mathcal{I}_e] = 0 \tag{9–34}$$

which is a system of e equations in the e unknowns of $\mathcal{I}_e$. For lack of a better designation these e equations may be called the e-system.

The e-system of equations is rarely if ever used to determine the electrical behavior of a network. Instead, two different alterations of these equations are used which *reduce the number of equations that must be solved simultaneously*. One of these methods, the mesh method, is presented next.

The mesh system of equations is based on a change of variables. In turn this change of variables is based on a fundamental property of the vertex and circuit matrices, namely, that if the columns of $\mathcal{A}$ and of $\mathcal{B}$ are ordered to correspond to the same elements,

$$\mathcal{A}\mathcal{B}' = 0 \quad \text{and} \quad \mathcal{B}\mathcal{A}' = 0 \tag{9–35}$$

This last relation is easily verified for any particular case—Problems 9–19 and 9–20. The change in variables used to establish the mesh system involves a *reduction* in the number of variables as well as a reduction in the number of equations.

Formally, let

$$\mathcal{I}_e = \mathcal{B}'\mathcal{I}_m \tag{9–36}$$

where $\mathcal{I}_m$ is a set of $e - v + 1$ variables, with $\mathcal{I}_e$ and $\mathcal{B}$, and so $\mathcal{B}'$, as defined in the foregoing. Substitution of this last relation in equation 9–34 gives

$$\mathcal{A}\mathcal{B}'\mathcal{I}_m \equiv 0 \tag{9–37}$$
$$\mathcal{B}\mathcal{E}_e + \mathcal{B}\mathfrak{Z}_e\mathcal{B}'\mathcal{I}_m = 0 \tag{9–38}$$

Because of equation 9–35, equation 9–37 is satisfied for any $\mathcal{I}_m$ whatsoever. Then if equation 9–38 is used to determine $\mathcal{I}_m$, the vertex and circuit equations are both always satisfied by the $\mathcal{I}_e$ in equation 9–36.

Equation 9–38 is the set of $e - v + 1$ equations in $e - v + 1$ unknowns, $\mathcal{I}_m$, which is to be solved. This system is known as the system of mesh equations. An alternative symbolic form of this equation is convenient; namely,

$$-\mathcal{E}_m = \mathfrak{Z}_m\mathcal{I}_m \tag{9–39}$$

where

$$\mathcal{E}_m = \mathcal{B}\mathcal{E}_e \tag{9–40}$$
$$\mathfrak{Z}_m = \mathcal{B}\mathfrak{Z}_e\mathcal{B}' \tag{9–41}$$

The requirement that equation 9–39 determine $\mathcal{I}_m$ is that $\mathfrak{Z}_m$ have an inverse, i.e., that $\mathfrak{Z}_m$ is non-singular or that the determinant of $\mathfrak{Z}_m$ does not vanish. Formally, if $|\mathfrak{Z}_m| \neq 0$,

$$\mathcal{I}_m = -\mathfrak{Z}_m^{-1}\mathcal{E}_m \tag{9–42}$$

Example 9:7 Establish the mesh system of equations for the diagram in Fig. 9–7.

Solution The matrices $\mathcal{E}_e$, $\mathfrak{Z}_e$, and $\mathcal{I}_e$ are all given in Example 9:6. This diagram should be considered as connected. Without actually carrying out the process, imagine the two circuits as connected at *one* point, say 6 of the lower circuit and 5 of the upper circuit. There are, then, three vertices—2 of the upper diagram, 65 of the combined diagram, and 3 of the lower diagram. For the connected graph, therefore, $e - v + 1 = 4 - 3 + 1 = 2$. A circuit matrix is, for clockwise c-sensing,

$$\mathcal{B} = \begin{matrix} \text{upper circuit} \\ \text{lower circuit} \end{matrix} \begin{bmatrix} 0 & 0 & 1 & 1 \\ 1 & 1 & 0 & 0 \end{bmatrix}$$

Matrix multiplication, then, specifies

$$\mathcal{E}_m = \mathcal{B}\mathcal{E}_e = \begin{bmatrix} 0 & 0 & 1 & 1 \\ 1 & 1 & 0 & 0 \end{bmatrix} \begin{bmatrix} -E_1 \\ 0 \\ -E_2 \\ 0 \end{bmatrix} = \begin{bmatrix} -E_2 \\ -E_1 \end{bmatrix}$$

$$\mathfrak{Z}_m = \begin{bmatrix} 0 & 0 & 1 & 1 \\ 1 & 1 & 0 & 0 \end{bmatrix} \begin{bmatrix} Z_1 & Z_{AB} & 0 & Z_{AF} + Z_{AG} \\ Z_{AB} & Z_2 & 0 & Z_{BF} + Z_{BG} \\ 0 & 0 & Z_3 & 0 \\ Z_{AF} + Z_{AG} & Z_{BF} + Z_{BG} & 0 & Z_4 + 2Z_{FG} \end{bmatrix} \begin{bmatrix} 0 & 1 \\ 0 & 1 \\ 1 & 0 \\ 1 & 0 \end{bmatrix}$$

$$= \begin{bmatrix} Z_3 + Z_4 + 2Z_{FG} & Z_{AF} + Z_{AG} + Z_{BF} + Z_{BG} \\ Z_{AF} + Z_{AG} + Z_{BF} + Z_{BG} & Z_1 + Z_2 + 2Z_{AB} \end{bmatrix}$$

In the absence of mutual induction this matrix, $\mathfrak{Z}_m$, becomes a diagonal matrix.

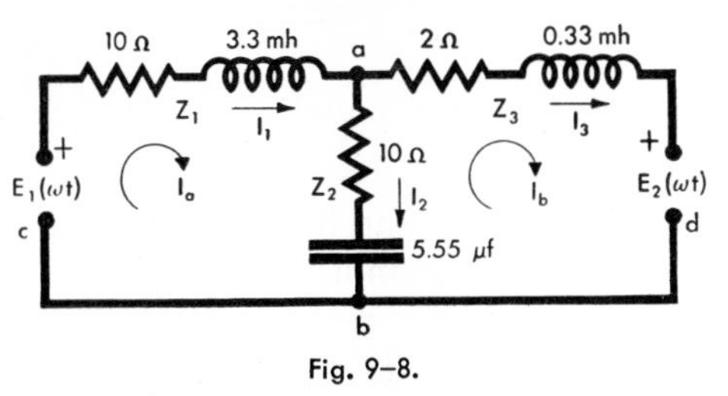

Fig. 9–8.

Example 9:8 Use the mesh system to determine $\mathcal{I}_e$ for Fig. 9–8 if $E_1(t) = 20\epsilon^{j6000t}$, and $E_2(t) = 40\epsilon^{j(6000t+45)}$.

Solution The $t = 0$ values of $E_1(t)$ and $E_2(t)$ specify E_1 and E_2; hence

$$\mathcal{E}_e = \begin{bmatrix} -E_1 \\ 0 \\ E_2 \end{bmatrix} = \begin{bmatrix} -20 + j0 \\ 0 \\ 28.3 + j28.3 \end{bmatrix}$$

In the absence of mutual induction the matrix, $\mathfrak{Z}_e$, is diagonal and is

$$\mathfrak{Z}_e = \begin{bmatrix} Z_1 & 0 & 0 \\ 0 & Z_2 & 0 \\ 0 & 0 & Z_3 \end{bmatrix} = \begin{bmatrix} 10 + j20 & 0 & 0 \\ 0 & 10 - j30 & 0 \\ 0 & 0 & 2 + j2 \end{bmatrix}$$

If the curved arrows specify the two $(e - v + 1)$ circuits and c-sense these circuits, the circuit matrix is

$$\mathcal{B} = \begin{bmatrix} 1 & 1 & 0 \\ 0 & -1 & 1 \end{bmatrix}$$

By matrix multiplication

$$\mathcal{E}_m = \mathcal{B}\mathcal{E}_e = \begin{bmatrix} -E_1 \\ E_2 \end{bmatrix}$$

$$\mathfrak{Z}_m = \mathcal{B}\mathfrak{Z}_e\mathcal{B}' = \begin{bmatrix} 20 - j10 & -10 + j30 \\ -10 + j30 & 12 - j28 \end{bmatrix}$$

The inverse of $\mathfrak{Z}_m$ is

$$\mathfrak{Z}_m^{-1} = \frac{1}{760 - j80} \begin{bmatrix} 12 - j28 & 10 - j30 \\ 10 - j30 & 20 - j10 \end{bmatrix}$$

From equation 9–42, then,

$$\mathcal{I}_m = -\mathfrak{Z}_m^{-1}\mathcal{E}_m = \begin{bmatrix} I_a \\ I_b \end{bmatrix} = \begin{bmatrix} -1.16 - j0.114 \\ -0.72 - j1.24 \end{bmatrix} = \begin{bmatrix} 1.17\epsilon^{j185.7} \\ 1.43\epsilon^{j239.8} \end{bmatrix}$$

Finally

$$\mathcal{I}_e = \begin{bmatrix} I_1 \\ I_2 \\ I_3 \end{bmatrix} = \mathcal{B}'\mathcal{I}_m = \begin{bmatrix} 1 & 0 \\ 1 & -1 \\ 0 & 1 \end{bmatrix} \begin{bmatrix} -1.16 - j0.114 \\ -0.72 - j1.24 \end{bmatrix} = \begin{bmatrix} -1.16 - j0.114 \\ -0.44 + j1.126 \\ -0.72 - j1.24 \end{bmatrix}$$

As functions of t

$$\mathcal{I}_e(t) = \begin{bmatrix} I_1(t) \\ I_2(t) \\ I_3(t) \end{bmatrix} = \begin{bmatrix} 1.17\epsilon^{j(6000t+185.7)} \\ 1.2\epsilon^{j(6000t+111.3)} \\ 1.43\epsilon^{j(6000t+239.8)} \end{bmatrix}$$

9.14 Mesh System of Network Equations—Direct from the Network Diagram.

The mesh system of equations can be written directly from a network diagram. If there is little or no mutual induction in the network, the direct-from-the-network method is rather easy. On the other hand, extensive mutual induction makes this process difficult. Both methods should therefore be in the repertory of an electrical engineer.

Any attempt at explaining just how the results of the matrix multiplications of equations 9–40 and 9–41 can be effected from a network diagram is almost certain to lead to more complexity than clarity. The statement of rules for carrying out this direct-from-the-network process is therefore all that is done here.

Formation of $\mathcal{E}_m$ Enter in any particular row of $\mathcal{E}_m$ the sum of the E_k of the circuit corresponding to that row. Use $+E_k$ for all E_k of the diagram with e- and c-sensing coincident, and $-E_k$ for all E_k of the diagram with e- and c-sensing non-coincident.

Formation of $\mathfrak{Z}_m$ (1) Enter in any particular main diagonal position of $\mathfrak{Z}_m$ the sum of all the self-impedance Z's of the circuit corresponding to that position. Add to this sum, for each pair of mutually coupled inductors A and B, both of which are in the corresponding circuit, $+2Z_{AB}$ if the e-sensing and the c-sensing coincide in both inductors or do not coincide in both; or $-2Z_{AB}$ if only one of the e-sensings coincides with the c-sensing.

(2) Enter in *two* of the off-the-main-diagonal positions, i-row and j-column and j-row and i-column, $+Z_k$ or $-Z_k$ if Z_k is common to the i-circuit and j-circuit and if the c-sensings of the two circuits are respectively the same or opposite for the Z_k element—$+Z_8$ and $-Z_5$ for Fig. 9–3.

Add in the i-row and j-column and j-row and i-column positions, for each mutual coupling of an inductor A of the i-circuit and an inductor B of the j-circuit, $+Z_{AB}$ if the e-sensings of A and B both do or both do not coincide respectively with the c-sensings of the i- and j-circuits, or $-Z_{AB}$ if only one of these pairs of sensings does not coincide.

These rules for forming $\mathfrak{Z}_m$ lead to an easy technique for simple networks and should certainly be learned for use in simple cases.

9.15 The E-Shift (Blakesley).

A useful alteration in a network diagram is considered next. This network diagram alteration, pointed out by Blakesley, consists in shifting an $e(t)$ function in any element into all the other elements at a vertex, as

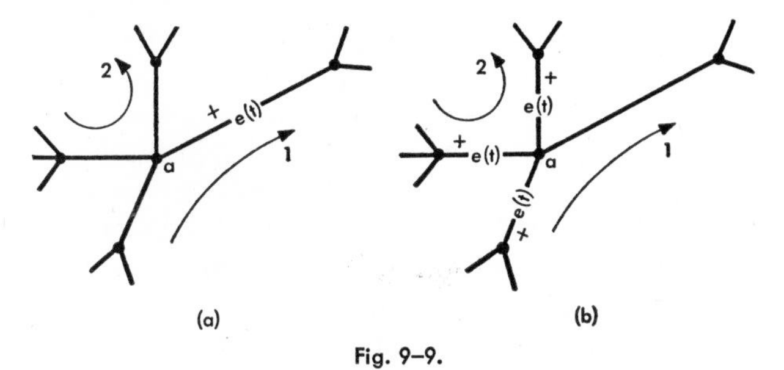

Fig. 9–9.

shown in Fig. 9–9. This E-shift does not alter the mesh system of equations since it does not alter $\mathcal{E}_m$. This fact is evident almost at a glance. Consider the two diagrams and the two c-sensing arrows in Fig. 9–9. The function $e(t)$ certainly would appear in $\mathcal{E}_m$ for both such circuits in exactly the same way. Since these two are the only possible patterns for

$e(t)$ appearing in $\mathcal{E}_m$, the E-shift cannot alter $\mathcal{E}_m$ no matter how many E-shifts are employed. Since $\mathcal{E}_m$ is unaltered by a set of E-shifts, so also are $\mathcal{I}_m$ and $\mathcal{I}_e$ unaltered—equations 9–42 and 9–36. The v-functions for the terminals of the network element are altered, however. This alteration is simple, though, and is easily corrected for by adding or subtracting the $e(t)$ wherever required to restore the original $e(t)$ pattern.

Example 9:9 Suppose an E-shift is applied to $E_1(\omega t)$ in Fig. 9–8. Determine the terminal voltage values in the altered and original network.

Solution Since $\mathcal{I}_e$ is the same for the altered and original networks, $\mathcal{I}_e$ of Example 9:8 applies to the altered network also.

For the altered network, then, since $E_1(\omega t)$ is no longer in element ac,

$$V_{ac}' = -Z_1I_1 = -(10 + j20)\ (-1.16 - j0.114) = 9.32 + j24.34$$

The original network value of V_{ab}, then, may be computed by

$$V_{ab} = V_{ac}' + E_1 = (9.32 + j24.34) + (20 + j0) = 29.32 + j24.34$$

9.16 Node System of Network Equations—Matrix Method.

The node system of equations, $v - 1$ in number, is essentially the system of vertex equations altered by an appropriate change in variables. The main idea in forming the node system is the same as that in forming the mesh system. In the mesh system an appropriate change in variables is applied to the circuit equations and in the node system to the vertex equations; in both a reduction in the number of equations which must be solved simultaneously is sought. The node system may be derived by first considering equation 9–33.

The first requirement for the existence of the node system of equations is that $\mathfrak{z}_e$ in equation 9–33 have an inverse. Customarily it does. There is, however, one obvious case of practical import where $\mathfrak{z}_e^{-1}$ does not exist, namely, in networks containing a regulated (fixed) terminal voltage. Such a condition corresponds to $Z = 0$ for the regulated element, and so $\mathfrak{z}_e$ contains a row and column of zeros and $|\mathfrak{z}_e| = 0$ and $\mathfrak{z}_e^{-1}$ does not exist.

Suppose, though, that the E-shift is used on all such regulated elements. The $Z = 0$ element (short circuit) can be then removed by combining the two end vertices into one. The row and column of zeros of $\mathfrak{z}_e$ corresponding to the regulated element thus do not enter the $\mathfrak{z}_e$ for the altered network. An obvious obstruction to the existence of $\mathfrak{z}_e^{-1}$ is thereby removed.

An easy although important change in the pattern of the vertex equations permits an extension of these equations, and hence the node system, to include "driving" current-functions as well as "driving" voltage-functions.

Consider first the extension of the vertex equations. For the diagram in Fig. 9–10, the vertex equations are (the subscript a indicates amplified)

$$\mathcal{A}_a\mathcal{I}_a = \begin{matrix} 1 \\ 2 \\ 3 \\ 5 \end{matrix}\begin{bmatrix} 1 & 1 & 0 & 0 & 0 & 0 & 1 & 0 & 0 \\ 0 & -1 & 1 & 1 & 0 & 0 & 0 & 1 & 0 \\ 0 & 0 & 0 & -1 & 0 & -1 & 0 & 0 & -1 \\ -1 & 0 & -1 & 0 & 1 & 0 & 0 & 0 & 0 \end{bmatrix}\begin{bmatrix} I_1 \\ I_3 \\ I_4 \\ I_5 \\ I_6 \\ I_7 \\ J_a \\ J_b \\ J_c \end{bmatrix}$$

This last matrix equation can be altered to the form

$$\mathcal{A}_a\mathcal{I}_a = \begin{bmatrix} 1 & 1 & 0 & 0 & 0 & 0 \\ 0 & -1 & 1 & 1 & 0 & 0 \\ 0 & 0 & 0 & -1 & 0 & -1 \\ -1 & 0 & -1 & 0 & 1 & 0 \end{bmatrix}\begin{bmatrix} I_1 \\ I_3 \\ I_4 \\ I_5 \\ I_6 \\ I_7 \end{bmatrix} + \begin{bmatrix} 1 & 0 & 0 \\ 0 & 1 & 0 \\ 0 & 0 & -1 \\ 0 & 0 & 0 \end{bmatrix}\begin{bmatrix} J_a \\ J_b \\ J_c \end{bmatrix}$$

$$= \mathcal{A}\mathcal{I}_e + \mathcal{A}_j\mathcal{I}_e = 0 \tag{9–43}$$

Notice that $\mathcal{A}$ is the vertex matrix for the diagram with only the I_k being considered, and $\mathcal{A}_j$ is the vertex matrix for the *same* set of vertices and in the same order with *only* the J's being considered. The vertex equations can always be expressed in the form of equation 9–43. Furthermore, any vertex may be omitted in forming the vertex equations. Also, as indicated in Problem 9–39, any one of the J's need not be specified because the others determine the one.

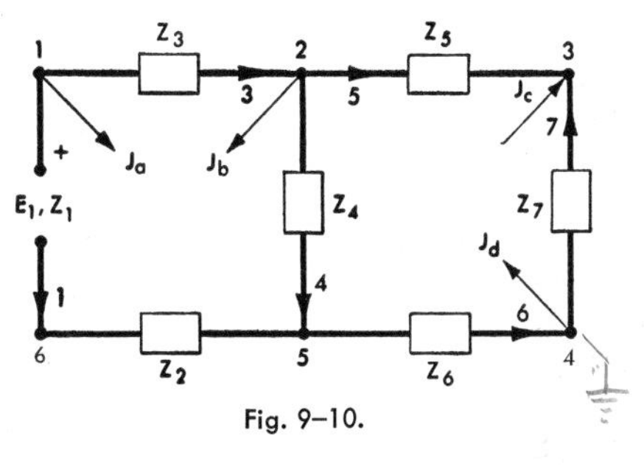

Fig. 9–10.

Return now to equation 9–33 and assume that $\mathfrak{z}_e$ has an inverse. Then

$$\mathcal{I}_e = \mathfrak{z}_e^{-1}[\mathcal{V}_{et} - \mathcal{E}_e] \tag{9–44}$$

If this last relation is substituted in equation 9–43, the vertex equations are

$$\mathcal{A}\mathfrak{z}_e^{-1}[\mathcal{V}_{et} - \mathcal{E}_e] + \mathcal{A}_j\mathcal{I}_e = 0 \tag{9–45}$$

Consider now a transformation of variables

$$\mathcal{V}_{et} = \mathcal{A}'\mathcal{V}_n \tag{9–46}$$

where $\mathcal{V}_n$ is a set of $v - 1$ variables. If this transformation is substituted in the circuit equations (equation 9–31) and the vertex equations as given by equation 9–45, the result is

$$\mathcal{B}\mathcal{V}_{et} = \mathcal{B}\mathcal{A}'\mathcal{V}_n \equiv 0 \tag{9–47}$$
$$\mathcal{A}\mathfrak{Z}_e^{-1}\mathcal{A}'\mathcal{V}_n = \mathcal{A}\mathfrak{Z}_e^{-1}\mathcal{E}_e - \mathcal{A}_j\mathcal{J}_e \tag{9–48}$$

In contrast with the mesh system, it is now the circuit equations that are satisfied for all $\mathcal{V}_n$. Consequently, the $v - 1$ variables of $\mathcal{V}_n$, if determined by equation 9–48, satisfy both the circuit and vertex equations. Equation 9–46 determines $\mathcal{V}_{et}$ once $\mathcal{V}_n$ is determined, and equation 9–44 determines $\mathcal{I}_e$.

A briefer symbolism may be convenient. Equation 9–48, the node system, may be expressed as

$$\mathcal{J}_{ne} - \mathcal{J}_{nj} = \mathcal{Y}_n\mathcal{V}_n \tag{9–49}$$

where $\mathcal{Y}_n = \mathcal{A}\mathfrak{Z}_e^{-1}\mathcal{A}'$ (9–50)

$\mathcal{J}_{ne} = \mathcal{A}\mathfrak{Z}_e^{-1}\mathcal{E}_e$ (9–51)

$\mathcal{J}_{nj} = \mathcal{A}_j\mathcal{J}_e$ (9–52)

In order that equation 9–49 determine $\mathcal{V}_n$, the inverse of $\mathcal{Y}_n$ must exist. If this inverse does exist,

$$\mathcal{V}_n = \mathcal{Y}_n^{-1}[\mathcal{J}_{ne} - \mathcal{J}_{nj}] \tag{9–53}$$

Example 9:10 Use the node system to determine $\mathcal{I}_e$ for the diagram in Fig. 9–11. This network diagram represents a direct-voltage, direct-current

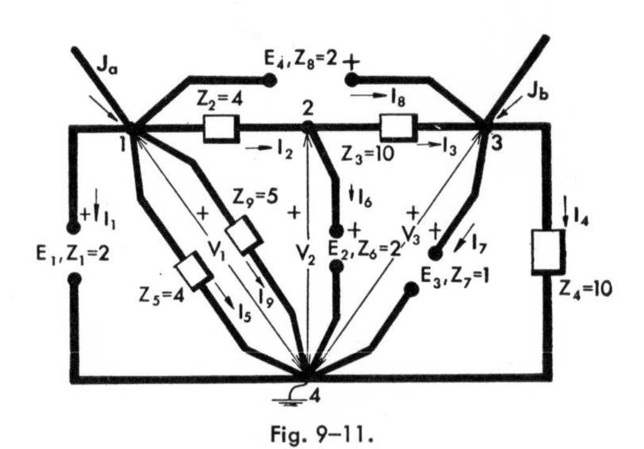

Fig. 9–11.

network with $E_1 = 10$ volts, $E_2 = 20$ volts, $E_3 = -10$ volts, $E_4 = -20$ volts, $J_a = 10$ amp, and $J_b = -10$ amp.

Solution The vertex matrices $\mathcal{A}$ and $\mathcal{A}_j$, are: from considering only the I's

$$\mathcal{A} = \begin{matrix} \\ 1 \\ 2 \\ 3 \end{matrix}\begin{matrix} \begin{matrix} 1 & 2 & 3 & 4 & 5 & 6 & 7 & 8 & 9 \end{matrix} \\ \begin{bmatrix} 1 & 1 & 0 & 0 & 1 & 0 & 0 & 1 & 1 \\ 0 & -1 & 1 & 0 & 0 & 1 & 0 & 0 & 0 \\ 0 & 0 & -1 & 1 & 0 & 0 & 1 & -1 & 0 \end{bmatrix} \end{matrix}$$

and from considering only the J's

$$\mathcal{A}_j = \begin{matrix} & a & b \\ 1 & -1 & 0 \\ 2 & 0 & 0 \\ 3 & 0 & -1 \end{matrix}$$

The inverse of $\mathfrak{Z}_e$, a diagonal matrix with $\dfrac{1}{R_k}$ in the main diagonal positions, and $\mathcal{E}_e$, are

$$\mathfrak{Z}_e^{-1} = \begin{bmatrix} \frac{1}{2} & 0 & 0 & 0 & 0 & 0 & 0 & 0 & 0 \\ 0 & \frac{1}{4} & 0 & 0 & 0 & 0 & 0 & 0 & 0 \\ 0 & 0 & \frac{1}{10} & 0 & 0 & 0 & 0 & 0 & 0 \\ 0 & 0 & 0 & \frac{1}{10} & 0 & 0 & 0 & 0 & 0 \\ 0 & 0 & 0 & 0 & \frac{1}{4} & 0 & 0 & 0 & 0 \\ 0 & 0 & 0 & 0 & 0 & \frac{1}{2} & 0 & 0 & 0 \\ 0 & 0 & 0 & 0 & 0 & 0 & \frac{1}{1} & 0 & 0 \\ 0 & 0 & 0 & 0 & 0 & 0 & 0 & \frac{1}{2} & 0 \\ 0 & 0 & 0 & 0 & 0 & 0 & 0 & 0 & \frac{1}{5} \end{bmatrix}; \quad \mathcal{E}_e = \begin{bmatrix} E_1 \\ E_2 \\ E_3 \\ E_4 \\ E_5 \\ E_6 \\ E_7 \\ E_8 \\ E_9 \end{bmatrix} = \begin{bmatrix} 10 \\ 0 \\ 0 \\ 0 \\ 0 \\ 20 \\ -10 \\ 20 \\ 0 \end{bmatrix}$$

Performing the matrix multiplication of equation 9–50 gives

$$\mathcal{Y}_n = \mathcal{A}\mathfrak{Z}_e^{-1}\mathcal{A}' = \begin{bmatrix} \frac{1}{2}+\frac{1}{4}+\frac{1}{4}+\frac{1}{2}+\frac{1}{5} & \frac{-1}{4} & \frac{-1}{2} \\ \frac{-1}{4} & \frac{1}{4}+\frac{1}{10}+\frac{1}{2} & \frac{-1}{10} \\ \frac{-1}{2} & \frac{-1}{10} & \frac{1}{10}+\frac{1}{10}+\frac{1}{1}+\frac{1}{2} \end{bmatrix} = \begin{bmatrix} \frac{17}{10} & -\frac{1}{4} & -\frac{1}{2} \\ \frac{-1}{4} & \frac{17}{20} & \frac{-1}{10} \\ \frac{-1}{2} & \frac{-1}{10} & \frac{17}{10} \end{bmatrix}$$

The numerical form of equation 9–51 is

$$\mathcal{J}_e = \mathcal{A}\mathfrak{Z}_e^{-1}\mathcal{E}_e = \begin{bmatrix} 15 \\ 10 \\ -20 \end{bmatrix}$$

and of equation 9–52 it is

$$\mathcal{J}_{nj} = \mathcal{A}_j \mathcal{J}_e = \begin{bmatrix} -1 & 0 \\ 0 & 0 \\ 0 & -1 \end{bmatrix} \begin{bmatrix} J_a \\ J_b \end{bmatrix} = \begin{bmatrix} -10 \\ 0 \\ 10 \end{bmatrix}$$

The combination of these various matrices in accordance with equation 9–49 specifies the node equations as

$$\begin{bmatrix} 25 \\ 10 \\ -30 \end{bmatrix} = \begin{bmatrix} \frac{17}{10} & -\frac{1}{4} & -\frac{1}{2} \\ -\frac{1}{4} & \frac{17}{20} & -\frac{1}{10} \\ -\frac{1}{2} & -\frac{1}{10} & \frac{17}{10} \end{bmatrix} \begin{bmatrix} V_1 \\ V_2 \\ V_3 \end{bmatrix}$$

Note that the subscripts on V_1, V_2, V_3 are the same as the vertex labels corresponding to the rows and their order in $\mathcal{A}$. The solution of this matrix equation determines $\mathcal{V}_n$ as

$$\mathcal{V}_n = \begin{bmatrix} V_1 \\ V_2 \\ V_3 \end{bmatrix} = \frac{4000}{8383} \begin{bmatrix} \frac{287}{200} & \frac{19}{40} & \frac{9}{20} \\ \frac{19}{40} & \frac{66}{25} & \frac{59}{200} \\ \frac{9}{20} & \frac{59}{200} & \frac{553}{400} \end{bmatrix} \begin{bmatrix} 25 \\ 10 \\ -30 \end{bmatrix} = \begin{bmatrix} 12.94 \\ 14.04 \\ -13.02 \end{bmatrix}$$

Next, using this $\mathcal{V}_n$ and equations 9–46 and 9–44, specifies that

$$\mathcal{V}_{et} = \mathcal{A}'\mathcal{V}_n = \begin{bmatrix} V_{1t} \\ V_{2t} \\ V_{3t} \\ V_{4t} \\ V_{5t} \\ V_{6t} \\ V_{7t} \\ V_{8t} \\ V_{9t} \end{bmatrix} = \begin{bmatrix} 12.94 \\ -1.10 \\ 27.06 \\ -13.02 \\ 12.94 \\ 14.04 \\ -13.02 \\ 25.96 \\ 12.94 \end{bmatrix}; \mathcal{J}_e = \mathfrak{Z}_e^{-1}[\mathcal{V}_{et} - \mathcal{E}_e] = \begin{bmatrix} I_1 \\ I_2 \\ I_3 \\ I_4 \\ I_5 \\ I_6 \\ I_7 \\ I_8 \\ I_9 \end{bmatrix} = \begin{bmatrix} 1.47 \\ -0.28 \\ 2.71 \\ -1.30 \\ 3.24 \\ -2.98 \\ -3.02 \\ 2.98 \\ 2.59 \end{bmatrix}$$

The foregoing example indicates the node system procedure for a network with little or no complications. Consider, in contrast, the following example.

Example 9:11 Determine $\mathcal{J}_e$ for the network diagram in Fig. 9–12*a* by the node method.

Solution Since the diagram under consideration has two elements (7 and 8) with regulated terminal voltages, the E-shift must be employed. Fig. 9–12*b* shows the altered diagram subsequent to two applications of the E-shift. Note that the E's shifted into the J-elements has no effect so may be ignored.

The vertex matrix, $\mathfrak{A}$, is

$$\mathfrak{A} = \begin{array}{r} \\ 3 \\ 6,2 \\ 5 \end{array}\begin{array}{c} \begin{array}{cccccccc} 1 & 2 & 3 & 4 & 5 & 6 & 9 & 10 \end{array} \\ \begin{bmatrix} -1 & 1 & 1 & 0 & 0 & 0 & -1 & 0 \\ 0 & -1 & 0 & 0 & 0 & -1 & 1 & -1 \\ 0 & 0 & -1 & -1 & -1 & 1 & 0 & 1 \end{bmatrix} \end{array}$$

and the matrices $\mathfrak{A}_j$ and $\mathcal{J}_e$ are

$$\mathfrak{A}_j = \begin{bmatrix} 0 & 0 \\ 1 & -1 \\ 0 & 0 \end{bmatrix}; \; \mathcal{J}_e = \begin{bmatrix} J_2 \\ \\ J_6 \end{bmatrix} = \begin{bmatrix} 20 \\ \\ 25 \end{bmatrix}$$

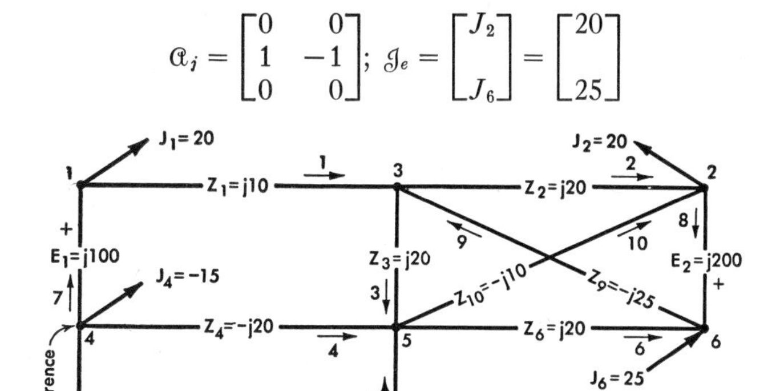

(a)

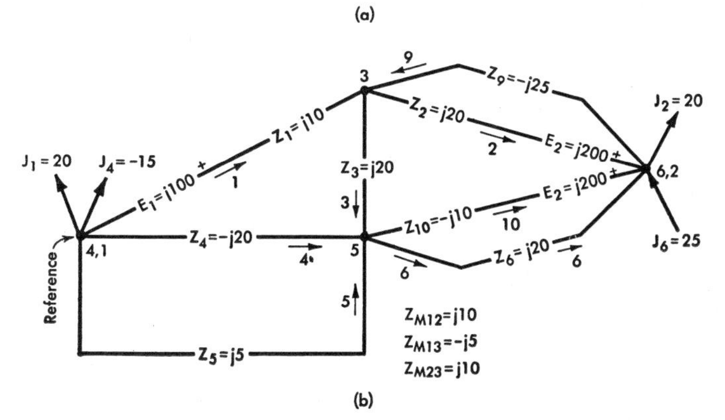

(b)

Fig. 9–12.

Since mutual induction appears in the network being considered, it is not possible to write $\mathfrak{Z}_e^{-1}$ immediately from the diagram. First, then,

$$\mathfrak{Z}_e = \begin{array}{r} 1 \\ 2 \\ 3 \\ 4 \\ 5 \\ 6 \\ 9 \\ 10 \end{array}\begin{bmatrix} j10 & j10 & -j5 & 0 & 0 & 0 & 0 & 0 \\ j10 & j20 & j10 & 0 & 0 & 0 & 0 & 0 \\ -j5 & j10 & j20 & 0 & 0 & 0 & 0 & 0 \\ 0 & 0 & 0 & -j20 & 0 & 0 & 0 & 0 \\ 0 & 0 & 0 & 0 & j5 & 0 & 0 & 0 \\ 0 & 0 & 0 & 0 & 0 & j20 & 0 & 0 \\ 0 & 0 & 0 & 0 & 0 & 0 & -j25 & 0 \\ 0 & 0 & 0 & 0 & 0 & 0 & 0 & -j10 \end{bmatrix}; \; \mathcal{E}_e = \begin{bmatrix} E_1 \\ E_2 \\ E_3 \\ E_4 \\ E_5 \\ E_6 \\ E_9 \\ E_{10} \end{bmatrix} = \begin{bmatrix} -j100 \\ -j200 \\ 0 \\ 0 \\ 0 \\ 0 \\ 0 \\ -j200 \end{bmatrix}$$

and so, according to Art. 9.3,

$$\mathfrak{Z}_e^{-1} = \begin{bmatrix} j0.6 & -j0.5 & j0.4 & 0 & 0 & 0 & 0 & 0 \\ -j0.5 & j0.35 & -j0.3 & 0 & 0 & 0 & 0 & 0 \\ j0.4 & -j0.3 & j0.2 & 0 & 0 & 0 & 0 & 0 \\ 0 & 0 & 0 & j0.05 & 0 & 0 & 0 & 0 \\ 0 & 0 & 0 & 0 & -j0.2 & 0 & 0 & 0 \\ 0 & 0 & 0 & 0 & 0 & -j0.05 & 0 & 0 \\ 0 & 0 & 0 & 0 & 0 & 0 & j0.04 & 0 \\ 0 & 0 & 0 & 0 & 0 & 0 & 0 & j0.1 \end{bmatrix}$$

Using these numerical results in equation 9–50

$$\mathcal{Y}_n = \mathfrak{A}\mathfrak{Z}_e^{-1}\mathfrak{A}' = \begin{bmatrix} j0.79 & -j0.59 & j0.50 \\ -j0.59 & j0.44 & -j0.35 \\ j0.50 & --j0.35 & j0.10 \end{bmatrix}$$

Then, from equations 9–51 and 9–52,

$$\mathcal{J}_{ne} = \mathfrak{A}\mathfrak{Z}_e^{-1}\mathcal{E}_e = \begin{bmatrix} 40 \\ -40 \\ 40 \end{bmatrix}; \mathcal{J}_{nj} = \mathfrak{A}_j \mathcal{J}_e = \begin{bmatrix} 0 \\ -5 \\ 0 \end{bmatrix}$$

The combination of the numerical matrices now established according to equation 9–49 gives the node equations as

$$\begin{bmatrix} 40 \\ -35 \\ 40 \end{bmatrix} = \begin{bmatrix} j0.79 & -j0.59 & j0.50 \\ -j0.59 & j0.44 & -j0.35 \\ j0.50 & -j0.35 & j0.10 \end{bmatrix} \begin{bmatrix} V_3 \\ V_{6,2} \\ V_5 \end{bmatrix}$$

The solution of this last equation is

$$\mathcal{V}_n = \begin{bmatrix} V_3 \\ V_{6,2} \\ V_5 \end{bmatrix} = \begin{bmatrix} j1169.2 \\ j1861.5 \\ j269.2 \end{bmatrix}$$

Finally, then, this "node" voltage matrix, $\mathcal{V}_n$, specifies the complete solution, from equations 9–46 and 9–44, as

$$\mathcal{V}_{et} = \mathfrak{A}'\mathcal{V}_n = \begin{bmatrix} -j1169.2 \\ -j692.3 \\ j900 \\ -j269.2 \\ -j269.2 \\ -j1592.3 \\ j692.3 \\ -j1592.3 \end{bmatrix} = \begin{bmatrix} V_{1t} \\ V_{2t} \\ V_{3t} \\ V_{4t} \\ V_{5t} \\ V_{6t} \\ V_{9t} \\ V_{10t} \end{bmatrix}; \mathcal{J}_e = \mathfrak{Z}_e^{-1} [\mathcal{V}_{et} - \mathcal{E}_e] = \begin{bmatrix} 35.37 \\ -92.30 \\ 100 \\ 13.46 \\ -53.84 \\ -79.62 \\ -27.69 \\ 139.23 \end{bmatrix} = \begin{bmatrix} I_1 \\ I_2 \\ I_3 \\ I_4 \\ I_5 \\ I_6 \\ I_9 \\ I_{10} \end{bmatrix}$$

This $\mathcal{J}_e$ is the same as that for the original network diagram in Fig. 9–12*a* since the E-shift does not affect $\mathcal{J}_e$. However, elements 7 and 8 are missing from Fig. 9–12*b*. Computation of I_7 and I_8 may be effected by using the vertex equations at vertices 1 and 2, respectively, in Fig. 9–12*a*. Thus

$$I_7 = I_1 + J_1 = 55.37$$
$$I_8 = I_2 + I_{10} - J_2 = 26.94$$

The terminal voltage values of elements 1, 2, and 10 as calculated for Fig. 9–12*b* differ from those of the original diagram by the values of E_1 and E_2. The corrected terminal voltage values which apply to Fig. 9–12*a* are

$$V_{13} = V_{1t} + E_1 = -j1169.2 + j100 = -j1069.2$$
$$V_{32} = V_{2t} + E_2 = -j692.3 + j200 = -j492.3$$
$$V_{52} = V_{10t} + E_2 = -j1592.2 + j200 = -j1392.2$$

9.17 Node System of Network Equations—Directly from the Network Diagram.

The node system of equations, in the form of equation 9–49, can be written directly from the network diagram but only in the absence of mutual induction. However, much work of importance is done with networks having no mutual induction; hence obtaining the node system directly from the diagram is very often a time-saver. The node system is a little easier to write directly from the diagram than the mesh method because the pattern of signs in $\mathcal{Y}_n$ is simpler than in $\mathfrak{z}_m$. The matrices in Example 9:10 exemplify the method which is presented in the following word description.

The node system of equations may be written directly from the network diagram (no mutual induction) as follows:

(*a*) Form $\mathcal{Y}_n$ by adding all admittances associated with the elements incident to a vertex and enter this sum in the main diagonal position corresponding to the vertex.

Enter in the i-row and j-column and the j-row and i-column positions $(i \neq j)$ of $\mathcal{Y}_n$ the negative of the sum of all admittances of the elements incident to both the i and j vertices; see Problem 9–42.

(*b*) Form $\mathcal{J}_{ne}$ by entering, in the position corresponding to the i-vertex, the sum of $\pm$ $\mathrm{E}_k\mathrm{Y}_k$ terms, one for each element incident to the i-vertex which contains an E_k. Use a plus sign if the e-sense is away from the vertex.

(*c*) Form $\mathcal{J}_{nj}$ as indicated by equation 9–52; i.e., form the vertex equation at the i-vertex, considering the J's only, and enter this sum in the appropriate position in $\mathcal{J}_{nj}$.

One further point of utility should be noted. The variables $\mathcal{V}_n$ can be identified with voltages between the other vertices and the reference vertex, the reference vertex being the one at which no KCE is written. For example, V_3, $V_{6,2}$, V_5 of $\mathcal{V}_n$ in Example 9:11 specify respectively the voltages between the reference vertex (4,1) and vertices 3; 6,2; and 5 in Fig. 9–12*b* (reference plus at vertices 3; 6,2; and 5). The entries in $\mathcal{V}_n$ can always be identified with the voltages from the reference to the other vertices. These voltages to a common reference vertex are called node voltages. The reference plus for node voltages is always at the nonreference vertex. These node voltages determine all the terminal voltages of the network.

One final point in connection with the node system should be noted. For each regulated terminal voltage which can be identified with a node voltage, one equation may be omitted from the node system. This fact is evident from the E-shift pattern. In Fig. 9–12*a*, with vertex 4 as reference, the E-shift need not be applied to element 7 and an equation at vertex 1 is not to be attempted. The E-shift must be used on element 8. The node equations for Fig. 9–12*a* can then be precisely those for Fig. 9–12*b*. If the reference vertex is taken as vertex 2 or 6, then the E-shift must be applied to element 7 but not to element 8, and a vertex equation is not written at vertex 6 or 2, respectively.

PROBLEMS

9–1 Substitute the values of y_1, y_2, and y_3 as given by equation 9–7 in equations 9–1 and show thereby that equation 9–9 is correct if $\mathcal{A}\mathcal{B}$ is as shown in equation 9–10.

9–2 Given three matrices:

$$\mathcal{A} = \begin{bmatrix} 1 & 2 & 3 \\ 3 & 2 & 1 \\ 1 & 0 & 2 \end{bmatrix} \quad \mathcal{B} = \begin{bmatrix} 2 & 2 & 2 \\ 4 & 1 & 2 \\ 3 & 2 & 2 \end{bmatrix} \quad \mathcal{C} = \begin{bmatrix} 3 & 0 & 3 \\ 2 & 1 & 4 \\ 6 & 1 & 1 \end{bmatrix}$$

Determine the products: $\mathcal{A}\mathcal{B}$, $\mathcal{B}\mathcal{A}$, $\mathcal{A}\mathcal{C}$, $\mathcal{C}\mathcal{A}$, $(\mathcal{A}\mathcal{B})\mathcal{C}$, $\mathcal{A}(\mathcal{B}\mathcal{C})$, $\mathcal{C}(\mathcal{A}\mathcal{B})$, and $(\mathcal{C}\mathcal{A})\mathcal{B}$. These latter products illustrate the *associative* law for matrix algebra.

9–3 Compute the inverses of the three matrices in the preceding problem. Multiply each of these matrices and their inverses in both orders and show that the unit matrix $\mathcal{U}$ is the result each time. Multiply $\mathcal{A}\mathcal{U}$, $\mathcal{U}\mathcal{A}$, $\mathcal{B}\mathcal{U}$, $\mathcal{U}\mathcal{B}$ and thus show that $\mathcal{U}$ corresponds to unity in the algebra of numbers.

9–4 Use the matrices in Problem 9–2 to show that equations 9–20 and 9–21 are valid for these matrices.

9–5 Verify equation 9–22 in terms of the four matrices

$$\mathcal{A} = \begin{bmatrix} 1 & 2 & 3 \\ 2 & -1 & 0 \\ 0 & -1 & 1 \end{bmatrix}, \quad \mathcal{B} = \begin{bmatrix} 2 & 1 \\ 1 & 1 \\ 3 & 4 \end{bmatrix}, \quad \mathcal{C} = \begin{bmatrix} 1 & 1 & 1 & 1 \\ 0 & -1 & 2 & 0 \end{bmatrix}, \quad \mathcal{D} = \begin{bmatrix} 2 & 1 & 2 & 1 \\ 0 & -1 & 0 & 1 \\ 3 & 3 & 1 & 1 \\ 2 & -1 & -1 & -2 \end{bmatrix}$$

9–6 Choose two symmetric matrices $\mathcal{A}$ and $\mathcal{B}$ such that $\mathcal{A}\mathcal{B}$ can be evaluated. Show that $\mathcal{A}\mathcal{B}$ is not generally symmetric, even though $\mathcal{A}$ and $\mathcal{B}$ are symmetric.

9–7 Use equation 9–23 to show that if $\mathfrak{z}$ is symmetric, $\mathfrak{z} = \mathfrak{z}'$, then

$$[\mathcal{A}'\mathfrak{z}\mathcal{A}]' = \mathcal{A}'\mathfrak{z}\mathcal{A}$$

i.e., the product $\mathcal{A}'\mathfrak{z}\mathcal{A}$ is also symmetric.

9–8 Indicate, for the diagram in Fig. 9–13, five paths of four elements each, ten paths of three elements each, and fifteen circuits of four elements each. Indicate these paths and circuits, each on a separate complete diagram; use an arrow to indicate the path or circuit, and heavier lines to indicate the elements of the path or circuit.

9–9 Establish ten trees for the diagram in Fig. 9–13. Form these trees so that each of the ten elements in the diagram is in at least one of the trees. This problem suggests that perhaps each element of a connected graph can be made a branch of some tree. This is acutally the situation.

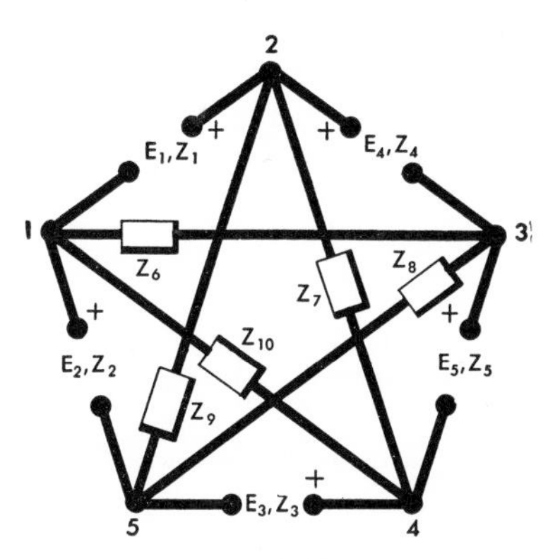

Fig. 9–13.

9–10 Show on separate diagrams, similar to that in Fig. 9–1*f*, five different sets of c-circuits for the diagram in Fig. 9–13.

9–11 Establish six sets of c-circuits for the diagram in Fig. 9–14, so that each element is a chord for at least one of the sets of c-circuits. Establish the e-sensing arrows all pointing toward the vertex with the highest number.

9–12 Give an argument, other than multiplication by minus one, for proving that the relations given by equations 9–24, 9–25, and 9–26 are valid with all signs changed. Consider as part of this discussion reversing the connections of all the meters. Also consider changing the direction of the deflection assumed as the a-deflection.

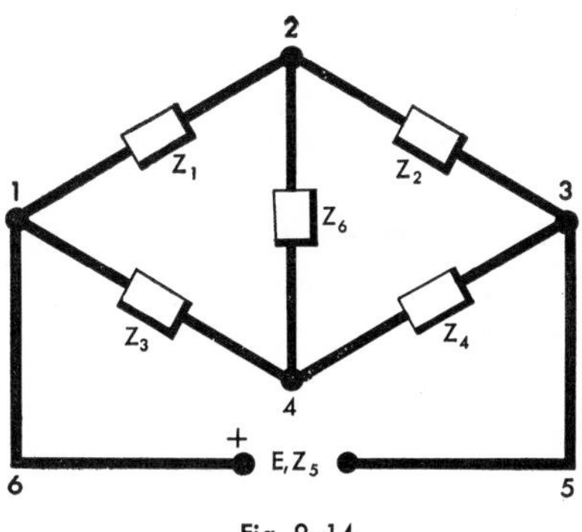

Fig. 9–14.

9–13 Assign an e-sensing to the elements of the diagram in Fig. 9–13 clockwise for the pentagon and toward the smallest numbered vertex for each of the other elements. Establish a 5-rowed incidence matrix for this diagram. Note that each column contains all zeros except for one +1 and one −1. All such incidence matrices have this characteristic. Why?

9–14 On the basis of the result in the preceding problem, show that any one row of the incidence matrix for all vertices is the negative of the sum of all the other rows. Hence all the vertex equations are not independent. Why?

9–15 (*a*) Show that the first, second, third, and fifth columns of the incidence matrix in Example 9:3 form a non-zero fourth-order determinant. These columns correspond to a tree in Fig. 9–3.

(*b*) Choose another set of four columns which correspond to a tree and show that this determinant also is not zero.

(*c*) Show that the determinant formed by the first four columns of $\mathcal{A}$ in Example 9:3 is zero.

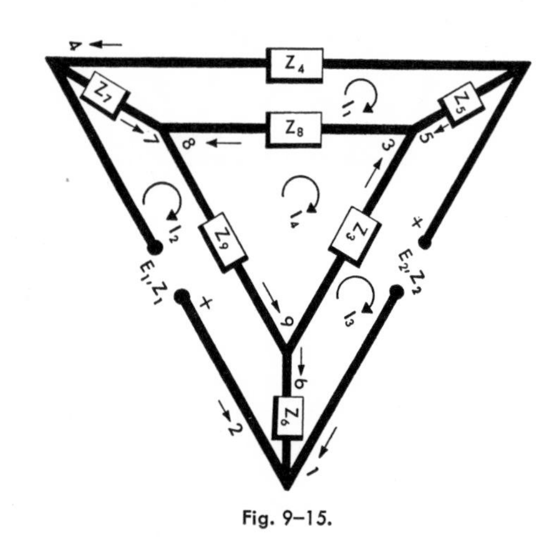

Fig. 9–15.

The properties shown by this problem hold true for all incidence matrices—the columns corresponding to any tree form a non-zero determinant and any $(v - 1)$ order determinant vanishes if any of its columns correspond to a circuit.

9–16 Show that the set of equations for the thirteen circuits indicated in Art. 9.11 for the diagram in Fig. 9–3 are *not* independent. How many of them are?

9–17 Establish the c-circuit matrix for the trees, the branches of which are the elements: (*a*) 1–2–3–6, (*b*) 1–5–6–3, and (*c*) 1–4–5–8 in Fig. 9–13. Use the e-sensing in Problem 9–13.

9–18 Establish the circuit matrix $\mathcal{B}$ for two sets of circuits according to criterion 2. Form this matrix so that a triangular matrix is in the leading position. Use Fig. 9–13. Use the e-sensing in Problem 9–13.

9–19 Establish an incidence matrix, $\mathcal{A}$, a c-circuit matrix, $\mathcal{B}_c$, and a non-c-circuit matrix, $\mathcal{B}$, for Fig. 9–14. Show that $\mathcal{A}\mathcal{B}_c^1 = 0$, $\mathcal{A}\mathcal{B}^1 = 0$. Use the e-sensing in Problem 9–11.

9–20 Establish a c-circuit matrix, $\mathcal{B}_c$, for Fig. 9–15, and the circuit matrix, $\mathcal{B}$, for the circuits indicated on this figure. Form an incidence matrix and show that $\mathcal{A}\mathcal{B}_c' = 0$, $\mathcal{B}_c\mathcal{A}' = 0$. Also that $\mathcal{A}\mathcal{B}' = 0$, and $\mathcal{B}\mathcal{A}' = 0$.

9–21 Consider Fig. 9–7 as consisting of the four elements:

(1) E_2, R_2, coil F and coil G.
(2) C_2.
(3) E_1, R_1, coil A, and coil B.
(4) C_1.

Determine the detailed form of equation 9–33 for this diagram.

9–22 Repeat Problem 9–21 for the four elements defined as:

(1) R_2, coil F.
(2) E_2, C_2, coil G.
(3) E_1, R_1, coil A.
(4) C_1, coil B.

9–23 Establish the matrix $\mathfrak{z}_e$ for the diagram in Fig. 9–3. Assume mutual induction between elements 7 and 8 only. Show this matrix in a detailed form of equation 9–33.

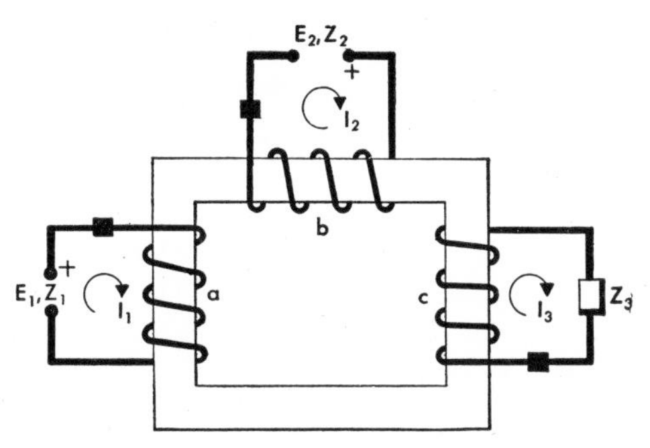

Fig. 9–16.

9–24 Establish the e-system of equations—equations 9–34—for the diagram in Fig. 9–16. Consider this diagram as of six elements. Let E_1, Z_1; E_2, Z_2; and Z_3 be three of the six elements. Also let the curved arrows indicate both the e-sensing of the appropriate elements and the c-sensing.

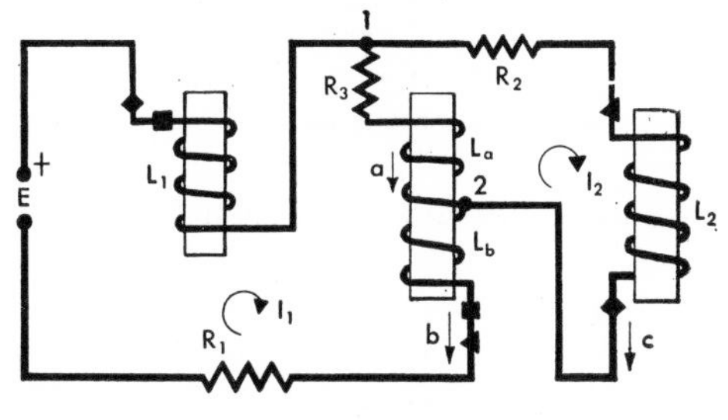

Fig. 9–17.

9–25 Establish the e-system for the diagram in Fig. 9–17. Let the curved arrows indicate the circuits for forming $\mathfrak{B}$.

9–26 Establish $\mathcal{E}_m$ and $\mathfrak{z}_m$ for Fig. 9–14. (*a*) Each element has mutual induction with all other elements. (*b*) There is no mutual induction. Use the e-sensing in Problem 9–11.

9–27 Repeat Problem 9–26 for Fig. 9–15.

9–28 Repeat Problem 9–26 for Fig. 9–13. Use the e-sensing in Problem 9–13.

9–29 Use the mesh system of equations—matrix method—to determine $\mathcal{I}_e$ for Fig. 9–16. Let $Z_1 = 10 + j0$ ohms, $Z_2 = 5 + j0$ ohms, $Z_3 = 20 + j0$ ohms, $L_a = 0.1$ henry, $L_b = 0.1$ henry, $L_c = 0.05$ henry, $E_1 = 10\epsilon^{j0}$, $E_2 = 50\epsilon^{j30}$, $\omega = 100$; the coefficients of coupling are $k_{ab} = 0.8$, $k_{ac} = 0.6$, and $k_{bc} = 0.4$.

9–30 Determine $\mathcal{I}_e$ for Fig. 9–8 for $E_1(t) = 10\epsilon^{j6000t}$, $E_2(t) = 4\epsilon^{j6000t}$. Use the mesh method.

9–31 For Fig. 9–13, $E_1 = 100\epsilon^{j50}$, $E_2 = 100\epsilon^{j72}$, $E_3 = 100\epsilon^{j144}$, $E_4 = 100\epsilon^{j216}$, and $E_5 = 100\epsilon^{j288}$. Each of the 10 elements contains a pure resistor of 10 ohms resistance. Determine the 10 entries of $\mathcal{I}_e$. Use an e-sensing according to the element ordering: 1–2, 3–2, 4–3, 4–5, 1–5, 2–5, 2–4, 3–1, 3–5, 1–4. Use the mesh method.

9–32 Consider the diagram in Fig. 9–18. All the Z's are purely reactive: $Z_1 = 0 + j10$, $Z_2 = 0 + j5$, $Z_3 = 0 - j10$, $Z_4 = 0 + j20$, $Z_5 = 0 + j10$, $Z_6 = 0 - j30$, and $Z_7 = 0 + j10$. Also $E_1 = 10 + j0$ and $E_2 = 20 + j0$. Use the mesh system to determine $\mathcal{I}_e$.

9–33 Repeat Problem 9–26, but write the equations directly from the diagram. Put the result directly into the final matrix form.

9–34 Redo Problem 9–27 by establishing the $\mathcal{E}_m$ and $\mathfrak{Z}_m$ directly from the diagram.

9–35 Redo Problem 9–28 by establishing $\mathcal{E}_m$ and $\mathfrak{Z}_m$ directly from the diagram.

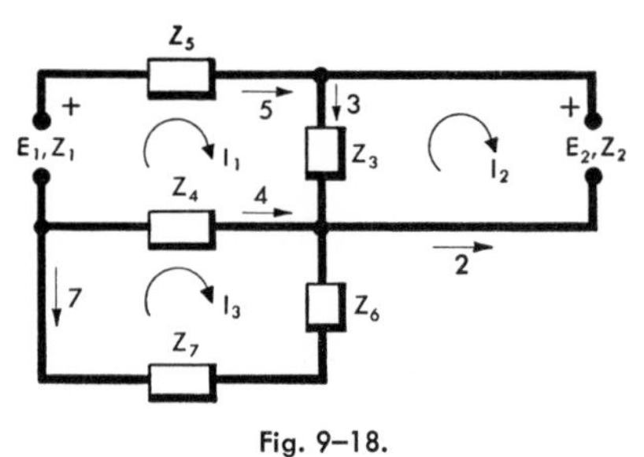

Fig. 9–18.

9–36 Establish $\mathcal{E}_m$ and $\mathfrak{Z}_m$ directly from the network in numerical form for Fig. 9–18.

9–37 Assume $Z_1 = 0 + j0$ in Example 9–8. Use the E-shift on $E_1(t)$. (*a*) Determine $\mathcal{I}_e$ for the altered diagram. Check these results by using the mesh system of equations on the original diagram, i.e., the diagram with $Z_1 = 0 + j0$.

(*b*) Calculate the values of the terminal voltages of the altered diagram and correct to the original diagram. Check the results by calculating the terminal voltage values of the original network diagram—$Z_1 = 0 + j0$.

9–38 Present an argument to show that use of the E-shift on network diagram elements, no matter how many are used, does not change the number of circuits unless there is a circuit of regulated terminal voltages only.

9–39 To the four equations preceding equation 9–43, add the equation at vertex 4 in Fig. 9–10, and thereby show that

$$J_a + J_b + J_d - J_c = 0$$

Generalize, and prove in the same way, the general pattern corresponding to this equation.

9–40 Solve the problem in Example 9:11 (node method) except that the E-shift is to be employed through vertices 4 and 6 instead of 1 and 2 as in the example.

9–41 Use the node method to determine $\mathcal{G}_e$ for Fig. 9–8. Add to this figure: $J_a(t) = 5\epsilon^{j6000t}$ with sensing arrow toward vertex a, and $J_b(t) = -5\epsilon^{j6000t}$ with sensing arrow toward vertex b.

9–42 Solve the same problem in Example 9:10, but use vertex 3 as reference. Write $\mathcal{Y}_n$ directly from the network diagram. Note that elements 5 and 9 "couple" vertices 1 and 4. Therefore, the term $-(Y_5 + Y_9) = -(\frac{1}{4} + \frac{1}{5})$ appears in the off-diagonal position corresponding to vertices 1 and 4.

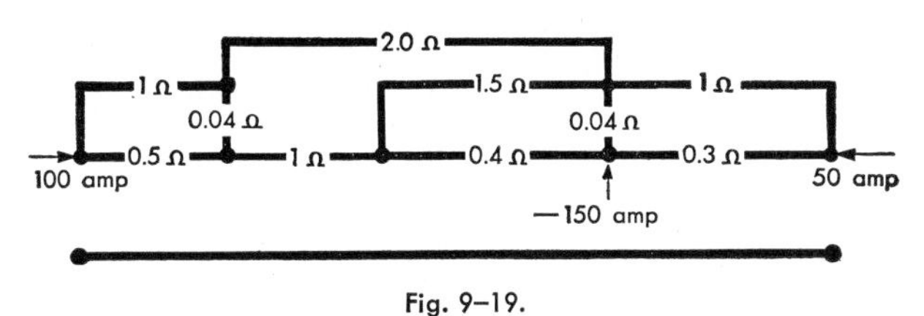

Fig. 9–19.

9–43 Determine the current distribution in the overhead trolley structure in Fig. 9–19. Point all e-sensing arrows from left to right.

9–44 Assume a current of 1 amp into a and out of b of Fig. 10–28. Determine all the branch currents, using the node method. These currents are known as the distribution factors of a network. In order to determine the currents in any branch of this network for any current other than 1 amp at a requires merely a multiplication of the input current by the distribution factor of the particular branch concerned. From the distribution factors find the current in the circuit of Fig. 10–28 for 25 amp into a and out of b.

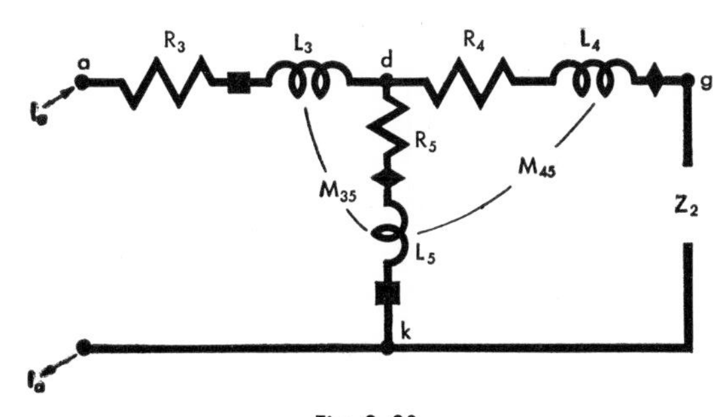

Fig. 9–20.

9–45 Determine currents in the network of Fig. 9–20 if $R_3 = R_4 = R_5 = 0$, $Z_3 = 0 + j10$, $Z_4 = 0 + j5$, $Z_5 = 0 + j4$, $Z_2 = 0 + j20$, $|X_{45}| = 0 + j1$ ohms, $|X_{35}| = 0 + j2$, and $I_a = 0 + j10$ amperes.

9–46 Form the node equations for the circuit in Fig. 9–3. Assume that Z_4, and Z_2 are zero.

9–47 Write the node equations for the circuit in Fig. 9–16. From the data given in Problem 9–29 for this curcuit, use the node equations to find the currents in the circuit.

9–48 Form the node equations for the circuit in Fig. 9–17.

9–49 The incidence matrix determines the form of the network diagram, the e-sensing of the elements of the diagram and the sensing and location of the driving-current elements. The incidence matrix for a network diagram is

$$\mathfrak{A} = \begin{array}{c} \\ a \\ b \\ c \end{array}\begin{array}{c} \begin{array}{cccccc} 1 & 2 & 3 & 4 & 5 & 6 \end{array} \\ \begin{bmatrix} 1 & 0 & 0 & 0 & -1 & -1 \\ -1 & -1 & -1 & 0 & 0 & 0 \\ 0 & 0 & 1 & -1 & 0 & 1 \end{bmatrix} \end{array}$$

(*a*) Establish the network diagram and its e-sensing.

The impedance matrix for the elements of the network diagram is

$$\mathfrak{Z}_e = \begin{array}{c} 1 \\ 2 \\ 3 \\ 4 \\ 5 \\ 6 \end{array}\begin{bmatrix} 0+j1 & 0 & 0 & 0 & 0 & 0 \\ 0 & 0-j2 & 0 & 0 & 0 & 0 \\ 0 & 0 & 0+j10 & 0 & 0 & 0 \\ 0 & 0 & 0 & 0-j5 & 0 & 0 \\ 0 & 0 & 0 & 0 & 0+j2 & 0 \\ 0 & 0 & 0 & 0 & 0 & 0-j4 \end{bmatrix}$$

(*b*) Determine the mesh impedance matrix $\mathfrak{Z}_m$ for the c-circuits corresponding to the tree 1–2–3.

(*c*) Determine the mesh impedance matrix for the circuits *a-b-c-a*, *b-c-d-b*, *a-c-d-a*.

The matrix of driving voltage-functions is

$$\mathcal{E}_e(t) = \begin{array}{c} 1 \\ 2 \\ 3 \\ 4 \\ 5 \\ 6 \end{array}\begin{bmatrix} 10 \sin \omega t \\ 0 \\ 2 \sin \omega t \\ 0 \\ 5 \sin \omega t \\ 0 \end{bmatrix}$$

(*d*) Determine $\mathcal{I}_m$, and $\mathcal{I}_m(t)$ for the c-circuits of (*b*).

(*e*) Determine $\mathcal{I}_e$ and $\mathcal{I}_e(t)$.

9–50 The incidence matrix for a network diagram is

$$\mathfrak{A}_a = \begin{array}{c} \\ a \\ b \\ c \end{array}\begin{array}{c} \begin{array}{cccccccc} 1 & 2 & 3 & 4 & 5 & a & b & c \end{array} \\ \begin{bmatrix} 0 & 1 & -1 & 0 & 0 & 1 & 0 & 0 \\ 1 & 0 & 0 & -1 & 1 & 0 & 1 & 0 \\ 0 & 0 & 1 & 1 & 0 & 0 & 0 & 1 \end{bmatrix} \end{array}$$

(*a*) Determine the form and e-sensing of the network diagram. The impedance matrix $\mathfrak{Z}_e$ for this network is

$$\mathfrak{Z}_e = \begin{matrix} 1 \\ 2 \\ 3 \\ 4 \\ 5 \end{matrix}\begin{bmatrix} 2+j2 & 0 & 0 & 0 & 0 \\ 0 & 1-j2 & 0 & 0 & 0 \\ 0 & 0 & 0 & 0 & 0 \\ 0 & 0 & 0 & 5+j0 & 0 \\ 0 & 0 & 0 & 0 & 0-j10 \end{bmatrix}$$

(*b*) Determine $\mathcal{Y}_n$ for vertex a as reference.
(*c*) Determine $\mathcal{Y}_n$ for vertex b as reference.
(*d*) Determine $\mathcal{Y}_n$ for vertex c as reference.
(*e*) Determine $\mathcal{Y}_n$ for vertex d as reference.
The matrices of driving voltage-functions and driving current-functions are

$$\mathcal{E}_e(t) = \begin{matrix} 1 \\ 2 \\ 3 \\ 4 \\ 5 \end{matrix}\begin{bmatrix} 100 \sin \omega t \\ 50 \sin \omega t \\ 50 \cos \omega t \\ 0 \\ 200 \sin(\omega t + 45°) \end{bmatrix}; \quad \mathcal{J}_e(t) = \begin{matrix} a \\ b \\ c \end{matrix}\begin{bmatrix} 10 \sin \omega t \\ 10 \cos \omega t \\ -10\sqrt{2} \sin(\omega t + 45°) \end{bmatrix}$$

(*f*) Determine the terminal voltage complex number matrix, $\mathcal{V}_{e_t}$, and the matrix of terminal voltage-functions of t, $\mathcal{V}_{e_t}(t)$, from $\mathcal{Y}_n$ of (*b*).
(*g*) Determine the $\mathcal{I}_e$ matrix and the $\mathcal{I}_e(t)$ matrix also.

CHAPTER 10

Some Electrical Network Theorems

Probably one of the most striking characteristics of electrical networks is that so few properties can be formulated which are applicable to *all* networks. Kirchhoff's current and voltage laws are, of course, valid for all electrical networks, but they are practically the only laws of universal applicability. One reason for this is that a network theorem to be valid for *all* networks must be valid for a simple series circuit. Obviously, there are relatively few possibilities apparent in a one-mesh network. Certain other laws, some of them of less than the universal applicability of Kirchhoff's laws and designated as network theorems, have been established and have been found useful in establishing the properties of many kinds of electrical networks. Some of these theorems are considered in this chapter. A different approach to these theorems from the one here presented can be found in other books.*

A few definitions and statements concerning network elements will facilitate the discussion of network theorems. A *linear* network element, R, L, or C, by definition has an unvarying value, i.e., it is constant. Actually, there is no such circuit element. All of them vary in one way or another—with time, current, voltage, temperature, age, shape, etc. These variations are frequently small enough that they may be neglected, so that the assumption of linearity (constancy) is often justifiable.

Network elements are also classified as *bilateral* and *unilateral* as well as linear or non-linear. A *bilateral* element conducts the same in both directions, and a *unilateral* element conducts differently in the two directions, or perhaps not at all in one direction. Electron tubes are examples of unilateral network elements.

* T. E. Shea, *Transmission Networks and Wave Filters*, D. Van Nostrand Co., 1929; W. L. Everitt, *Communication Engineering*, McGraw-Hill Book Co., 1937; E. A. Guillemin, *Communication Networks*, Vol. II, John Wiley & Sons, 1935; M.I.T., E. E. Staff, *Electric Circuits*, John Wiley & Sons, 1940; A. T. Starr, *Electric Circuits and Wave Filters*, Pitman and Sons, 1938; J. D. Ryder, *Networks, Lines and Fields*, Prentice-Hall, 1955.

10.1 General Expression for the Currents in a Bilateral Linear Network.

As a preliminary to developing the proof of some network theorems, a formula for the mesh currents of a linear, bilateral network will be established.

The Kirchhoff voltage equations of an n-mesh network may be written in terms of mesh currents as

$$\begin{aligned} E_1 &= Z_{11}I_1 + Z_{12}I_2 + Z_{13}I_3 + \cdots + Z_{1n}I_n \\ E_2 &= Z_{21}I_1 + Z_{22}I_2 + Z_{23}I_3 + \cdots + Z_{2n}I_n \\ E_3 &= Z_{31}I_1 + Z_{32}I_2 + Z_{33}I_3 + \cdots + Z_{3n}I_n \\ &\cdot \quad \cdot \quad \cdot \quad \cdot \quad \cdot \quad \cdot \quad \cdot \\ E_n &= Z_{n1}I_1 + Z_{n2}I_2 + I_{n3}I_3 + \cdots + Z_{nn}I_n \end{aligned} \tag{10-1}$$

where for j and $k = 1, 2, \cdots, n$,

E_k = the algebraic *sum* of all the source voltages in the kth mesh,
Z_{kk} = the *sum* of all the impedances in the kth mesh,
Z_{jk} = the coupling impedance between the jth and kth meshes.

The algebraic sum E_k may consist of positive terms, negative terms, or a combination of them, or it may be zero. The reference polarity of the source voltages and the reference direction of the mesh currents will determine the signs. The terms Z_{kk} and Z_{jk} may also consist of positive and/or negative terms in any combination. The location of the polarity marks on magnetically coupled coils, and the reference directions of mesh currents will determine just what form Z_{jk} and Z_{kk} take.

The solution of equation 10–1 for the current in the kth mesh can be written as

$$I_k = \frac{\begin{vmatrix} Z_{11} & Z_{12} \cdots Z_{1,k-1} & E_1 & Z_{1,k+1} \cdots Z_{1n} \\ Z_{21} & Z_{22} \cdots Z_{2,k-1} & E_2 & Z_{2,k+1} \cdots Z_{2n} \\ Z_{31} & Z_{32} \cdots Z_{3,k-1} & E_3 & Z_{3,k+1} \cdots Z_{3n} \\ \cdot & \cdot \qquad \cdot & \cdot & \cdot \qquad \cdot \\ \cdot & \cdot \qquad \cdot & \cdot & \cdot \qquad \cdot \\ \cdot & \cdot \qquad \cdot & \cdot & \cdot \qquad \cdot \\ Z_{n1} & Z_{n2} \cdots Z_{n,k-1} & E_n & Z_{n,k+1} \cdots Z_{nn} \end{vmatrix}}{\begin{vmatrix} Z_{11} & Z_{12} & \cdots\cdots\cdots & Z_{1n} \\ Z_{21} & Z_{22} & \cdots\cdots\cdots & Z_{2n} \\ Z_{31} & Z_{32} & \cdots\cdots\cdots & Z_{3n} \\ \cdot & \cdot & & \cdot \\ \cdot & \cdot & & \cdot \\ \cdot & \cdot & & \cdot \\ Z_{n1} & Z_{n2} & \cdots\cdots\cdots & Z_{nn} \end{vmatrix}} \tag{10-2}$$

An abbreviating symbolism is required to make the formula for I_k compact enough to work with. So let

$$D = \begin{vmatrix} Z_{11} & Z_{12} \cdots Z_{1n} \\ Z_{21} & Z_{22} \cdots Z_{2n} \\ \cdot & \cdot & \cdot \\ \cdot & \cdot & \cdot \\ \cdot & \cdot & \cdot \\ Z_{n1} & Z_{n2} \cdots Z_{nn} \end{vmatrix} \qquad (10\text{–}3)$$

and d_{jk} = cofactor of the jth row and kth column of D, i.e., it is D after the jth row and kth column have been removed and the remaining determinant multiplied by $(-1)^{j+k}$.

The kth mesh current may now be expressed by expanding the numerator of equation 10–2 by the kth column. The result is

$$I_k = E_1 \frac{d_{1k}}{D} + E_2 \frac{d_{2k}}{D} + \cdots + E_k \frac{d_{kk}}{D} + \cdots + E_n \frac{d_{nk}}{D} \qquad (10\text{–}4)$$
$$= \sum_{i=1}^{n} \frac{E_i d_{ik}}{D}$$

This formula will be useful in proving some of the theorems which follow.

10.2 Superposition Theorem.

The superposition theorem may be stated as follows. *If an electrical network consists of linear, bilateral elements and if more than one generator is located in the network, the current response of the network may be obtained by computing the currents due to each harmonic of each source voltage separately and adding all the corresponding currents thus obtained.*

The proof of this theorem at any particular frequency can be established in terms of equation 10–4. For suppose, as the theorem states, that all but one of the source voltages, or particular harmonic thereof, are reduced to zero without removing or altering the internal impedance of any of the sources. Then if this remaining voltage is represented by E_a, the current I_{ka} of the kth mesh is

$$I_{ka} = \sum_{j=1}^{n} E_{ja} \frac{d_{jk}}{D} \qquad (10\text{–}5)$$

where E_{ja} is equal to $\pm E_a$ or zero depending on whether the I_j reference arrow is or is not through E_a. The determinant and cofactors of this last equation are the same as those of equation 10–4 since the current reference arrows of the network are not to be changed. A similar equation can be written for each source voltage E_b, E_c, $\cdots$. Then if all the currents I_{ka}, I_{kb}, $\cdots$ are added, such sums as $(E_{1a} + E_{1b} + E_{1c} + \cdots)\, d_{1k}/D$, $(E_{2a} + E_{2b} + E_{2c} + \cdots)\, d_{2k}/D$, etc., will appear. But E_{1a} is zero unless

E_a is in the mesh of I_1, E_{1b} is zero unless E_b is in the mesh of I_1 and so on. Hence for any one of these voltage sums, say the jth,

$$E_{ja} + E_{jb} + E_{jc} + \cdots = E_j$$

Therefore, for m generators in the network

$$I_k = \sum_{j=1}^{m} I_{kj}$$

which proves the theorem for a set of voltages all at the same frequency. The foregoing proof, however, can be carried through without change for *any* particular frequency; therefore, the sum of all currents of a particular mesh calculated separately from all harmonics of all generators gives the actual current of that mesh.

The superposition theorem has already been used in the discussion of Fourier series applications in solving for the currents of a network for each of the harmonics of the source voltages, and then adding the results to obtain the total currents.

If the superposition theorem is used with the node equations of a circuit, it follows that *the node voltages may be computed for each generator or input current and the corresponding resultant node voltages added.* The demonstration of this fact is very similar to the proof already given for the current solution.

Example 10:1 The circuit of Fig. 10–1 will be used to illustrate the superposition principle by computing its behavior for each voltage separately and adding the results. This illustration is based on the node equations.

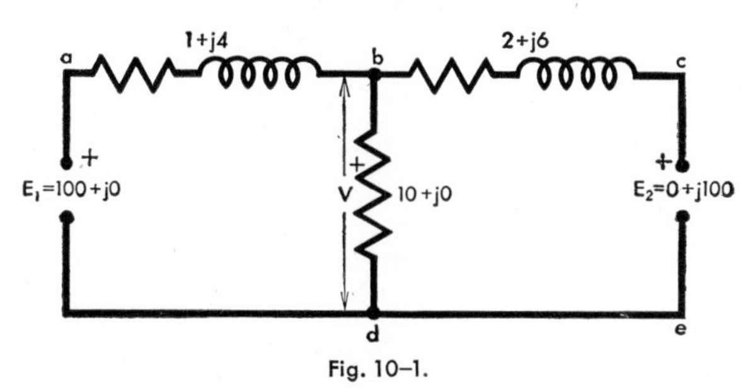

Fig. 10–1.

Solution The one node equation required for the circuit of Fig. 10–1—$E_2 = 0$—is, at node b, with node d as reference,

$$-E_1 Y_{ab} + V(Y_{ab} + Y_{bd} + Y_{bc}) = 0$$

Numerically, this equation is

$$-(100 + j0)\frac{1}{1 + j4} + V\left(\frac{1}{1 + j4} + \frac{1}{10 + j0} + \frac{1}{2 + j6}\right) = 0$$

from which

$$V = 53.6 - j13.78$$

Then

$$
\begin{aligned}
I_{bd} &= 5.36 - j1.378 \\
V_{cb} &= -V = -53.6 + j13.78 \\
I_{cb} &= \frac{V_{cb}}{Z_{cb}} = \frac{-53.60 + j13.78}{2 + j6} = -0.6136 + j8.729 \\
V_{ab} &= (100 + j0) - V = 46.40 + j13.78 \\
I_{ab} &= \frac{V_{ab}}{Z_{ab}} = \frac{46.40 + j13.78}{1 + j4} = 5.972 - j10.10
\end{aligned}
$$

For E_1 zero, the node equation of Fig. 10–1 is

$$-E_2 Y_{bc} + V(Y_{ab} + Y_{bd} + Y_{bc}) = 0$$

which becomes numerically

$$-(0 + j100)\frac{1}{2 + j6} + V\left(\frac{1}{1 + j4} + \frac{1}{10 + j0} + \frac{1}{2 + j6}\right) = 0$$

and

$$V = 6.269 + j35.53$$

From this result,

$$
\begin{aligned}
I_{bd} &= \frac{V}{Z_{bd}} = 0.627 + j3.553 \\
V_{cb} &= (0 + j100) - V = -6.27 + j64.47 \\
I_{cb} &= \frac{V_{cb}}{Z_{cb}} = \frac{-6.27 + j64.47}{2 + j6} = 9.357 + j4.164 \\
V_{ab} &= -V = -6.27 - j35.53 \\
I_{ab} &= \frac{V_{ab}}{Z_{ab}} = \frac{-6.27 - j35.53}{1 + j4} = -8.729 - j0.615
\end{aligned}
$$

Adding these two sets of results gives

$$
\begin{aligned}
V &= 59.87 + j21.75 \\
I_{bd} &= 5.99 + j2.18 \\
V_{cb} &= -59.87 + j78.25 \\
I_{cb} &= 8.74 + j12.89 \\
V_{ab} &= 40.12 - j21.75 \\
I_{ab} &= -2.76 - j10.72
\end{aligned}
$$

These same results also arise from solving the equation

$$-E_1 Y_{ab} + V(Y_{ab} + Y_{bd} + Y_{bc}) - E_2 Y_{bc} = 0$$

for V, and then computing the currents and other voltages of the circuit.

10.3 Reciprocity Theorem.

The reciprocity theorem may be stated as: *If at any particular frequency the only generator of a linear, bilateral network, located in the* i*th branch, and an impedance in the* k*th branch equal to the internal impedance of the generator are interchanged, the current of the* k*th branch before the interchange is the same as the current in the* i*th branch after the interchange.*

The proof of the reciprocity theorem may be deduced as follows. Writing the equations—at any particular frequency—for the mesh current in the kth and ith meshes of an n-mesh, bilateral, linear network in accordance with equation 10–4 gives

$$I_k = E_1 \frac{d_{1k}}{D} + \cdots + E_i \frac{d_{ik}}{D} + \cdots + E_k \frac{d_{kk}}{D} + \cdots + E_n \frac{d_{nk}}{D} \qquad (10\text{–}6)$$

$$= \sum_{p=1}^{n} E_p \frac{d_{pk}}{D}$$

$$I_i = E_1 \frac{d_{1i}}{D} + \cdots + E_i \frac{d_{ii}}{D} + \cdots + E_k \frac{d_{ki}}{D} + \cdots + E_n \frac{d_{ni}}{D} \qquad (10\text{–}7)$$

$$= \sum_{p=1}^{n} E_p \frac{d_{pi}}{D}$$

Because the circuit equations 10–1 can always be written so that D is symmetric, i.e., $Z_{ij} = Z_{ji}$, the same set of elements in corresponding positions appear in the same numbered rows and columns of D. Then whether the ith row and kth column is omitted from D, or the kth row and ith column, is immaterial. Consequently

$$d_{ik} = d_{ki} \qquad (10\text{–}8)$$

Using this result makes it evident that equations 10–6 and 10–7 are equal for any network, i.e., for any set of cofactors and determinants, if and only if all E's of equation 10–6 are zero except E_i, all E's of equation 10–7 are zero except E_k, and if $E_k = E_i = E$. The kth mesh current with E in the ith mesh is then

$$I_k = E \frac{d_{ik}}{D} \qquad (10\text{–}9)$$

and the ith mesh current with E in the kth mesh is

$$I_i = E \frac{d_{ki}}{D} \qquad (10\text{–}10)$$

But the reciprocity theorem has been stated in terms of ***branch*** currents and not ***mesh*** currents, so that the conditions under which these last two equations represent branch currents must be examined.

If, in Fig. 10–2a, the generator is located as shown, the mesh currents indicated cannot be used to produce equations like 10–9 and 10–10 because E will appear in two different mesh voltage equations, i.e., in two different positions on the left of equations 10–1, so that the solution for any mesh current will contain two terms and not one as required. On the other hand, the mesh current arrangement of Fig. 10–2b can be used to demonstrate the reciprocity theorem for branches a–b and a–d or b–d; or Fig. 10–2c can be used for branches a–b and a–c or b–c. In fact, it is in general true that the relatively little restraint which the mesh method of writing circuit equations imposes on the location of the assumed mesh currents always makes it possible to locate the mesh currents so that any two branches of a network can have only one mesh current through each.

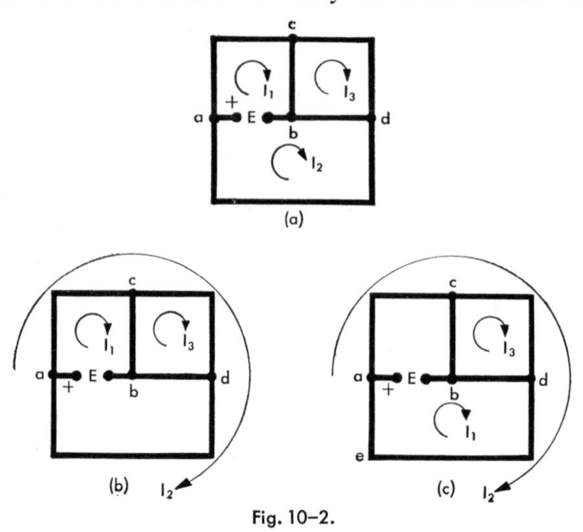

Fig. 10–2.

Equations 10–9 and 10–10 therefore represent any two branch currents under the conditions of the reciprocity theorem, and since these two currents are equal the theorem is proved.

The fact that the reciprocity theorem applies if the one generator of the network produces a non-sinusoidal voltage follows immediately from the superposition theorem. For the reciprocity theorem applies for each of the Fourier series components of the source voltage and so to the sum of these components.

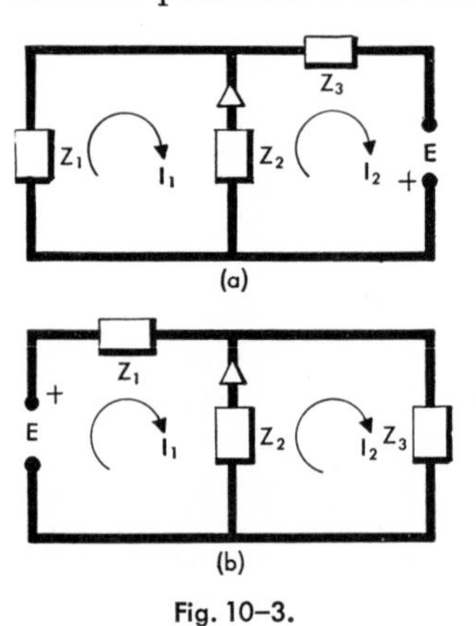

Fig. 10–3.

The proof that the reciprocity theorem does not apply to a unilateral network may be seen by an examination of Figs. 10–3*a* and *b*. If, in Fig. 10–3*a*, the unilateral element Z_2 will permit current to flow with E of polarity shown, no current will flow in Z_2 in Fig. 10–3*b*. Therefore, I_1 of Fig. 10–3*a* cannot be equal to the current I_2 of Fig. 10–3*b*.

The proof that the reciprocity theorem does not apply to a non-linear circuit can be demonstrated by the solution of Prob. 10–5.

The reciprocity theorem is valuable because it shows that the behavior of a linear, bilateral network between any two pairs of terminals is the same from either pair of terminals to the other. Thus it is necessary to calculate the behavior of many networks, such as transmission lines and filters, in only one direction.

10.4 Compensation Theorem.

If the subscript a represents *after* and the subscript b represents *before* an impedance change ΔZ, the compensation theorem may be stated as: *Any change, $\Delta Z = Z_a - Z_b$, in the impedance of a branch of any electrical network (linear or not) can be compensated for (network restored to its original condition) by inserting in the altered branch a generator of zero internal impedance and generated voltage $\Delta E = -\Delta Z I_b$.*

The proof of this theorem follows from Fig. 10–4, which represents an n-mesh network, any one branch of which is shown in detail. The voltage V_k for this branch is

$$V_k = E_k + Z_k I_k + \Delta Z_k I_k + \Delta E_k$$

But suppose

$$\Delta E_k = -\Delta Z_k I_k \tag{10–11}$$

then

$$\begin{aligned} V_k &= E_k + Z_k I_k + (\Delta Z_k I_k - \Delta Z_k I_k) \\ &= E_k + Z_k I_k \end{aligned}$$

But this result is the same as though no impedance ΔZ_k or generated voltage ΔE_k were present. Therefore, the generated voltage ΔE_k exactly cancels the $\Delta Z_k I_k$ voltage *with the current equal to its value with neither ΔE_k nor $\Delta Z_k I_k$ present*, i.e., I_b of the theorem statement. The theorem is thus proved not only for linear networks but also for *any* network with the possible exception of networks with hysteresis effects.

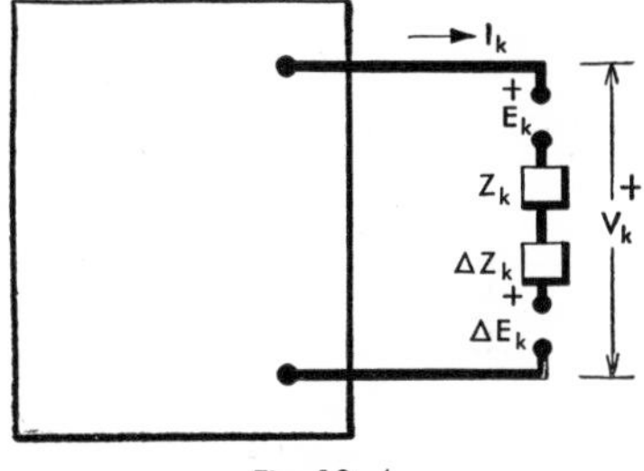

Fig. 10–4.

It should be noted that the reference polarity of ΔE_k is plus to minus in the reference direction of the branch current.

The compensation theorem, as here stated, covers both the addition and removal of impedance from a branch of a network. If impedance is removed, the voltage ΔE_k has exactly the magnitude and polarity of the voltage across the impedance before its removal and so restores the circuit to its original condition by compensating completely for the impedance removed. Alternatively, if impedance is added, the voltage ΔE_k has the same magnitude but opposite polarity to the voltage across the added impedance, and so once more restores the network to its original condition.

A special case of the compensation theorem can be used to compute the effect on a network of opening a branch of the network. Application of the compensation theorem requires a knowledge of the current in the branch before the impedance removal or addition. An open-circuited branch, of course, has zero current. Also changing the impedance of a branch from open circuit to any finite impedance amounts to subtracting an infinite impedance from the branch. The corresponding ΔZ is thus $\Delta Z = Z_a - \infty = -\infty$. The ΔE which results is $\Delta E = -\Delta Z I_b = \infty \times 0$, an indeterminate form which requires special treatment for evaluation. If, instead of an open circuit, Z_b represents the impedance in the branch before the change, ΔZ and ΔE are both finite and the actual ΔE for open circuit can be determined from the finite ΔE by establishing the limit as Z_b increases without limit. The following example illustrates these statements.

Example 10:2 Suppose that the branch *bd* of the network represented by Fig. 10–1 is to be opened. Use the compensation theorem to determine the effect on the network of opening this branch.

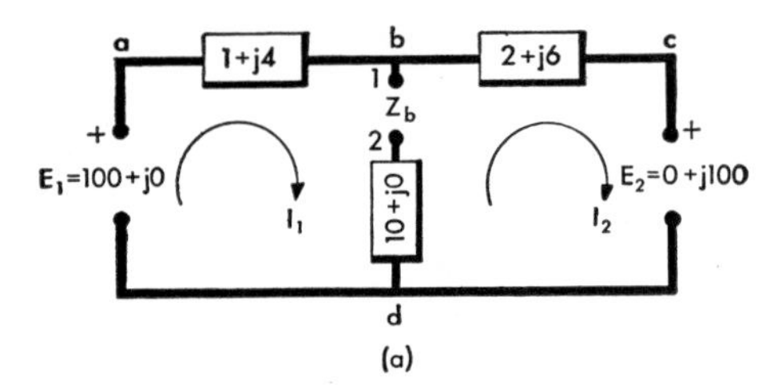

(a)

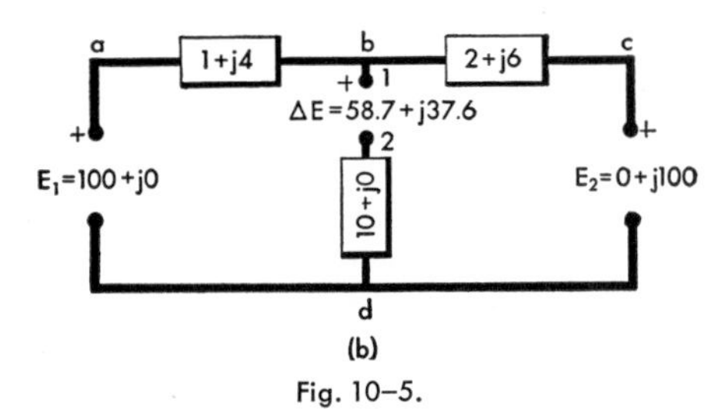

(b)

Fig. 10–5.

Solution In Fig. 10–5*a* the network of Fig. 10–1 is shown with Z_b in place of an open circuit in the branch *bd*. This impedance Z_b is to be removed and a $\Delta' E$ placed in the branch to compensate for the removal. The limit of $\Delta' E$ as Z_b increases without limit will then determine the compensating ΔE.

The currents of the circuit in terms of Z_b may be computed from the mesh equations

$$\begin{aligned} E_1 &= (Z_{ab} + Z_b + Z_{2d})I_1 - (Z_b + Z_{2d})I_2 \\ -E_2 &= -(Z_b + Z_{2d})I_1 + (Z_{bc} + Z_b + Z_{2d})I_2 \end{aligned}$$

If numerical values are substituted, these equations become

$$\begin{aligned} 100 + j0 &= (Z_b + 11 + j4)I_1 - (Z_b + 10 + j0)I_2 \\ 0 - j100 &= -(Z_b + 10 + j0)I_1 + (Z_b + 12 + j6)I_2 \end{aligned}$$

Solving for the currents gives

$$I_1 = \frac{(100 - j100)Z_b + 1200 - j400}{(Z_b + 11 + j4)(Z_b + 12 + j6) - (Z_b + 10)^2}$$

$$I_2 = \frac{(100 - j100)Z_b + 1400 - j1100}{(Z_b + 11 + j4)(Z_b + 12 + j6) - (Z_b + 10)^2}$$

In terms of a finite Z_b,

$$\Delta' E = -\Delta Z I_b = -(Z_a - Z_b)(I_1 - I_2)$$
$$= \frac{Z_b(-200 + j700)}{(Z_b + 11 + j4)(Z_b + 12 + j6) - (Z_b + 10)^2}$$

The limit of this expression as Z_b increases indefinitely by l'Hôpital's rule—differentiation of numerator and denominator separately with respect to Z_b—is

$$\Delta E = \lim_{Z_b \to \infty} \Delta' E = \lim_{Z_b \to \infty} \frac{-200 + j700}{(Z_b + 11 + j4) + (Z_b + 12 + j6) - 2(Z_b + 10)}$$
$$= \frac{-200 + j700}{3 + j10} = 58.7 + j37.6$$

Placing this voltage ΔE in the altered network as shown in Fig. 10–5*b* will compensate for the impedance change from open circuit to $Z_{bd} = 10 + j0$, i.e., restore the network to its open circuit condition.

As a check on the compensating effect of the computed ΔE, the voltage V_{bd} of Fig. 10–5*b* will be computed. Using the one node equation required to solve for this voltage (d as reference) gives

$$-\frac{100+j0}{1+j4} - \frac{0+j100}{2+j6} - \frac{58.7+j37.6}{10+j0} + V_{bd}\left(\frac{1}{1+j4} + \frac{1}{10+j0} + \frac{1}{2+j6}\right) = 0$$

and the solution is

$$V_{bd} = 58.7 + j37.6$$

But since in the branch bd, ΔE and the total voltage are identical there can be no impedance voltage in the branch and so no current. The result is thus equivalent to an open circuit.

10.5 Alteration Theorem.

The problem of determining the effect on a network of altering an impedance of the network is sometimes encountered. One obvious way to solve such a problem is, of course, to make the impedance change and calculate or measure the currents in the changed network. A more useful approach to this problem is to determine the change in the network currents in terms of the change in impedance. The following theorem, which will here be known as the *alteration theorem*, specifies the method of computing the effect of changes in an impedance in a linear, bilateral network.

The change ΔI *at any particular frequency in any current in a linear, bilateral network caused by changing the impedance of any branch of the network by* $\Delta Z = Z_a - Z_b$ *can be obtained by reducing all generator voltages to zero (internal impedances unchanged) and inserting a properly oriented generator of zero internal impedance and generated voltage* $\Delta E = \Delta Z I_b$ *into the altered branch.* The subscript a represents *after* and the subscript b *before* the impedance change. Also the reference plus-to-minus polarity of ΔE is in the reference positive direction of the branch current I_b.

The proof of the alteration theorem can be formulated in terms of a compensating voltage ΔE, in a branch of a linear network, producing compensating current components ΔI throughout the network. Thus by the compensation theorem, a properly oriented voltage $\Delta' E_j$ in the j-branch of the altered network, where

$$\Delta' E_j = -\Delta Z_j I_{jb}$$

with ΔZ_j the change $Z_{ja} - Z_{jb}$ of the j-branch, and

I_{jb} the I of the j-branch before the change in Z,

restores the network I's to their *before*, or unaltered, state. By the superposition theorem, this $\Delta' E_j = -\Delta Z_j I_{jb}$ acting alone (all other E's $= 0$) in the altered network specifies the negative of the change in I's (compensates); i.e., $\Delta' E_j$ in the altered network determines $-\Delta I_k$ of the k-branch where ΔI_k is the change in I_k associated with the network change ΔZ_j, or

$$\Delta I_k = I_{ka} - I_{kb} \tag{10–12}$$

Consequently, if

$$\Delta E_j = \Delta Z_j I_{jb} \tag{10–13}$$

is located with proper orientation in the j-branch of the altered network, the I's thereby determined in the altered network are the changes in the I_{kb} associated with the change in impedance, ΔZ_j. If, then, I_{kb} is known, ΔI_k can be calculated and equation 10–12 thereby determines I_{ka}. Note that the current of the altered branch is also specified in the foregoing discussion merely by setting $k = j$. The theorem is thus proved.

The alteration theorem is most useful for calculating *changes* from known (before) conditions rather than for determining an original state of a network.

Further interpretation and some uses for the alteration theorem are indicated in the following examples.

Example 10:3 Suppose that 5 ohms are to be removed from the branch bd of Fig. 10–1. Determine the currents in the circuit after the change, by the alteration theorem.

Solution From Example 10–1, the current in branch bd before the change in resistance occurs is

$$I_{bd} = 5.99 + j2.18$$

and because the resistance is removed

$$\Delta Z = Z_a - Z_b = 5–10 = -5$$

The voltage ΔE is

$$\begin{aligned}\Delta E_{bd} &= \Delta Z I_{b,bd} \\ &= -5(5.99 + j2.18) = -29.95 - j10.9\end{aligned}$$

This voltage is shown in the *altered* network in Fig. 10–6.

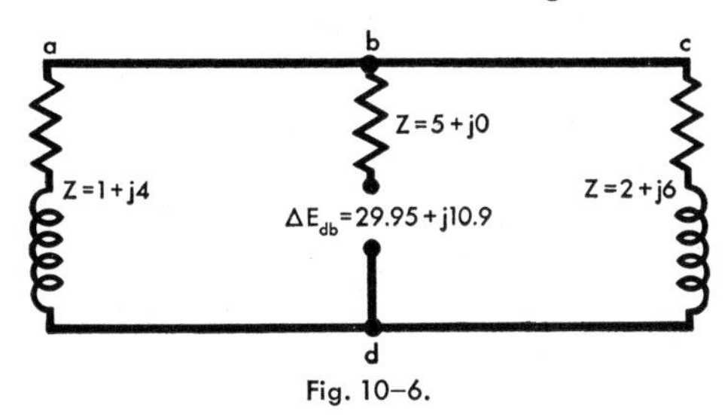

Fig. 10–6.

The currents ΔI, which the circuit of Fig. 10–6 determine, may be computed by using series-parallel impedance combinations, by using two simultaneous mesh voltage equations, or by using one node equation. The last method will be used. The node equation, for b as the reference node, is

$$-\Delta E_{db} Y_{db} + V_{db}(Y_{ad} + Y_{bd} + Y_{cd}) = 0$$

which, on substituting numerical values, becomes

$$-(29.95 + j10.9)\frac{1}{5 + j0} + V_{db}\left(\frac{1}{1 + j4} + \frac{1}{5 + j0} + \frac{1}{2 + j6}\right) = 0$$

Solving this equation establishes

$$V_{db} = 4.14 + j12.23$$

The currents of Fig. 10–6 can be determined immediately from this voltage as

$$\begin{aligned}\Delta I_{ab} &= \frac{V_{db}}{1 + j4} = 3.12 - j0.25 \\ \Delta I_{cb} &= \frac{V_{db}}{2 + j6} = -2.04 - j0.01 \\ \Delta I_{db} &= \Delta I_{ba} + \Delta I_{bc} = -1.08 + j0.26\end{aligned}$$

These ΔI are the *changes* in the branch currents caused by removing 5 ohms from the coupling branch of Fig. 10–1.

The currents in the *altered* network are finally, from the alteration theorem,

$$\begin{aligned}I_{ab}' = \Delta I_{ab} + I_{ab} &= (-2.76 - j10.72) + (3.12 - j0.25) \\ &= 0.36 - j10.97 \\ I_{cb}' = \Delta I_{cb} + I_{cb} &= (8.74 + j12.89) + (-2.04 - j0.01) \\ &= 6.70 + j12.88 \\ I_{db}' = \Delta I_{db} + I_{db} &= (-5.99 - j2.18) + (-1.08 + j0.27) \\ &= -7.07 - j1.92\end{aligned}$$

One more illustration of the use of the alteration theorem will be given. This example shows the method to be used in applying this theorem to the problem of determining the effect on a network of opening a branch of a network.

Example 10:4 By means of the alteration theorem compute the effect of opening the branch *ab* of the network of Fig. 10–1.

Solution Assume first that a *finite* ΔZ is inserted in the branch a–b of Fig. 10–1. From the results of Example 10–1, the current before the change is

$$I_{ab} = -2.76 - j10.72$$

and, correspondingly,

$$\Delta E = \Delta Z I_{ab} = \Delta Z(-2.76 - j10.72)$$

This ΔE should be placed in the altered network with all source voltages reduced to zero as in Fig. 10–7a, and the resulting currents are the ΔI caused by inserting ΔZ.

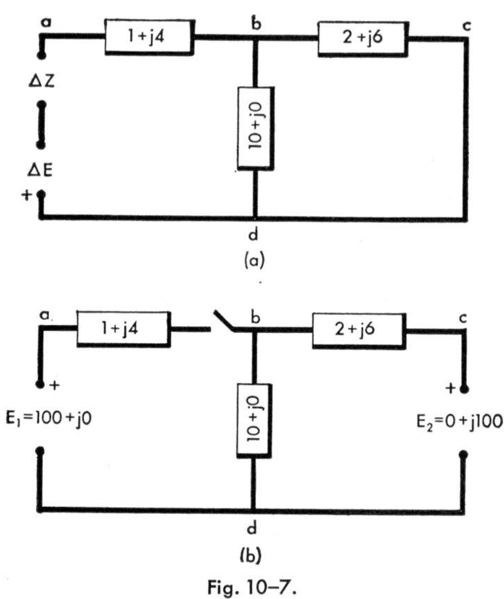

Fig. 10–7.

The ΔI will be computed from the node equation written at b with d as the reference, i.e.,

$$\frac{\Delta E}{\Delta Z + Z_{ab}} + V_{bd}\left(\frac{1}{\Delta Z + Z_{ab}} + \frac{1}{Z_{bd}} + \frac{1}{Z_{bc}}\right) = 0$$

On replacing ΔE by its already computed equivalent and solving for V_{bd}, there results

$$V_{bd} = \frac{-\Delta Z I_{ab} Z_{bd} Z_{bc}}{(\Delta Z + Z_{ab})(Z_{bd} + Z_{bc}) + Z_{bd} Z_{bc}}$$

The currents $\Delta I_{ab}'$ are then, for a finite ΔZ,

$$\Delta I_{ab}' = \frac{-V_{bd} - \Delta E}{\Delta Z + Z_{ab}} = \frac{-\Delta Z I_{ab}(Z_{bd} + Z_{bc})}{(\Delta Z + Z_{ab})(Z_{bd} + Z_{bc}) + Z_{bd} Z_{bc}}$$

$$\Delta I_{bd}' = \frac{V_{bd}}{Z_{bd}} = \frac{-\Delta Z I_{ab} Z_{bd} Z_{bc}}{Z_{bd}[(\Delta Z + Z_{ab})(Z_{bd} + Z_{bc}) + Z_{bd} Z_{bc}]}$$

$$\Delta I_{bc}' = \frac{V_{bd}}{Z_{bc}} = \frac{-\Delta Z I_{ab} Z_{bd} Z_{bc}}{Z_{bc}[(\Delta Z + Z_{ab})(Z_{bd} + Z_{bc}) + Z_{bd} Z_{bc}]}$$

If ΔZ is allowed to increase indefinitely, these ΔI give the change in current due to opening the branch a–b of Fig. 10–7. In the limit, therefore,

$$\Delta I_{ab} = \lim_{\Delta Z \to \infty} \Delta I_{ab}' = -I_{ab} = 2.76 + j10.72$$

$$\Delta I_{bd} = \lim_{\Delta Z \to \infty} \Delta I_{bd}' = \frac{-Z_{bc}}{Z_{bd} + Z_{bc}} I_{ab} = \frac{2 + j6}{12 + j6} I_{ab} = -2.66 + j4.49$$

$$\Delta I_{bc} = \lim_{\Delta Z \to \infty} \Delta I_{bc}' = \frac{-Z_{bd}}{Z_{bd} + Z_{bc}} I_{ab} = \frac{10 + j0}{12 + j6} I_{ab} = 5.41 + j6.23$$

Adding these current changes to the original currents taken from Example 10–1 gives

$$I_{ab} + \Delta I_{ab} = I_{ab} - I_{ab} = 0$$
$$I_{bd} + \Delta I_{bd} = (5.99 + j2.18) + (-2.66 + j4.49) = 3.33 + j6.67$$
$$I_{bc} + \Delta I_{bc} = (-8.74 - j12.89) + (5.41 + j6.22) = -3.33 - j6.67$$

which are the currents of Fig. 10–7*b*, i.e., Fig. 10–1 with branch a–b open.

10.6 Theorem on the Equivalence of a *T* or π Network to Other Networks.*

A network equivalence of considerable importance, both theoretically and practically, may be stated as: *At any particular frequency, any linear, bilateral, three- or four-terminal, passive network can be replaced by an equivalent three- or four-terminal* π *(delta) or* T *(wye) passive network which may or may not be physically realizable.*

The proof of this theorem follows from the general equations for the networks shown in Figs. 10–8*a* and 10–8*b*. If all source voltages in these two networks are zero except the ones shown, the general equations for either network are of the form given in equations 10–1 except that V_1 and $-V_2$ replace E_1 and E_2, respectively, and all other E's are zero. The input and output currents I_1 and I_2 are accordingly (equation 10–4)

$$I_1 = V_1 \frac{d_{11}}{D} - V_2 \frac{d_{21}}{D}$$
$$I_2 = V_1 \frac{d_{12}}{D} - V_2 \frac{d_{22}}{D} \qquad (10\text{-}14)$$

But, if d_{12} and d_{21} are equal and if the last equation is multiplied by -1, which, of course, does not alter the equation, these equations are exactly the *node* equations for the π circuit of Fig. 10–8*c* or the delta circuit of Fig. 10–8*d*. That $d_{12} = d_{21}$ has already been shown in the discussion preceding equation 10–8. The circuits of Figs. 10–8*c* and 10–8*d*, therefore, have the same currents I_1 and I_2 for the same terminal voltages V_1 and V_2 as the general four- and three-terminal networks of Figs. 10–8*a* and 10–8*b*, respectively, and so are equivalent.

---

* Myril B. Reed, "General Formulas for "T"—and "π"—Network Equivalents, *Proc. I.R.E.*, December, 1945, vol. 33, No. 12, Pt. 1, pp. 897–899.

The formulas for the impedances of the equivalent π and delta networks taken directly from Figs. 10–8*c* and *d* are, therefore,

$$
\begin{aligned}
Z_1 &= \frac{D}{d_{11} - d_{21}} \\
Z_2 &= \frac{D}{d_{12}} \\
Z_3 &= \frac{D}{d_{22} - d_{12}}
\end{aligned}
\tag{10–15}
$$

The equivalence established by these last equations is valid at any one frequency only if the π or delta network is to be physically constructed or represented by single impedances consisting of a series combination

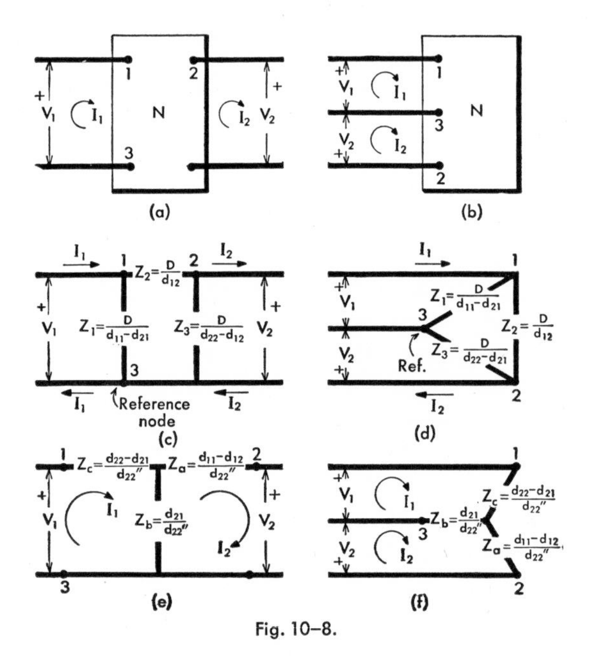

Fig. 10–8.

of R, L, and C. If, however, Z_1, Z_2, and Z_3 are to be treated as functions of frequency defined by equations 10–15, the π and delta networks are equivalent to the original networks at all frequencies. This latter equivalence can be realized only mathematically since no series combination of R, L, and C can have the frequency variation specified by the Z_1, Z_2, and Z_3 defining equations.

The fact that it may be impossible to represent Z_1, Z_2 and Z_3 for certain networks by any *real* or physically possible impedance will be demonstrated in one of the following examples.

Next, if the two equations 10–14 are solved for V_1 and $-V_2$, the result is

$$V_1 = \frac{d_{22}}{DD'} I_1 - \frac{d_{21}}{DD'} I_2$$
$$-V_2 = \frac{-d_{12}}{DD'} I_1 + \frac{d_{11}}{DD'} I_2 \qquad (10\text{–}16)$$

where

$$D' = \frac{1}{D^2}\begin{vmatrix} d_{11} & d_{21} \\ d_{12} & d_{22} \end{vmatrix} \qquad (10\text{–}17)$$

In accordance with a theorem of algebra,* that if d_{kq}'' represents the remainder of d_{11} after removing the kth row and qth column, and if k and q are equal,

$$d_{kq}d_{11} - d_{k1}d_{1q} = \begin{vmatrix} d_{11} & d_{1q} \\ d_{k1} & d_{kq} \end{vmatrix} = Dd_{kq}''(k = q) \qquad (10\text{–}18)$$

But the determinant of cofactors of equation 10–17 fits this theorem relation exactly for $k = q = 2$. Therefore,

$$D' = \frac{Dd_{22}''}{D^2} = \frac{d_{22}''}{D} \qquad (10\text{–}19)$$

where d_{22}'' = the remainder of D after the first two rows and first two columns are removed.

Equations 10–16 thus become

$$V_1 = \frac{d_{22}}{d_{22}''} I_1 - \frac{d_{21}}{d_{22}''} I_2$$
$$-V_2 = \frac{-d_{12}}{d_{22}''} I_1 + \frac{d_{11}}{d_{22}''} I_2 \qquad (10\text{–}20)$$

But these are exactly the equations for the T and wye circuits of Figs. 10–8e and 10–8f, and directly from these circuits the equivalent T and wye impedances are

$$Z_a = \frac{d_{11} - d_{12}}{d_{22}''}$$
$$Z_b = \frac{d_{21}}{d_{22}''} \qquad (10\text{–}21)$$
$$Z_c = \frac{d_{22} - d_{21}}{d_{22}''}$$

In exact correspondence with the restrictions on the equivalent π, the equivalent T is only equivalent at any one frequency if physical realizability is desired, and it may actually be impossible to obtain a physically

* M. Bocher, *Introduction to Higher Algebra*, The Macmillan Co., 1938, p. 33.

realizable equivalent even at the particular frequency desired. If equations 10–21 are treated as functions of frequency the networks are *mathematically* equivalent at all frequencies.

Example 10:5 The T and π equivalent circuits for the network shown in Fig. 10–9*a* are to be computed. A pure resistance network is used to facilitate computation.

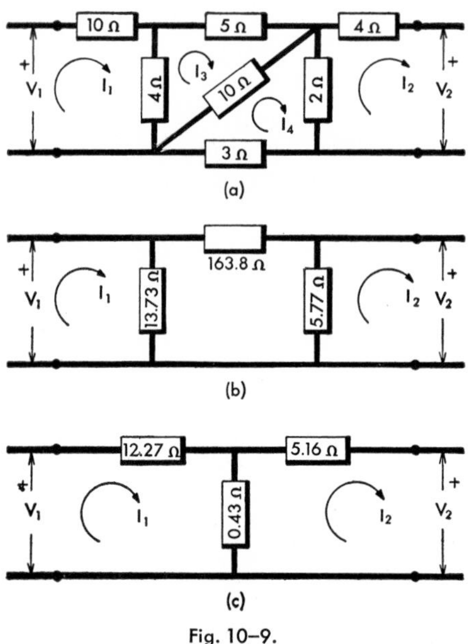

Fig. 10–9.

Solution The separate factors appearing in equation 10–15 and 10–21 will be computed first. The determinant of the equations for Fig. 10–9*a*, for currents in order I_1, I_2, I_3, and I_4 is

$$D = \begin{vmatrix} 14 & 0 & -4 & 0 \\ 0 & 6 & 0 & -2 \\ -4 & 0 & 19 & -10 \\ 0 & -2 & -10 & 15 \end{vmatrix} = 13{,}100$$

The cofactor of the first row and first column is

$$d_{11} = \begin{vmatrix} 6 & 0 & -2 \\ 0 & 19 & -10 \\ -2 & -10 & 15 \end{vmatrix} = 1034$$

The cofactor of the first row and second column, d_{12}, equal to the cofactor of the second row and first column, d_{21}, is

$$d_{12} = d_{21} = -\begin{vmatrix} 0 & 0 & -2 \\ -4 & 19 & -10 \\ 0 & -10 & 15 \end{vmatrix} = 80$$

The cofactor of the second row and second column is

$$d_{22} = \begin{vmatrix} 14 & -4 & 0 \\ -4 & 19 & -10 \\ 0 & -10 & 15 \end{vmatrix} = 2350$$

Also removing the first two rows and columns of D leaves

$$d_{22}'' = \begin{vmatrix} 19 & -10 \\ -10 & 15 \end{vmatrix} = 185$$

Then from equation 10–15,

$$Z_1 = \frac{D}{d_{11} - d_{21}} = \frac{13{,}100}{1034 - 80} = \frac{13{,}100}{954} = 13.73 \text{ ohms}$$

$$Z_2 = \frac{D}{d_{12}} = \frac{13{,}100}{80} = 163.8 \text{ ohms}$$

$$Z_3 = \frac{D}{d_{22} - d_{12}} = \frac{13{,}100}{2350 - 80} = \frac{13{,}100}{2270} = 5.77 \text{ ohms}$$

The π network equivalent to Fig. 10–9*a* is, therefore, as shown in Fig. 10–9*b*.
Substituting into equations 10–21 gives

$$Z_a = \frac{d_{11} - d_{12}}{d_{22}''} = \frac{1034 - 80}{185} = \frac{954}{185} = 5.16 \text{ ohms}$$

$$Z_b = \frac{d_{21}}{d_{22}''} = \frac{80}{185} = 0.43 \text{ ohms}$$

$$Z_c = \frac{d_{22} - d_{21}}{d_{22}''} = \frac{2350 - 80}{185} = \frac{2270}{185} = 12.27 \text{ ohms}$$

Consequently the T network equivalent to Fig. 10–9*a* is as shown in Fig. 10–9*c*.

10.7 T (Wye) and π (Delta) Equivalence Theorem.

The fact that a π (delta) or a T (wye) network can be established which is equivalent to any particular four- or three-terminal network suggests that an equivalence relation exists between a π and T network. Such is in fact the case, for: *A* T *(wye) network (not necessarily physically realizable) can be determined which is equivalent at any particular frequency to any given π (delta) network, and vice versa.*

First, to determine the equivalent π network, if the mesh equations of the T network of Fig. 10–8*e* are inverted, and the two resulting current equations are considered as the node equations of a three-node network, the equivalent π network results. Thus, from Fig. 10–8*e*,

$$V_1 = (Z_c + Z_b)I_1 - Z_bI_2$$
$$-V_2 = -Z_bI_1 + (Z_a + Z_b)I_2$$

Solving these equations for I_1 and I_2 (inverting) leads to

$$I_1 = \frac{Z_a + Z_b}{Z_aZ_b + Z_aZ_c + Z_bZ_c} V_1 + \frac{Z_b}{Z_aZ_b + Z_aZ_c + Z_bZ_c}(-V_2)$$
$$I_2 = \frac{Z_b}{Z_aZ_b + Z_aZ_c + Z_bZ_c} V_1 + \frac{Z_b + Z_c}{Z_aZ_b + Z_aZ_c + Z_bZ_c}(-V_2) \quad (10\text{–}22)$$

which may be viewed as the node equations of a three-node network. But the node equations of the three-node π network of Fig. 10–8*c* are

$$I_1 = (Y_1 + Y_2)V_1 + Y_2(-V_2)$$
$$I_2 = Y_2V_1 + (Y_2 + Y_3)(-V_2) \quad (10\text{–}23)$$

Comparing these last two sets of equations shows that, for the corresponding currents to be equal for all possible voltages V_1 and V_2, it is sufficient that

$$Z_1 = \frac{1}{Y_1} = \frac{Z_aZ_b + Z_aZ_c + Z_bZ_c}{Z_a}$$
$$Z_2 = \frac{1}{Y_2} = \frac{Z_aZ_b + Z_aZ_c + Z_bZ_c}{Z_b} \quad (10\text{–}24)$$
$$Z_3 = \frac{1}{Y_3} = \frac{Z_aZ_b + Z_aZ_c + Z_bZ_c}{Z_c}$$

These equations specify, in terms of T impedances, the impedances which should be connected as the π network (Figs. 10–8*e* and *c*) equivalent to the given T network.

The T impedances in terms of π impedances, which specify a T network equivalent to the π network, can be obtained by solving (inverting) the node equations for the π circuit (equations 10–23) for the voltages. The result after replacing each admittance by the reciprocal of the corresponding impedance leads to

$$V_1 = \frac{Z_1Z_3 + Z_1Z_2}{Z_1 + Z_2 + Z_3} I_1 - \frac{Z_1Z_3}{Z_1 + Z_2 + Z_3} I_2$$
$$-V_2 = -\frac{Z_1Z_3}{Z_1 + Z_2 + Z_3} I_1 + \frac{Z_2Z_3 + Z_1Z_3}{Z_1 + Z_2 + Z_3} I_2$$

But viewing these two equations as the mesh equations of a T network (Fig. 10–8*e*) it follows immediately from the circuit and these equations that it is sufficient for equivalence (T in terms of π) that

$$Z_a = \frac{Z_2Z_3}{Z_1 + Z_2 + Z_3}$$
$$Z_b = \frac{Z_1Z_3}{Z_1 + Z_2 + Z_3} \quad (10\text{–}25)$$
$$Z_c = \frac{Z_1Z_2}{Z_1 + Z_2 + Z_3}$$

Example 10:6 Determine the π equivalent of the T network shown in Fig. 10–10a.

Solution A comparison of Figs. 10–10a and 10–8e shows that $Z_c = Z_{13}$, $Z_b = Z_{34}$, and $Z_a = Z_{3a}$ and a comparison of Figs. 10–8c and 10–10b shows that $Z_{34\pi} = Z_1$, $Z_{65\pi} = Z_3$, and $Z_{35\pi} = Z_2$; consequently substitution into equations 10–24 gives

$$Z_{34\pi} = \frac{(2+j4)(4+j4)+(2+j4)(3+j6)+(4+j4)(3+j6)}{4+j4}$$

$$= \frac{-38+j84}{4+j4} = 5.75 + j15.25$$

$$Z_{65\pi} = \frac{-38+j84}{2+j4} = 13 + j16$$

$$Z_{35\pi} = \frac{-38+j84}{3+j6} = 8.67 + j10.67$$

If these impedances are placed in a π section, as in Fig. 10–10b, the current in the generator and the voltage across the load impedance Z_r will not be altered.

The impedances of both these wye and delta equivalents are physically realizable, i.e., all resistances are positive. But suppose that $Z_{13} = 1 - j5$, $Z_{a3} = 2 - j6$, and $Z_{43} = 2 + j0$ in Fig. 10–10a. Then

$$Z_{35\pi} = -11 - j19$$
$$Z_{65\pi} = 6.46 - j5.69$$
$$Z_{34\pi} = 4.6 - j5.2$$

and the equivalent set of π impedances cannot be physically realized because a negative resistance is required. Therefore, although the formulas 10–24 always specify an equivalent delta (or π) in terms of a given wye (or T) which may be used for numerical computations or symbolic manipulation, the equivalents are not always physically realizable.

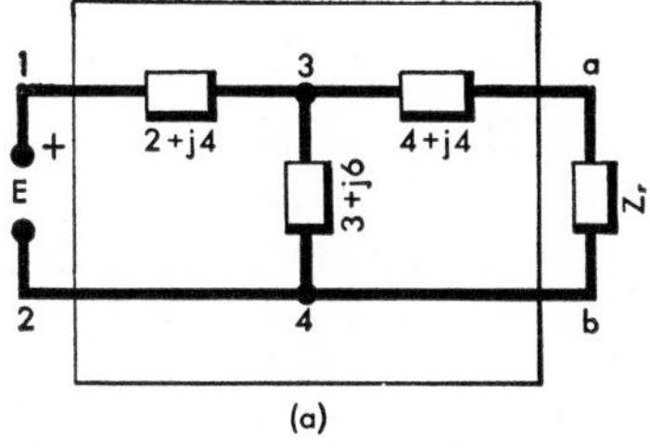

(a)

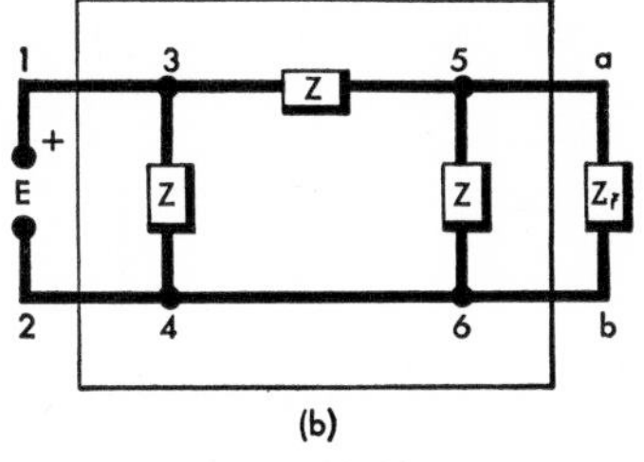

(b)

Fig. 10–10.

Similarly, a physically realizable wye (or T) equivalent to a delta (or π) is not always possible. For example, if $Z_1 = Z_3 = |Z|\epsilon^{j\sigma}$ are both inductive with σ greater than 45 degrees, and Z_2 is such that the angle of $Z_1 + Z_2 + Z_3$ is less than $2\sigma - 90°$, then the real part of Z_b of equations 10–25 is negative and so physically unrealizable. Many other impedance combinations in delta will of course produce this same effect.

The appearance of physically unrealizable impedances in a numerical calculation has no effect on the calculation itself. It can still be carried through as far as desired. Only in the event that a physical representation is desired does a negative resistance offer any difficulties.

Wye-to-delta (or T-to-π) transformations, or vice versa, can be effectively used in computing equivalent circuits which do not allow the use of series-parallel equivalence combinations to be applied throughout. By successive application of series-parallel and T-π equivalence transformations, any two-terminal network can be reduced to a single impedance at any particular frequency.

10.8 Thévenin's Theorem.

Thévenin's theorem may be stated in several slightly different forms, of which the following is typical. *At any particular frequency any linear network of bilateral elements viewed from any two terminals of the network can be replaced by a generated voltage* E_0 *and impedance* Z_i *in series, where* E_0 *is the open circuit voltage measured across the terminals in question and* Z_i *is the impedance of the network viewed from these same terminals with all generators replaced by their internal impedances.*

The proof of Thévenin's theorem may be developed by computing the open circuit voltage and input impedance of part of a network as follows. The open circuit voltage is computed first. Consider Fig. 10–11*a*. The impedance Z is connected across the terminals for which the open circuit voltage is to be determined. This open circuit voltage can be computed by calculating the limit of the voltage across Z as Z approaches infinity.

The equations for the network of Fig. 10–11*a* are most useful if the Z shown is not submerged in the determinant and cofactors. Thus the solution for I_1 can be written as

$$I_1 = \frac{\begin{vmatrix} E_1 & Z_{12} & Z_{13} \cdots Z_{1n} \\ E_2 & Z_{22} & Z_{23} \cdots Z_{2n} \\ \cdot & \cdot & \cdot \quad \cdot \\ \cdot & \cdot & \cdot \quad \cdot \\ \cdot & \cdot & \cdot \quad \cdot \\ E_n & Z_{n2} & Z_{n3} \cdots Z_{nn} \end{vmatrix}}{\begin{vmatrix} Z_{11}+Z & Z_{12} & Z_{13} \cdots Z_{1n} \\ Z_{21} & Z_{22} & Z_{23} \cdots Z_{2n} \\ \cdot & \cdot & \cdot \quad \cdot \\ \cdot & \cdot & \cdot \quad \cdot \\ \cdot & \cdot & \cdot \quad \cdot \\ Z_{n1} & Z_{n2} & Z_{n3} \cdots Z_{nn} \end{vmatrix}} \tag{10–26}$$

which may be also represented by

$$I_1 = \sum_{k=1}^{n} \frac{E_k d_{k1}}{D + Zd_{11}} \tag{10–27}$$

if the determinants are expanded by the first column.

The voltage across the external impedance of Fig. 10–11a is then

$$V = ZI_1 = \sum_{k=1}^{n} \frac{E_k Z d_{k1}}{D + Z d_{11}} \tag{10–28}$$

and the open circuit value of this voltage which results from opening the circuit at the cross mark of Fig. 10–11a may be obtained by taking the limit of equation 10–28 as Z increases indefinitely. Therefore, the open circuit voltage is

$$E_0 = V_0 = \lim_{z\to\infty} V = \lim_{z\to\infty} \sum_{k=1}^{n} \frac{E_k d_{k1}}{\dfrac{D}{Z} + d_{11}} = \sum_{k=1}^{n} E_k \frac{d_{k1}}{d_{11}} \tag{10–29}$$

Consider next the determination of the equation for the impedance looking into the network N. In order to calculate or measure this impedance a known voltage across the terminals a–b, as in Fig. 10–11b, will

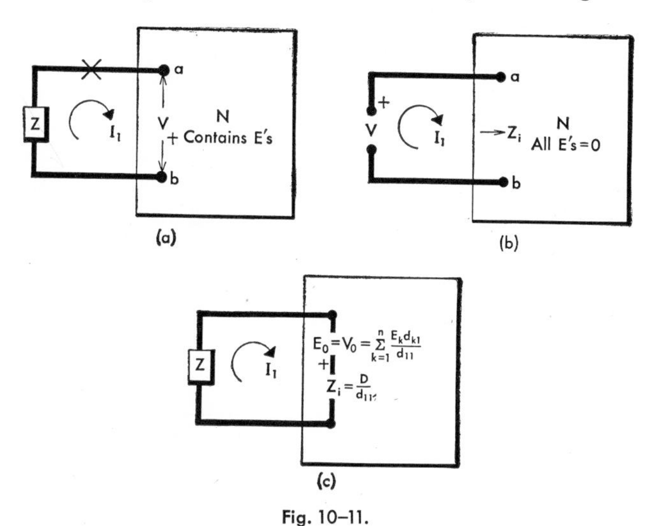

Fig. 10–11.

determine the current into the network, and the voltage-current ratio specifies the input impedance. For the purposes of calculation the equations for this circuit are the same as equations 10–1 except that E_1 is replaced by V and all other E's are zero. The current I_1, therefore, consists of only the term

$$I_1 = V\frac{d_{11}}{D} \tag{10–30}$$

Consequently, the impedance looking into N is from this equation,

$$Z_i = \frac{V}{I} = \frac{D}{d_{11}} \tag{10–31}$$

Incidentally, it should be noted that this expression for the impedance looking into any two terminals of a linear, bilateral network is in itself a very useful formula. It can be used in place of or to supplement the series-parallel and wye-delta or T-π equivalence relations in many cases with a resultant saving in time and effort.

The necessary preliminary relations required for proving Thévenin's theorem have now been established. Combining them as indicated by the theorem statement leads to Fig. 10–11*c*, where the network has been replaced by the open circuit voltage V_0 and the input impedance Z_i in series. The voltage equation for this mesh is

$$-V_0 + I_1(Z + Z_i) = 0$$

or

$$I_1 = \frac{V_0}{Z + Z_i} = \frac{E_0}{Z + Z_i} \qquad (10\text{–}32)$$

Substituting from equations 10–29 and 10–31 into this equation gives

$$I_1 = \sum_{k=1}^{n} \frac{E_k d_{k1}}{\left(Z + \frac{D}{d_{11}}\right) d_{11}} = \sum_{k=1}^{n} \frac{E_k d_{k1}}{D + Z d_{11}} \qquad (10\text{–}33)$$

which is exactly equation 10–27 for the actual current in Z of Fig. 10–11*a*. The circuits of Figs. 10–11*a* and 10–11*c* are therefore equivalent and a two-terminal linear, bilateral network may be replaced by its open circuit voltage in series with its input impedance. Thévenin's theorem is thus proved.

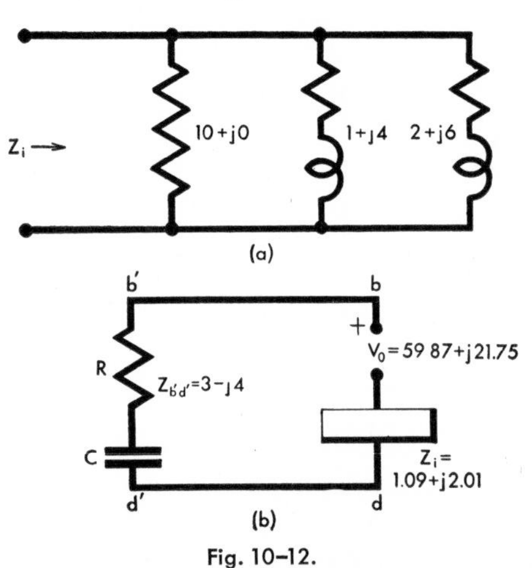

Fig. 10–12.

Thévenin's theorem is useful in many ways,* two of the most evident of which are illustrated in the following examples.

Example 10:7 The effect on the circuit of connecting an additional impedance $Z = 3 - j4$ across the branch b–d of Fig. 10–1 is to be determined by Thévenin's theorem.

Solution The open circuit voltage and input impedance at the terminals b and d of Fig. 10–1 will be determined first. The voltage across b–d *before* $Z = 3 - j4$ is connected is, from Example 10–1, $V_{bd} = 59.87 + j21.75$. The impedance looking into this circuit, with both E_1 and E_2 zero, is the impedance of the circuit of Fig. 10–12*a* and is

$$Z_i = 1.09 + j2.01$$

*E. L. Harder, "Thévenin's Theorem," *Electric Journal*, October, 1938, vol. 35, pp. 307–401.

Then, from Thévenin's theorem, Fig. 10–12*b* represents the behavior of the circuit of Fig. 10–1, with $Z = 3 - j4$ added across the terminals *b* and *d*. The equation for Fig. 10–12*b* is

$$-V_0 + (Z_i + Z_{b'd'})I_{b'd'} = 0$$

and the current through the added impedance is

$$I_{b'd'} = \frac{(59.87 + j21.75)}{4.09 - j1.99} = 9.74 + j10.06$$

Therefore, for $Z = 3 - j4$ in place across *bd* of Fig. 10–1,

$$V_{b'd'} = V_{bd} = I_{b'd'}(3 - j4) = 69.46 - j8.78$$

This example shows one of the most useful properties of Thévenin's theorem. For by means of the theorem the behavior of any addition to a linear network may be computed from measured or calculated open circuit voltage and input impedance. If the original network is a complex communication or power system, considerable saving in time and labor is possible.

A second effective use of Thévenin's theorem is:

Example 10:8 The current and voltage of *any* branch of a linear network can be determined by using Thévenin's theorem. To illustrate this use, the current in branch *ad* of Fig. 10–13*a* and the voltage across these terminals will be computed by means of the theorem for $\omega = 1000$.

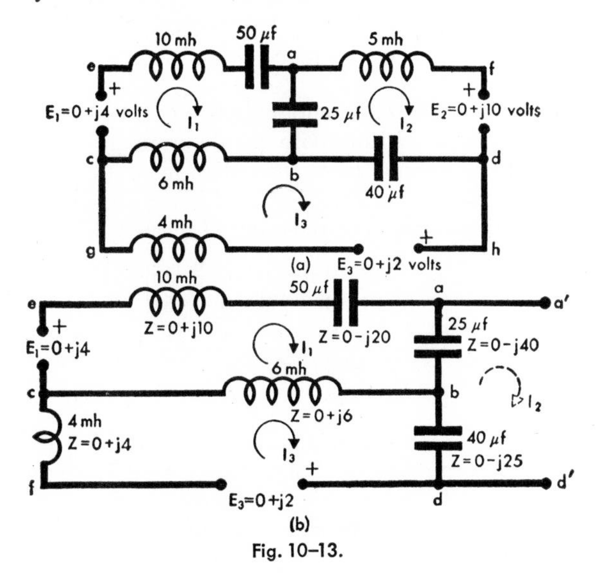

Fig. 10–13.

Solution The open circuit voltage across terminals *ad* and the impedance Z_i looking into the network from these points is required. First, the open circuit voltage may be obtained by computing $V_0 = V_{ad}$ of Fig. 10–13*b*. To this end the two component voltages V_{ab} and V_{bd} will be computed after the currents in branches *ab* and *bd* are determined. The single node equation required, written from node *b* with node *c* as reference, is

$$-E_1Y_{bac} - E_3Y_{bdc} + V_{bc}(Y_{bac} + Y_{bc} + Y_{bdc}) = 0$$

or, numerically,

$$\frac{0 + j4}{0 - j50} + \frac{0 + j2}{0 - j21} = V_{bc}\left(\frac{1}{0 - j50} + \frac{1}{0 + j6} + \frac{1}{0 - j21}\right)$$

and

$$V_{bc} = -j1.77$$

The current I_1 may then be obtained from the equation of mesh 1 as

$$E_1 = I_1(0 + j10 + 0 - j20 + 0 - j40) + V_{bc}$$

and

$$I_1 = \frac{E_1 - V_{bc}}{0 - j50} = -0.1154$$

Therefore,

$$V_{ab} = I_1(0 - j40) = j4.62$$

Similarly, for mesh 3,

$$I_3 = \frac{-E_3 + V_{bc}}{0 - j21} = 0.18$$

and

$$V_{bd} = (0 - j25)I_3 = -j4.5$$

The open circuit voltage $V_0 = V_{ad}$ is, therefore,

$$V_0 = V_{ad0} = V_{ab} + V_{bd} = j0.12$$

The input impedance Z_i can be computed from equation 10–31 as readily as any other way. Therefore, writing both the determinant D and the cofactor of the first row and first column from D from an inspection of the now three-mesh circuit with points a' and d' of Fig. 10–13*b* connected across a constant voltage—mesh equations written in the order of mesh 2, 1, and 3—gives

$$Z_i = \frac{D}{d_{11}} = \frac{\begin{vmatrix} 0 - j65 & 0 + j40 & 0 + j25 \\ 0 + j40 & 0 - j44 & 0 - j6 \\ 0 + j25 & 0 - j6 & 0 - j15 \end{vmatrix}}{\begin{vmatrix} 0 - j44 & 0 - j6 \\ 0 - j6 & 0 - j15 \end{vmatrix}} = 0 - j1.7$$

According to Thévenin's theorem, the network to the left of the terminals *a* and *d* of Fig. 10–13*a* can now be replaced by a series connection of the V_0 and Z_i just computed. Therefore, Fig. 10–14 represents a network which is equivalent to Fig. 10–13*a* at the terminals *a* and *d*. The voltage equation of Fig. 10–14 is

$$-E_2 = (Z_i + Z)I_2 - V_0$$

or

$$I_2 = \frac{-E_2 + V_0}{Z_i + Z} = \frac{-j9.87}{0 + j3.3} = -2.99$$

which is the current in branch *ad* of Fig. 10–13*a*. In addition, the voltage across the terminals *ad* of Figs. 10–13*a* and 10–14 is

$$V_{ad} = V_0 - Z_i I_2 = j0.12 - j5.08$$
$$= -j4.96$$

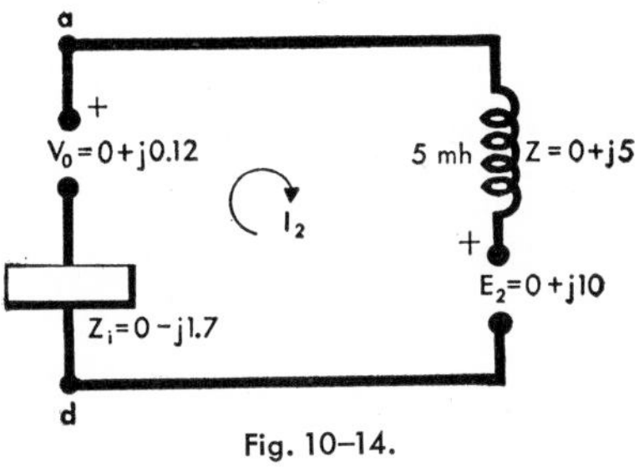

Fig. 10–14.

10.9 Norton's Theorem.

Norton's theorem may be stated as follows: *Any linear bilateral network viewed from any two terminals of the network may be replaced at any particular frequency by a current generator of constant current* I *in parallel with an impedance* Z_i, *where* I *is the current delivered into a short circuit of the two terminals in question, and* Z_i *is the impedance looking into the network from these terminals with all generators replaced by their internal impedances.*

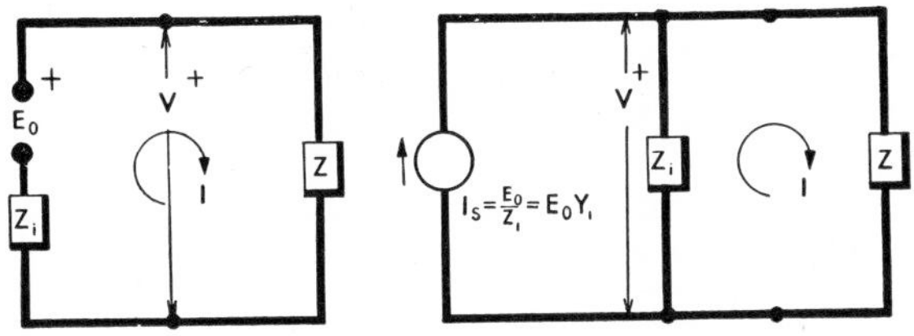

(a) (b)

Fig. 10–15.

This theorem can be proved by using Thévenin's theorem. In Fig. 10–15*a* the series combination E_0 and Z_i represents any two-terminal network from Thévenin's theorem. The voltage equation for this circuit is then

$$E_0 = Z_i I + V$$

or

$$I - \frac{E_0}{Z_i} + \frac{V}{Z_i} = I - E_0 Y_i + V Y_i = 0 \qquad (10\text{–}34)$$

But this equation is the node equation for the circuit shown in Fig. 10–15*b*. The currents I of the networks of Fig. 10–15 are therefore the same, and the networks are equivalent so far as producing this current is concerned. The current $E_0 Y_i$ of the constant current generator is the current into a short circuit of the two-terminal network represented by its Thévenin's theorem equivalent on the left of Fig. 10–15*a*. Norton's theorem is thus proved.

Incidentally it should be noted that the foregoing proof has also shown, that in general the constant current generator *paralleled* by Z_i in Fig. 10–15*b* is equivalent to a constant voltage source in *series* with Z_i.

10.10 Maximum Power Transfer Theorem.*

In communication systems the power available to operate receiving equipment is always low. It is consequently of major importance that the system be designed to deliver the largest part possible of the total power input.

As will be shown in the following, the maximum power delivery occurs at the low value of 50 per cent efficiency. However, high efficiency is relatively unimportant in communications. On the other hand, it is of major importance in power systems. Therefore, maximum power transfer would ordinarily be avoided in a power system as a steady operating condition. In spite of this fact, the maximum power properties of a power network must be studied, because it has been found that if the power delivered over a power network exceeds a certain amount, the network becomes unstable and serious operational difficulties arise. It is essential, therefore, that the power limits of both communication and power systems be understood.

Maximum power transfer can be formulated on the basis of the simple circuit of Fig. 10–16. The power delivered to Z_R by the generator is

$$P_R = |I|^2R_R = \left|\frac{E}{Z + Z_R}\right|^2 R_R = \frac{|E|^2R_R}{(R + R_R)^2 + (X + X_R)^2} \qquad (10\text{–}35)$$

The maximum value of this expression is to be determined. If the load or receiving impedance Z_R is considered the variable, there are several ways in which this impedance may be varied, the most important of which are: R_R and X_R may be varied independently and without restriction or the range of variation of X_R and R_R may be limited.

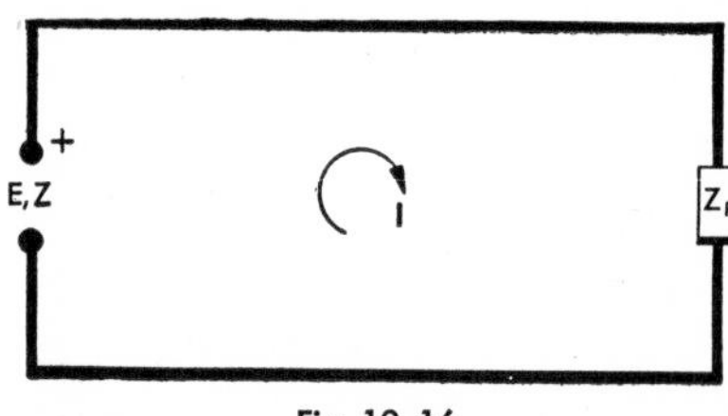

Fig. 10–16.

Considering equation 10–35 as a function of R_R and X_R only (in geometrical terms a power surface plotted above the $X_R - R_R$ plane) would give a complete picture of the variation of the power delivered to Z_R as X_R and R_R are varied. Since the flat surface of a page of this book does

---

* Myril B. Reed, "Maximum Power Transfer," *Radio News*, Engineering Department, October, 1945, vol. 5, No. 4, pp. 11, 22.

not permit such a three-dimensional representation, the next best and fundamentally as effective a representation will be presented—a contour map. The establishment of the power contour map can be accomplished through the use of a few equations, which will now be derived.

The partial derivatives of P_R with respect to X_R and R_R will be useful. These derivatives are

$$\frac{\partial P_R}{\partial X_R} = \frac{-|E|^2 R_R\, 2(X + X_R)}{[(R + R_R)^2 + (X + X_R)^2]^2} \tag{10–36}$$

and

$$\frac{\partial P_R}{\partial R_R} = \frac{|E|^2[(R + R_R)^2 + (X + X_R)^2 - 2R_R(R + R_R)]}{[(R + R_R)^2 + (X + X_R)^2]^2} \tag{10–37}$$

Also the equation for the intersection of the P_R surface and planes parallel to the $X_R - R_R$ plane, i.e., equation 10–35 with P_R a constant, is

$$(R + R_R)^2 - \frac{|E|^2}{P_R} R_R + (X + X_R)^2 = 0$$

This equation represents a circle, for, on combining the first two terms, completing the squares, and rearranging, there results

$$\left[R_R - \left(\frac{|E|^2}{2P_R} - R\right)\right]^2 + (X + X_R)^2 = \frac{|E|^2}{P_R}\left[\frac{|E|^2}{4P_R} - R\right] \tag{10–38}$$

The eccentric circles shown in Fig. 10–17 are these *constant power circles* projected onto the $X_R - R_R$ plane. The general shape of the power-supplied surface can now be determined.

The contour circles indicate that the power surface rises to a peak at the point $X_R = -X$ and $R_R = R$ and may be crudely described, above the $X_R - R_R$ plane where R_R is positive, as a lop-sided cone which tapers off to zero at the boundaries of the first and second quadrants. Further information about the shape of the power surface can be obtained from the partial derivatives.

First, equation 10–36 is equal to zero if $X_R = -X$. Consequently, the intersections of the power surface and planes parallel to X_R and perpendicular to the $R_R - X_R$ plane will all have maximum values directly above the $X_R = -X$ line shown in Fig. 10–17. Second, solving for R_R, from equation 10–37 set equal to zero, gives

$$R_R = \sqrt{R^2 + (X + X_R)^2} \tag{10–39}$$

The graph of this equation on the $X_R - R_R$ plane produces the hyperbola shown on Fig. 10–17. Therefore, the line intersections of the power surface and planes parallel to R_R and perpendicular to the $X_R - R_R$ plane have maximum values directly above this hyperbola. The values to which R_R and X_R should be adjusted for maximum power absorption can now be formulated in terms of the power surface picture presented in the foregoing.

As suggested by the peak of the power surfaces, where $X_R = -X$, and $R_R = R$, a maximum power transfer theorem may be stated as:

Maximum Power Transfer Theorem.

If at any particular frequency the resistance and reactance of a two-terminal, linear, bilateral, passive network are varied independently, the maximum power is delivered to this network by an active two-terminal, linear,

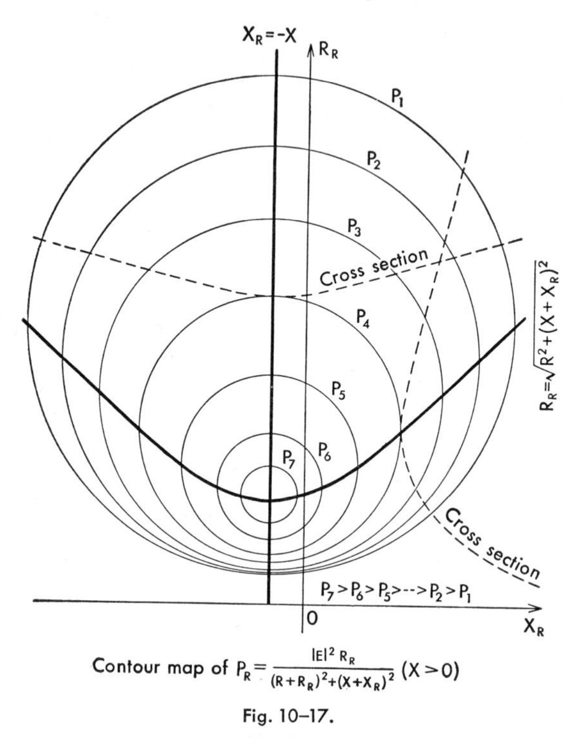

Contour map of $P_R = \dfrac{|E|^2 R_R}{(R + R_R)^2 + (X + X_R)^2}$ $(X > 0)$

Fig. 10–17.

bilateral network when the impedances looking into the two networks are conjugates. Because of Thévenin's theorem the circuit of Fig. 10–16 represents the two networks—active on the left and passive on the right—mentioned in the theorem.

Note that the conditions $X_R = -X$ and $R_R = R$ for maximum power absorption by Z_R of Fig. 10–16 corresponds to *series resonance* for Z and Z_R in series. Note also that because $R = R_R$ the power loss inside the generator is the same as that delivered to the impedance Z_R. Thus maximum power delivery means 50 per cent efficiency. As already indicated, this condition would be very undesirable in a power system since it would require tremendous generators merely to dissipate the heat developed. In communication systems, on the other hand, maximum power delivery is sought by deliberate design of equipment. The power available to operate loud-speakers, telephone receivers, etc., is so small that the maximum possible power should be delivered at all times.

In the event that the impedance Z_R of the network absorbing power cannot be fully adjusted to meet the requirements for a full maximum power absorption, the question arises of how to adjust Z_R within whatever physical limits are possible. If once more the nature of the power surface is recalled and a climber on this surface is imagined, it is evident that, as any X_R line is followed, higher points on the surface are reached until $X_R = -X$. Also by following any R_R line, higher points on the surface will be reached until points above the hyperbola $R_R = \sqrt{R^2 + (X + X_R)^2}$ are reached. Consequently, an auxiliary power transfer theorem may be stated as:

Partial Maximum, Power Transfer Theorem.

If at any particular frequency, two linear, bilateral, two-terminal networks (one active and one passive) are connected, the maximum power is associated with the passive network when X_R *is first adjusted to as near* $-X$ *as possible and* R_R *is then adjusted to as near* $\sqrt{R^2 + (X + X_R)^2}$ *as possible* (X_R and R_R independently variable).

One interesting fact immediately evident from this theorem is that if $X_R = 0$, the load resistance R_R should equal the magnitude of the internal impedance of the generator for the maximum possible power associated with R_R.

Example 10:9 (*a*) Determine the load impedance which will absorb the maximum power from a generator of internal impedance $2 + j3$ ohms. (*b*) Determine the load impedance adjustment which will cause this impedance to absorb maximum power if it can only be varied over the ranges: $4 \leqslant X_R \leqslant 10$, and $1 \leqslant R_R \leqslant 5$.

Solution (*a*) The maximum power will be delivered when the load and source impedances are conjugates. Hence $Z_R = 2 - j3$ will absorb maximum power.

(*b*) The reactance X_R can be adjusted no closer to -3 ohms than $X_R = 4$. For maximum power R_R should be (equation 10–39)

$$R_R = \sqrt{4 + (3 + 4)^2} = \sqrt{53} = 7.27$$

However, R_R can only be adjusted to a maximum of 5 ohms. Therefore, if $Z_R = 5 + j4$ it will absorb the maximum power possible under the restrictions given.

If X_R and R_R are not independently variable, the adjustment to be made for maximum power is not so easy to determine. In any event, a clear picture of the nature of the power surface, as presented in the foregoing, permits a solution to be reached (see Problem 10–26).

10.11 Foster's Two-Terminal Reactance Theorem.

One of the most important and at the same time most difficult problems in the theory of electrical networks is that of determining a network—synthesis—which will produce a certain specified current variation for a given source voltage. Foster's reactance theorem is perhaps the most widely known and one of the most useful of the various attempts at the solution of the synthesis problem. This theorem may be stated as:

Foster's Reactance Theorem.

Considered as a function of frequency, the input impedance $Z(\omega)$ *of any two-terminal, linear, bilateral, pure reactance network (no resistance) can be expressed as a ratio of two polynomials in* ω — $Z(\omega) = D(\omega)/d_{11}(\omega)$. *The derivative of this function,* $dZ(\omega)/j\, d\omega$, *is positive for every* ω. *Also, if* $\omega_1, \omega_3, \omega_5, \cdots$ *locate the zeros of* $Z(\omega)$ *(values of* ω *for which* $Z[\omega] = 0$, *i.e., short circuit) and if* $\omega_2, \omega_4, \omega_6, \cdots$ *locate the poles of* $Z(\omega)$ *(values of* ω *for which* $Z(\omega)$ *is infinite, i.e., open circuit) the* ω_i *are related by* $0 \leqslant \omega_1 < \omega_2 < \omega_3 < \omega_4 < \omega_5 \cdots$. *The zeros of* $Z(\omega) = D(\omega)/d_{11}(\omega)$ *are determined by the roots of* $D(\omega) = 0$ *and the poles from the roots of* $d_{11}(\omega) = 0$. *The zeros and poles so located determine the parameter values of a Foster simplified network when they are used to express* $Z(\omega)$ *in factored form.*

Furthermore, if the location of a set of zeros and poles are not derived from a known network but are simply specified in correspondence with the separation property $0 \leqslant \omega_1 < \omega_2 < \omega_3 < \omega_4 \cdots$, *and if* $Z(\omega)$ *is specified properly at any other frequency, the parameter values of a real Foster reactance network can be determined which has the input impedance value and the poles and zeros specified.*

The proof of Foster's reactance theorem will not be given here but will be illustrated in terms of discussion and illustrative examples. Other books may be consulted to obtain a proof of its validity and further properties.*

Foster's reactance theorem has two important restrictions which should not be lost sight of; namely, it applies only to purely reactive networks and only to two-terminal networks. In spite of these restrictions, the theorem is of great usefulness in further theoretical studies and in designing other than two-terminal networks by combinations of two-terminal networks designed from Foster's reactance theorem.

The purely reactive restriction is not so serious as might at first be

* R. M. Foster, *Bell System Technical Journal*, April, 1924, p. 259; A. T. Starr, *Electric Circuits and Wave Filters*, Pitman and Sons, 1938; E. A. Guillemin, *Communication Networks*, John Wiley & Sons, 1935, Vol. II; T. E. Shea, *Transmission Networks and Wave Filters*, D. Van Nostrand Co., 1929.

supposed because by design many classes of circuits are constructed to have as little resistance as possible, so that the reactance theorem expresses, as a good approximation, the behavior of many actual two-terminal networks. Even if this latter condition were not true, Foster's reactance theorem would be useful in specifying a mathematical expression from which the synthesis of networks could at least be approached, whereas otherwise such synthesis might be largely experimental and, therefore, wasteful of time and effort.

The impedance looking into any two-terminal network has already been expressed by equation 10–31 as $Z = D/d_{11}$. Since for a purely reactive network any branch impedance must be one of the three types

$$j\omega L, \frac{1}{j\omega C}, \text{ or } j\omega L + \frac{1}{j\omega C}$$

both of the determinants D and d_{11} will be polynomials in ω, so that the input impedance may be expressed as

$$Z(\omega) = \frac{D(\omega)}{d_{11}(\omega)} \tag{10–40}$$

It is so evident as hardly to need mentioning that the values of ω for which $D(\omega) = 0$ correspond to zeros of $Z(\omega)$, i.e., short circuits, and that the values of ω for which $d_{11}(\omega) = 0$ correspond to poles of $Z(\omega)$, i.e., open circuit. Therefore, the roots of $D(\omega) = 0$ determine the zeros and the roots of $d_{11}(\omega) = 0$ determine the poles of $Z(\omega)$.

Proof will not be given here of the fact that, for any physically possible combination of inductors and capacitors which form a two-terminal network, the derivative $dZ(\omega)/d\omega$ divided by j—$dZ(\omega)/jd\omega$—is positive for every value of ω, or of the fact that the poles and zeros are separated by pole-zero-pole-zero-etc. $(0 \leqslant \omega_1 < \omega_2 < \omega_3 < \omega_4 \cdots)$. The next example will illustrate these points.

Example 10:10 Determine the reactance function $Z(\omega)$ of Fig. 10–18a and locate its poles and zeros.

Solution The formula for the input impedance to this two-terminal network is

$$Z(\omega) = \frac{D(\omega)}{d_{11}(\omega)} = \frac{\begin{vmatrix} j\omega L_1 & -j\omega L_1 & 0 \\ -j\omega L_1 & j\omega L_{13} + \dfrac{1}{j\omega C_{13}} & -\dfrac{1}{j\omega C_1} \\ 0 & -\dfrac{1}{j\omega C_1} & j\omega L_2 + \dfrac{1}{j\omega C_{12}} \end{vmatrix}}{\begin{vmatrix} j\omega L_{13} + \dfrac{1}{j\omega C_{13}} & -\dfrac{1}{j\omega C_1} \\ -\dfrac{1}{j\omega C_1} & j\omega L_2 + \dfrac{1}{j\omega C_{12}} \end{vmatrix}}$$

where

$$L_{13} = L_1 + L_3$$
$$C_{13} = \frac{C_1C_3}{C_1 + C_3};\ C_{12} = \frac{C_1C_2}{C_1 + C_2}$$

Expanding the two determinants, combining terms, and canceling common denominators leave

$$Z(\omega) = j\omega L_1 \frac{L_2L_3\omega^4 - \omega^2\left(\frac{L_3}{C_{12}} + \frac{L_2}{C_{13}}\right) + \frac{1}{C_{12}C_{13}} - \frac{1}{C_1^2}}{L_2L_{13}\omega^4 - \omega^2\left(\frac{L_2}{C_{13}} + \frac{L_{13}}{C_{12}}\right) + \frac{1}{C_{12}C_{13}} - \frac{1}{C_1^2}}$$

Substituting from Fig. 10–18*a* for the L and C values of this equation leads to

$$Z(\omega) = j\omega \frac{1}{60} \frac{\omega^4 - 4.25 \times 10^7\omega^2 + 2 \times 10^{14}}{\omega^4 - 4.125 \times 10^7\omega^2 + 1.67 \times 10^{14}}$$

as the input impedance as a function of frequency.

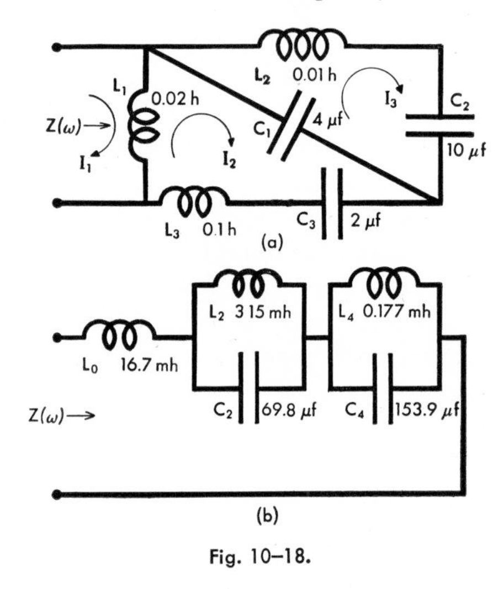

Fig. 10–18.

The poles and zeros can be located by using the quadratic formula to determine the roots of the quadratics in ω^2 which appear in both numerator and denominator. Thus from the numerator the roots are

$$\omega^2 = \frac{4.25 \times 10^7 \pm \sqrt{(4.25 \times 10^7)^2 - 4 \times 2 \times 10^{14}}}{2}$$
$$= 5.4 \times 10^6 \text{ and } 3.71 \times 10^7$$

From the denominator the roots are

$$\omega^2 = \frac{4.125 \times 10^7 \pm \sqrt{(4.125 \times 10^7)^2 - 4 \times 1.67 \times 10^{14}}}{2}$$
$$= 4.54 \times 10^6 \quad \text{and} \quad 3.67 \times 10^7$$

Using these results in the expression for $Z(\omega)$ gives

$$Z(\omega) = j\omega \frac{1}{60} \frac{(\omega^2 - 5.4 \times 10^6)(\omega^2 - 3.71 \times 10^7)}{(\omega^2 - 4.54 \times 10^6)(\omega^2 - 3.67 \times 10^7)}$$

The poles and zeros are completely specified by this last equation. Evidently zeros (short circuits) occur at

$$f_1 = 0,\ f_3 = \frac{\sqrt{5.4 \times 10^6}}{2\pi} = 369,\ f_5 = \frac{\sqrt{3.71 \times 10^7}}{2\pi} = 969$$

and poles (open circuits) occur at

$$f_2 = \frac{\sqrt{4.54 \times 10^6}}{2\pi} = 339,\ f_4 = \frac{\sqrt{3.67 \times 10^7}}{2\pi} = 961,\ f_6 = \infty$$

Note that these poles and zeros are separated in accordance with $0 \leqslant f_1 < f_2 < f_3 < f_4 < f_5 < \infty$, as stated in the theorem, since from Fig. 10–18*a* itself a zero at $\omega = 0$ and a pole at $\omega = \infty$ is required.

It is a comparatively simple matter to express $Z(\omega)$ mathematically in factored form from a specified location or computation of poles and zeros. For example, suppose that $Z(\omega)$ is to have three *interior* zeros,

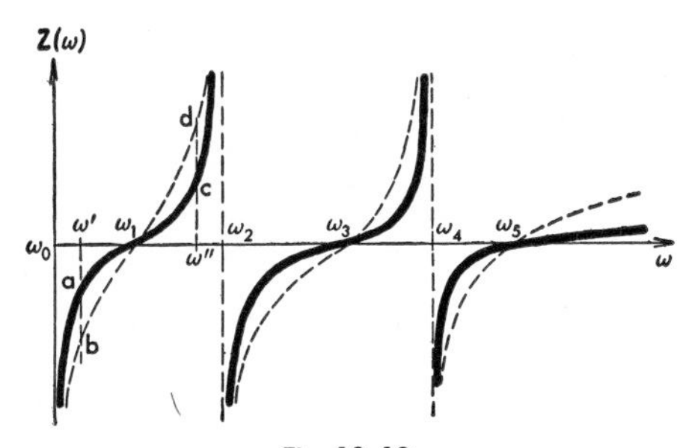

Fig. 10–19.

and four poles, two interior and two others at $\omega = 0$ and $\omega = \infty$. The curve of Fig. 10–19 represents a reactance function having these properties. The input impedance to such a network may be expressed as

$$Z(\omega) = j\omega H \frac{(\omega^2 - \omega_1{}^2)(\omega^2 - \omega_3{}^2)(\omega^2 - \omega_5{}^2)}{\omega^2(\omega^2 - \omega_2{}^2)(\omega^2 - \omega_4{}^2)} \quad (H > 0) \quad (10\text{–}41)$$

An examination shows that this relation is the ratio of two polynomials, with zero and infinite values of the required number and position. It can also be shown that this last equation has the other properties stated in Foster's reactance theorem.

Further algebraic manipulation of equation 10–41 leads to the establishment of the Foster network. Thus if this equation is expressed in partial fraction form, after dividing once to reduce the numerator to lower degree than the numerator, the result is

$$Z(\omega) = j\omega H\left[1 + \frac{A_0}{\omega^2} + \frac{A_2}{\omega^2 - \omega_2^2} + \frac{A_4}{\omega^2 - \omega_4^2}\right] \tag{10–42}$$

where the A's are unknown constants which may be determined as follows. If equations 10–41 and 10–42 are equated and if each side of the resultant equality is multiplied by ω^2, the result is

$$\frac{(\omega^2 - \omega_1^2)(\omega^2 - \omega_3^2)(\omega^2 - \omega_5^2)}{(\omega^2 - \omega_2^2)(\omega^2 - \omega_4^2)} = \omega^2 + A_0 + \frac{\omega^2 A_2}{\omega^2 - \omega_2^2} + \frac{\omega^2 A_4}{\omega^2 - \omega_4^2} \tag{10–43}$$

Now if zero is substituted for ω, immediately

$$A_0 = \frac{(-\omega_1^2)(-\omega_3^2)(-\omega_5^2)}{(-\omega_2^2)(-\omega_4^2)} \tag{10–44}$$

Similarly, if equations 10–41 and 10–42 are equated and then multiplied by $\omega^2 - \omega_2^2$, the result is

$$\frac{(\omega^2 - \omega_1^2)(\omega^2 - \omega_3^2)(\omega^2 - \omega_5^2)}{\omega^2(\omega^2 - \omega_4^2)} = (\omega^2 - \omega_2^2) + \frac{(\omega^2 - \omega_2^2)A_0}{\omega^2} + A_2 + \frac{(\omega^2 - \omega_2^2)A_4}{\omega^2 - \omega_4^2} \tag{10–45}$$

But if ω is replaced by ω_2, immediately

$$A_2 = \frac{(\omega_2^2 - \omega_1^2)(\omega_2^2 - \omega_3^2)(\omega_2^2 - \omega_5^2)}{\omega_2^2(\omega_2^2 - \omega_4^2)} \tag{10–46}$$

Likewise, A_4 can be computed as

$$A_4 = \frac{(\omega_4^2 - \omega_1^2)(\omega_4^2 - \omega_3^2)(\omega_4^2 - \omega_5^2)}{\omega_4^2(\omega_4^2 - \omega_2^2)} \tag{10–47}$$

Equation 10–42 is thus completely determined in terms of known factors from equation 10–41.

Next consider equation 10–42 in more detail. The equation as a whole represents an impedance, and the sum of terms must, therefore, represent a sum of impedances. The first term $j\omega H$ represents a coil of inductance $L = H$ henrys. The second term represents a capacitor, for

$$\frac{1}{j\omega C} = j\omega\frac{-\frac{1}{C}}{\omega^2} = j\omega\frac{HA_0}{\omega^2}$$

so that

$$C = \frac{-1}{HA_0} \text{ (farads)} \tag{10–48}$$

Finally, all terms of the type remaining represent parallel combinations of L and C, for the impedance of such a combination is

$$\frac{j\omega L \dfrac{1}{j\omega C}}{j\omega L + \dfrac{1}{j\omega C}} = j\omega \frac{-\dfrac{1}{C}}{\omega^2 - \dfrac{1}{LC}}$$

Therefore, from this result and the third term of equation 10–42,

$$-\frac{1}{C_2} = HA_2$$

or

$$C_2 = \frac{-1}{HA_2} \text{ (farads)} \tag{10–49}$$

Also, comparing further,

$$\omega_2{}^2 = \frac{1}{L_2C_2}$$

so that

$$L_2 = \frac{1}{\omega_2{}^2C_2} \text{ (henrys)} \tag{10–50}$$

Therefore, if equation 10–42 is known completely, the network represented by Fig. 10–20*a* can be determined completely. Furthermore, the Foster network of Fig. 10–20*a* has exactly the same frequency response as that of equation 10–42. Note that the Foster network has poles at all frequencies at which a parallel combination is in resonance, as for example $\omega_2 = 1/L_2C_2$, and that the exterior poles are determined by the series L and C.

Example 10:11 Determine the Foster network equivalent to the network represented in Fig. 10–18*a*.

Solution The partial fraction representation of $Z(\omega)$ must be obtained first. From example 10–10,

$$Z(\omega) = j\omega \frac{1}{60} \frac{\omega^4 - 4.25 \times 10^7\omega^2 + 2 \times 10^{14}}{\omega^4 - 4.125 \times 10^7\omega^2 + 1.67 \times 10^{14}}$$

which on dividing to reduce the numerator to lower degree than the denominator and then expressing the denominator in factored form produces

$$Z(\omega) = j\omega \frac{1}{60}\left[1 + \frac{-1.25 \times 10^6\omega^2 + 3.33 \times 10^{13}}{(\omega^2 - 4.54 \times 10^6)(\omega^2 - 3.67 \times 10^7)}\right]$$

As a partial fraction sum this relation becomes

$$Z(\omega) = j\omega \frac{1}{60}\left[1 + \frac{A_2}{\omega^2 - 4.54 \times 10^6} + \frac{A_4}{\omega^2 - 3.67 \times 10^7}\right]$$

Equating the last two equations and multiplying both sides by $(\omega^2 - 4.54 \times 10^6)$ gives

$$A_2 = \lim_{\omega^2 \to 4.54 \times 10^6} \frac{-1.25 \times 10^6 \omega^2 + 3.33 \times 10^{13}}{\omega^2 - 3.67 \times 10^7} = -8.6 \times 10^5$$

Similarly,

$$A_4 = \lim_{\omega^2 \to 3.67 \times 10^7} \frac{-1.25 \times 10^6 \omega^2 + 3.33 \times 10^{13}}{\omega^2 - 4.54 \times 10^6} = -3.9 \times 10^5$$

Therefore,

$$Z(\omega) = j\omega \frac{1}{60} \left[1 + \frac{-8.6 \times 10^5}{\omega^2 - 4.54 \times 10^6} + \frac{-3.9 \times 10^5}{\omega^2 - 3.67 \times 10^7} \right]$$

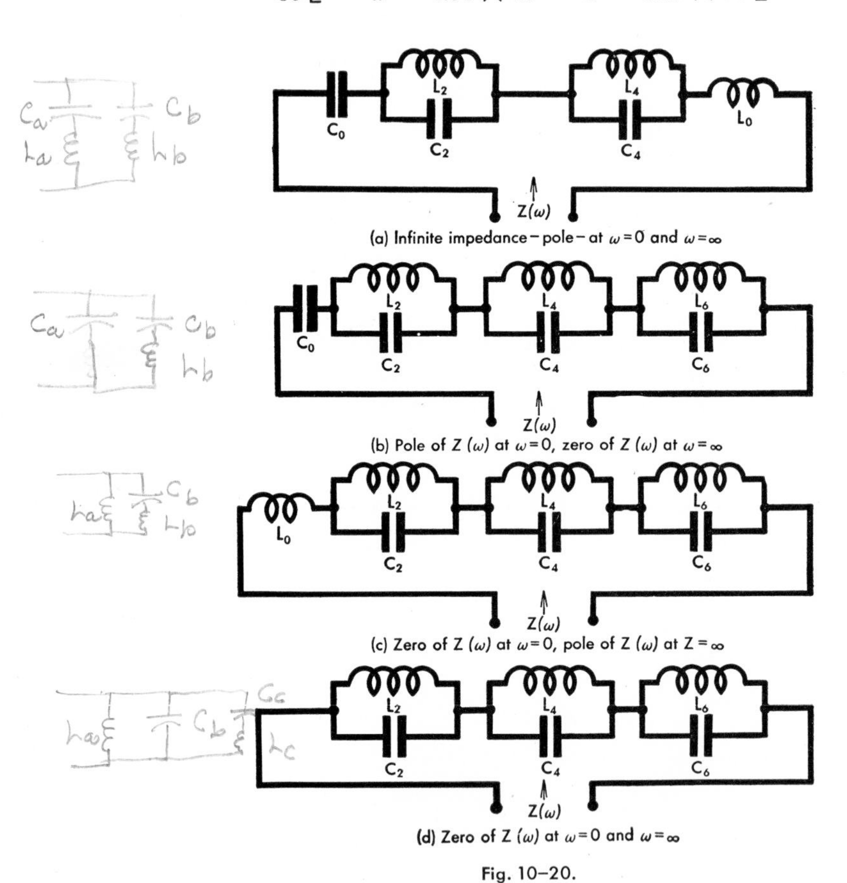

Fig. 10–20.

From this equation the Foster network is, as shown in Fig. 10–18*b*, an inductor in series with two L and C parallel circuits. The inductor is

$$L_0 = \frac{1}{60} = 0.0167 \text{ henry or } 16.7 \text{ mh}$$

From equations 10–49 and 10–50 the other inductors and capacitors are

$$C_2 = \frac{-1}{\frac{1}{60}(-8.6 \times 10^5)} = 69.8 \times 10^{-6} \text{ farad or } 69.8\ \mu\text{f}$$

$$L_2 = \frac{1}{4.54 \times 10^6 \times 69.8 \times 10^{-6}} = 0.00315 \text{ henry, or } 3.15 \text{ mh}$$

$$C_4 = \frac{-1}{\frac{1}{60}(-3.9 \times 10^5)} = 153.9 \times 10^{-6} \text{ farad, or } 153.9\ \mu\text{f}$$

$$L_4 = \frac{1}{3.67 \times 10^7 \times 153.9 \times 10^{-6}} = 0.000177 \text{ henry, or } 0.177 \text{ mh}$$

There are four mathematical forms which the input impedance $Z(\omega)$ can assume. One of these has already been given in equations 10–41 and 10–42 and another in Examples 10–10 and 10–11. The $Z(\omega)$ of equations 10–41 and 10–42 represents a network with a pole at $\omega = 0$ and at $\omega = \infty$. The network of Examples 10–10 and 10–11 has a zero at $\omega = 0$ and a pole at $\omega = \infty$. The other two possibilities are: pole at $\omega = 0$ and a zero at $\omega = \infty$; and a zero at $\omega = 0$ and a zero at $\omega = \infty$. The equations, in symbolic form for the three possibilities different from equations 10–41 and 10–42, are now given.

If $Z(\omega)$ has a pole at $\omega = 0$ and a zero at $\omega = \infty$, the Foster network will be as shown in Fig. 10–20*b* with a reactance function as plotted in Fig. 10–21*a* for three internal poles. Mathematically then,

$$Z(\omega) = -j\omega H \frac{(\omega^2 - \omega_1{}^2)(\omega^2 - \omega_3{}^2)(\omega^2 - \omega_5{}^2)}{\omega^2(\omega^2 - \omega_2{}^2)(\omega^2 - \omega_4{}^2)(\omega^2 - \omega_6{}^2)} \quad (H > 0) \qquad (10\text{–}51)$$

The minus sign must be used for $H > 0$, since the positive derivative property of $Z(\omega)$ makes $Z(\omega)$ negative for $0 \leqslant \omega < \omega_1$. But over this range of ω both the numerator and the denominator of equation 10–51 are negative so that the fraction is positive; hence the minus sign is necessary to make $Z(\omega)$ negative as required.

Because the numerator of the ratio in equation 10–51 is of lower degree than the denominator, the partial fraction form of this equation is

$$Z(\omega) = j\omega H \left[\frac{A_0}{\omega^2} + \frac{A_2}{\omega^2 - \omega_2{}^2} + \frac{A_4}{\omega^2 - \omega_4{}^2} + \frac{A_6}{\omega^2 - \omega_6{}^2}\right] \qquad (10\text{–}52)$$

This equation, of course, represents Fig. 10–20*b*.

Establishment of the remaining two forms of $Z(\omega)$ is very similar to the foregoing so that only the results will be given. If $Z\ (\omega)$ has a pole at $\omega = \infty$ and a zero at $\omega = 0$,

$$Z(\omega) = j\omega H \frac{(\omega^2 - \omega_3{}^2)(\omega^2 - \omega_5{}^2)(\omega^2 - \omega_7{}^2)}{(\omega^2 - \omega_2{}^2)(\omega^2 - \omega_4{}^2)(\omega^2 - \omega_6{}^2)} \quad (H > 0) \qquad (10\text{–}53)$$

and

$$Z(\omega) = j\omega H \left[1 + \frac{A_2}{\omega^2 - \omega_2{}^2} + \frac{A_4}{\omega^2 - \omega_4{}^2} + \frac{A_6}{\omega^2 - \omega_6{}^2}\right] \qquad (10\text{–}54)$$

The Foster network corresponding to these equations is shown in Fig. 10–20c and the reactance function in Fig. 10–21b. Finally, if $Z(\omega)$ has a zero at both $\omega = 0$ and $\omega = \infty$,

$$Z(\omega) = -j\omega H \frac{(\omega^2 - \omega_3^2)(\omega^2 - \omega_5^2)}{(\omega^2 - \omega_2^2)(\omega^2 - \omega_4^2)(\omega^2 - \omega_6^2)} \quad (H > 0) \qquad (10\text{–}55)$$

and

$$Z(\omega) = j\omega H \left[\frac{A_2}{\omega^2 - \omega_2^2} + \frac{A_4}{\omega^2 - \omega_4^2} + \frac{A_6}{\omega^2 - \omega_6^2} \right] \qquad (10\text{–}56)$$

The corresponding Foster network and the reactance function are shown in Figs. 10–20d and 10–21c.

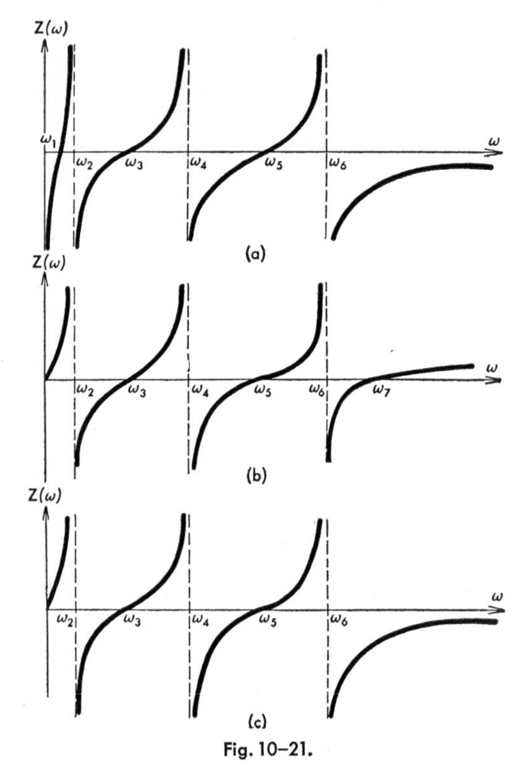

Fig. 10–21.

An examination of the equations which have now been given for $Z(\omega)$ indicates that, if the values of ω at the poles and zeros are known and if a value of $Z(\omega)$ is known at some other frequency so that H can be computed, the reactance function $Z(\omega)$ is completely determined. It is thus possible to determine a Foster network from a statement of the properties of the network as well as from a given network not of the Foster form. To obtain a physically possible structure the poles and zeros must be specified in accordance with the separation property and the value of

$Z(\omega)$ at some other frequency must be specified so that the reactance function can have a positive slope. For example, if the Foster network is to have poles and zeros in accordance with Fig. 10–21*c*, $Z(\omega)$ must be specified as positive for any ω less than ω_2, negative for $\omega_2 < \omega < \omega_3$, etc.

Example 10:12 Determine the Foster reactance network which has poles at $\omega = 0$ and $\omega = 1000$, and zeros at $\omega = 600$ and $\omega = \infty$. Also $Z(\omega)$ is to have a value of $j10$ at $\omega = 700$.

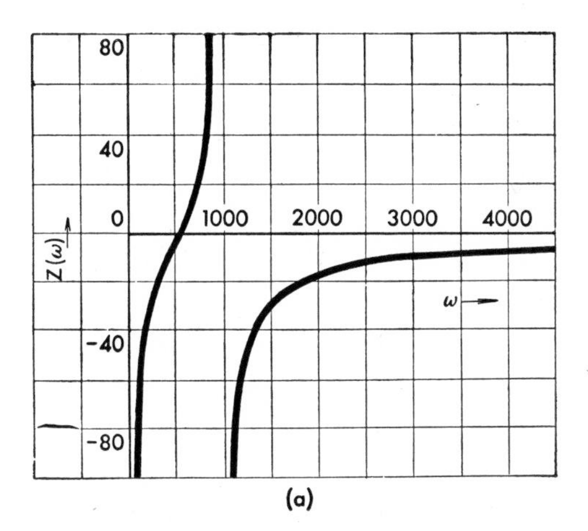

(a)

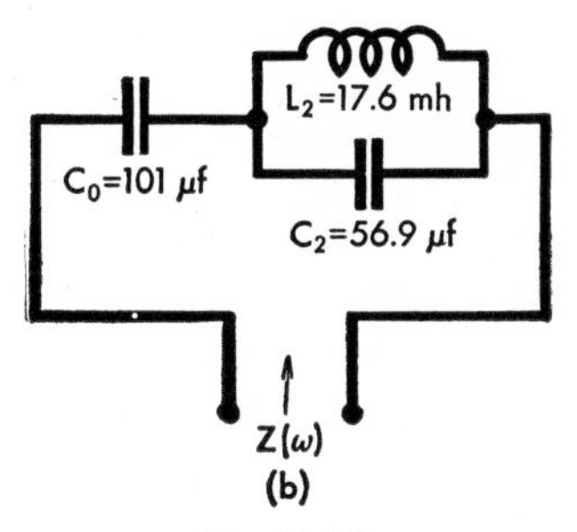

(b)

Fig. 10–22.

Solution The nature of the reactance function can be sketched immediately as shown in Fig. 10–22*a* and the form of the physical structure is as shown in Fig. 10–22*b*. Also the reactance function can be expressed immediately as—equations 10–51 and 10–52—

$$Z(\omega) = -j\omega H \frac{\omega^2 - \omega_1^2}{\omega^2(\omega^2 - \omega_2^2)} = -j\omega H \frac{\omega^2 - 36 \times 10^4}{\omega^2(\omega^2 - 10^6)}$$

or as

$$Z(\omega) = j\omega H \left[\frac{A_0}{\omega^2} + \frac{A_2}{\omega^2 - \omega_2^2}\right] = j\omega H \left[\frac{A_0}{\omega^2} + \frac{A_2}{\omega^2 - 10^6}\right]$$

The coefficients A_0 and A_2 may be determined from

$$A_0 = \lim_{\omega \to 0} \frac{-(\omega^2 - 36 \times 10^4)}{\omega^2 - 10^6} = -0.36$$

$$A_2 = \lim_{\omega \to 1000} \frac{-(\omega^2 - 36 \times 10^4)}{\omega^2} = -0.64$$

The coefficient H may now be determined from $Z(700) = j10$ or

$$j10 = j700H\left[\frac{-0.36}{49 \times 10^4} + \frac{-0.64}{49 \times 10^4 - 10^6}\right]$$

and

$$H = 2.75 \times 10^4$$

The reactance function is, therefore,

$$Z(\omega) = j2.75 \times 10^4\omega\left[\frac{-0.36}{\omega^2} + \frac{-0.64}{\omega^2 - 10^6}\right]$$

The values of the parameters of the network of Fig. 10–22*b* may now be obtained immediately from equations 10–48, 10–49, and 10–50 as

$$C_0 = \frac{-10^6}{HA_0} = \frac{-10^6}{2.76 \times 10^4(-0.36)} = 101 \ \mu\text{f}$$

$$C_2 = \frac{-10^6}{HA_2} = \frac{-10^6}{2.75 \times 10^4(-0.64)} = 56.8 \ \mu\text{f}$$

$$L_2 = \frac{10^6}{C_2\omega_2^2} = \frac{10^6}{56.8 \times 10^6} = 0.0176 \text{ henry}$$

which completely specifies the reactance network.

Three other physical forms of reactance networks which have the same frequency response as any particular Foster network established as in the foregoing are possible. The books mentioned at the beginning of this article indicate what these network equivalents are and give instructions how to obtain them.

10.12 Flux Linkage Theorem.

The term *flux linkage* has been derived directly from Faraday's law, expressed as

$$v(t)_i = \frac{d}{dt}[n\phi(t)]$$

The term in brackets is known as the flux linkage from the fact that $n\phi(t)$ represents the product of n turns which are linked by the flux $\phi(t)$.

In terms of current the self-induction voltage must be expressed as

$$v(t)_i = \frac{d}{dt}[L(i)i(t)] \tag{10–57}$$

which for linear circuits, where $L(i)$ is a constant L, becomes

$$v(t)_i = L\frac{di(t)}{dt} \tag{10–58}$$

Accordingly, the product $L(i)i(t)$ is also known as flux linkages since it bears exactly the same relation to the induction voltage as $n\phi(t)$.

The voltages of mutual induction are also given by

$$v(t)_M = \frac{d}{dt}[M(i)i(t)] \tag{10–59}$$

and the flux linkages are then $M(i)i(t)$.

In spite of the urgent need for a solution to the problem of the transient behavior of power generators so that they could be adequately protected from short circuits, and in order to maintain continuity of service of the power system, many years and much labor went into the transient problem before a solution was reached. In fact, until the notion of flux linkage was used and until the property of flux linkages, which is now known as the constant flux linkage theorem, was established, the transient behavior of power-generating machinery could be established only by the wasteful process of direct experimentation. It is now possible with the aid of the flux linkage theorem to predict mathematically with very satisfactory accuracy the transient behavior of the power generators for the first few cycles after any type of short circuit, and circuit breakers can be expected to remove the short circuit by that time.

No attempt will be made here to give details of just how the flux linkage theorem helps in solving alternator transient problems. It will be recalled, however, that in the presence of very low resistances the transient dies out slowly. Synchronous machines, in addition to having low resistance in comparison with their inductive effects, also have relatively negligible capacitive effects. As a consequence, during the short time between the occurrence of a fault and the opening of the circuit breakers which clear the fault, an alternator can be considered as a purely inductive circuit. Even with all these simplifications, the non-linearity of the magnetic circuits of these generating machines presents a problem which is not solved without effort. Suffice it to say here that these hurdles have been cleared and that the flux linkage theorem is the key device used in clearing them.

The flux linkage theorem will now be presented and proved to round out the set of network theorems which have been found useful in the study and application of electrical networks.

Continuity of Flux Linkage Theorem.

The sum of the flux linkages in any closed path of a purely inductive network is continuous from the instant of making any change in the physical structure of the network or through an abrupt change in one or more source voltages.

The proof of this statement follows almost at once from the voltage equation for any closed path of the network. Such a voltage equation, in general terms, can be written as

$$\sum e(t) = \sum \frac{d}{dt}[L(i)i(t)] + \sum \frac{d}{dt}[M(i)i(t)] \tag{10–60}$$

If this equation is integrated, the result is

$$\int \sum e(t)\, dt + K = \sum L(i)i(t) + \sum M(i)i(t) \tag{10–61}$$

Since an integral, if it exists, is continuous, the left-hand side of this equation is continuous from the instant of any physical change in the network. The continuity of flux linkage theorem is proved. It may be well to note that equation 10–61 is still essentially the same if $e(t)$ is replaced by a sum of source voltages, resistor voltages, and capacitor voltages. The theorem of flux linkage continuity is thus *valid for any network.*

One caution should be noted in connection with interpreting equation 10–61. It is sometimes erroneously assumed that this equation implies continuity of flux linkages even through a physical change in the circuit. But equation 10–61 *does not apply unchanged both before and after a change in the inductance of a circuit* so that a particular equation cannot possibly represent the network behavior both before and after the change.

Note also that if no change is made in the physical structure of the network, the right-hand side of equation 10–61 will not change in form. Furthermore, even though the voltage sum under the integral on the left of this equation is changed abruptly, the integral is still continuous and so the flux linkage sum is continuous even though the source voltage may be changed discontinuously. This fact suggests another flux linkage theorem or corollary to the one already stated, namely:

Constant Flux Linkage Theorem.

The sum of the flux linkages in a purely inductive network around any closed path of the network is constant from the instant of short-circuiting all source voltages of the network.

This theorem follows immediately from equation 10–61 and the accompanying discussion if the $e(t)$ sum is set equal to zero.

Example 10:13 Determine the mesh currents in the inductive network of Fig. 10–23 from the instant of closing the switch.

Solution This problem fits the continuity flux linkage theorem since the source voltage is to be changed abruptly from zero to $e(t)$.

In terms of flux linkages the equations for Fig. 10–23 are (switch closed)

$$\int e(t)\,dt + K_1 = (L_1 + L_2)i_1(t) - L_2 i_2(t)$$
$$K_2 = -L_2 i_1(t) + (L_2 + L_3)i_2(t) \tag{10–62}$$

The constants of integration appearing in these equations must be evaluated in terms of known conditions on the flux linkages. Energy conditions indi-

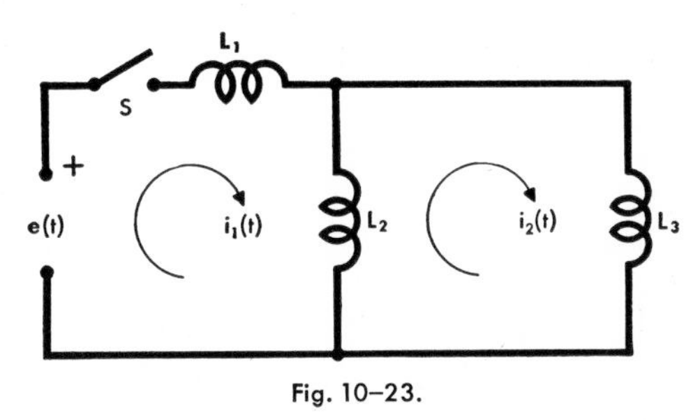

Fig. 10–23.

cate that the flux linkages will not change abruptly on closing the switch, so that at $t = 0$ the flux linkage sum of both meshes is zero and

$$K_1 = -\int e(t)\,dt\Big|_{t=0}$$
$$K_2 = 0$$

Substituting these results into equations 10–62 and solving for the currents give

$$i_1(t) = \frac{L_2 + L_3}{L_1L_2 + L_2L_3 + L_1L_3}\left[\int e(t)\,dt - \int e(t)\,dt\Big|_{t=0}\right]$$
$$i_2(t) = \frac{L_2}{L_1L_2 + L_2L_3 + L_1L_3}\left[\int e(t)\,dt - \int e(t)\,dt\Big|_{t=0}\right]$$

These currents represent the approximate behavior of the network of Fig. 10–23 —steady state and transient—for a short time following the closing of the switch.

The foregoing method of solving for the currents cannot be applied if the switch is opened rather than closed. In the first place, both equations 10–62 do not apply—only the second one. In the second place, the $t = 0$ value of the flux linkages of the mesh of $i_2(t)$ is not known because during the short time of opening the switch a circuit readjustment takes place with the current in L_1 decreasing to zero.

Example 10:14 Suppose that both s_1 and s_2 of Fig. 10–24 are closed with $e_1(t) = |E_m| \sin(\omega t + \phi)$ and $e_2(t) = 0$. When the circuit is operating under steady state the source voltage $e_1(t)$ is short-circuited. Determine the currents in the network from the instant of applying the short circuit.

Solution The equations for the circuit must be written after application of the short circuit. Consequently,

$$\begin{aligned} K_1 &= L_1 i_1(t) + M i_2(t) \\ K_2 &= M i_1(t) + L_2 i_2(t) \end{aligned} \tag{10–63}$$

The constants must be evaluated from the $t = 0$ values of the flux linkages which may be obtained from the equations of the circuit written before $e_1(t)$ is short-circuited and then evaluated at $t = 0$; i.e., from

$$\int e(t)\,dt\Big|_{t=0} = \frac{-|E_m|\cos\phi}{\omega} = L i_1(0) + M i_2(0)$$

$$0 = M i_1(0) + L_2 i_2(0)$$

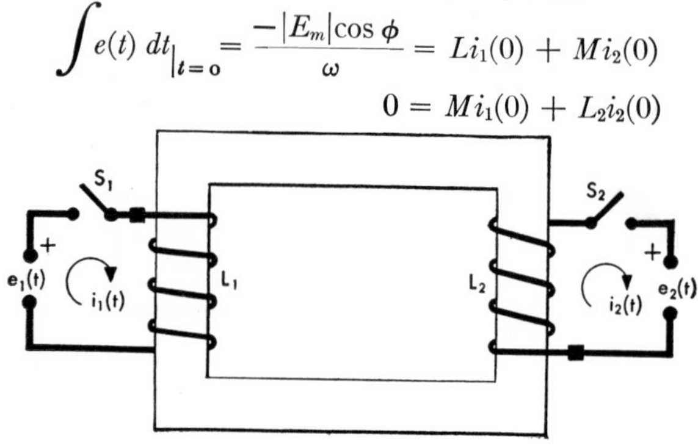

Fig. 10–24.

The constants of equation 10–63 are thus $K_1 = \dfrac{-|E_m|\cos\phi}{\omega}$

$$K_2 = 0$$

and equations 10–63 become

$$\begin{aligned} |E_m|\sin\phi &= L_1 i_1(t) + M i_2(t) \\ 0 &= M i_1(t) + L_2 i_2(t) \end{aligned}$$

The solution of these linear equations determines the approximate behavior, for a short time after shorting the generator, of a transformer in which the reactances are high compared to the resistances.

PROBLEMS

10–1 Using the superposition theorem, compute the currents in each branch of the network of Fig. 10–13*a*. Compute these currents for each voltage separately and add the results. Check by computing the currents for all voltages acting simultaneously. A pure reactance network is used to simplify the arithmetic. In many circuits it is permissible to neglect the resistance for first calculations. Assume $\omega = 1000$.

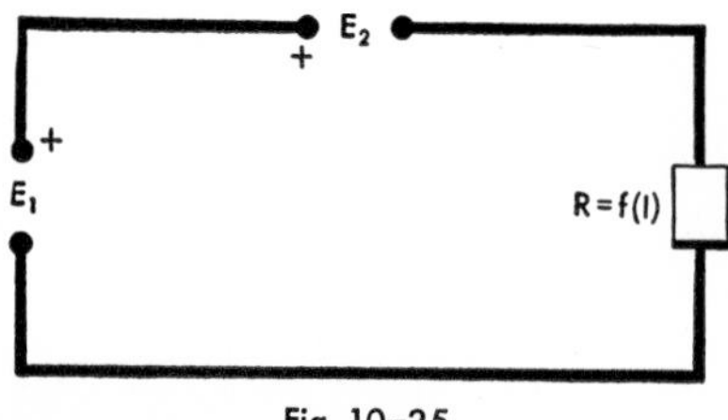

Fig. 10–25.

10–2 As an example of a circuit for which the superposition theorem does not apply, consider Fig. 10–25. The resistance is a function of the current. Suppose that $R = f(I) = 2I$, $E_1 = 10$ volts, and $E_2 = 30$ volts. Apply the superposition theorem and check its failure to be valid by computing the current which actually flows.

10–3 Repeat Problem 10–2 if $R = f(I) = 2I^2$.

10–4 Use the node equations and the superposition theorem to determine the voltages which will appear across the galvanometer of the Wheatstone bridge arrangement of Fig. 10–26 due to a voltage ΔE appearing in branch 3 as a result of an external magnetic field.

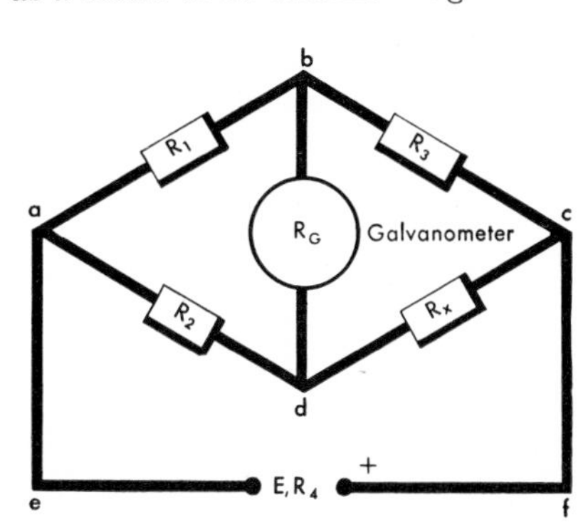

Fig. 10–26.

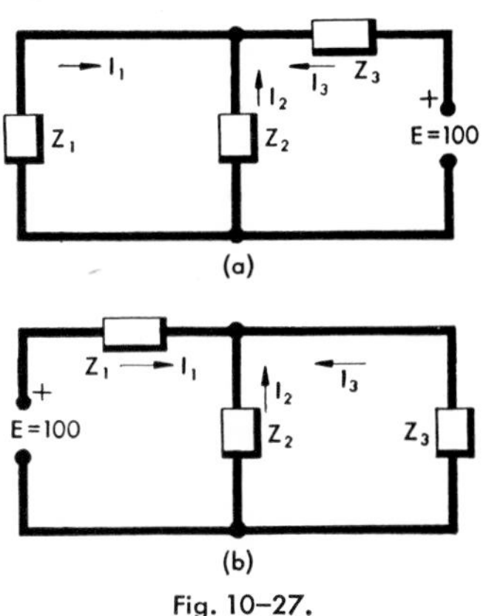

Fig. 10–27.

10–5 The circuits of Fig. 10–27 have non-linear resistances $Z_1 = 2I_1$, $Z_2 = 3I_2$, and $Z_3 = I_3$. The generated voltages are located according to the reciprocity theorem statement, and if the theorem applies, I_1 of Fig. 10–27*a* should be equal to I_3 of Fig. 10–27*b*. Show that these currents are not equal and, therefore, that the theorem does not apply to non-linear networks.

10–6 Sketch the mesh current arrangements for the circuit of Fig. 10–2, required for the application of the reciprocity theorem successively to all branches of the network. Assume E as shown.

10–7 Demonstrate the validity of the reciprocity theorem for branches *ac* and *bd* of Fig. 10–13*a*. The voltages E_2 and E_3 are to be taken as zero.

10–8 Use the compensation theorem to determine the voltage which appears across the galvanometer of Fig. 10–26 if the branch *cd* is opened. $R_1 = 10$ ohms, $R_2 = 9$ ohms, $R_3 = 20$ ohms, $R_4 = 2$ ohms, $R_G = 100$ ohms, and $E = 2$ volts.

10–9 A resistance of 4 ohms is added in series to the branch *bc* of Fig. 10–1. Use the alteration theorem to determine the effect on the currents of this circuit of the resistance change. Verify the results obtained by solving directly for the currents of the changed network. Refer to Example 10–1 for the currents of the unchanged network.

10–10 Use the alteration theorem to calculate the effect of opening branch *bc* of Fig. 10–1. Verify the result by calculating the network behavior directly with branch *bc* open.

10–11 Use the alteration theorem to determine the behavior of the network of Fig. 10–10*a* if branch *ab* is opened.

10–12 Consider Fig. 10–13*a* as a four-terminal network between point-pairs *ec* and *fd*. Assume $E_3 = 0$. Determine the equivalent T network at $\omega = 1000$.

10–13 Find the equivalent T network for the circuit of Fig. 9–15 between the generator terminals. The impedances of the network are $Z_3 = 2$, $Z_4 = 5$, $Z_5 = 3$, $Z_6 = 10$, $Z_7 = 5$, $Z_8 = 2$, and $Z_9 = 8$ ohms.

10–14 Use the delta-to-wye transformation to establish the equivalent impedance at the battery terminals of the Wheatstone bridge circuit of Fig. 10–26. Consider $Z_{ab} = 2 + j6$, $Z_{bc} = 3 - j8$, $Z_{dc} = 3 + j3$, $Z_{ad} = 7 + j2$, and $Z_{bd} = 10 + j0$ ohms. Find the current I_{ef}.

10–15 (*a*) Compute the impedance looking into the circuit from the generator of Fig. 10–28, i.e., compute the equivalent impedance of the load connected to the generator. Use the delta-to-wye or wye-to-delta transformation, whichever is more convenient. If the internal impedance of the generator is $1 + j3$ ohms and $E = 200$ volts, determine the generator current. (*b*) Use equation 10–31 to determine the input impedance. Compare the two methods.

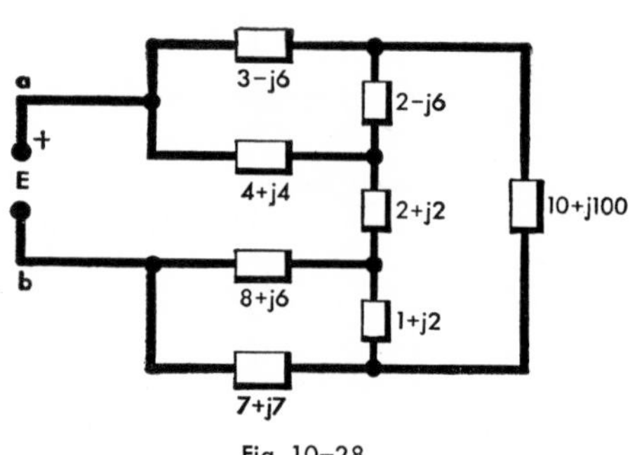

Fig. 10–28.

10–16 Use Thévenin's theorem to compute the current and voltage of branch *cb* of Fig. 10–13*a*. $\omega = 10^3$.

10–17 Use Thévenin's theorem to compute the current and voltage of branch *ab* of Fig. 10–13*a*. $\omega = 10^3$.

10–18 Use Thévenin's theorem to compute the current and voltage of an impedance $Z = 10 + j10$ paralleled across branch *ab* of Fig. 10–13*a* ($\omega = 2000$).

10–19 Use Thévenin's theorem to determine the current in branch *ba* of Fig. 10–1.

10–20 Use Norton's theorem to work Problem 10–16.

10–21 Use Norton's theorem to solve Problem 10–17.

10–22 Solve Problem 10–18 by the use of Norton's theorem.

10–23 Determine the maximum power which may be delivered into a receiver impedance, Z_R, from the generator and telephone transmission line shown in Fig. 10–29. The resistive inductors and capacitor arrangement shown represent rather accurately a transmission line at any one frequency. Thévenin's theorem is useful for solving this problem.

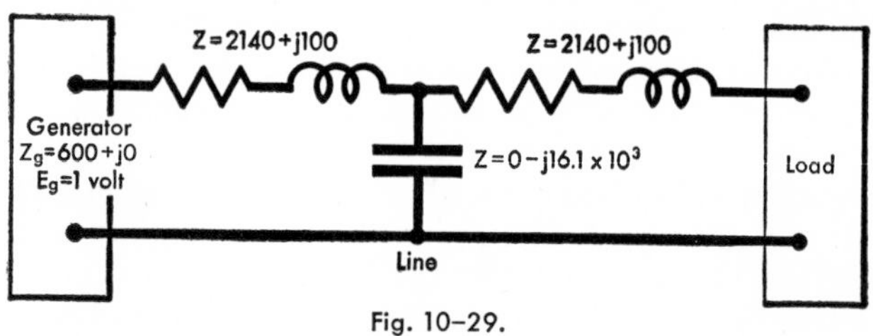

Fig. 10–29.

10–24 Determine the maximum power which the generator and network of Fig. 10–1 could deliver into an impedance Z_R which replaces E_2. Determine the value of Z_R.

10–25 Suppose an oscillator has an internal impedance of $400 + j100$ ohms with a generated voltage of 3 volts at $\omega = 1000$.

(*a*) What is the impedance into which this oscillator will deliver maximum power? What is this maximum power?

(*b*) A coil, the inductance of which can be varied from 0.0001 henry to 0.01 henry, and a variable resistor are connected in series across the oscillator. What value of L and of R give maximum power delivery? What is this maximum power?

(*c*) A capacitor and variable resistor in series are connected across the oscillator. The reactance of the capacitor is $X_C = -50$ ohms. What value of resistance will establish maximum power delivery? What is this maximum power?

(*d*) A coil of resistance equal to 300 ohms and variable inductance—0.0001 to 0.01 henry—is connected across the oscillator. What value of L causes maximum power absorption by the resistor? What is this maximum power?

10–26 Suppose that a generator of internal impedance $2 + j4$ ohms is paralleled with an impedance $10 + j0$. This combination is network A. Network B consists of an impedance $4 - j4$ paralleled with a variable resistor R. What value of resistance should R have for maximum power delivery to network B? What is the maximum power if the generator voltage is 100 volts? *Hint.* From one node equation find $V_B(G)$, i.e., the voltage value, across network B, as a function of G ($G = 1/R$). Then find $I_B(G)$, the total current value for network B. Then find $P_B(G) = V_B(G) \cdot I_B(G)$, i.e., use the scalar product of Art. 2.8 to determine the average power $P_B(G)$. Then, finally, find the value of G which maximizes $P_B(G)$.
What is the maximum power if the generator voltage is 100 volts?

10–27 Determine the Foster network for a circuit similar to that of Fig. 10–18*a*, for which L_3 is placed in series with C_1 and C_2 in series with L_1.

10–28 Determine the Foster network for a circuit consisting of $L_0 =$ 1 henry, in parallel with $L_3 = 0.1$ henry and $C_3 = 10$ μf in series, and these two branches in parallel with $L_5 = 0.2$ henry in series with $C_5 = 5$ μf.

10–29 Determine the Foster network for a circuit similar to Fig. 10–18*a* if in the branch of L_1 a capacitor of 20 μf is added in series and in the branch of C_1 a coil of $L = 1$ henry is added in series.

10–30 Determine the Foster reactance network which has a pole at $\omega = 0$, $\omega = 10{,}000$, and ω infinite; zeros at $\omega = 400$ and $\omega = 20{,}000$, and $Z(\omega) = j10$ at $\omega = 700$.

10–31 Determine the Foster reactance network and function for poles at $\omega = 500{,}000$ and ω infinite, zeros at $\omega = 0$ and $\omega = 10^6$. Also $Z(800{,}000) = -j1000$.

10–32 Determine the Foster reactance network and impedance function for poles at $\omega = 0$, $\omega = 15{,}000$, and $\omega = 100{,}000$; and zeros at $\omega = 10{,}000$, $\omega = 30{,}000$, and ω infinite. The impedance function is $Z(12{,}000) = j20$.

10–33 Determine the eight forms of $Y(\omega)$ for Foster's reactance theorem. Sketch the $Y(\omega)$ vs. ω curves, and the physical structure of the networks corresponding.

10–34 Use the constant flux linkage theorem to determine the approximate short circuit currents for a very short time after closing s_1 of Fig. 10–24, if s_2 is already closed and $e(t)_1 = E_1$, $e(t)_2 = 0$.

10–35 Consider a series circuit of two pure inductors in series, $L_1 =$ 0.01 henry, $L_2 = 0.02$ henry, and $M_{12} = 0.01$ henry. A voltage $e(t) = 100 \sin 1000t$ is connected across this series arrangement. If coil 2 is shorted at $t = 0$, determine the currents.

CHAPTER 11

Three-Phase Wye- and Delta-Connected Power Distribution Systems

The general scheme for writing and solving the steady state equations of an electric circuit, the basic elements of the transient behavior of a circuit, and a few fundamental network theorems have now been studied. Theoretically, consideration of electric circuits might be stopped at this point and attention turned to other fields, but all has not been said in any investigation when the general mathematical relations are written.

Fig. 11–1. Control panel of a power plant showing measuring devices. (Courtesy, Leeds & Northrup Co.)

Frequently, consideration of special circuits and special cases of these circuits leads to many very fruitful results. Special series and parallel circuits have already been considered, and, now, and throughout the remainder of the book, various other special forms of circuits are discussed.

In this chapter the so-called three-phase, or polyphase, systems are considered. Such polyphase systems, in three-phase form, are used almost exclusively in distributing the vast quantities of energy taken from the

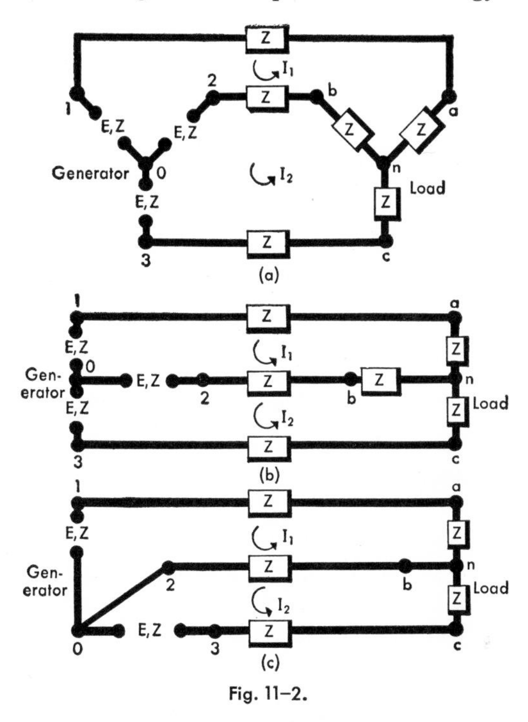

Fig. 11–2.

power-generating stations of the world. Except for the break caused by the Rocky Mountains, the United States, for example, is fairly well covered with an interconnected power network of three-phase lines connecting loads and generators. Several illustrations of generators and transmission lines are to be found in this book at various places. This vast network of power units operates almost entirely on 60 cps. The illustration of Fig. 11–1, for example, shows a portion of the control and measuring panel in a power plant and indicates that 60 cps is the operating frequency.

The first energy transfer by means of alternating current was effected over a two-wire, single-phase system, i.e., a single generator was connected to a load by means of two wires. The next form of transmission line used was the a-c form of the Edison three-wire system as shown in Fig. 11–2*c*. This system consists of generators connected between points 1 and 0 and between points 0 and 3. These generators are so arranged that their voltages have the relation $E_{01} = E_{30}$, i.e., the generator voltages are kept in phase in the order given by the subscripts. This system may be viewed as a special case of the three-phase system to be considered in detail in this chapter.

In chronological order the next circuit used for power distribution was called a two-phase system. The circuit used was the same as for the single-phase three-wire system, but the generator voltages of the two-phase system were related by $E_{01} = jE_{03}$ (see Fig. 11–2c). Because of certain unsymmetrical properties of this system both in the generator and on the transmission line, it was discarded in favor of the more symmetrical three-phase system. Two-phase systems, except for occasional old installations, have ceased to exist.

The three-phase generator is essentially a set of three generators, or, in actual practice, three windings in a single generator, which, for so-called balanced conditions, have their voltages 120 degrees out of phase, i.e., the voltages are related by $E_{30} = aE_{20} = a^2E_{10}$ or $E_{30} = a^2E_{20} = aE_{10}$, where $a = \epsilon^{j120}$ (Fig. 11–2a and b).

11.1 General Circuit Relations—Three-Phase Wye or Star.

A three-phase wye- or star-connected generator and load are shown in the conventional manner in Fig. 11–2a. An actual wye connection is shown on the transformers of Fig. 11–3. The reason for the wye connection designation is evident from the diagram of Fig. 11–2a. Of course, there is no real necessity for drawing the circuit as in this figure; Fig. 11–2b represents the same circuit. However, if a wye circuit is drawn as in Fig. 11–2a, the type of circuit is evident at a glance, i.e., *by convention* Fig. 11–2a is understood to represent a three-phase wye connection in which the generator voltages are approximately or exactly 120 degrees apart, whereas Fig. 11–2b has not been conventionalized to have any particular meaning unless $E_{20} = 0$, in which case the figure represents a three-wire single-phase circuit.

The wye-to-wye circuit of Fig. 11–2a is a two-node or two-mesh network. The mesh equations are

$$\begin{aligned} E_{01}+E_{20} &= (Z_{10}+Z_{20}+Z_{2b}+Z_{bn}+Z_{na}+Z_{a1})I_1-(Z_{20}+Z_{2b}+Z_{bn})I_2 \qquad (11\text{–}1) \\ E_{02}+E_{30} &= -(Z_{20}+Z_{2b}+Z_{bn})I_1+(Z_{20}+Z_{30}+Z_{3c}+Z_{cn}+Z_{nb}+Z_{b2})I_2 \end{aligned}$$

and may be shortened to

$$\begin{aligned} E_{01} + E_{20} &= Z_{11}I_1 - Z_{12}I_2 \\ E_{02} + E_{30} &= -Z_{12}I_1 + Z_{22}I_2 \qquad (11\text{–}2) \end{aligned}$$

for convenience of reference. The meaning of the symbols in these last two equations should be evident from a comparison with the preceding two sets of equations.

Fig. 11–3. A bank of power transformers showing a three-phase wye connection. (Courtesy, Allis-Chalmers Mfg. Co.)

The node equation for this two-node circuit is (written away from the node, with n as reference)

$$E_{10}\frac{1}{Z_{10}+Z_{1a}+Z_{an}}+E_{20}\frac{1}{Z_{20}+Z_{2b}+Z_{bn}}+E_{30}\frac{1}{Z_{30}+Z_{3c}+Z_{cn}} + \left[\frac{1}{Z_{10}+Z_{1a}+Z_{an}}+\frac{1}{Z_{20}+Z_{2b}+Z_{bn}} + \frac{1}{Z_{30}+Z_{3c}+Z_{cn}}\right]V_{0n}=0 \tag{11–3}$$

The electrical properties of any three-phase wye-to-wye connection can be deduced from equations 11–2 or 11–3. The actual solution of these sets of equations is a relatively simple matter and should lead to no difficulty. Obviously, the electrical properties of any particular three-phase wye will depend on the particular voltages connected and the impedances of the network. However, a few important properties possessed by *all* three-phase wye circuits can be deduced.

As a preliminary to the deduction of such properties of three-phase wye units, two voltage conventions will be stated. The voltages between the points 1–2, 2–3, 3–1, and a–b, b–c, c–a of Fig. 11–2a are known as the line or line-to-line voltages corresponding to the fact that these voltages appear between the three wires, or lines, connecting the three-phase generator and the three-phase load. The voltages between the points

1–0, 2–0, 3–0, and a–n, b–n, c–n are known as line-to-neutral or phase voltages.

The line and line-to-neutral voltages are related by the equations

$$\begin{aligned} V_{ab} &= V_{an} + V_{nb} \\ V_{bc} &= V_{bn} + V_{nc} \\ V_{ca} &= V_{cn} + V_{na} \end{aligned} \tag{11–4}$$

If these equations are added, the right-hand side adds to zero so that

$$V_{ab} + V_{bc} + V_{ca} = 0 \tag{11–5}$$

for any wye-connected system. Therefore, the individual phase or line-to-neutral voltages may have any values whatsoever and the sum of the line voltages will still be zero. Another simple way to demonstrate this fact is to write Kirchhoff's voltage equations through the points abc or 123. The sum of the voltages so obtained is zero. In fact, this demonstration will show that the sum of the voltages taken in consecutive order between any set of wires is zero, provided these voltages are considered in the direction required to form a closed path.

The sum of the line currents of *any ungrounded wye generator or load* is also zero since at either the 0 or n junction of Fig. 11–2a, Kirchhoff's current law gives

$$I_{na} + I_{nb} + I_{nc} = 0 \tag{11–6}$$

Also the corresponding *line currents and generator or load phase currents of any wye connection are identical.*

11.2 General Circuit Relations—Three-Phase Delta or Mesh.

In addition to the wye connection, a second and very generally used connection is the delta, or mesh, connection shown schematically in

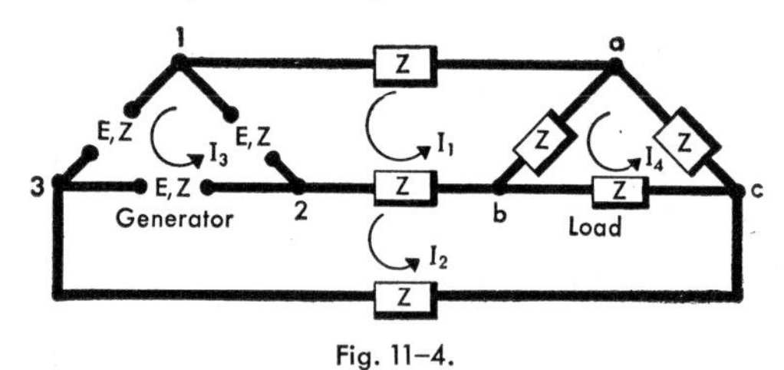

Fig. 11–4.

Fig. 11–4, and for a particular installation in Fig. 11–5. This circuit has four meshes and will, therefore, require a minimum of four mesh equations for its solution. One set of such equations is

$$\begin{aligned} E_{21} &= (Z_{12} + Z_{2b} + Z_{ba} + Z_{a1})I_1 - Z_{2b}I_2 - Z_{12}I_3 - Z_{ab}I_4 \\ E_{32} &= -Z_{2b}I_1 + (Z_{23} + Z_{3c} + Z_{cb} + Z_{b2})I_2 - Z_{23}I_3 - Z_{bc}I_4 \\ E_{31} + E_{23} + E_{12} &= -Z_{12}I_1 - Z_{23}I_2 + (Z_{13} + Z_{32} + Z_{21})I_3 \\ 0 &= -Z_{ab}I_1 - Z_{bc}I_2 + (Z_{ab} + Z_{bc} + Z_{ca})I_4 \end{aligned} \tag{11–7}$$

Fig. 11–5. Delta connection on low-voltage side. (Courtesy, Utah Power & Light Co.)

The solution of this system of equations will determine the complete behavior of any delta generator connected to a delta load. There would be no point in writing or using the node equations for this circuit since five of them would be required.

As for the wye connection, a few general properties can be established which are valid for all delta connections. In particular, *the properly ordered sum of the line voltages is zero for a delta connection.* This fact is immediately evident at the load, or at any three points along the connecting lines, by writing the voltage equation about a closed mesh connecting such points. *The generator terminal voltage sum is also zero no matter what the generated voltages* since around a closed path between the lines as near the generator terminals as desired, the voltage sum is zero, i.e.,

$$V_{12} + V_{23} + V_{31} = 0 \tag{11-8}$$

The sum of the line currents into a delta generator or load is also zero. Thus, from Kirchhoff's current law, the line currents in terms of load currents are

$$\begin{aligned} I_{a1} &= I_{ba} + I_{ca} \\ I_{b2} &= I_{ab} + I_{cb} \\ I_{c3} &= I_{bc} + I_{ac} \end{aligned} \tag{11-9}$$

If these equations are added, it is evident that

$$I_{a1} + I_{b2} + I_{c3} = 0 \tag{11–10}$$

for all possible values of the load currents.

The sum of the load or phase currents of a delta may or may not be zero, depending on the nature of the impedances and generated voltages.

A fact so obvious as hardly to need mentioning is that at the generator or load terminals the line voltages and phase voltages of a delta connection are equal. A glance at the circuit of Fig. 11–4 will show this relation.

11.3 Wye and Delta Combinations.

Three-phase systems in which some of the generators, loads, transformers, etc., are connected delta and some wye may be and are used. The diagrams of Fig. 11–6 represent two arrangements—delta-connected load and wye-connected generator, and vice versa.

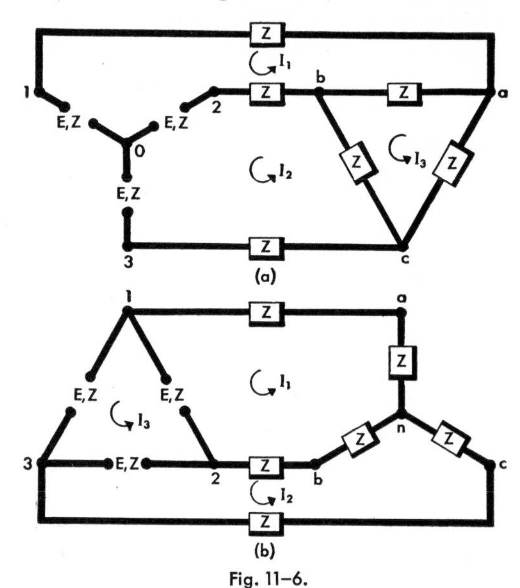

Fig. 11–6.

Of course, the general conclusions reached in the preceding articles also apply to these mixed circuits—the sum of the line currents and line voltages is zero, phase and line voltages are equal at the delta end, phase and line currents are equal at the wye end, and the sum of the phase voltages of the wye or phase currents of the delta may or may not be equal to zero.

11.4 Four-Wire Wye Connection.

The three-phase circuit shown in Fig. 11–7 is also used some in three-phase applications—increasingly in recent years because of the added voltages thereby made available. This circuit arrangement is designated as four-wire three-phase for obvious reasons. A set of three voltage equations or *one* node equation is required for a solution. Note that the node

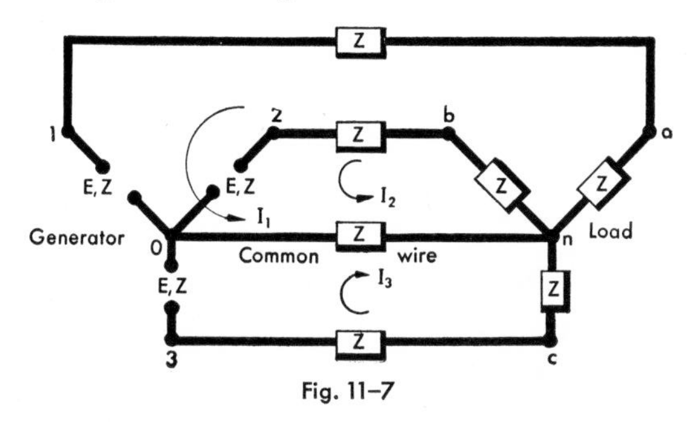

Fig. 11–7

equation 11–3 needs only to be modified by adding $1/Z_{0n}$ in the brackets to make it apply to the four-wire wye system.

The sum of the line voltages is always zero, and the sum of the line currents is the current through the common wire.

11.5 Balanced Three-Phase Voltages.

Three-phase systems can usually be treated with a very high degree of accuracy by assuming a certain amount of symmetry, or equality, among the various elements comprising the system. For example, three-phase generators—usually connected wye and often with common point grounded—are built symmetrically so that the generated voltages are equal in magnitude and 120 degrees apart in time phase. Three-phase lines are frequently built so that the impedance per phase is the same for all phases. Also most three-phase loads are constructed so that the three impedances in the three phases are identical. Therefore, a special case of the general wye-connected three-phase unit, which is a good approximation to many of the installations used in practice, is a balanced and constant voltage system, where a balanced voltage system is such that the three phase-generated voltages are equal in magnitude and displaced from each other by 120 degrees or 240 degrees in time phase (see Fig. 11–8*b* and *d*).

Before discussing these relations further, a few general observations regarding vector diagrams will be made. In the first place, according to their complex number representation, all vectors are represented as originating at a common point. But by common consent, a vector which is moved parallel to its original position to any new origin is considered as the *same* vector. The force polygons with which the reader is no doubt familiar are examples of such parallel displacements of vectors. In the vector diagrams of earlier parts of this book, certain voltage vectors were moved parallel to their original positions to form closed voltage polygons in order to make the pictorial representation of the circuit behavior more descriptive. This same technique will be used in the vector diagrams of polyphase systems, to an even greater extent, to enhance the pictorial effectiveness of the diagrams. The vector diagrams of Art. 11–11 serve as illustrations. Note that these diagrams show at a glance the extent to which the triangles differ from equilateral and, therefore, from the ideal—a balanced set of voltages. Also removing some of the vectors

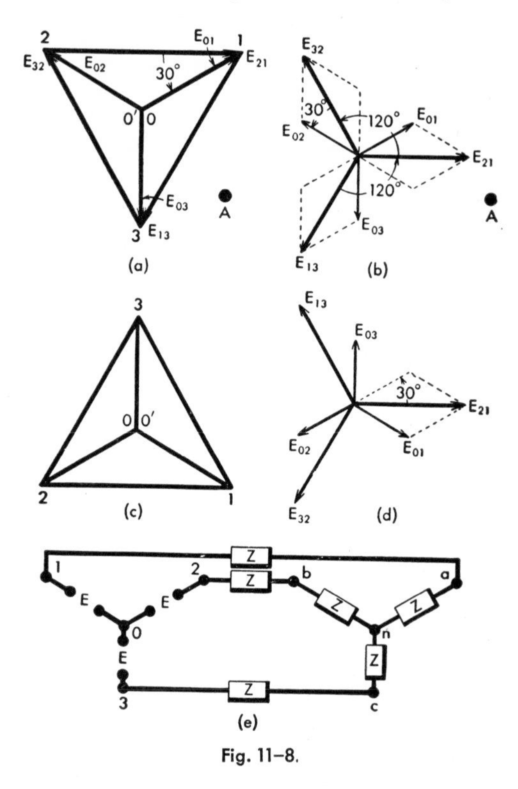

Fig. 11–8.

from about the origin helps in the interpretation of the remaining voltage vectors. This particular idea will be carried still further by removing the current vectors to the line-voltage-triangle vertices, as shown in Figs. 11–16, 11–17, and 11–18.

Returning now to the balanced wye connection of Fig. 11–8*e*, the line voltages are formed by adding the phase voltages in accordance with Kirchhoff's voltage law, as shown in Fig. 11–8*b*. The results are voltage vectors equal in magnitude, larger than the phase voltages, and successively 120 degrees apart. It is important to notice that these systems of line and phase voltages may be oriented in two fundamentally different ways as shown in Figs. 11–8*b* and *d*, or Figs. 11–8*a* and *c*. Consider Figs. 11–8*b* and *d* first. These diagrams may be changed one into the other by rotating the system out of the paper about any axis in the paper. But such a rotation is not simply a change in the arbitrary reference axis, since a change in reference axis means rotation *in the plane of the paper*. Reflecting back into the circuit, what does the change from the vector diagram of Fig. 11–8*b* to that of Fig. 11–8*d* mean? Consider Fig. 11–9*a*. Three coils are located so that as the magnet is rotated clockwise at uniform velocity, voltages of induction appear in the coils in the order shown

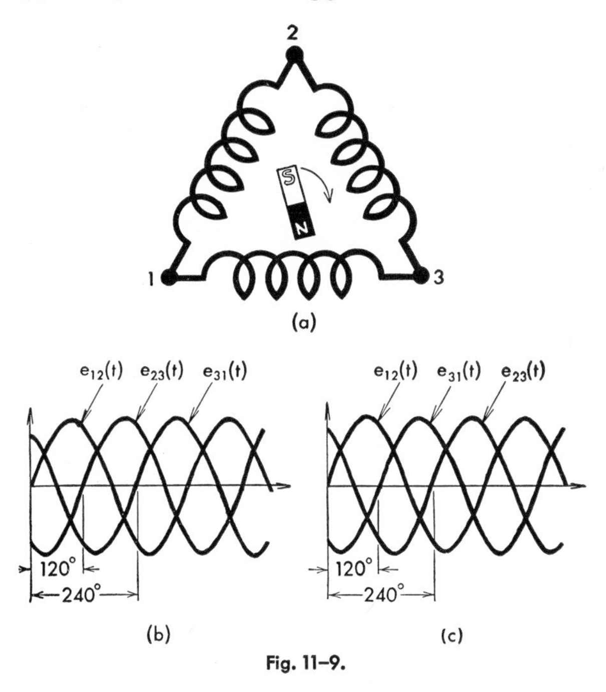

Fig. 11–9.

in Fig. 11–9*b*. But suppose the magnet is rotated in the opposite, or counterclockwise, direction; the voltages then appear in the order shown in Fig. 11–9*c*. Furthermore, if the coils are spread out properly and the magnet (actually an electromagnet) is properly shaped, all of which is done in practice, the voltages appearing in the coils will be practically sinusoids. Representing the voltages by vectors, then, note that the system given in Fig. 11–8*d* corresponds to clockwise rotation in Fig. 11–9*a*, and Fig. 11–8*b* corresponds to counterclockwise rotation of the magnet of Fig. 11–9*a*. Since there are only two ways to revolve a machine rotor, only two *phase sequences*, as the order of occurrence of the maxima of the waves is called, are possible. The two possible phase sequences are designated as the *a–b–c* or 1–2–3 or as the *a–c–b* or 1–3–2 sequence. The voltage systems represented by Figs. 11–8*a* and *b* and 11–9*c* have a phase sequence of *a–c–b* or 1–3–2 which is designated as *negative;* and the voltage systems represented by Figs. 11–8*c* and *d* and

Fig. 11–9*b* have a phase sequence of *a–b–c* or 1–2–3 which is defined as the *positive* sequence.

One way to determine the phase sequence of a set of voltages (or currents) from the vector diagram is to imagine standing at A as in Figs. 11–8*a* and *b* and noting the order in which the vectors or triangle vertices go by as the vector system is imagined rotated counterclockwise. Thus, by this rule, Fig. 11–8*a* gives a phase sequence of 1–3–2, and Fig. 11–8*b* gives voltage maxima occurring in the order 21, 13, 32, or the first, third, and second voltages as they are usually ordered; hence the sequence is also 1–3–2.

When the voltages are balanced, as represented in Fig. 11–8, a *simple numerical* relation exists between the phase and line voltage magnitudes. As shown in this figure, each line voltage is a difference of two phase voltages. For example,

$$E_{21} = E_{20} + E_{01} = -E_{02} + E_{01} \tag{11–11}$$

From the vector diagram it is evident that E_{01} and $-E_{02}$ are 60 degrees apart, and because $|E_{01}| = |E_{02}|$ the difference E_{21} will be halfway between them. Therefore, E_{21} is, in magnitude,

$$|E_{21}| = 2|E_{01}| \cos 30° = \sqrt{3}\,|E_{01}| \tag{11–12}$$

Symbolizing the magnitudes of the line voltages by $|E_l|$ and of the phase voltages by $|E_p|$

$$|E_l| = \sqrt{3}\,|E_p| \tag{11–13}$$

for all line and phase voltages of a *balanced* wye generator or load.

A corresponding voltage relation for a delta connection does not exist since obviously the phase-generated voltages and line-generated voltages of a delta are the same.

11.6 Balanced Three-Phase Voltages and Unbalanced Impedances.

Electrical power systems are operated in such a manner that the voltage at the load is maintained practically constant. Automatic voltage regulators (see Fig. 11–10) are used at transmission line terminals and at various points in the distribution networks to maintain constant voltages for all loads. An important result of such an operating condition is that the load behavior is practically independent of the generators and connecting lines for normal operation. Such a condition, of course, cannot be assumed for transients or any unusual disturbance of the power system, but for the usual steady state operation the behavior of the loads on a power system can be determined without any knowledge of the power distribution network.

The behavior of certain unbalanced systems of impedances connected to a balanced constant voltage system is of interest and will now be considered. Suppose that the wye load of Fig. 11–11*c* has a *positive* sequence

Fig. 11–10a. Indoor type of induction voltage regulators. (Courtesy, Westinghouse Electric & Mfg. Co.)

set of constant voltages at its terminals. This system of voltages is shown in Figs. 11–11*a* and *b*. Note, from these figures, that the letters *a*, *b*, and *c* at the vertices of the voltage triangle of Fig. 11–11*b* determine completely the position of V_{ab}, V_{bc}, V_{ca}, etc., and that adding arrow heads to the diagram, therefore, contributes nothing to its utility and will henceforth be frequently omitted. The balanced voltages of the vector diagram of Fig. 11–11*a* and *b* can be expressed by means of an operator $a = \epsilon^{j120}$ $(a^2 + a + 1 = 0)$ as

$$\begin{aligned} V_{ba} &= aV_{cb} \\ V_{ac} &= a^2 V_{cb} = aV_{ba} \end{aligned} \tag{11–14}$$

and with this symbolism the two voltage equations for the constant and balanced, positive sequence terminal voltage, wye network of Fig. 11–11*c* are

$$V_{cb} = (Z_{cn} + Z_{bn})I_{cn} - Z_{bn}I_{na} \tag{11–15}$$

$$V_{ba} = aV_{cb} = -Z_{bn}I_{cn} + (Z_{bn} + Z_{an})I_{na} \tag{11–16}$$

The solution of these equations is

$$I_{cn} = \frac{\begin{vmatrix} V_{cb} & -Z_{bn} \\ aV_{cb} & (Z_{bn} + Z_{an}) \end{vmatrix}}{\begin{vmatrix} (Z_{cn} + Z_{bn}) & -Z_{bn} \\ -Z_{bn} & (Z_{bn} + Z_{an}) \end{vmatrix}} = \frac{[Z_{bn}(1 + a) + Z_{an}]V_{cb}}{Z_{cn}Z_{bn} + Z_{cn}Z_{an} + Z_{an}Z_{bn}}$$

$$= \frac{(-a^2 Z_{bn} + Z_{an})V_{cb}}{Z_{cn}Z_{bn} + Z_{cn}Z_{an} + Z_{an}Z_{bn}} \tag{11–17}$$

Fig. 11–10*b*. Feeder voltage regulator. (Courtesy, Allis-Chalmers Mfg. Co.)

Fig. 11–10c. Voltage regulators. (Courtesy, Allis-Chalmers Mfg. Co.)

Similarly,

$$I_{na} = \frac{[aZ_{cn} + Z_{bn}(1 + a)]V_{cb}}{Z_{cn}Z_{bn} + Z_{cn}Z_{an} + Z_{an}Z_{bn}} = \frac{(aZ_{cn} - a^2Z_{bn})V_{cb}}{Z_{cn}Z_{bn} + Z_{cn}Z_{an} + Z_{an}Z_{bn}} \quad (11\text{–}18)$$

The voltages across the wye-connected loads are then

$$V_{na} = Z_{na}I_{na} = \frac{(aZ_{cn} - a^2Z_{bn})Z_{na}V_{cb}}{Z_{cn}Z_{bn} + Z_{cn}Z_{an} + Z_{an}Z_{bn}} = \frac{(aZ_{cn} - a^2Z_{bn})Z_{na}}{K} \quad (11\text{–}19)$$

$$V_{nb} = Z_{nb}(I_{cn} - I_{na}) = \frac{(Z_{an} - aZ_{cn})V_{cb}Z_{nb}}{Z_{cn}Z_{bn} + Z_{cn}Z_{an} + Z_{an}Z_{bn}} = \frac{(Z_{an} - aZ_{cn})Z_{nb}}{K} \quad (11\text{–}20)$$

$$V_{nc} = Z_{nc}I_{nc} = \frac{(a^2Z_{bn} - Z_{an})V_{cb}Z_{nc}}{Z_{cn}Z_{bn} + Z_{cn}Z_{an} + Z_{an}Z_{bn}} = \frac{(a^2Z_{bn} - Z_{an})Z_{nc}}{K} \quad (11\text{–}21)$$

These equations in terms of the three arbitrary phase impedances express the impedance voltages of these phases for a positive sequence of balanced line voltages. The corresponding equations for a negative

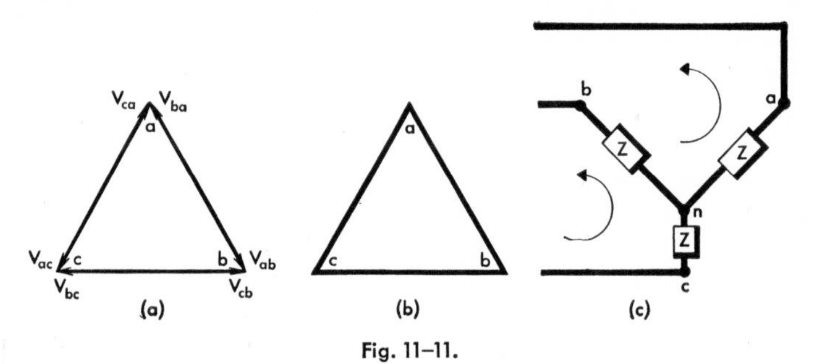

Fig. 11–11.

sequence of applied voltages may be obtained from these equations by replacing a with a^2 and a^2 with a wherever they appear. The phase voltages for an a–c–b sequence are, therefore,

$$V_{na} = \frac{(a^2Z_{cn} - aZ_{bn})Z_{na}}{K} \tag{11–22}$$

$$V_{nb} = \frac{(Z_{an} - a^2Z_{cn})Z_{nb}}{K} \tag{11–23}$$

$$V_{nc} = \frac{(aZ_{bn} - Z_{an})Z_{nc}}{K} \tag{11–24}$$

Because the impedances are assumed to have any possible values, little more can be said concerning these equations without placing some restrictions on the impedances. Suppose that, if possible, the phase impedances are such that the denominator of the voltage equations is zero. If impedances can be found to produce such a result, the phase voltages will be infinite no matter how small the balanced line voltages. In order to investigate the possibility of such a circuit condition, the denominator will be equated to zero. The result is

$$Z_{cn}Z_{bn} + Z_{cn}Z_{an} + Z_{an}Z_{bn} = 0 \tag{11–25}$$

Solving this equation for Z_{an} gives

$$Z_{an} = \frac{-Z_{cn}Z_{bn}}{Z_{bn} + Z_{cn}} = \frac{-1}{\dfrac{1}{Z_{cn}} + \dfrac{1}{Z_{bn}}} \tag{11–26}$$

Because of the negative sign, satisfying this relation requires that Z_{an} be physically unrealizable; i.e., have a *negative* resistance component, because the reciprocal of any realizable impedance is a realizable admittance, the sum of two such admittances is a realizable admittance, and, finally, the reciprocal of a realizable admittance is a realizable impedance. Actual impedances, therefore, will not satisfy equation 11–25. Suppose, however, that for the moment it is assumed that the impedances are purely reactive. Then equation 11–26 can be satisfied for *any pair* of reactances Z_{cn} and Z_{bn}. Evidently, therefore, if the resistances of the phase impedances are low, the phase voltages of an unbalanced set of wye impedances may be *very large* no matter what the balanced line voltages. Note that a capacitor and inductor must be included among the three impedances to satisfy relation 11–26.

The result just deduced shows one of the disadvantages of an unbalanced wye system; namely, that very large voltages may appear from line to neutral even though the balanced line voltages are normal.

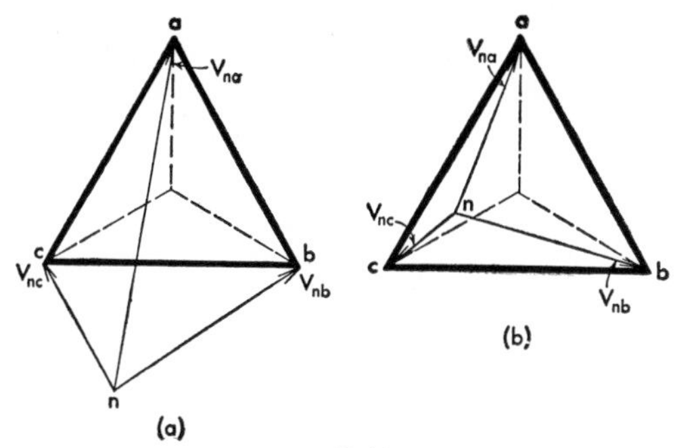

Fig. 11–12.

The line-to-neutral voltages will be unbalanced in some such fashion as shown in Fig. 11–12. The dashed lines on these diagrams correspond to a set of *balanced* line-to-neutral voltages.

It should not be supposed, on the basis of the foregoing, that the wye connection is not useful. In actual practice unbalance as extreme as inductance in one phase and capacitance in another does not occur. In fact, commercial wye load voltages are nearly balanced, and thus ordinarily lead to no difficulties.

Another interesting property of a particular type of unbalanced wye-connected load with balanced line voltages appears under change in phase sequence of line voltages. Suppose that $Z_{nc} = Z_{nb}$ in equations 11–19 through 11–24. Then equations 11–19 and 11–22 are *negative equals* as are equations 11–20 and 11–24 and equations 11–21 and 11–23. Thus, stating these results in a more compact form, if V^+ refers to positive sequence voltages and V^- refers to negative sequence voltages, for $Z_{nc} = Z_{nb}$,

$$V^+{}_{na} = -V^-{}_{na}$$
$$V^+{}_{nb} = -V^-{}_{nc}$$
$$V^+{}_{nc} = -V^-{}_{nb}$$

These relations are illustrated in the vector diagrams of Fig. 11–13, in which the point n of these vector diagrams may or may not be inside the triangle of balanced line voltages. Therefore, *if two of the phase impedances of a wye load are equal, by merely changing the phase sequence*—reversing the direction of rotation of the generator, or interchanging *any two of the three line* wires—*the magnitudes of the voltages across the two equal impedances will be interchanged.* The third phase voltage does not change in magnitude. The interchanging voltages across the two equal impedances may or may not be equal. If the interchanging voltages are equal a change in phase sequence will not cause a change in any of the phase voltage magnitudes (see Fig. 11–13c).

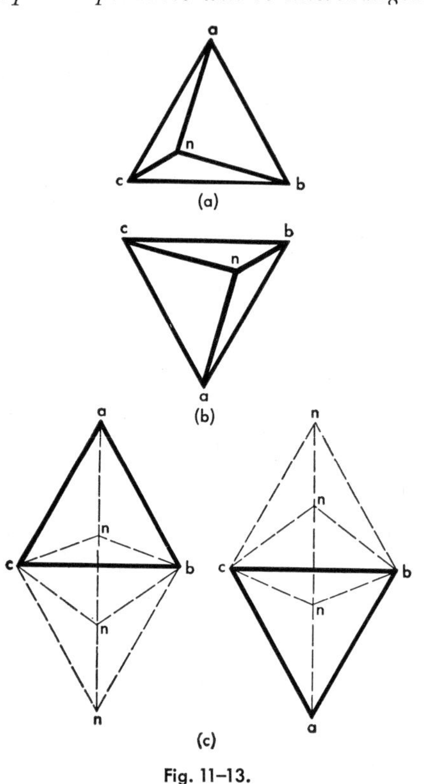

Fig. 11–13.

On the basis of these results a phase sequence indicator may be constructed for balanced or very nearly balanced three-phase voltages. If any two equal impedances—perhaps two lamps or two voltmeters—are connected in wye with a third impedance *which does not have the same phase angle as the equal impedances*, the relative brightness of the lamps or the relative size of the voltmeter indications may be used to indicate the phase sequence. For example, *if the two equal impedances (lamps) of the wye set are connected to lines* b *and* c, *the phase sequence is positive if the lamp connected to line* b *is brighter* (Fig. 11–13a), *and the sequence is negative if lamp* c *is brighter*, provided Z_{an} is capacitive.

As already indicated this phase sequence meter will not work if all three of the wye impedances have the same phase angle. For, as will now be shown, a change in phase sequence of the balanced voltages connected to such a sequence meter *will not change the magnitudes* of the voltages from line-to-neutral of the meter.

Equations 11–19 through 11–24 represent the line-to-neutral voltages of any set of wye impedances connected to the two sequences of balanced line-to-line voltages. In order for the line-to-neutral voltages to remain unchanged in magnitude under change in phase sequence a comparison of corresponding equations of this group of equations shows that the line-to-neutral impedances must be related by

$$|aZ_{cn} - a^2Z_{bn}| = |a^2Z_{cn} - aZ_{bn}| \tag{11-27}$$

$$|Z_{an} - aZ_{cn}| = |Z_{an} - a^2Z_{cn}| \tag{11-28}$$

$$|a^2Z_{bn} - Z_{an}| = |aZ_{bn} - Z_{an}| \tag{11-29}$$

The simultaneous solution of this set of equations cannot be carried out by a set of formal rules as would be possible if absolute values had not been equated. The simplest way to solve these equations is to obtain by inspection a solution for one of them which satisfies the other two. Thus equation 11–28 will be valid if Z_{an} and Z_{cn} have the same phase angle (equal X/R ratios) as a complex number diagram of this relation will show. But equations 11–27 and 11–29 also are valid if Z_{bn} has the same phase angle as the already equal angles of Z_{an} and Z_{cn}. Accordingly, therefore, the line-to-neutral voltages of a wye set of impedances will not change in magnitude under a change in phase sequences of balanced line-to-line voltage if all the wye impedances have the same X/R ratio.

An examination of complex number diagrams representing the relations of equations 11–27, 11–28, and 11–29 will show that in addition to the foregoing conditions, if Z_{an}, Z_{bn}, and Z_{cn} are any combination of pure inductors and/or capacitors the equations are satisfied. Consequently, the line-to-neutral voltage of any purely reactive wye connection will not change in magnitude with change in phase sequence of balanced line-to-line voltages.

If balanced voltages are connected to an unbalanced set of impedances in delta, nothing corresponding to the foregoing wye phase voltage relations occurs. The delta phases are connected directly across the lines, and the phase voltages are simply the balanced line voltages.

Consider next the currents of balanced voltage, three-phase wye-connected loads. Because the line-to-neutral voltages are directly across the corresponding line-to-neutral impedances, it follows immediately that: (*a*) if all the line-to-neutral voltages change under a change in phase sequence the phase and line currents will probably also change; (*b*) if the line-to-neutral voltages across two equal line-to-neutral impedances interchange under phase sequence change, the currents in these two impedances will also interchange; and (*c*) if no change in line-to-neutral voltage magnitude occurs under phase sequence change, there will be no change in current magnitudes.

Exactly the same conclusion can be reached regarding a delta connection; namely, the line currents will not change *in magnitude* under a change in voltage sequence if the impedances all have the same phase angle. The reader should establish this result as suggested in Problem 11–13.

Example 11:1 The impedances of a wye load (Fig. 11–2*a*) are

$$Z_{na} = 8.66 + j5.0 = 10\epsilon^{j30}$$
$$Z_{nb} = 4.33 + j2.5 = 5\epsilon^{j30}$$
$$Z_{nc} = 17.32 + j10.0 = 20\epsilon^{j30}$$

All other impedances will be assumed equal to zero. The balanced generator phase voltages are $|E_{10}| = |E_{20}| = |E_{30}| = 173.2$. Show that the magnitudes of the line currents are not changed by a change in the phase sequence of the source voltages. Use a reference axis coinciding with $V_{co} = E_{30}$ for the *acb* sequence.

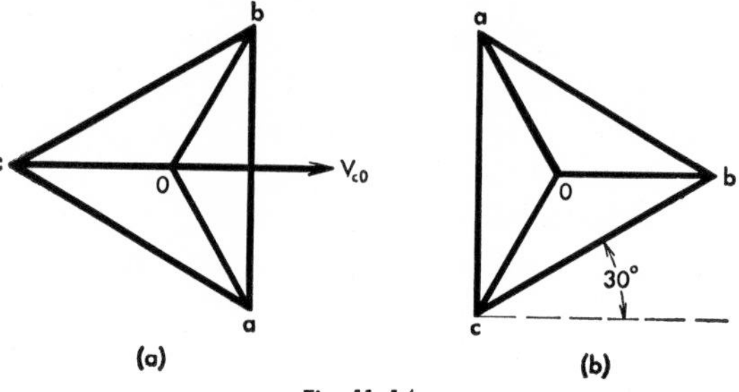

Fig. 11–14.

Solution Since the current formulas—equations 11–17 and 11–18—are expressed in terms of V_{cb}, and since V_{cb} was assumed the same for both sequences, the vector diagrams of Fig. 11–14 show the voltage triangles for the present problem. From the fact that the balanced line voltages are $\sqrt{3}$ times as large as the balanced phase voltages (equation 11–13) and from Fig. 11–14

$$V_{cb} = 173.2\sqrt{3}\,\epsilon^{j30} = 300\epsilon^{j30}$$

Then from equations 11–17 and 11–18, for the *abc* sequence

$$I_{cn} = \frac{(-\epsilon^{j240}\,5 + 10)300}{5 \times 20 + 10 \times 20 + 5 \times 10} = \frac{3}{3.5}(10 + 2.5 + j4.33)$$
$$= 10.71 + j3.71$$
$$I_{na} = \frac{(\epsilon^{j120}\,20 - \epsilon^{j240}\,5)300}{350} = \frac{3}{3.5}(-7.5 + j21.65)$$
$$= -6.43 + j18.6$$
$$I_{nb} = I_{cn} + I_{an} = 17.14 - j14.89.$$

If a and a^2 of equations 11–17 and 11–18 are replaced respectively by a^2 and a, the currents become, for the negative or *acb* sequence,

$$I_{cn} = \frac{(-\epsilon^{j120}\,5 + 10)300}{350} = \frac{3}{3.5}(10 + 2.5 - j4.33) = 10.71 - j3.71$$
$$I_{na} = \frac{(\epsilon^{j240}\,20 - \epsilon^{j120}\,5)300}{350} = \frac{3}{3.5}(-7.5 - j21.65) = -6.43 - j18.6$$
$$I_{nb} = I_{cn} + I_{an} = 17.14 + j14.89$$

A comparison of the two sets of currents shows that they have not changed in magnitude.

11.7 Ideal Neutral, or Center of Gravity, of a Triangle.

One of the well-known properties of a triangle is that its center of gravity is located at the intersection of the medians—lines drawn from the vertices to the center of the opposite sides, as in Fig. 11–15, lines *ap*, *br*, and *cq*. An important property of three-phase systems may be developed in terms of the voltages to the center of gravity, or ideal neutral of the line voltage triangle. These ideal-neutral voltages do not always exist as voltages which may be measured, but as will now be shown, they may be calculated from a known set of line voltages, and in turn the line voltages may be calculated from a known set of center-of-gravity (c-g) voltages.

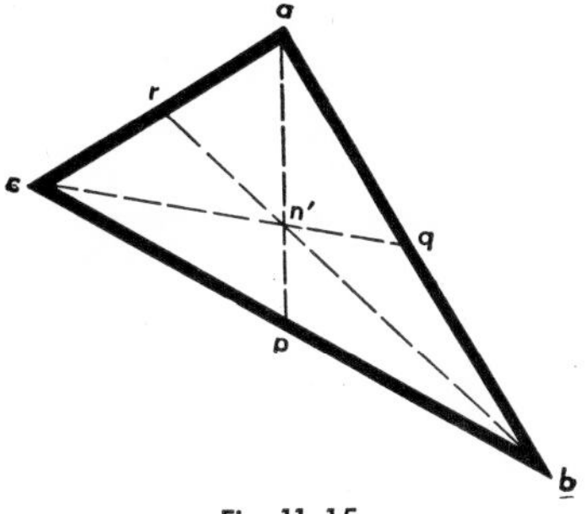

Fig. 11–15.

The intersection of the medians of a triangle occurs at a point two-thirds of the distance from any vertex along the corresponding median, e.g., from Fig. 11–15,

$$\begin{aligned} V_{an'} &= \tfrac{2}{3}V_{ap} \\ V_{bn'} &= \tfrac{2}{3}V_{br} \\ V_{cn'} &= \tfrac{2}{3}V_{cq} \end{aligned} \qquad (11\text{–}30)$$

From the diagram of Fig. 11–15, these voltages may be expressed in terms of the line voltages, or sides of the triangle, as

$$\begin{aligned} V_{n'a} &= \tfrac{2}{3}V_{pa} = \tfrac{2}{3}\left(V_{ca} + \frac{V_{bc}}{2}\right) = \tfrac{2}{3}V_{ca} + \frac{V_{bc}}{3} \\ V_{n'b} &= \tfrac{2}{3}V_{rb} = \tfrac{2}{3}\left(V_{ab} + \frac{V_{ca}}{2}\right) = \tfrac{2}{3}V_{ab} + \frac{V_{ca}}{3} \\ V_{n'c} &= \tfrac{2}{3}V_{qc} = \tfrac{2}{3}\left(V_{bc} + \frac{V_{ab}}{2}\right) = \tfrac{2}{3}V_{bc} + \frac{V_{ab}}{3} \end{aligned} \qquad (11\text{–}31)$$

One property of the c-g voltages appears immediately from these equations, namely,

$$V_{n'a} + V_{n'b} + V_{n'c} = 0 \qquad (11\text{–}32)$$

because the sum of the line voltages is zero, i.e., because

$$V_{ab} + V_{bc} + V_{ca} = 0 \qquad (11\text{–}33)$$

This last equation can be of further use, for by means of it equations 11–31 can be expressed through substitution (for say V_{bc} in the first equation) as

$$\begin{aligned} V_{n'a} &= \tfrac{1}{3}(V_{ba} + V_{ca}) \\ V_{n'b} &= \tfrac{1}{3}(V_{ab} + V_{cb}) \\ V_{n'c} &= \tfrac{1}{3}(V_{ac} + V_{bc}) \end{aligned} \qquad (11\text{–}34)$$

The line voltages can be expressed in terms of the ideal neutral voltages from Fig. 11–15 as

$$\begin{aligned} V_{ab} &= V_{an'} + V_{n'b} \\ V_{bc} &= V_{bn'} + V_{n'c} \\ V_{ca} &= V_{cn'} + V_{n'a} \end{aligned} \tag{11–35}$$

11.8 Unbalanced Voltages Connected to Balanced Impedances.

Suppose that a system of balanced impedances, connected in delta as in Fig. 11–16*a*, is connected to a set of unbalanced line voltages represented by the *closed* triangle of Fig. 11–16*b*. If the three impedances so connected are all equal, then, as will now be shown, *the currents in the lines are out of phase with the ideal neutral voltages by the power factor angle of the equal impedances.*

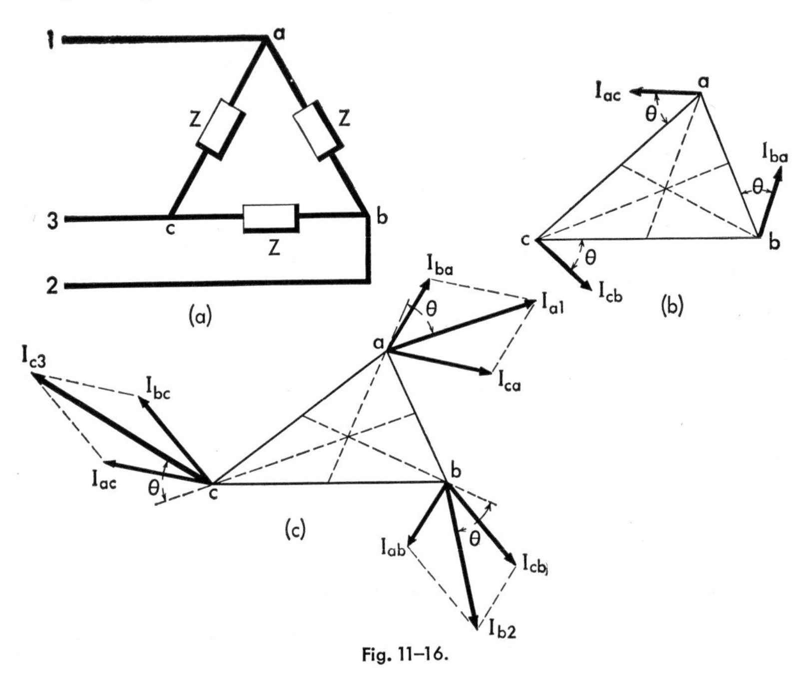

Fig. 11–16.

The line currents will first be expressed in terms of the ideal neutral voltages. Thus, if the common phase impedance is designated by Z, I_{a1} of Fig. 11–16*a* is

$$I_{a1} = I_{ba} + I_{ca} = \frac{V_{ba}}{Z} + \frac{V_{ca}}{Z}$$

Writing similar relations for the other two line currents, and using equations 11–35, gives

$$I_{a1} = \frac{V_{ba}}{Z} + \frac{V_{ca}}{Z} = \frac{V_{bn'} + V_{n'a} + V_{cn'} + V_{n'a}}{Z} = 3\frac{V_{n'a}}{Z}$$
$$I_{b2} = \frac{V_{ab}}{Z} + \frac{V_{cb}}{Z} = \frac{V_{an'} + V_{n'b} + V_{cn'} + V_{n'b}}{Z} = 3\frac{V_{n'b}}{Z} \quad (11\text{–}36)$$
$$I_{c3} = \frac{V_{bc}}{Z} + \frac{V_{ac}}{Z} = \frac{V_{bn'} + V_{n'c} + V_{an'} + V_{n'c}}{Z} = 3\frac{V_{n'c}}{Z}$$

These equations show immediately that *the line currents and ideal neutral voltages of a delta connection are out of phase by the power factor angle of the common (balanced) load impedance for all possible sets of line voltages—balanced or not.*

A graphical demonstration of the foregoing conclusion can be shown as follows. The currents in the phases of the delta are shown typically on the diagram of Fig. 11–16*b* for a lagging power factor angle of θ degrees for each equal impedance. If the line currents are determined from an application of Kirchhoff's current law at the junctions of the delta and if the vector sums indicated by these equations are carried out and the results located as shown in Fig. 11–16*c*, it will be found that all the line currents lag the extension of the ideal neutral voltages by the phase angle θ as shown.

A similar demonstration is even easier for a wye set of three *equal* impedances connected to a system of *unbalanced* three-phase line voltages, for then *the line-to-neutral voltages are actually the ideal neutral voltages*, and the phase currents and voltages are, of course, related by the common phase angle. See Problem 11–17 for instructions as to the procedure for showing these results.

11.9 Balanced Voltages and Balanced Impedances.

Three-phase circuits take on a very simple form, so far as calculations are concerned, if both the voltages and impedances are balanced. Under these conditions the complete behavior of a three-phase system can be predicted without the use of complex numbers. Real numbers and a vector diagram are all that are needed.

It no doubt seems that specializing a three-phase circuit to the extent of complete balance makes any results deduced for the circuit of merely academic interest. Actually there is considerable use in commercial practice for the formulas for balanced three-phase systems. Motors and generators are built so as to require and produce balanced voltages and currents, and other unbalanced loads are so arranged in a power system that the main transmission lines and generators operate at practically balanced conditions.

Consider first a completely balanced wye-wye connection as shown in Fig. 11–17*a*. For positive sequence the constant generated voltages are related as shown by Fig. 11–17*b*. The circuit point 0 is at the potential represented by the ideal neutral of the equilateral triangle. The line voltages add to zero as do the phase voltages, i.e.,

$$E_{12} + E_{23} + E_{31} = 0$$
$$E_{01} + E_{02} + E_{03} = E_{10} + E_{20} + E_{30} = 0 \qquad (11\text{–}37)$$

Specializing the impedances corresponding to the usual commercial practice, suppose that $Z_p = Z_{10} + Z_{1a} + Z_{an} = Z_{20} + Z_{2b} + Z_{bn} = Z_{30} + Z_{3c} + Z_{cn}$. The diagram of Fig. 11–17*a* can then be used to represent a completely balanced wye-wye circuit. The equations for this

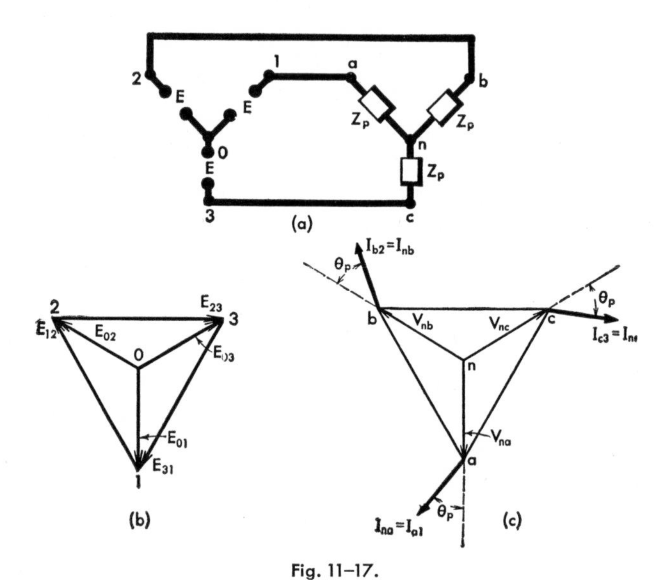

Fig. 11–17.

circuit have already been written (Art. 11–6) so using equations 11–17 and 11–18, for positive sequence,

$$I_{na} = (a - a^2)\frac{V_{cb}}{3Z_p} = \frac{V_{cb}}{\sqrt{3}\,Z_p}\,\epsilon^{j90}$$
$$I_{nb} = (1 - a)\frac{V_{cb}}{3Z_p} = \frac{V_{cb}}{\sqrt{3}\,Z_p}\,\epsilon^{-j30}$$
$$I_{nc} = (a^2 - 1)\frac{V_{cb}}{3Z_p} = \frac{V_{cb}}{\sqrt{3}\,Z_p}\,\epsilon^{j210} \qquad (11\text{–}38)$$

These currents are obviously equal in magnitude and spaced 120 degrees. Furthermore, the total line-to-neutral voltage is

$$
\begin{aligned}
Z_pI_{na} &= \frac{V_{cb}}{\sqrt{3}}\,\epsilon^{j90} \\
Z_pI_{nb} &= \frac{V_{cb}}{\sqrt{3}}\,\epsilon^{-j30} \\
Z_pI_{nc} &= \frac{V_{cb}}{\sqrt{3}}\,\epsilon^{j210}
\end{aligned}
\tag{11–39}
$$

These voltages are also all equal in magnitude and spaced 120 degrees on a vector diagram, and are exactly as shown by the vector diagram of Fig. 11–17*c*.

One very important implication of the diagrams of Figs. 11–17*b* and *c* is that

$$
\begin{aligned}
E_{10} &= V_{an} \\
E_{20} &= V_{bn} \\
E_{30} &= V_{cn}
\end{aligned}
\tag{11–40}
$$

Thus, even though the circuit points 0 and n do *not* coincide physically, the circuit acts as though they were connected through an impedanceless conductor. *No current would flow through such a fourth wire* so that the four-wire system of Art. 11–4 under balanced conditions acts exactly like a three-wire circuit. The phases appear to act *independently* of each other if the load and voltages are both balanced. The node equation 11–3 shows immediately that $V_{0n} = 0$ for balanced voltages and impedances.

It should also be noted that the load of Fig. 11–17*a* will take the same currents and consequently have the same set of balanced voltages if the generator is delta connected. This fact is evident from the expression for the currents of equation 11–38 because it requires only a *line* voltage and the phase impedance for their complete determination.

The currents of a balanced wye load for the phase angle θ_p lagging are shown on Fig. 11–17*c*. Notice that the current vectors are related to the ideal-neutral voltages by the phase power factor angle θ_p.

A delta set of balanced (equal) impedances connected to a balanced set of three-phase voltages naturally differs somewhat in its analysis from a wye system. Thus, from Fig. 11–18*a*, the currents in the lines leading to the delta-connected load are

$$
\begin{aligned}
I_{a1} &= I_{ba} + I_{ca} \\
I_{b2} &= I_{ab} + I_{cb} \\
I_{c3} &= I_{ac} + I_{bc}
\end{aligned}
\tag{11–41}
$$

These currents are shown, for lagging power factor impedances and balanced line voltages, on the vector diagram of Fig. 11–18*b*. The phase currents are located first with respect to the proper phase, or line, voltage, and then the vector sum is formed by adding the two equal current vectors 60 degrees apart. The resultant vector lies exactly midway between the two component vectors and is $\sqrt{3}$ times as long as either of them. *The line currents of a balanced delta system are, therefore, $\sqrt{3}$ times as large as the phase currents.*

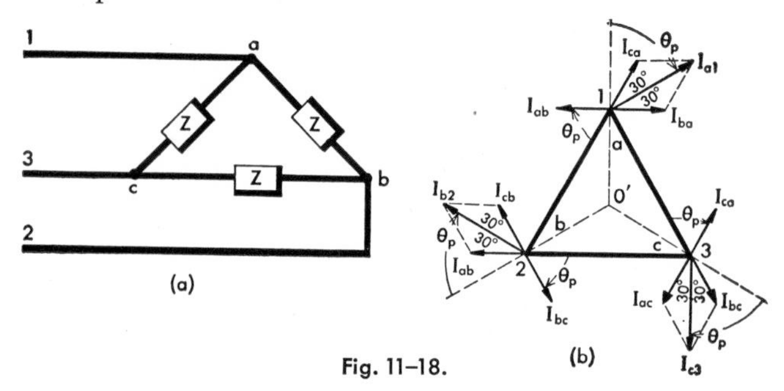

Fig. 11–18.

Mathematically this result follows immediately from equations 11–36. For with balanced voltages the hypothetical ideal neutral voltages and line voltages are related by

$$|V_l| = \sqrt{3}\,|V_{cg}| \tag{11–42}$$

so that each of the currents of 11–36 can be expressed as

$$|I_l| = \frac{3|V_{cg}|}{|Z_p|} = \frac{3|V_l|}{\sqrt{3}\,|Z_p|} = \sqrt{3}\,\frac{|V_l|}{|Z_p|} = \sqrt{3}\,|I_p| \tag{11–43}$$

11.10 Apparent or Vector Power, Power, and Reactive Volt-Amperes in a Three-Wire Wye System.

One of the many advantages of a three-phase over a single-phase system is the relatively steady flow of energy through a three-phase system. As the reader may recall, or will note on reference to Art. 1–7, the power in a unity power factor single-phase system varies from zero to a maximum twice each cycle. If the power factor is not equal to unity, the power is actually negative for a short time twice each cycle. For a three-phase system, on the other hand, for a completely balanced system, the total *instantaneous power*—the sum of the instantaneous power of the three phases—is a *constant*, as will now be shown.

Suppose the following three voltages represent the wye or delta phase voltages at any instant,

$$\begin{aligned} v(t)_1 &= |V_{m1}| \sin(\omega t + \phi_1) \\ v(t)_2 &= |V_{m2}| \sin(\omega t + \phi_2) \\ v(t)_3 &= |V_{m3}| \sin(\omega t + \phi_3) \end{aligned} \tag{11–44}$$

and the corresponding phase currents are

$$\begin{aligned} i(t)_1 &= |I_{m1}| \sin(\omega t + \phi_1 + \theta_1) \\ i(t)_2 &= |I_{m2}| \sin(\omega t + \phi_2 + \theta_2) \\ i(t)_3 &= |I_{m3}| \sin(\omega t + \phi_3 + \theta_3) \end{aligned} \tag{11–45}$$

The total instantaneous power absorbed by the wye or delta is the sum of the power absorbed in the three phases and is

$$p(t)_0 = \sum_{k=1}^{3} |V_{mk}|\ |I_{mk}| \sin(\omega t + \phi_k) \sin(\omega t + \phi_k + \theta_k) \quad (11\text{–}46)$$

This expression may be written by means of equation 1–21 as

$$p(t)_0 = \sum_{k=1}^{3} \frac{|V_{mk}|\ |I_{mk}|}{2} \cos\theta_k - \sum_{k=1}^{3} \frac{|V_{mk}|\ |I_{mk}|}{2} \cos(2\omega t + 2\phi_k + \theta_k) \quad (11\text{–}47)$$

If the three-phase connection is balanced,

$\theta_1 = \theta_2 = \theta_3 = \theta_p;\ \phi_1 = 0,\ \phi_2 = \pm 120°,\ \phi_3 = \pm 240°;\ |I_{m1}| = |I_{m2}| = |I_{m3}|$ and $|V_{m1}| = |V_{m2}| = |V_{m3}|$

then the second sum on the right of equation 11–47 is zero since it can be represented by three equal rotating vectors separated by 120 degrees. Therefore, for balanced systems, equation 11–47 becomes

$$p(t)_0 = 3|V_p|\ |I_p| \cos\theta_p = P_0 \quad (11\text{–}48)$$

Thus the *instantaneous power absorbed by a balanced three-phase system is a constant* so it absorbs power at the same *non-pulsating* rate as a d-c system, which is one of the principal reasons for the use of three-phase power.

On the other hand, the total *average* power of a three-phase wye or delta is, of course, the sum of the average power in the three phases, i.e.,

$$P_0 = V_1 \cdot I_1 + V_2 \cdot I_2 + V_3 \cdot I_3 \quad (11\text{–}49)$$

which for a *balanced* circuit becomes

$$P_0 = 3V_p \cdot I_p = 3|V_p|\ |I_p| \cos\phi_p \quad (11\text{–}50)$$

which is the same as the *instantaneous* power of equation 11–48. Accordingly, the total *instantaneous* power of a *balanced* three-phase system is exactly the *average* power of this same system.

Because of its importance, and the desirability of expressing the power in terms other than the wye and delta phases, the average power relation of equation 11–50 may be expressed in terms of *line* currents and *line* voltages as

$$P_0 = \sqrt{3}\ |V_l|\ |I_l| \cos\theta_p \quad (11\text{–}51)$$

by making use of the already derived balanced circuit relations, namely,

$$|I_l| = |I_p|;\ |V_l| = \sqrt{3}\ |V_p| \text{ (wye connection)}$$
$$|I_l| = \sqrt{3}\ |I_p|;\ |V_l| = |V_p| \text{ (delta connection)}$$

Corresponding to the total average power expression of equation 11–51, the total apparent or vector power of a balanced three-phase system is

$$|U| = 3|V_p|\,|I_p| = \sqrt{3}\,|V_l|\,|I_l| \tag{11–52}$$

for a wye or delta, and the reactive volt-amperes are

$$Q = 3|V_p|\,|I_p| \sin\theta_p = \sqrt{3}\,|V_l|\,|I_l| \sin\theta_p \tag{11–53}$$

By combining these two relations the vector power may be expressed as a complex number:

$$\begin{aligned} U &= P + jQ = 3|V_p|\,|I_p|\,(\cos\theta_p + j\sin\theta_p) \\ &= \sqrt{3}\,|V_l|\,|I_l|\,(\cos\theta_p + j\sin\theta_p) \end{aligned} \tag{11–54}$$

and power diagrams like those used in Art. 5–12 may be used to represent balanced three-phase systems as a whole, with the simple diagrams developed for a single-phase load.

Example 11:2 Two balanced wye-connected loads—a three-phase induction motor of 100 kw at 0.7 power factor lag, and a three-phase 200-kva synchronous motor load of 0.8 power factor lead—are connected, in parallel, with negligible resistance leads to a regulated wye generator of 2300 volts from line to neutral. Determine the following: total power, P_0; total vector volt-amperes, U_0; total reactive volt-amperes, Q_0; current in each generator phase, the impedance of each load, and the generator power factor.

Solution The determination of the total power is very simple. It is necessary only to add the total power absorbed by each load. Thus

$$P_0 = 100 + 200(0.8) = 260 \text{ kw}$$

The total volt-amperes may best be determined by adding the complex vector power expressions, as though the system were single phase.

For the induction motor

$$\begin{aligned} U &= P + jQ = P + j\frac{P}{pf}rf = P + j\frac{P}{\cos\theta}\sin\theta \\ &= 100 - j\frac{100}{0.7}\sqrt{1 - 0.7^2} = (100 - j102) \text{ kva} \end{aligned}$$

and for the synchronous motor

$$\begin{aligned} U &= P + jQ = |U|pf + j|U|rf = |U|\cos\theta + j|U|\sin\theta \\ &= 200(0.8) + j200\sqrt{1 - 0.8^2} = (160 + j120) \text{ kva} \end{aligned}$$

The total apparent power is, then, the sum of these values or

$$U_0 = 260 + j18$$

and the total reactive volt-amperes are

$$Q_0 = 18 \text{ kva leading}$$

In order to determine the magnitude of the currents, use may be made of the fact that $|U| = \sqrt{P^2 + Q^2}$, which follows from equation 11–54; then, by using equation 11–52 for the wye system being considered,

$$|I_l| = |I_p| = \frac{|U|}{3|V_p|} = \frac{1000\sqrt{260^2 + 18^2}}{3 \times 2300} = 37.8 \text{ amp}$$

The phase impedances are, since the system is completely balanced,

$$Z_p = \frac{|V_p|}{|I_p|} = \frac{2300}{37.8} = 60.9 \text{ ohms}$$

The power factor may be determined from any of the expressions

$$pf = \frac{R}{Z} = \frac{R|I_p|^2}{Z|I_p|^2} = \frac{P_p}{|V_p|\,|I_p|} = \frac{P_p}{|U_p|} = \frac{3P_p}{3|U_p|} = \frac{P_0}{|U_0|}$$

If the last one is used,

$$pf = \frac{P_0}{|U_0|} = \frac{260}{\sqrt{260^2 + 18^2}} = 0.997$$

The impedance per phase may be determined by dividing the total apparent power by $\hat{I}_{na}I_{na}$, for, by using the relation of equation 5–56,

$$\frac{U_0}{\hat{I}_{na}I_{na}} = \frac{3\hat{V}_{na}I_{na}}{\hat{I}_{na}I_{na}} = 3\hat{Z}_{na}$$

and

$$Z_{na} = \frac{1}{3}\frac{\hat{U}_0}{|I_{na}|^2} = \frac{(260 - j18)1000}{3(37.77)^2} = 60.7 - j4.21$$

Then

$$pf = \frac{R}{|Z|} = \frac{60.7}{60.9} = 0.997$$

as before.

Example 11:3 A balanced wye-connected load of impedances $10 + j10$ ohms is connected in parallel with a balanced delta load of impedance $5 + j8.66$ ohms across a balanced positive sequence system of three-phase voltages constant at 200 volts between lines. Determine the currents and voltages and the total power absorbed. What is the total vector power? Compare with the vector power sum of the two systems. Draw the vector diagram. Use V_{cb} as reference.

Solution Computing the voltages first, the voltages across the phases are (see Fig. 11–19*a*)

$$|V_{na'}| = \frac{|V_l|}{\sqrt{3}} = \frac{200}{\sqrt{3}} = 115.5 \text{ volts for the wye connection}$$

$$|V_{ab}| = |V_{a''b''}| = |V_l| = 200 \text{ volts for the delta connection}$$

The phase currents are thereby

$$|I_{na'}| = \frac{|V_{na'}|}{|Z_{na'}|} = \frac{115.5}{14.14} = 8.17 \text{ amp for the wye connection}$$

$$|I_{a''b''}| = \frac{|V_{a''b''}|}{|Z_{a''b''}|} = \frac{200}{10} = 20 \text{ amp for the delta connection}$$

These currents are shown at n and at a, b, and c on the vector diagram of Fig. 11–19b. The line currents are

$$|I_{a'a}| = |I_{na'}| = 8.17 \text{ amp for the wye}$$

and

$$|I_{a''a}| = \sqrt{3}\,|I_{a''b''}| = 20\sqrt{3} = 34.6 \text{ amps for the delta}$$

Note, as shown on the vector diagram (Fig. 11–19b) that these line currents lag the voltage to the ideal neutral of the voltage triangle by the phase power factor angle for both the wye and delta.

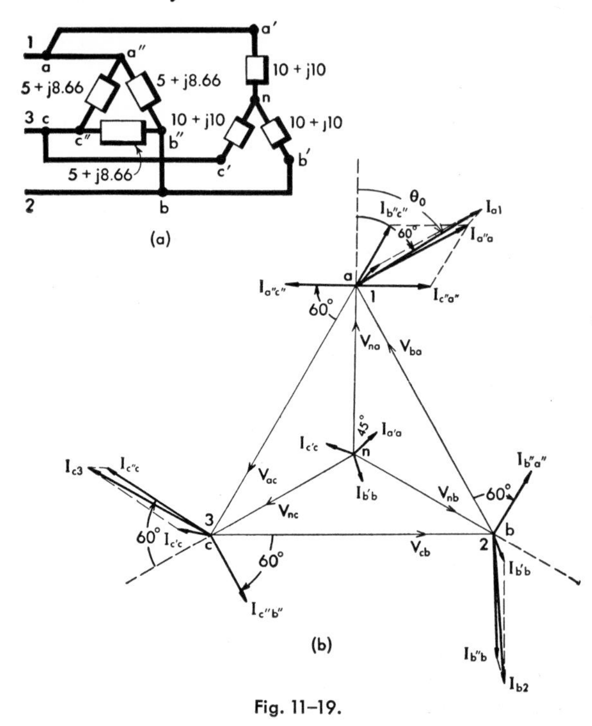

Fig. 11–19.

The total current in the line $a1$ from the generator is the sum

$$I_{a1} = I_{a'a} + I_{a''a}$$

This vector sum is indicated at the vertex a of the vector diagram. The other total line currents are shown vectorially at the b and c vertices of the vector diagram. In order to determine the magnitude of the total line currents, the currents $I_{a'a}$ and $I_{a''a}$ *must be added vectorially*. This addition may be performed in the simplest manner by assuming for the moment that $I_{a''a}$ is the reference axis and is, therefore,

$$I_{a''a} = 34.6 + j0$$

The current $I_{a'a}$ is 15 degrees ahead of $I_{a''a}$; hence

$$I_{a'a} = 8.17\epsilon^{j15} = 7.89 + j2.11$$

and the total line current in each of the generator lines is

$$|I_l| = |I_{a1}| = |(34.6 + j0) + (7.89 + j2.11)| = |42.6\epsilon^{j2.75}| \text{ amperes}$$
$= 42.6$ amp 2.75 degrees ahead of $I_{a''a}$ or 57.25 degrees lagging the ideal neutral (Fig. 11–19)

The simplest way to get the total power is to use the $|I|^2R$ relation. For the wye, the total power is

$$P_Y = 3(8.17)^2 10 = 2000 \text{ watts}$$

and for the delta the total power is

$$P_\Delta = 3(20)^2 5 = 6000 \text{ watts}$$

The total power is the sum of the wye and delta power, or

$$P = 8000 \text{ watts} = 8 \text{ kw}$$

The vector power of the wye is

$$U_Y = 3[|I_p|^2 R_p - j|I_p|^2 X_p] = 3[(8.17)^2 10 - j(8.17)^2 10] = 2000 - j2000$$

and of the delta

$$U_\Delta = 3[|I_p|^2 R_p - j|I_p|^2 X_p] = 3[(20)^2 5 - j(20)^2 8.66] = 6000 - j10{,}392$$

The total vector power for the two systems is the sum of U_Y and U_Δ:

$$U_0 = 8000 - j12{,}392 \text{ volt-amperes}$$
$$|U_0| = \sqrt{8^2 + (12.39)^2} = 14.75 \text{ kva}$$

In order to calculate the total vector power at the generator, from the generator conditions

$$|U_0| = \frac{\sqrt{3}|V_l|\,|I_l|}{1000} = \frac{\sqrt{3} \times 200 \times 42.6}{1000} = 14.75 \text{ kva}$$

as for the sum of the two loads. The complex form of the total generator kva is also the same as that determined from the sum of the loads, or it is, because the angle between the total line current and the ideal-neutral voltage is -57.25 degrees,

$$U_0 = 14.75(\cos\theta_0 + j\sin\theta_0) = 14.75(\cos 57.25° - j\sin 57.25°)$$
$$= 8.0 - j12.39 \text{ kva}$$

as before.

The last part of the foregoing example brings out an important fact; namely, that *the complex number forms for volt-amperes add directly from each part of the balanced circuit to give the correct total even though some parts of the system may be wye and others delta.*

11.11 Illustrative Examples.

Some further examples of calculations for determining the behavior of three-phase systems are presented in this article.

Example 11:4 A completely balanced three-wire wye-wye connection (see Fig. 11–2*a*) has impedances $Z_{na} = 5 - j5$, $Z_{a1} = 1 + j2$, and $Z_{10} = 0.5 + j2$ connected to a balanced set of line-to-neutral voltages of 100 volts. The phase sequence is *a–c–b*, and the reference axis is E_{02}. Find the currents and all the voltages, and draw the complete vector diagram.

Solution Since the system is completely balanced, the problem is relatively easy. If the results are computed for one of the phases, which, as has already been shown, act independently of each other, the other phase conditions may be obtained by applying the rotators a or a^2 in an order determined by the phase sequence. The reference axis may even be ignored for the first computations. From the fact that the line-to-neutral voltages at the generator are 100 volts, the line voltages are

$$|E_{12}| = |E_{23}| = |E_{31}| = \sqrt{3}|E_{10}| = \sqrt{3}|E_p| = \sqrt{3} \times 100 = 173.2 \text{ volts}$$

The currents are

$$|I_{na}| = |I_{nb}| = |I_{nc}| = \frac{|E_p|}{|Z_p|} = \frac{100}{|6.5 - j1|} = \frac{100}{6.58} = 15.2 \text{ amp}$$

The voltages across the load impedances are

$$|V_{na}| = |V_{nb}| = |V_{nc}| = |Z_{na}|\,|I_p| = |5 - j5|15.2 = 107.5 \text{ volts}$$

The voltages along the lines between generator and load are

$$|V_{a1}| = |V_{b2}| = |V_{c3}| = |Z_{a1}|\,|I_p| = |1 + j2|15.2 = 34.0 \text{ volts}$$

and the internal voltages per phase in the generator are

$$|V_{10}| = |V_{20}| = |V_{30}| = |Z_{10}|\,|I_p| = |0.5 + j2|15.2 = 31.3 \text{ volts}$$

The terminal voltages at the load are

$$|V_{ab}| = |V_{bc}| = |V_{ca}| = \sqrt{3}|V_{na}| = \sqrt{3}\,107.5 = 186.2 \text{ volts}$$

which, it should be noted, are *greater than the generator* line voltages.

In order to compute the terminal voltages of the generator, some of the voltages already computed must be added in *complex form.* Since E_{02} has been specified as the reference vector, the voltage equation for the second phase will be used. Then, since for balanced systems, the points 0 and n are at the same potential,

$$E_{02} = V_{nb} + V_{b2} + V_{20} = (Z_{nb} + Z_{b2} + Z_{20})I_{nb}$$

and

$$E_{02} - V_{20} = V_{b2} + V_{nb} = V_{n2} \text{ phase voltage to the terminal of the generator}$$

Therefore, since $E_{02} = 100 + j0$ referred to the assigned reference axis,

$$I_{nb} = \frac{E_{02}}{Z_{20} + Z_{2b} + Z_{nb}} = \frac{100 + j0}{6.5 - j1} = \frac{100\epsilon^{j0}}{6.58\epsilon^{-j8.75}} = 15.2\epsilon^{j8.75} = 15 + j2.3,$$

and

$$V_{n2} = 100 + j0 - (0.5 + j2)(15 + j2.3) = 97.1 - j31.2 = 102\epsilon^{-j17.8}$$

This calculation gives the curious result, already noted for the terminal voltages, that the *voltage per phase in the load external to the generator is greater than the generated voltage per phase.* This effect is typical of leading currents through inductances.

Since the load is balanced, the terminal voltages of the generator are

$$|V_{12}| = |V_{23}| = |V_{31}| = \sqrt{3} \times 102 = 176.7 \text{ volts}$$

In order to draw the vector diagram, the following additional complex number voltages must be computed:

$$V_{b2} = Z_{b2}I_{nb} = 34\epsilon^{j72.2} = 10.4 + j32.4$$
$$V_{20} = Z_{20}I_{nb} = 31.3\epsilon^{j84.7} = 2.9 + j31.2$$

The vector diagram is, then, as shown in Fig. 11–20. Plotting E_{02}, V_{20}, V_{b2} and V_{nb} according to the Kirchhoff's voltage equation

$$E_{02} = V_{nb} + V_{b2} + V_{20}$$

gives the part of Fig. 11–20 shown in heavy lines, which is plotted on E_{02} along the horizontal. The remainder of the vector diagram may be plotted

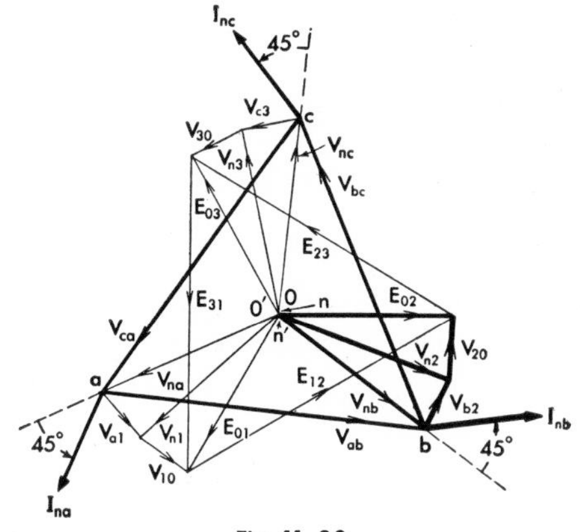

Fig. 11–20.

by simply rotating this whole system 120 degrees and 240 degrees as shown, or by plotting the numerical results of the following:

$$E_{10} = a^2E_{20};\ V_{10} = a^2V_{20};\ V_{a1} = a^2V_{b2};\ V_{na} = a^2V_{nb};\ \text{and } I_{na} = a^2I_{nb}$$
$$E_{30} = aE_{20};\ V_{30} = aV_{20};\ V_{c3} = aV_{b2};\ V_{nc} = aV_{nb};\ \text{and } I_{nc} = aI_{nb}$$

Example 11:5 The balanced impedances of a delta-delta connection are: receiving end, or load, impedance $Z_r = 10 + j10$, line impedance $Z_l = 2 + j6$, and generator, or sending-end, internal impedance $Z_s = 0.4 + j2.4$ (Fig. 11–4). A positive sequence of constant generated voltages of 200 volts line-to-line appear in the generator. Determine all currents, and voltages, and draw the complete vector diagram. Use V_{ba} as the reference axis.

Solution Once the currents are determined, the voltages follow immediately; hence the currents will be determined first. From the result given in Problem 11–28, the phase current can be determined from the phase voltages of the delta-connected alternator. The impedance factor required is

$$Z_s + 3Z_l + Z_r = 16.4 + j30.4 = 34.5\epsilon^{j61.7}$$

Only the magnitude of this impedance sum is required to determine the currents and voltages because the system is *balanced*. The phase currents of the generator and of the load are

$$|I_{ps}| = |I_{pr}| = \frac{|E_p|}{|Z_s + 3Z_l + Z_r|} = \frac{200}{34.5} = 5.8 \text{ amp}$$

The currents in the connecting lines are

$$|I_l| = \sqrt{3}|I_p| = \sqrt{3} \times 5.8 = 10.04 \text{ amp}$$

The line-to-line voltages of the load are

$$|V_r| = |I_{pr}|\,|Z_r| = 5.8 \times 14.14 = 82 \text{ volts}$$

The voltages of the lines connecting generator and load are

$$|V_l| = |I_l|\,|Z_l| = 10.04 \times 6.3 = 63.25 \text{ volts}$$

and the internal impedance voltages in the phases of the generator are

$$|V_{si}| = |I_{ps}|\,|Z_s| = 5.8 \times 2.43 = 14.1 \text{ volts}$$

Finally, the terminal voltages of the generator are

$$|V_s| = |Z_r + 3Z_l|\,|I_{pr}| = |16 + j28|\,|I_{pr}| = 32.25 \times 5.8 = 187.1 \text{ volts}$$

The results of these calculations are shown on the vector diagram of Fig. 11–21. Since V_{ba} is specified as the reference vector, the voltage triangle of the load voltages is constructed first as an equilateral triangle, 82 volts to the side. The line currents may then be plotted at the load power factor angle from the voltages to the ideal neutral of the triangle just formed. These currents are shown on the diagram radiating from the vertices of the load voltage triangle at the points marked *a*, *b*, and *c*. The phase currents may also be located at these vertices as shown.

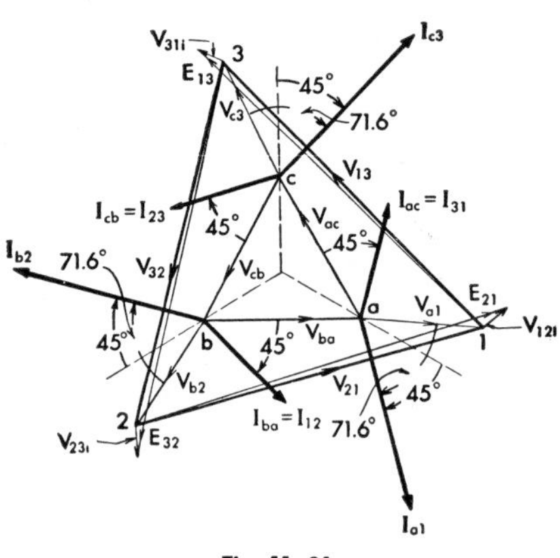

Fig. 11–21.

The line voltages, V_{a1}, V_{b2}, and V_{c3}, may then be plotted from these same vertices, leading the respective line currents by the line power factor angle of 71.6 degrees. The closed triangle formed with the ends of these vectors gives the triangle marked 1, 2, and 3. This triangle represents the terminal voltages of the generator.

The generated voltage may next be located by means of the equation, written from the circuit diagram of Fig. 11–4 (V_i is the internal impedance voltage in the generator phase),

$$E_{21} - V_{12i} = V_{21} \quad \text{or} \quad E_{21} = V_{21} + V_{12i}$$

and, of course, similar ones for the other phases. The internal impedance voltages are plotted at the vertices 1, 2, and 3 of Fig. 11–21, and the generator voltages are drawn as shown. These voltages are not shown forming a closed triangle but they will if properly located.

Example 11:6 Suppose that to the unbalanced three-phase circuit of Fig. 11–22, the unbalanced voltages $E_{01} = 100 + j0$, $E_{02} = -100 + j30$, and $E_{03} = 0 - j150$ are connected. Find the currents of the circuit and draw the complete vector diagram.

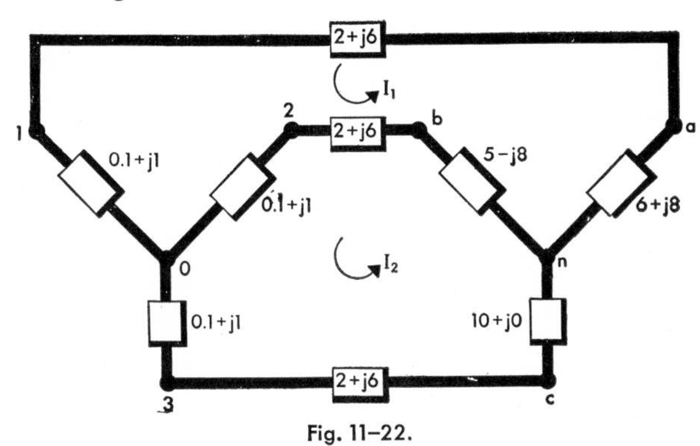

Fig. 11–22.

Solution The currents may be obtained from equations 11–2 which take the form

$$202\epsilon^{-j8.54} = 200 - j30 = (15.2 + j14)I_1 - (7.1 - j1)I_2$$
$$206\epsilon^{j119.1} = -100 + j180 = -(7.1 - j1)I_1 + (19.2 + j6)I_2$$

The currents, obtained by solving these equations, are

$$I_1 = I_{10} = 7.7 - j5.9 = 9.7\epsilon^{-j37.4} = I_{na}$$
$$I_2 = I_{03} = -0.45 + j6.9 = 6.9\epsilon^{j93.7} = I_{cn}$$

and from these results

$$I_{nb} = I_{20} = I_{01} + I_{03} = -8.15 + j12.8 = 15.2\epsilon^{j122.5}$$

In order to draw the vector diagram, it will be necessary to compute the voltages for various parts of the circuit. The load impedance voltages in the load phases are

$$V_{na} = Z_{na}I_{na} = 10\epsilon^{j53.1} \times 9.7\epsilon^{-j37.4} = 97\epsilon^{j15.7} = 93.4 + j26.2$$
$$V_{nb} = Z_{nb}I_{nb} = 9.43\epsilon^{-j58} \times 15.2\epsilon^{j122.5} = 143.3\epsilon^{j64.5} = 61.7 + j129.3$$
$$V_{nc} = Z_{nc}I_{nc} = 10\epsilon^{j0} \times 6.9\epsilon^{j273.7} = 69\epsilon^{j273.7} = 4.5 - j68.9$$

The impedance voltages of the lines are

$$V_{a1} = Z_{a1}I_{na} = 6.32\epsilon^{j71.6} \times 9.7\epsilon^{-j37.4} = 61.3\epsilon^{j34.2} = 50.7 + j34.4$$
$$V_{b2} = Z_{b2}I_{nb} = 6.32\epsilon^{j71.6} \times 15.2\epsilon^{j122.5} = 96.1\epsilon^{j194.1} = -93.0 - j23.4$$
$$V_{c3} = Z_{c3}I_{nc} = 6.32\epsilon^{j71.6} \times 6.9\epsilon^{j273.7} = 43.6\epsilon^{j345.3} = 42.2 - j11.1$$

and the internal impedance voltages of the generator phases are

$$V_{10} = Z_{01}I_{na} = 1.00\epsilon^{j84.3} \times 9.7\epsilon^{-j37.4} = 9.7\epsilon^{j46.9} = 6.62 + j7.08$$
$$V_{20} = Z_{02}I_{nb} = 1.00\epsilon^{j84.3} \times 15.2\epsilon^{j122.5} = 15.2\epsilon^{j207.1} = -13.57 - j6.85$$
$$V_{30} = Z_{03}I_{nc} = 1.00\epsilon^{j84.3} \times 6.9\epsilon^{j273.7} = 6.9\epsilon^{-j2.0} = 6.9 - j0.24$$

The numerical results necessary to draw the complete vector diagram for the circuit represented by Fig. 11–22 have now been computed with the voltage E_{01} coinciding with or parallel to the reference axis. The vectors of the system could, therefore, be plotted without difficulty with some point on the reference axis as the common origin. Instead of doing this, the diagram can be explained more easily if the common point, n, of the load phases is considered as the starting point. Note that it is *not* necessary to draw the diagram in this fashion. It is merely convenient.

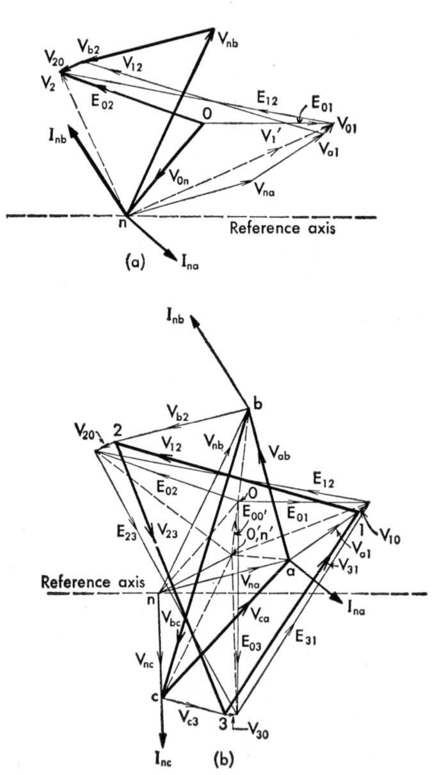

Fig. 11–23.

Consider the vector diagram of Fig. 11–23*a* first. From any point on the reference axis draw the vector representing V_{nb}. In order to establish the vectors to be added to form the polygon of voltages of phase b, the voltage equation of that phase must be written from the diagram of the physical connections of the circuit, namely, Fig. 11–22. This voltage equation is

$$E_{02} = V_{0n} + V_{nb} + V_{b2} + V_{20}$$

So if V_{b2} is drawn from the end of V_{nb}, i.e., added to V_{nb}, and V_{20} added to this sum, the resultant, V_2' (shown dashed in Fig. 11–23*a*), is the total impedance voltage in the conductor—load, line, and generator—of phase b. Then if E_{02} is located as shown from the end of V_{20}, the vector V_{0n} drawn as shown completes the polygon of voltages for phase b. A similar polygon may be drawn for phase a as shown (Fig. 11–23*a*).

If once more the circuit diagram is referred to, the terminal voltage of the generator between points 1 and 2 is

$$V_{12} = V_{1a} + V_{an} + V_{nb} + V_{b2} = -V_{a1} - V_{na} + V_{nb} + V_{b2}$$

But the difference between two vectors is the vector joining the terminals of these vectors, when they are drawn from a common origin, and directed from the vector which is subtracted. Hence V_{12} is as shown in the vector diagram of Fig. 11–23*a*.

Similarly since, from the circuit diagram,

$$\begin{aligned} E_{12} &= V_{01} + V_{1a} + V_{an} + V_{nb} + V_{b2} + V_{20} \\ &= -V_{10} - V_{a1} - V_{na} + V_{nb} + V_{b2} + V_{20} \end{aligned}$$

this vector, E_{12}, is as shown in Fig. 11–23*a*.

If the voltage polygon of phase c is added to the diagram of Fig. 11–23*a*, and if the triangles of line voltages are formed by plotting V_{23}, V_{31}, E_{23}, V_{ab}, etc., the resultant diagram is as shown in Fig. 11–23*b*. Note that the shape of the voltage triangles shows immediately whether the voltages between lines is an equilateral triangle or to what extent these voltages deviate from this ideal equilateral triangle. In this particular example, the line voltages at the load differ considerably from the ideal, whereas the generator terminal voltages and generator internal-generated voltages are near the ideal—equal in magnitude and 120 or 240 degrees out of phase. Several points of interest appear on the diagram. The point n is outside the triangle of line voltages at the load, whereas the point 0 is inside the triangle of generator line voltages. The fact that the voltages to the points 0 and n of the circuit do not originate at $0'$ and n', the center of gravity, or ideal neutral, of the triangles, is also of interest. Also the ideal neutral of *all* the voltage triangles coincides. The diagram shows, too, that the points 0 and n of the circuit have a potential difference between them, and this voltage is shown in magnitude and phase position by the dashed line joining points 0 and n on the vector diagram. In fact, the voltage between any two points in the actual circuit may be determined from the vector diagram by measuring the length and position of the vectors between the same points on the vector diagram.

The currents are drawn from the vertices of the load line voltage triangle to facilitate keeping the diagram as descriptive as possible, and they are associated with the vertex corresponding to the line in which the current appears.

11.12 Non-Sinusoidal Voltages Connected to a Three-Phase System.

The reaction of a three-phase circuit to a set of balanced, or nearly balanced, non-sine waves has important practical applications. Suppose that the three balanced non-sinusoidal voltages are

$$\begin{aligned} e(\alpha)_1 &= \sum_{k=1}^{\infty} |E_{m1k}| \sin(k\alpha) \\ e(\alpha)_2 &= \sum_{k=1}^{\infty} |E_{m2k}| \sin(k\alpha \pm k120) \qquad (11\text{–}55) \\ e(\alpha)_3 &= \sum_{k=1}^{\infty} |E_{m3k}| \sin(k\alpha \pm k240) \end{aligned}$$

where the minus signs produce a positive or 1–2–3 sequence, and the plus signs a negative sequence. If k is allowed to take on integral values, the voltage sequences change as k changes. For example, if the minus signs of these equations are used, the sequence is positive for $k = 1$. Then, if $k = 2$, because $e(\alpha)_2$ is now 240 degrees behind $e(\alpha)_1$ and $e(\alpha)_3$ is 480 degrees or 120 degrees behind $e(\alpha)_1$, the sequence is negative. Carrying out similar substitutions for further values of k and for the negative sequence will give the results of the following tabulation:

k	Positive sequence for $k = 1$	Negative sequence for $k = 1$
1	1–2–3	1–3–2
2	1–3–2	1–2–3
3	in phase	in phase
4	1–2–3	1–3–2
5	1–3–2	1–2–3
6	in phase	in phase
7	1–2–3	1–3–2
8	1–3–2	1–2–3
9	in phase	in phase

This tabulation shows that if the fundamental is of positive sequence, the harmonics alternate in sequence except that all multiples of the third harmonic are not *three phase* but are three voltages *all in phase.* As shown, a similar relation is true if the fundamentals are of negative sequence.

The fact that alternate harmonic systems are of opposite sequence points to one undesirable feature of non-sine waves for three phase systems. Since the direction of rotation of motors is determined by the sequence of the applied voltages, some of the harmonic systems will cause a motor torque in opposition to the fundamental, thus reducing the effective torque output of the motor.

The three-phase connection has certain filtering or harmonic elimination characteristics which are important. Thus, if the voltages of equations 11–55 are wye connected line-to-neutral voltages, since the voltage between any two lines is the difference between line-to-neutral voltages, *all multiples of the third harmonic disappear from between the lines if the phase voltages are balanced.* If the voltages are not balanced, of course, all harmonics will appear between the lines, and each harmonic system will be three phase except multiples of the third.

If the three non-sine voltages are connected in delta, multiples of the third harmonic once more do not appear between the lines if, *in addition to balanced voltages, the impedances in the delta are balanced.* Thus, around the closed delta of an unloaded generator, for any particular harmonic

$$(E_{21k} - I_k Z_{12k}) + (E_{32k} - I_k Z_{23k}) + (E_{13k} - I_k Z_{31k}) = 0 \quad (11\text{–}56)$$

Each of the combinations, $V_{ijk} = E_{jik} - I_k Z_{ijk}$, represents the terminal voltage of the generator. If $k = 3$, or a multiple of three, the generated voltages are all *in phase* and will cause a circulating current. If the impedances are all alike and the voltages balanced, each V_{ijk} will vanish for the third harmonic and its multiples because $I_k Z_{12k}$, $I_k Z_{23k}$, and $I_k Z_{31k}$ will be equal and each one equal to $(E_{21k} + E_{32k} + E_{13k})/3 = E_{21k} = E_{32k} = E_{13k}$. Accordingly, the third harmonic and its multiples will not appear across the generator terminals even though they are, in a sense, directly across these terminals.

For k not a multiple of three, the sum of the harmonic generator voltages will be zero if the system is balanced, and I_k—the delta circulating current—will be zero. If the voltages for any harmonic are not balanced, a resultant generated voltage will cause a circulating current in the delta which will make the terminal voltages at no load different from the generated voltages per phase. These terminal voltages, V_{ijk}, will not be individually zero although their sum is zero.

11.13 Commercial Three-Phase System Computations.

Consider the three-phase circuit representation of Fig. 11–24*a*. From left to right this diagram represents a wye-connected generator (alternator), a delta-wye bank of three, two-winding transformers, a transmission line, a wye-delta bank of three, two-winding transformers, and finally a wye-connected load. It is not at all uncommon for three-phase systems to be as diverse so far as wye and delta connections are concerned as in Fig. 11–24*a*. Determining the complete behavior of this net-

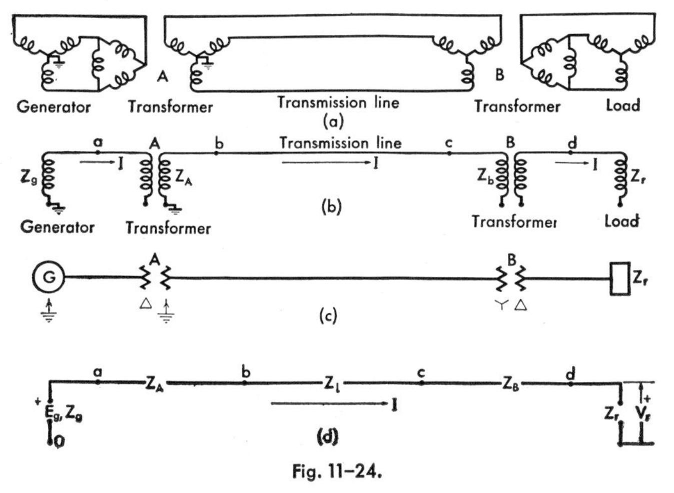

Fig. 11–24.

work by the mesh current method requires the simultaneous solution of eight equations—at best a very tedious job. To make matters worse, the network of Fig. 11–24*a* is a very simple one relative to the actual three-phase networks in use. Fortunately, however, certain simplifications are possible which reduce the work of solution very much. Thus by deliberate design and connection three-phase systems under normal operating conditions are practically balanced; and the balance is so good that computations on the basis of complete balance are generally used. The resulting simplifications which are possible reduce the computation required very greatly. For example, the network of Fig. 11–24*a* can be reduced to the one shown in Fig. 11–24*c* or *d* for balanced conditions as follows.

On the basis of the results given in Problems 11–44 and 11–45, it is evident that for balanced conditions a wye-delta combination, as at either end of Fig. 11–24*a*, can be replaced by a wye-wye combination, where for the replaced delta the equivalent wye voltages are the delta ideal neutral voltages and the wye impedances are the equivalent of the delta impedances, i.e., $Z_Y = Z_\Delta/3$. Also, according to the results given in Problem 11–28, a delta-delta combination can be replaced by an equivalent wye-wye combination, for in a balanced delta circuit (for negative sequence)

$$\left.\begin{aligned} E_{21} &= \sqrt{3}\, E_{0'1}\epsilon^{j30} \\ I_{a1} &= \sqrt{3}\, I_{ba}\epsilon^{-j30} \end{aligned}\right\} \text{for positive sequence}$$

$$\left.\begin{aligned} E_{21} &= \sqrt{3}\, E_{0'1}\epsilon^{-j30} \\ I_{a1} &= \sqrt{3}\, I_{ba}\epsilon^{j30} \end{aligned}\right\} \text{for negative sequence}$$

so that the first equation of Problem 11–28 is

$$E_{21} = \sqrt{3}\, E_{0'1}\epsilon^{\pm j30} = (Z_s + 3Z_l + Z_r)I_{ba} = (Z_s + 3Z_l + Z_r)\frac{I_{a1}}{\sqrt{3}}\,\epsilon^{\pm j30}$$

Then dividing both sides of this equation by $\sqrt{3}\,\epsilon^{\pm j30}$ gives

$$E_{0'1} = \left(\frac{Z_s}{3} + Z_l + \frac{Z_r}{3}\right) I_{a1}$$

which in terms of the ideal neutral voltage, balanced impedance, and line current is the *a*-phase voltage equation for a wye-wye circuit equivalent to a delta-delta circuit.

The solution of the equations for one phase of the equivalent all-wye circuit determines the complete behavior of a balanced system because all phases appear to act independently of each other for balanced conditions, and differ from each other only in 120 and 240 degree time phase relations. Accordingly, the circuit of Fig. 11–24*a* can be replaced for computational purposes by its one-phase equivalent of Fig. 11–24*b*. The diagram of Fig. 11–24*c* is the form such one-phase equivalents take in commercial practice, and the diagram of Fig. 11–24*d* is the still further simplified circuit which may be used for the actual calculations.

The impedances to be used at all points are simply the wye or wye equivalents per phase. However, the presence of transformers with the consequent change in line-to-neutral voltages from one point in a system to another requires some adjustment in impedance magnitudes in accordance with the square of the ratio of turns (see equation 9–49). A scheme known as "per unit" or "per cent" constants has been developed for the express purpose of handling such impedance adjustments. The per unit method has the effect of transforming the network so that all transformations of voltages appear (line-to-line) as 1 : 1. Because it is not the purpose here to develop transformer theory or per unit constant techniques, in all following discussions in this chapter *line-to-line voltage* transformations will be considered as 1 : 1. The method of calculation used will then correspond to the scheme used in actual practice; yet transformer theory and per unit constant methods need not be developed for an understanding of the calculations.

The self-impedances Z_A and Z_B of Fig. 11–24*d* represent the total impedance effect from line-to-neutral of both windings of each of the three phases of the transformer banks. Because of the non-linear character of the transformers—coils of wire practically imbedded in iron—the impedance effect of the primary and secondary cannot be separated and so must be treated as a single unit, and this in spite of the fact that the separate windings of the transformer have separate and usually different self-impedances. For simplicity in thinking and calculating, the total impedance effect of the two windings of one phase of the transformer accordingly should be imagined as concentrated in one of the windings.

In terms of the delta-wye bank at *A* of Fig. 11–24*a*, suppose all the transformer impedance is imagined in the wye side and is Z_A. This impedance $Z_A = Z_{AY}$ is then the impedance to neutral of the transformer bank and is so indicated in Fig. 11–24*d*. Suppose, on the other hand, that the impedance of the transformer is imagined in the delta winding. An impedance which will be symbolized by $Z_{A\Delta}$ is then in each of the three windings of the delta side. But the voltages from line-to-line on each side of the transformers are to be of the same magnitude so for each of the three transformers the ratio of transformation is $\sqrt{3} = V_\Delta/V_Y$. Accordingly, because impedances on one side of a transformer are transferred to the other side by the square of the ratio of transformation, the equivalent impedance per transformer when assumed concentrated on the delta side is

$$Z_{A\Delta} = Z_{AY}(\sqrt{3})^2 = 3Z_{AY}$$

where Z_{AY} is the total impedance per transformer assumed concentrated on the wye side. But the relation of this last equation is exactly the one which specifies the wye and delta equivalences of balanced impedances. Therefore, *the equivalent line-to-neutral impedance* of a wye-delta, or similarly a delta-wye, bank of transformers under *balanced* conditions and line-to-line voltage transformation of 1 : 1 is the total transformer impedance from line-to-neutral viewed from the wye side, or one third of the total impedance of the transformer from line-to-line viewed from the delta side.

If the transformer bank is connected delta-delta, the ratio of transformation is 1 : 1 for a 1 : 1 line-to-line voltage ratio. Consequently the equivalent line-to-neutral impedance of a 1 : 1 delta-delta bank is simply one third of the line-to-line impedance viewed from either side.

After a balanced three-phase network has been transformed into an equivalent all-wye system, all ideal neutral and neutral points of the system are at the same potential. It may be assumed, therefore, that all ideal neutral and neutral points are joined by an impedanceless bus. As a result, the voltage from any point in the network to neutral can be computed by calculating the voltage between this point and the neutral point of the generators. Thus in Fig. 11–24*d* the voltage from the point *b* (secondary terminal of the transformer) to neutral may be obtained from the equation of the mesh 0–*a*–*b*–0

$$E_g = (Z_g + Z_A)I + V_{bn}$$

from which

$$V_{bn} = E_g - (Z_g + Z_A)I \tag{11–57}$$

Example 11:7 The networks of Fig. 11–25*a* and *b* represent one phase of a balanced three-phase system feeding energy to a load. Suppose the load impedance is $Z_r = 13.2 + j10$ ohms. The generated internal line-to-neutral impedances are $Z_{g1} = 0.12 + j12$, $Z_{g2} = 0.1 + j11$. The other impedances are as given in the diagram of Fig. 11–25*b*. Assume the generator voltages are in phase and use these voltages as reference. Also assume that the generator terminal voltages are held constant at 13,200 volts between lines. Determine the currents of the network, the line-to-neutral voltages at *m*, *n*, *y*, and of the load. Note that the impedances given in the diagram for the delta-delta banks of transformers are actually one-third of the impedance of each of the three transformers connected in delta.

Solution Since there are six branches and four nodes in the network, three node equations or three mesh equations will serve to determine the node voltages or the currents. The mesh equations will be used.

The regulated (constant) terminal voltages of the alternators will be taken as reference, so that

$$V_{g1} = V_{g2} = \frac{13{,}200}{\sqrt{3}} + j0 = 7620 + j0$$

Because the terminal voltages of the alternators are held constant the internal impedances of the alternators will have no effect on the currents of the system.

The three mesh equations are then

$$0 = (0.108 + j0.91)I_{g1} - (0.09 + j0.71)I_{l1} - (0.018 + j0.2)I_r$$
$$0 = -(0.09 + j0.71)I_{g1} + (0.396 + j3.19)I_{l1} - (0.104 + j0.9)I_r$$
$$7620 + j0 = -(0.018 + j0.2)I_{g1} - (0.104 + j0.9)I_{l1} + (13.32 + j11.1)I_r$$

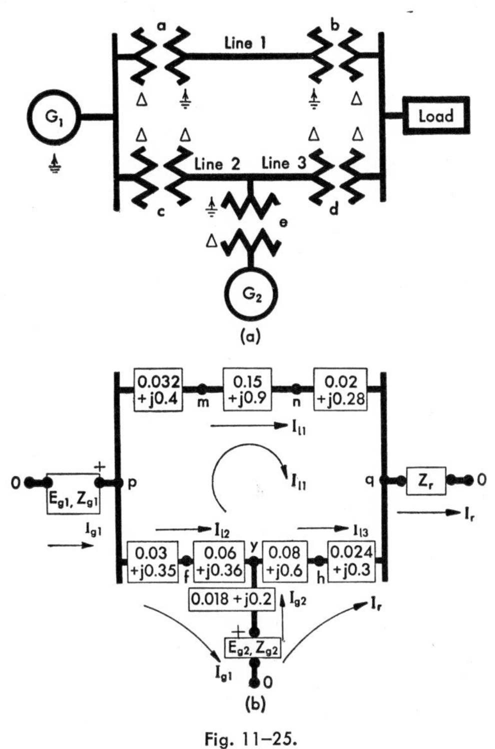

Fig. 11–25.

The solution of these equations for the current is a routine process and will not be indicated here. The results are

$$I_{g1} = 151.5 - j93.4$$
$$I_{l1} = 113.3 - j71.5$$
$$I_r = 283.5 - j179.6$$

The other currents in the circuit, namely I_{l2} and I_{l3} are

$$I_{l2} = I_{g1} - I_{l1} = 38.2 - j21.9$$
$$I_{l3} = I_r - I_{l1} = 170.2 - j108.1$$

The line-to-neutral voltage at point m can be determined from the equation for the closed path 0–p–m–0,

$$V_{g1} = (0.032 + j0.4)I_{l1} + V_{m0}$$

so

$$V_{m0} = (7620 + j0) - (0.032 + j0.4)(113.3 - j71.5)$$
$$= 7587.8 - j43.03$$

The magnitude of this voltage is

$$|V_{m0}| = 7588$$

and the voltage from line-to-line at the wye side of the transformers at a of Fig. 11–25a is

$$|V_{ml}| = \sqrt{3}|V_{m0}| = 13{,}142$$

Similarly at n for the path 0–g–n–0,

$$-I_r(13.2 + j10) - I_{l1}(0.02 + j0.28) + V_{n0} = 0$$

and

$$\begin{aligned} V_{n0} &= (13.2 + j10)(283.5 - j179.6) + (0.02 + j0.28)(113.3 - j71.5) \\ &= 5560.5 + j494.57 \end{aligned}$$

The voltage between lines at the wye terminals of the wye-delta transformer bank at b of Fig. 11–25a is

$$|V_{nl}| = \sqrt{3}\,|V_{n0}| = \sqrt{3}\,5561 = 9632$$

At y the voltage between lines may be calculated as follows:

$$V_{g2} = (0.018 + j0.2)I_{g2} + V_{y0}$$

from which

$$\begin{aligned} V_{y0} &= (7620 + j0) - (0.018 + j0.2)(132 - j86.2) \\ &= 7600.4 - j24.85 \end{aligned}$$

The voltage between lines at the junction of lines 1 and 2 is

$$|V_{yl}| = \sqrt{3}\,|V_{g0}| = 13{,}164$$

The line-to-neutral voltage at the terminals of load is simply

$$\begin{aligned} V_r &= Z_rI_r = (13.2 + j10)(283.5 - j179.6) \\ &= 5538 + j464 \end{aligned}$$

and the voltage between lines at the load is

$$|V_{rl}| = \sqrt{3}\,|V_r| = 9625$$

11.14 Some Useful Computational Methods and Network Equivalents.

It is often a practical necessity to know the currents in all parts of a system for short circuits at many different points. With the short circuit currents and voltages known, protective relays and other protective devices can be installed to assure continuous service. If the short circuit current distribution is not known, protecting a system is at best a hit-and-miss affair.

The method of calculating the behavior of balanced three-phase systems given in the preceding article can be used for even the most extensive networks. However, it has been found impractical to use this method for many of the system studies which must be carried out. Performing the computations required to determine the current distri-

Fig. 11–26. Network calculator. (Courtesy, Westinghouse Electric & Mfg. Co.)

bution, in even a simplified present-day power network, time after time as short circuits are assumed to be located at different places is simply not feasible. Instead, large numbers of variable resistors, inductors, and capacitors are assembled in a group. These units, together with some miniature generators and the appropriate controls, form a network calculator as shown in Fig. 11–26. The actual network under consideration is set in miniature on this calculator and the currents and voltages measured for any desired condition of the network. Very extensive studies of a network can be performed in a relatively short time by this test equipment.

As an auxiliary to the calculator certain computational techniques are helpful. In addition, these computational techniques are very helpful in many investigatory calculations.

One very common device employed in power network calculations and reductions is the wye-delta or delta-wye transformation of equation 10–25 or 10–24. The use of these transformations will be shown in Example 11–8.

It is often desirable to be able to determine the currents throughout a network for certain specified input currents. The node system of equations is effective for solving this problem. An illustration is given in Example 11–9.

Because of the prevalence of magnetically coupled parallel wires in power systems an equivalent circuit containing no magnetic coupling is sometimes useful. Such an equivalent circuit may be established as follows. The simple circuit of Fig. 11–27*a* represents two parallel wires joined at *a*. As a mutual induction device these wires should be polarity marked at the same ends of the wires as shown, because currents into

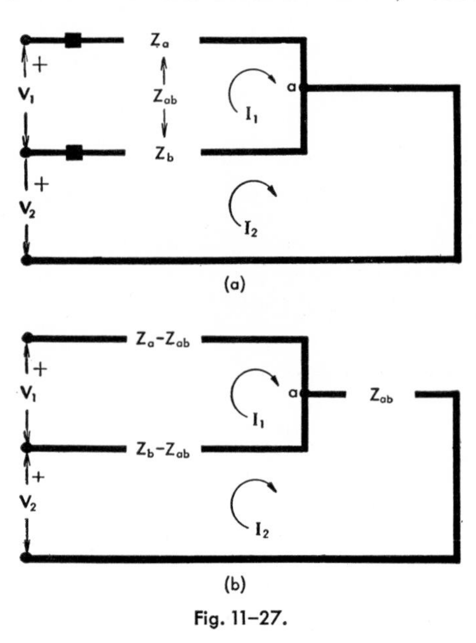

Fig. 11–27.

the wires at the polarity marks will produce magnetic fields in the same direction outside the wires. The magnetic field between the wires is, of course, not common to both wires. The voltage equations for the two meshes of Fig. 11–27*a* are

$$V_1 = (Z_a - Z_b)I_1 - 2Z_{ab}I_1 - Z_bI_2 + Z_{ab}I_2$$
$$V_2 = -Z_bI_1 + Z_{ab}I_1 + Z_bI_2 \qquad (11\text{–}58)$$

But these equations are also exactly the two equations for Fig. 11–27*b*. The two circuits of Fig. 11–27 are consequently equivalent. For many purposes the network of Fig. 11–27*b* which *contains no mutual induction* is simpler to handle than its counterpart containing mutual induction. Example 11–9 illustrates the use of "sliding of the mutual" off the end of the line, as forming the equivalent circuit of Fig. 11–27*b* is sometimes called.

Example 11:8 Calculate the balanced three-phase short circuit current into a short circuit at the load point q of Fig. 11–25*b*. Assume constant E_{g1} and E_{g2} in phase at 13,200 volts between lines with $Z_{g1} = 0.1 + j11$, $Z_{g2} = 0.12 + j12$.

Solution Examination of the impedances of Fig. 11–25*b* indicates that the ratio of the reactance to resistance is about 10. This is typical of power systems. As a consequence, short circuit calculations are usually based on pure reactance impedances. Under this assumption the network of Fig. 11–25*b* is as given in Fig. 11–28*a*.

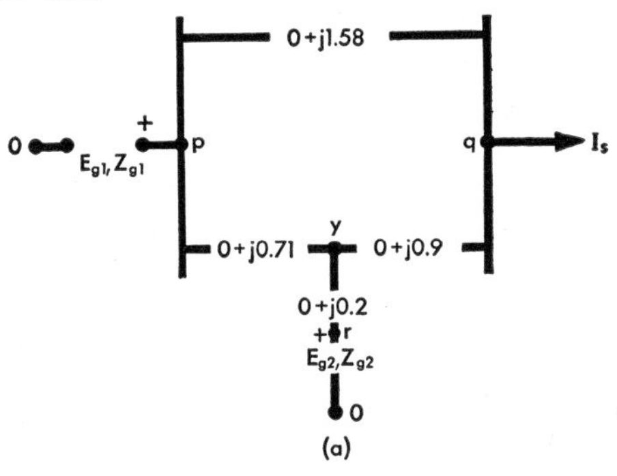

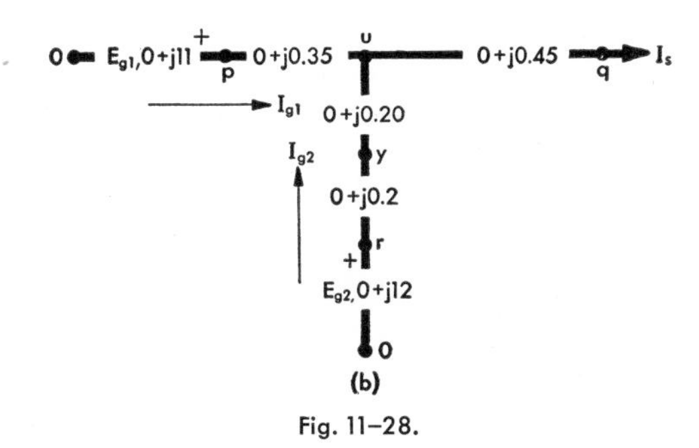

Fig. 11–28.

Since only the short circuit current is desired, the delta-wye transformation of equation 10–25 will permit the immediate simplification of Fig. 11–28*a* to Fig. 11–28*b*, for

$$Z_{pu} = \frac{Z_{pq}Z_{py}}{Z_{pq} + Z_{py} + Z_{yq}} = \frac{j1.58j0.71}{j3.19} = j0.352$$

$$Z_{qu} = \frac{Z_{pq}Z_{yq}}{Z_{pq} + Z_{py} + Z_{yq}} = \frac{j1.58j0.9}{j3.19} = j0.446$$

$$Z_{yu} = \frac{Z_{yq}Z_{yp}}{Z_{pq} + Z_{py} + Z_{yq}} = \frac{j0.9j0.71}{j3.19} = j0.20$$

Two mesh equations or one node equation will serve to determine the behavior of this *equivalent* network of Fig. 11–28*b*. The node equation at u is

$$-E_{g1}\frac{1}{j11.35} - E_{g2}\frac{1}{j12.4} + V_{u0}\left(\frac{1}{j11.35} + \frac{1}{j12.4} + \frac{1}{j0.45}\right) = 0$$

If the equal and inphase generator voltages are taken as reference, this equation becomes

$$\frac{-13200}{\sqrt{3}}\left(\frac{1}{j11.35} + \frac{1}{j12.4}\right) + V_{u0}\frac{2.39}{j} = 0$$

Solving for V_{u0} gives

$$V_{u0} = 538 \text{ volts}$$

The short circuit current is then

$$I_s = \frac{V_{u0}}{j0.45} = \frac{538}{j0.45} = -j1195 \text{ amperes}$$

in each of the three lines feeding into the short circuit at q.

The generator currents may be determined from the node voltage V_{u0} as follows. Through the generator connected to p the voltage equation is

$$E_{g1} = j11.35I_{g1} + V_{u0}$$

so that

$$I_{g1} = \frac{\dfrac{13{,}200}{\sqrt{3}} - 538}{j11.35} = -j624 \text{ amperes}$$

The generator terminal voltage may be obtained from

$$E_{g1} = I_{g1}j11 + V_{p0}$$

and

$$V_{p0} = 7620 - 6864 = 756 \text{ volts}$$

or, between lines,

$$V_{pl} = \sqrt{3}\, 756 = 1311 \text{ volts}$$

The other generator current is the difference between the short circuit current and the generator current just calculated and is

$$I_{g2} = -j571 \text{ amperes}$$

The generator terminal voltage may be obtained from

$$E_{g2} = j12I_{g2} + V_{r0}$$

and

$$V_{r0} = 7620 - 6852 = 768 \text{ volts}$$

Between lines the voltage at generator 2 is

$$V_{rl} = \sqrt{3}\, 768 = 1332 \text{ volts}$$

Example 11:9 Determine the current distribution in the balanced three-phase network represented by Fig. 11–29*a* for the input currents as shown.

Solution The node equations are the most effective means of solving this problem. The mutual induction may be separated from the self-induction of the lines in accordance with Fig. 11–29*b*. A total of four node equations is required for this circuit. Alternatively, in accordance with the equivalent circuits of Fig. 11–27, Fig. 11–29*b* can be modified to Fig. 11–29*c*. This circuit requires three node equations for its solution. Still another approach to determining the current distribution is possible. If the equivalent series-parallel, then the delta-wye, transformation is used on Fig. 11–29*c*, only a wye circuit is left with the three input currents feeding into the vertices of the wye. The current distribution of the wye is then determined. The current distribution must then be traced back through the preceding transformations. This process is awkward and not so effective as the straight node method, which will now be used.

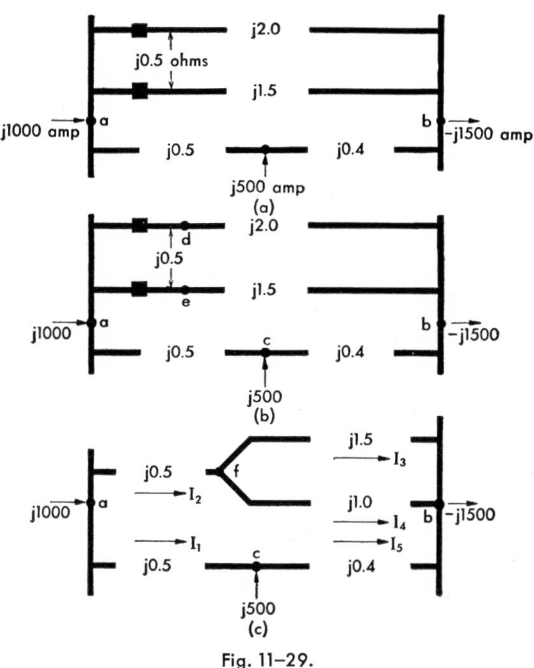

Fig. 11–29.

The node equations for Fig. 11–29*c* are (node *c* reference)

Node *a*:

$$-j1000 + V_a\left(\frac{1}{j0.5} + \frac{1}{j0.5}\right) - V_f\frac{1}{j0.5} = 0$$

Node *f*:

$$-V_a\frac{1}{j0.5} + V_f\left(\frac{1}{j0.5} + \frac{1}{j1.5} + \frac{1}{j1.0}\right) - V_b\left(\frac{1}{j1.5} + \frac{1}{j1.0}\right) = 0$$

Node *b*:

$$-j1500 - V_f\left(\frac{1}{j1.5} + \frac{1}{j1.0}\right) + V_b\left(\frac{1}{j1.5} + \frac{1}{j1.0} + \frac{1}{j0.4}\right) = 0$$

The solution of these equations can be expedited by combining and rearranging to give

$$\begin{aligned} -1000 &= 4V_a - 2V_f \\ 0 &= -2V_a + 3.67V_f - 1.67V_b \\ -1500 &= - 1.67V_f + 4.17V_b \end{aligned}$$

which, on solving, give

$$V_a = -525 \text{ volts}$$

and

$$I_1 = \frac{V_a}{j0.5} = j1050 \text{ amperes}$$

$$V_f = -550 \text{ volts}$$

and

$$I_2 = \frac{V_a - V_f}{j0.5} = \frac{25}{j0.5} = -j50 \text{ amperes}$$

$$V_b = -580 \text{ volts}$$

and

$$I_3 = \frac{V_f - V_b}{j1.5} = \frac{30}{j1.5} = -j20 \text{ amperes}$$

$$I_4 = \frac{V_f - V_b}{j1.0} = \frac{30}{j1.0} = -j30 \text{ amperes}$$

$$I_5 = \frac{-V_b}{j0.4} = \frac{580}{j0.4} = -j1450 \text{ amperes}$$

PROBLEMS

11–1 Write the equations for the circuit of Fig. 11–2*a* if the load impedances have mutual induction between them. Assume magnetic coupling polarity marks at *a*, *b*, and *c*.

11–2 A wye-connected load has the impedances as given in Example 11–4, with the following source voltages:

$$E_{10} = -100 - j50, \quad E_{20} = -50 + j0, \quad E_{30} = -100 + j50$$

Find the three load currents of the network. Draw a complete vector diagram on which all currents and voltages are represented.

11–3 The currents in the lines of a wye-wye connection (Fig. 11–2*a*) are $I_{a1} = 10 + j0$, $I_{b2} = 3 + j4$, and $I_{c3} = -13 - j4$. What are the generator terminal voltages? Draw the complete vector diagram. The circuit impedances are as given in Example 11–4.

11–4 Consider the single-phase three-wire circuit of Fig. 11–2*b*. Write the equations and compute the currents. The voltages are $E_{01} = 86.6 + j50$, $E_{20} = 0$, and $E_{30} = 80 + j60$. Draw the complete vector diagram. The impedances are: $Z_{1a} = Z_{2b} = Z_{3c} = 1 + j2$, $Z_{an} = 8 + j6$, $Z_{cn} = 10 - j10$, $Z_{bn} = 0$, $Z_{01} = Z_{03} = 0.2 + j1$, and $Z_{02} = 0$.

11–5 Repeat Problem 11–4 for the two-phase voltages $E_{01} = jE_{03} = j(100 + j0)$.

11–6 Solve Problem 11–2 by the node method.

11–7 Determine the currents in the circuit of Fig. 11–4 if the voltages and impedances are: $E_{12} = 100\epsilon^{j0}$, $E_{23} = 100\epsilon^{j120}$, and $E_{31} = 100\epsilon^{j240}$; $Z_{12} = Z_{23} = Z_{31} = 1 + j4$, $Z_{1a} = Z_{2b} = Z_{3c} = 0$, $Z_{ab} = 10 + j0$, $Z_{bc} = 0 + j10$, and $Z_{ca} = 0 - j10$. Show numerically that the sum of the load terminal voltages and of the generator terminal voltages is zero. Show that the sum of the line currents is zero. Draw a complete vector diagram.

11–8 Repeat Problem 11–7 for the set of generator voltages $E_{12} = 100\epsilon^{j0}$, $E_{23} = 100\epsilon^{j240}$, and $E_{31} = 100\epsilon^{j120}$.

11–9 Determine the currents in the circuit of Fig. 11–7, where $Z_{10} = Z_{20} = Z_{30} = 1 + j4$, $Z_{1a} = Z_{1b} = Z_{1c} = 2 + j3$, $Z_{0n} = 4 + j6$, and $Z_{an} = 10 + j0$, $Z_{bn} = 0 + j10$, $Z_{cn} = 0 - j10$. Draw the complete vector diagram. Also check the validity of the relations suggested in Art. 11–4. The generated phase voltages are balanced at 100 volts and of negative phase sequence. Use E_{20} as the reference.

11–10 Assume that a set of balanced voltages of 100 volts between lines are maintained at the terminals of a wye load of $Z_{bn} = 0.1 + j10$, $Z_{cn} = 1 - j20$, and $Z_{an} = 0.2 - j15$. Find the line-to-neutral voltages and compare in magnitude with the line voltages. Draw the vector diagram in the same general form as Fig. 11–16. Assume a positive sequence of voltages.

11–11 Suppose two identical voltmeters of internal resistance 10,000 ohms are connected in wye with a third impedance $10{,}000\epsilon^{j45}$ ohms. Determine the voltmeter indications for positive and negative phase sequences of balanced line voltages of 100 volts. Describe briefly but carefully the exact process by which this wye connection could be used as a phase sequence indicator.

11–12 Using the expressions of equations 11–17 and 11–18 show the relation of the currents in an unbalanced wye circuit, for balanced generator line voltages, under a change in phase sequence, if $Z_{cn} = Z_{bn}$.

11–13 Assume a set of three not equal impedances connected in delta. Assume further that the generator is regulated so that the load terminal voltages remain constant and exactly balanced. The line currents are then of the form (using equations 11–14):

$$I_{a1} = I_{ba} + I_{ca} = \frac{V_{ba}}{Z_{ba}} + \frac{V_{ca}}{Z_{ca}} = \left[\frac{a}{Z_{ba}} - \frac{a^2}{Z_{ca}}\right] V_{cb}$$

Show that the three line currents do or do not change in magnitude under a change in line voltage phase sequence if the impedances have the same phase angle.

11–14 Assume that the impedances $Z_{ab} = 10\epsilon^{j45}$, $Z_{bc} = 20\epsilon^{j45}$, $Z_{ca} = 30\epsilon^{j45}$ are connected in delta to a balanced set of line voltages of 300 volts magnitude. Show that the line currents do not change in magnitude for a change in voltage phase sequence. Use V_{cb} as the reference vector. See the preceding problem.

11–15 Prove that the center of gravity—ideal neutral—of a triangle is at the intersection of the medians and that this intersection is two-thirds of the distance from any vertex along the median.

11–16 Show how to derive equations 11–34 and give in words a rule for determining the ideal neutral voltages which equations 11–34 suggest.

11–17 Assume the line voltages connected to the wye of Fig. 11–11*c* are unbalanced but constant. Also assume that $Z_{na} = Z_{nb} = Z_{nc} = Z$. Show that the ideal neutral voltages and phase voltages are the same, i.e.,

$$V_{n'a} = V_{na}; \quad V_{n'b} = V_{nb}; \quad V_{n'c} = V_{nc}$$

by comparing a set of equations similar to equations 11–19, 11–20, and 11–21 for general conditions with equations 11–34. Also show that the line currents are out of phase with the ideal neutral voltages by the phase angle, σ, of the impedances.

11–18 A wye set of phase voltages is given as $|E_{10}| = 100$, $|E_{20}| = 200$, and $|E_{30}| = 300$. The complex numbers representing these voltages are oriented so that E_{20} leads E_{10} by 100°, and E_{30} lags E_{10} by 110°. Use a reference axis 30° ahead of E_{20}. Draw this system of voltages to scale. Can a closed triangle be formed from these voltages? Determine graphically the line voltages. Determine the complex number form of the line voltages from the diagram. Locate the ideal neutral of the triangle. Show graphically that the vector sum of the ideal neutral voltages is zero.

11–19 (*a*) A set of wye-phase voltages is given by $E_{10} = 50 + j86.6$, $E_{20} = 200 + j0$, and $E_{30} = -100 + j173.2$. Determine the line voltages and $E_{00'}$, where $E_{00'}$ is the voltage between the ideal neutral of the triangle and the common point 0 of the voltages. (*b*) The following voltages form a wye set: $E_{00'} = 200 + j200$, $E_{10'} = 100 + j0$, $E_{20'} = -50 + j86.6$, and $E_{30'} = -50 - j86.6$. Determine the line-to-neutral and line voltages. Solve both parts of this problem graphically by drawing vector diagrams and adding and subtracting the proper vectors.

11–20 A set of line-to-neutral voltages of phase sequence 1–2–3 are represented by vectors successively 120 degrees apart. The magnitudes of the voltages are $|E_{10}| = 50$ volts, $|E_{20}| = 100$ volts, and $|E_{30}| = 150$ volts. Use E_{10} as reference. These voltages are connected to a wye circuit made up of balanced impedances such that the impedance per phase is $Z_p = 7 + j7$. Assume the generator internal impedances are zero. Compute the currents and all voltages. Show that the line currents lag the voltage to the ideal neutral of the generator terminal triangle by 45 degrees. Draw the vector diagram.

11–21 A wye three-wire circuit has currents $I_{na} = 2 - j6$, and $I_{nb} = -6 + j3$. Assume that the terminal voltages of the generator are kept constant at the no-load value and that the connections between line and load are short and hence have negligible impedances. The load impedances are balanced and equal to $3 + j8$. Determine the line-to-neutral and line-to-line voltages at the load. Draw the vector diagram and show that all the line currents lag the voltages to the ideal neutral of the generator terminal voltage triangle by the load power factor angle.

11–22 Suppose that the generator voltages are kept constant at the values given in Problem 11–18. Suppose further that the internal impedances of the generator and the line impedances are negligible and that the wye load impedances are $Z_{na} = Z_{nb} = Z_{nc} = 2 - j6$. Determine the line-to-neutral load voltages, the load terminal voltages, and the currents. Use E_{12} as the reference axis. Draw the vector diagram.

11–23 A three-phase wye-connected motor is connected to a generator with constant terminal voltages of 200. The balanced phase impedances equivalent to the motor input are $Z_{na} = 6 + j8$ and of the connecting lines are $Z_{1a} = 1 + j4$. Determine the magnitudes of the line voltages of the load, the line-to-neutral voltages, connecting line voltages, and currents. Draw the complete vector diagram. Use E_{12} as the reference vector—positive phase sequence.

11–24 (*a*) A wye-connected motor is connected by negligible impedance leads to a constant voltage balanced three-phase circuit of 200 volts between lines (positive sequence). This load has equivalent impedances of $Z_{na} = Z_{nb} = Z_{nc} = 10 + j10$ ohms. Compute the currents and line-to-neutral voltages without using complex numbers. Sketch the vector diagram, not to scale but roughly in proportion. (*b*) Suppose Z_{na} is changed to $10 - j10$ by paralleling one phase of the motor with a capacitor. Compute the currents and voltages. Note the difference in the time and work required for the two solutions.

11–25 A delta set of impedances $Z_{ab} = 10 + j10$, $Z_{bc} = 8 + j8$, and $Z_{ca} = 6 - j8$ are connected to a balanced, positive sequence set of line voltages of 200 volts. Determine all the currents. Use V_{ba} as the reference vector.

11–26 Find the ratio of the delta line currents to the wye line currents if the same set of three equal impedances are connected to the same balanced three-phase system—first in delta then in wye.

11–27 Determine the phase and line currents of a delta-connected synchronous motor if $Z_p = 10 - j10$. The line voltages are 100 volts. Draw a complete vector diagram. Use the 1–3–2 sequence.

11–28 Show, for a delta-delta connection (Fig. 11–4) which is completely balanced but with three different balanced sets of impedances—one in the generator, Z_s, one on the line, Z_l, and one at the load, Z_r—that

$$E_{21} = (Z_s + 3Z_l + Z_r)I_{12} = (Z_s + 3Z_l + Z_r)I_{ba}$$
$$E_{32} = (Z_s + 3Z_l + Z_r)I_{23} = (Z_s + 3Z_l + Z_r)I_{cb}$$
$$E_{13} = (Z_s + 3Z_l + Z_r)I_{31} = (Z_s + 3Z_l + Z_r)I_{ac}$$

Write the general equations and solve them to establish this result.

11–29 (*a*) Determine the power absorbed by the load, the connecting lines, and the generator internal impedances for the circuit of Example 11–6. Determine the total power *delivered* by the generator, and check against the sum of the power *absorbed* by each part of the system. (*b*) Repeat for Example 11–1. (*c*) Repeat for Example 11–4.

11–30 A wye-connected synchronous motor has equivalent phase impedances of 10 ohms at 0.8 power factor lead. The line voltages of the generator are 2300 volts. Determine the total power. Use E_{20} as the reference vector and assume a phase sequence of *a–c–b*. Draw the vector diagram assuming that the line impedances and the internal impedances of the generator are zero.

11–31 Determine the complex form of the total apparent power for each of the circuits given in Examples 11–1, 11–4, and 11–6. Note that, while the power components of these results give a useful number, namely, the total watts absorbed by the system, the reactive volt-ampere component has very little if any significance for unbalanced circuits.

11–32 A set of completely balanced loads are connected to a wye generator, the positive sequence phase voltages of which are 200. The connected loads are: 20-kva induction motor of 0.75 power factor lag, 10-kw synchronous motor of 0.9 power factor lead, and 5 kva of lights at 1.0 power factor. Determine the generator currents, the total power, and the total reactive volt-amperes.

11–33 The load given in Problem 11–32 is to be corrected to give 0.8 leading power factor in each phase. What is the kva rating of each of the three static capacitors which must be connected in wye to make such a correction? What is the capacitance of the capacitors if the system operates at 60 cps? What are the generator phase currents with the capacitors installed? What is the equivalent impedance of the whole load?

11–34 A delta circuit has balanced impedances of $Z_r = 20 + j40$ at the load, and $Z_l = 3 + j6$ on the lines. The negative sequence terminal voltages of the generator are kept constant at 220 volts. Determine all currents and voltages, the total power absorbed by this system, the power absorbed by the load and by the line. Check the total power against the sum of the $|I^2|R$ losses. Draw the complete vector diagram using V_{cb} as reference. Solve this problem by using complex numbers only where absolutely necessary.

11–35 Connect, in parallel, the impedances $Z_{na} = 8 - j6$, $Z_{nb} = 6 + j8$, and $Z_{nc} = 10 + j10$ in wye, and the impedances $Z_{ab} = 8 + j8$, $Z_{bc} = 10 + j0$, $Z_{ca} = 4 + j10$ in delta, to a balanced three-phase circuit of 200 volts between lines. Determine the line currents required from the system. The phase sequence is positive and the reference axis is to be V_{ab}. What is the total power absorbed by the delta load and the wye load? Determine the total apparent power in complex form on the assumption of a wye-connected generator. Draw a vector diagram.

11–36 A balanced wye circuit of $10 + j10$ ohms per phase is connected in parallel with a balanced delta circuit of $8 + j6$ ohms per phase across a 220-volt, negative sequence, balanced system of voltages. Determine the total line currents taken from the system. What is the total power and what is the complex form for the total apparent power if the alternator is wye connected? How does the sum of the apparent power for each connection compare with the total apparent power as determined from the line currents? Use complex numbers in this problem only where necessary or convenient. Draw a vector diagram.

11–37 A wye network is made up of three impedances of $8 + j8$ ohms. A delta network made up of a second set of identical impedances is connected in parallel with the wye onto 110-volt three-phase positive sequence voltages. Determine all currents and voltages and the total power absorbed. Do not use any complex numbers. Draw the vector diagram.

11–38 Show that reversing *any* two terminals of a three-phase connection always changes the phase sequence.

11–39 An induction motor—lagging power factor—operates on a full-load kva of 1000 from 4000-volt three-phase lines. What is the line current? The power factor is 0.76. What is the power absorbed? Draw the current and voltage vector diagram.

11–40 The three currents $I_{a1} = 5 + j8.66$, $I_{b2} = -10 + j0$, and $I_{c3} = 5 - j8.66$ are in a three-phase connection. Is the circuit balanced? What is the power factor if V_{0a} is reference axis? What is the phase resistance and reactance if $|Z_p| = 10$ ohms wye connected? What are the line voltages, the total power, and the total reactive volt-amperes?

11–41 A three-phase circuit shows a power consumption of 3600 watts. Each branch of the load has an impedance of $3 + j4$ ohms. The voltage between lines is 173.2. Is the load connected wye or delta?

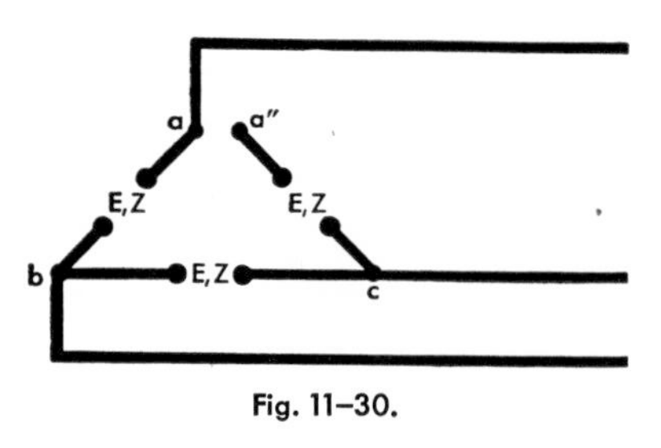

Fig. 11–30.

11–42 The delta impedances of Fig. 11–30 are all equal to $2 + j2$ ohms at fundamental frequency. The balanced 200-volt positive sequence generated voltages have a third harmonic of 10 volts. Compute the voltage at the gap aa''. If this gap is closed, compute the current and show that the third harmonic voltage does not appear between the lines.

11–43 If Z_{ab} of Fig. 11–30 is $1 + j1$ and the others $2 + j2$, compute the current if the gap aa'' is closed, and compute the component of third harmonic voltage appearing between each line.

11–44 Show by solving three-mesh equations simultaneously that, if the circuit of Fig. 11–6*a* is balanced,

$$E_a = E_{10} = \left(Z_g + Z_l + \frac{Z_r}{3}\right) I_{1a}$$

$$E_b = E_{20} = \left(Z_g + Z_l + \frac{Z_r}{3}\right) I_{2b}$$

$$E_c = E_{30} = \left(Z_g + Z_l = \frac{Z_r}{3}\right) I_{3c}$$

where $Z_g = Z_{10} = Z_{20} = Z_{30}$, $Z_l = Z_{1a} = Z_{2b} = Z_{3c}$, and $Z_r = Z_{ab} = Z_{bc} = Z_{ca}$. Since $Z_r/3$ is the balanced wye-phase impedance equivalent to the balanced delta-phase impedance Z_r, the above equations also demonstrate the wye-delta equivalence.

11–45 Show by solving three simultaneous mesh equations that, if the circuit of Fig. 11–6*b* is balanced,

$$E_{1n'} = \left(\frac{Z_g}{3} + Z_l + Z_r\right) I_{1a}$$

$$E_{2n'} = \left(\frac{Z_g}{3} + Z_l + Z_r\right) I_{2b}$$

$$E_{3n'} = \left(\frac{Z_g}{3} + Z_l + Z_r\right) I_{3c}$$

where $E_{1n'}$, $E_{2n'}$, and $E_{3n'}$ are the ideal neutral voltages of the generator, and Z_g, Z_l, and Z_r are the balanced impedances of generator, line, and load. The results given here show that a balanced delta-connected generator can be replaced by a balanced wye-connected generator with ideal neutral phase voltages and equivalent wye internal impedances.

11–46 Verify the results of Example 11–7 by the node method. Write node equations at nodes *y*, and *q* of Fig. 11–25*b*. An equation at node *p* is not required because this node voltage is determined by the constant terminal voltage of the alternator.

11–47 Determine all currents and the load terminal voltage to neutral and between lines for the balanced three-phase circuit represented by Fig. 11–31. The alternator generated voltages are regulated at 13,200 volts between lines. Use V_{g1} as reference and assume V_{g2} lags V_{g1} by 10 degrees.

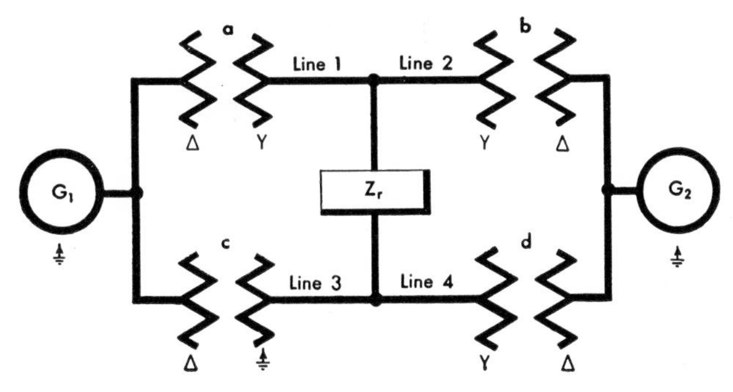

Fig. 11–31.

The impedances are $Z_{g1} = 0.08 + j8.0$, $Z_{g2} = 0.09 + j8.5$, $Z_{l1} = 0.14 + j0.86$, $Z_{l2} = 0.11 + j0.66$, $Z_{l3} = 0.1 + j0.6$, $Z_{l4} = 0.09 + j0.52$, $Z_r = 13.3 + j8.2$, $Z_{a\Delta} = 0.09 + j1.05$, $Z_{bY} = 0.02 + j0.28$, $Z_{c\Delta} = 0.075 + j0.9$, and $Z_{dY} = 0.032 + j0.39$. Draw the complete three-phase circuit this diagram represents.

11–48 Assume that a short circuit between all three phases occurs at the center of the line 1 of Fig. 11–31. Assume the data given in Problem 11–47 and calculate the currents in all parts of the circuit. What is the current into the short circuit? It is common practice to neglect all loads connected to three-phase systems and all resistance for short circuit calculations. Draw the complete circuit diagram represented by this figure.

11–49 Assume that a short circuit occurs at the load Z_r of Fig. 11–25. Neglect all resistance and calculate all currents and the generator terminal voltages. Use the data specified on Fig. 11–25*b* and in Example 11–7. The terminal voltages are not regulated but assume E_{g1} and E_{g2} constant at 13,200 volts line to line.

11–50 Assume that a balanced short circuit occurs at junction p of Fig. 11–25. Compute all currents and load and alternator terminal voltages. Use the data of Fig. 11–25 and Example 11–7. Assume the alternator terminal voltages are not held constant but E_{g1} and E_{g2} are, and neglect all resistance.

11–51 Suppose an additional load of $Z_r = 5 - j3$ ohms is connected at the center of line 1 of Fig. 11–25*a*. Determine all currents and load and alternator terminal voltages. Use the data of Fig. 11–25*b* and Example 11–7. Assume that the internal generator voltages E_{g1} and E_{g2} (line to neutral) are held constant at 7600 volts.

11–52 Assume that the lines of Fig. 11–25*a* are close enough together so that under short circuit condition they must be considered as magnetically coupled through $j0.2$ ohms between lines 1 and 2 and $j0.4$ ohms between lines 1 and 3. Assume currents out of the generators $|I_{g1}| = 1500$ amp, $|I_{g2}| = 2000$ amp and into a short circuit at the load 3500 amp. Determine the current distribution of the network. Use the reactance parameters of Fig. 11–25*b*. Neglect all resistance.

CHAPTER **12**

Power and Energy Measurements in Power Systems

The measurement of the energy absorbed by a load is one of the most important aspects of the operation of a power system. Both the owner and consumer are interested in these measurements because the total cost of using and the revenue from selling electrical energy are determined from energy measurements.

Measurement of single-phase energy and power is a problem only so far as the design of the meter itself is a problem. Although not nearly all the questions concerning meters have been answered, the watthour meter and indicating wattmeter in their present-day form are very accurate and rugged instruments, and are entirely satisfactory when operating under the conditions for which they are designed, namely, the substantially constant frequency and constant voltage of present-day power systems. If the frequency differs much from the 60 cps of power system fundamentals, if the voltage varies widely, or if the wave form differs much from a sine wave, the measurements are somewhat in error, and the accuracy of the meter should not be taken for granted.

A power-measuring instrument—indicating wattmeter—is shown in Fig. 1–14. This instrument indicates the average power at each instant. An energy-measuring instrument—integrating watthour meter—is shown in Fig. 1–21. This instrument measures the integrated sum of the product of the instantaneous power and time over which the meter is connected. Indicating and integrating meters are both widely used—the indicating meter in laboratories and for test purposes and the integrating meter for measuring the energy consumption of all loads connected to power systems.

The design and operating characteristics of these meters are rather extensive problems in themselves and will not be considered further here. Manufacturers' bulletins or other books* may be consulted for details.

---

* Edison Electric Institute, *Electrical Meterman's Handbook*, 5th Edition, 1940. G. W. Stubbings, *Commercial A. C. Measurements*, D. Van Nostrand Co., 2nd Edition, 1937.

The problem to be considered here is to determine the indication of power and energy meters as a result of their location at certain places in electric circuits, and not their indications as a result of temperature changes, position and types of coils used, the shape of iron cores, etc., in the meters themselves.

In the discussion to follow, it should be constantly kept in mind that so far as connecting them in the circuit is concerned, there is absolutely no difference between indicating and integrating power and energy meters. Accordingly, in subsequent discussions usually no attention will be paid to whether it is an energy- or a power-measuring meter which is to be connected. The results obtained can be applied to both, even though they will be deduced in terms of power symbols because the equations are thereby made a little simpler.

12.1 Power and Energy Measurement in a Two-Wire Single-Phase Circuit.

Typical connection diagrams for connecting indicating wattmeters (Fig. 12–1*a*) and integrating watthour meters (Fig. 12–1*b*) are simple and rarely lead to any difficulty. If for any reason either the current or

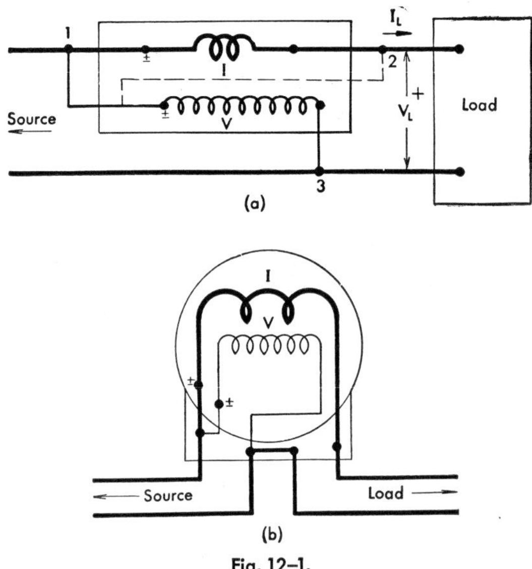

Fig. 12–1.

voltage coil has its connection reversed, of course, the meter will deflect backwards, but a reversal of either the current or voltage coil connections will rectify this difficulty immediately. A typical modern single-phase integrating watthour meter installation is shown in Fig. 1–21.

Aside from a reversal of current or voltage coil connections, the voltage coil connected to point 2 instead of 1 of Fig. 12–1*a* is the only other possible variation. The voltage coil connected to point 1 is known as the "outside" connection, and the voltage coil connected to point 2 is known as the "inside" connection. These connections have slightly different characteristics which are important in certain measurements. Consider, first, the "outside" connection. The power measured by the meter is the *scalar* product (Art. 2–8) of the voltage across the voltage coil terminals and the current through the current coil. Because a power or energy meter can be made to deflect backwards even on alternating current, it is desirable to have a computational technique which will permit the determination of the sign of the meter deflection as well as the magnitude. The polarity marks of power and energy meters—indicated by $\pm$ marks on Fig. 12–1—are placed so that, if the subscripts on the current and voltage symbols are written in the order from the marked to the unmarked terminal, the scalar product of the current and voltage will give both the magnitude and direction of the meter indication. A negative value of the scalar product means a backward indication. Therefore, for the "outside" connection of Fig. 12–1*a*, in accordance with the convention just indicated,

$$P_{13}{}^{12} = V_{13} \cdot I_{12} = (V_{12} + V_L) \cdot I_{12} = V_{12} \cdot I_{12} + V_L \cdot I_{12} \quad (12\text{–}1)$$
$$= P_I + P_L$$

i.e., the outside-connected meter indicates the power loss in the load *plus* the power loss in the *current coil.*

Next consider the "inside" connection. The power indicated by the meter is

$$P_{23}{}^{12} = V_{23} \cdot I_{12} = V_L \cdot (I_{23} + I_L) = V_L \cdot I_{23} + V_L \cdot I_L \quad (12\text{–}2)$$
$$= P_V + P_L$$

and the inside-connected meter indicates the power loss of the load *plus* the power loss of the *voltage coil.* A power or energy meter will, therefore, *always* indicate more than the load it is supposed to measure by the loss in one of its own coils.

The current and voltage coil losses are made small enough to be negligible for many commercial measurements, through designing voltage coils with impedances as *high* as possible and current coils with impedances as *low* as possible and still permit the development of large enough magnetic fields to give the required meter torque. The watthour meters in present-day practice are connected "outside" as shown in Fig. 12–1*b*. The customer thus pays for the loss in the intermittently excited current coil, and the power company supplies the losses of the constantly excited voltage coil. This particular arrangement has been standardized because with the inside connection the voltage coil loss tends to make the meter creep—just perceptibly rotate. With this compromise, no further attention is paid to the meter losses in commercial applications.

Obviously for any precise measurement, or for low-power or energy measurements, the meter losses must be accounted for. Wattmeters can be obtained with a special compensating coil in the meter which eliminates the self-loss measurement.

12.2 Reactive Volt-Ampere Measurements in a Single-Phase Two-Wire Circuit.

The measurement of reactive volt-amperes is confined almost entirely to being an adjunct to energy measurements in power systems. As has already been pointed out in Art. 1–7, reactive volt-amperes are a sort of discrepancy factor between the average power and total volt-amperes. Measuring a quantity from the electric circuit which corresponds to reactive volt-amperes, therefore, may be expected to require a rather special technique. Actually, however, the technique required is neither difficult nor very different from power measurements.

Reactive volt-amperes have already been defined as

$$Q = |V|\,|I| \sin \theta \tag{12–3}$$

for a sinusoidal system. If the currents and voltages are not sinusoidal, little more than a cursory examination is required to show that the concept of reactive volt-amperes is difficult to define so that it has any meaning. Power systems as a whole, being very nearly sinusoidal, permit the use of the formula 12–3.

The measurement of Q is carried out by a simple modification of a power meter. Thus, consider

$$|V|\,|I| \cos (90 \pm \theta) = \mp |V|\,|I| \sin \theta \tag{12–4}$$

Therefore, if an additional 90-degree phase shift can be added to the current-voltage relation in a wattmeter, reactive volt-amperes will be measured.

There are several methods of producing this 90-degree phase shift.* Only one of the simplest will be considered here.

The voltage coil of an indicating wattmeter is as nearly *non-inductive* as it is possible to make it, whereas the voltage coil of a watthour meter is very highly inductive at the operating frequency. A method of making an *indicating* Q (var) meter is suggested in Problem 12–2. Making a reactive component meter of a *watthour* meter can be accomplished as shown in Fig. 12–2*b*. A capacitor and resistor in parallel are connected in series with the highly inductive voltage coil of the meter shown in Fig. 12–2*b*. If the capacitance is properly adjusted, the circuit of Fig. 12–2*b* can be made largely capacitive so that the current I_{ab} can be made to lead the voltage V_{ab} by an angle close to 90 degrees. Thus an almost 180-degree shift in phase of the current of Fig. 12–2*b* from that of Fig. 12–

* G. W. Stubbings, *Commercial A. C. Measurements*, D. Van Nostrand Co., 2nd Edition, revised, 1937, Chapter VIII.

$2a$ is possible. But since only 90 degrees is required, obtaining the required phase shift is always possible. There is an additional requirement that the current magnitudes of these two circuits must be the same in order that the Q meter indicates $|V|\,|I|\sin\theta$ and not $|V|\,|kI|\sin\theta$.

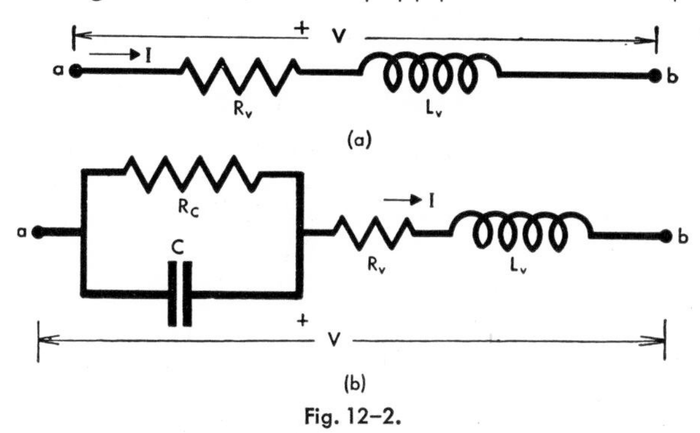

Fig. 12–2.

The parallel resistance, R_c is a second variable, such that by means of R_c and the capacitor C, the circuit can be adjusted so that the desired phase shift with no change in current magnitude can be established. The details of the process constitute a problem in series parallel circuit analysis (see Problem 12–3).

12.3 Power Measurement in a Single-Phase Three-Wire Circuit.

If more than two wires are used to supply energy to a load, more than one wattmeter, or one wattmeter with more than one driving element, is required, as is shown next.

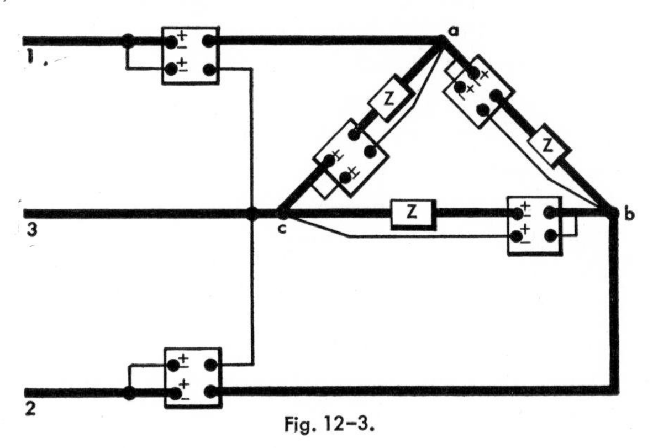

Fig. 12–3.

In terms of instantaneous values, the average power absorbed from the three wires by the load of Fig. 12–3 is

$$P_0 = P_{ab} + P_{bc} + P_{ca} = \frac{1}{T}\int_0^T [v(t)_{ab}i(t)_{ab} + v(t)_{bc}i(t)_{bc} + v(t)_{ca}i(t)_{ca}]\,dt \tag{12–5}$$

which is the sum of the indications of three wattmeters connected to the load as shown in the figure. This expression can be written in terms of line currents and line voltages by making use of the relations

$$\begin{aligned} i(t)_{1a} &= i(t)_{ab} - i(t)_{ca} \\ i(t)_{2b} &= i(t)_{bc} - i(t)_{ab} \end{aligned} \tag{12–6}$$

If $i(t)_{ca}$ and $i(t)_{bc}$ are eliminated from equation 12–5 by means of these last two equations,

$$\begin{aligned} P_0 &= \frac{1}{T}\int_0^T \{v(t)_{ab}i(t)_{ab} + v(t)_{bc}[i(t)_{2b} + i(t)_{ab}] + v(t)_{ca}[i(t)_{ab} + i(t)_{a1}]\}\, dt \\ &= \frac{1}{T}\int_0^T \{i(t)_{ab}[v(t)_{ab} + v(t)_{bc} + v(t)_{ca}] + v(t)_{bc}i(t)_{2b} + v(t)_{ca}i(t)_{a1}\}\, dt \end{aligned} \tag{12–7}$$

But

$$v(t)_{ab} + v(t)_{bc} + v(t)_{ca} = 0$$

from the circuit itself. Hence

$$\begin{aligned} P_0 &= \frac{1}{T}\int_0^T [v(t)_{bc}i(t)_{2b} + v(t)_{ac}i(t)_{1a}]\, dt \\ &= \frac{1}{T}\int_0^T v(t)_{bc}i(t)_{2b}\, dt + \frac{1}{T}\int_0^T v(t)_{ac}i(t)_{1a}\, dt \end{aligned} \tag{12–8}$$

which in terms of wattmeter indications may be expressed as

$$P_0 = P_{bc}{}^{2b} + P_{ac}{}^{1a} = V_{bc} \cdot I_{2b} + V_{ac} \cdot I_{1a} \tag{12–9}$$

The two wattmeters indicating these average power values are shown in the lines 1–a and 2–b in Fig. 12–3. The two wattmeters will measure the power absorbed by the load shown *no matter what the value of the impedance of the load or the voltages of the three wires* (see Problems 12–4 and 12–5) since in the foregoing derivation no restrictions have been placed on the impedances or voltages.

The conclusion reached in equation 12–9 has very important practical implications. For from this conclusion, instead of a three-wire load requiring three meters as suggested by the three-load impedances of Fig. 12–3, *two* meters will measure the total power absorbed. Metering installations are thereby made one-third cheaper.

It is not necessary that the two wattmeters, in the lines of Fig. 12–3, be connected in the particular two lines shown. Eliminating different currents from equation 12–5, by means of equations 12–6 and the third equation similar to these two, produces different forms for equation 12–9. All these forms are similar to equation 12–9, however. The only difference is that different line currents will appear associated with different voltages, but always so that the two wattmeters will have a common voltage connection on the line containing no wattmeter, and the polarity marks on the meters must be connected toward the source in the manner shown in Fig. 12–3.

Exactly the same conclusion can be reached for any wye load connected to any three-wire system, since a delta load can always be computed which is equivalent to any wye load. A direct derivation can also be used (see Problem 12–6). Therefore, since modifications of a delta load covers all possible loads which can be connected to a three-wire line, *two* wattmeters will measure the total power absorbed from *any three-wire* line.

In practice, meter men are never really satisfied with a metering installation until it has been reduced to using only *one* meter for each power circuit. The arrangement of Fig. 12–4 is the form of the electrical circuit

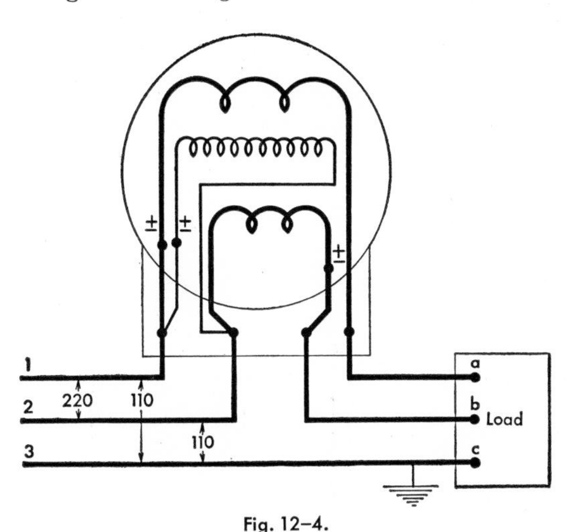

Fig. 12–4.

which has been devised for three-wire *single-phase* watthour meters. The current coils have half as many turns as would be required to measure the power for a particular current at the voltage V_{ab}. Also, the lower of the two current coils is wound oppositely to the upper coil. The correctness of the operation of the three-wire meter can be shown in three steps as follows:

Consider an impedance across *a–c* of Fig. 12–4. The power, because V_{ab} is twice $V_{ac} = V_{cb}$, is

$$P_{ac}{}^{1a} = V_{ac} \cdot I_{1a} = \frac{V_{ab}}{2} \cdot I_{1a} = V_{ab} \cdot \frac{I_{1a}}{2} \tag{12–10}$$

and the last term is exactly what the meter indicates. Similarly, for an impedance across *b–c*,

$$P_{bc}{}^{2b} = V_{bc} \cdot I_{2b} = -\frac{V_{ab}}{2} \cdot I_{2b} = V_{ab} \cdot \frac{I_{b2}}{2} \tag{12–11}$$

Fig. 12–5*a*. Three-phase three-wire metering installation showing meter and current transformers. (Courtesy, Public Service Co. of Colorado)

Fig. 12–5*b*. High-voltage three-phase metering; 13-kv current and voltage transformers and lightning protection devices shown. (Courtesy, Public Service Co. of Colorado)

Fig. 12–6a. Front view of three-phase three-wire watthour meter of two elements. (Courtesy, Westinghouse Electric & Mfg. Co.)

which once more represents the meter indication because the lower coil is wound oppositely to the upper coil. Finally, for a load across *a–b*, where $I_{1a} = I_{b2}$,

$$P_{ab}{}^{1a} = V_{ab} \cdot I_{1a} = V_{ab} \cdot \left(\frac{I_{1a}}{2} + \frac{I_{b2}}{2}\right)$$

$$= V_{ab} \cdot \frac{I_{1a}}{2} + V_{ab} \cdot \frac{I_{b2}}{2} \qquad (12\text{–}12)$$

which represents the meter indication.

If the voltages of the load are not exactly $V_{ab} = 2V_{ac} = 2V_{cb}$, measurement by a three-wire single-phase meter, of a load across the terminals *a–b* will be the only one which is correct. For such a load the meter voltage coil is operating at the voltage of the load and the load current is in the meter coils. Equation 12–12 still applies, therefore, unaltered. On the other hand, a load across either of the low-voltage pair of wires, for a voltage across them different from the one here assumed, will not

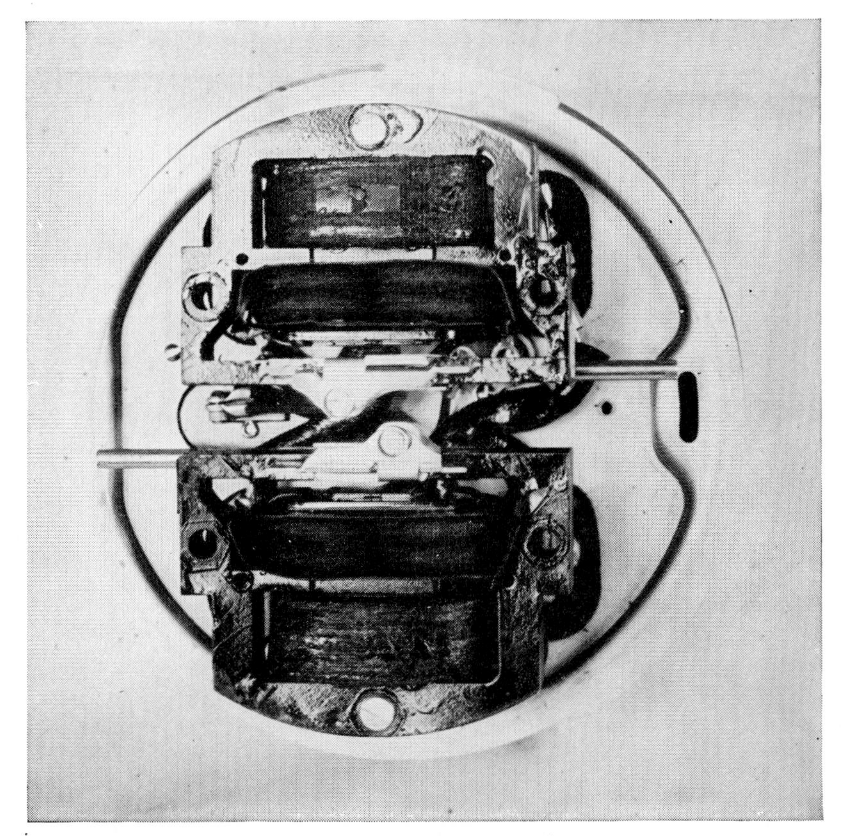

Fig. 12–6b. Rear view of the meter shown in Fig. 12–6a. (Courtesy, Westinghouse Electric & Mfg. Co.)

be correctly measured by the meter as the following shows. In particular for a load between the low-voltage wires *a–c*, the load power is

$$P_L = V_{ac} \cdot I_{1a} = kV_{ab} \cdot I_{1a}$$

where k is a complex or real number factor usually nearly equal to one half. The power indication of the meter is as given by equation 12–10. It is

$$P_m = V_{ab} \cdot \frac{I_{1a}}{2}$$

The decimal error is accordingly

$$\text{decimal error} = \frac{P_m - P_L}{P_L} = \frac{V_{ab} \cdot \dfrac{I_{1a}}{2} - kV_{ab} \cdot I_{1a}}{kV_{ab} \cdot I_{1a}} = \frac{(0.5 - k)V_{ab} \cdot I_{1a}}{kV_{ab} \cdot I_{1a}} \tag{12–13}$$

which, if k is *real*, becomes

$$\text{decimal error} = \frac{0.5 - k}{k}$$

Fig. 12–6c. Side view of the meter shown in Fig. 12–6a. (Courtesy, Westinghouse Electric & Mfg. Co.)

Example 12:1 Suppose the voltages across the load of Fig. 12–7 are $V_{ac} = 100 + j0$, $V_{cb} = 100 + j0$. Determine the indication of a three-wire meter connected in this circuit as in Fig. 12–4. Compare the meter indication with the actual power absorbed.

Solution The currents are

$$I_{1a} = V_{ac}\left(\frac{1}{Z_{ac}} + \frac{1}{Z_{de}}\right) = \frac{100 + j0}{8.66 + j5} + \frac{100 + j0}{10 + j0} = 18.66 - j5$$

$$I_{b2} = \frac{V_{cb}}{Z_{cb}} = \frac{100 + j0}{5 - j5} = 10 + j10$$

The meter connected as in Fig. 12–4 indicates the sum (equation 12–12)

$$P = V_{ab} \cdot \frac{I_{1a}}{2} + V_{ab} \cdot \frac{I_{b2}}{2} = V_{ab} \cdot \left(\frac{I_{1a}}{2} + \frac{I_{b2}}{2}\right)$$
$$= (200 + j0) \cdot (14.33 + j2.5) = 2866 \text{ watts}$$

Fig. 12–6*d*. Shaft and disks of the meter shown in Fig. 12–6*a*. (Courtesy, Westinghouse Electric & Mfg. Co.)

From the loads directly, the power is

$$P = V_{ac} \cdot I_{ac} + V_{ac} \cdot I_{ed} + V_{cb} \cdot I_{cb} = V_{ac} \cdot \frac{V_{ac}}{Z_{ac}} + V_{ac} \cdot \frac{V_{ac}}{Z_{ed}} + V_{cb} \cdot \frac{V_{cb}}{Z_{cb}}$$
$$= (100 + j0) \cdot (8.66 - j5) + (100 + j0) \cdot (10 + j0) + (100 + j0) \cdot (10 + j10)$$
$$= 866 + 1000 + 1000 = 2866 \text{ watts}$$

The meter thus measures the load exactly for equal voltages V_{ac} and V_{cb}.

12.4 Measurement of Three-Phase Three-Wire Power with Two Wattmeters.

The proof given in the preceding article that two wattmeters properly connected in a three-wire line will measure the power absorbed by any load connected to this line applies without any modification to a three-phase system. The two-meter connection shown in the lines of Fig. 12–3 corresponds to the requirement of this proof and represents the method of properly connecting two meters to measure three-phase, three-wire power or energy.

The pictures of Fig. 12–5 show actual installations. As for the three-wire single-phase system, only one meter is used for three-phase three-wire, but this three-phase three-wire watthour meter consists of *two* distinct elements, or meters, placed in vertical alignment in the same case so that a common shaft serves to support the two meter disks and to drive the common gear train connected to the indicating dials. The sum of the two meter indications required by equation 12–9 is thereby automatically computed by the two meters applying their torques to the common shaft. The pictures of Fig. 12–6 show several views of a two-element three-phase watthour meter.

Example 12:2 Compute the wattmeter indications for the meters of Fig. 12–7. The generator terminal voltages are balanced and constant at 100 volts. The phase sequence is *abc*.

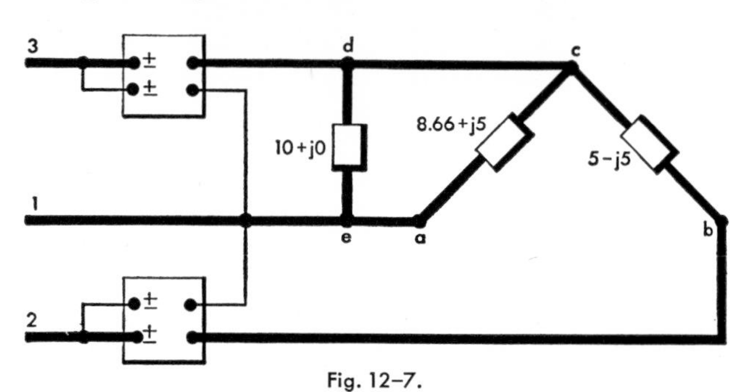

Fig. 12–7.

Solution Since the reference axis is arbitrary, the most convenient one will be chosen. The voltage V_{ca} should be most convenient because two of the loads are connected across it. Accordingly, since the voltage sequence is *a–b–c*,

$$V_{ca} = 100 + j0 = 100\epsilon^{j0}$$
$$V_{bc} = -50 + j86.6 = 100\epsilon^{j120}$$
$$V_{ab} = -50 - j86.6 = 100\epsilon^{j240}$$

The phase currents are

$$I_{ca} = \frac{V_{ca}}{Z_{ca}} = \frac{100\epsilon^{j0}}{10\epsilon^{j30}} = 10\epsilon^{-j30} = 8.66 - j5$$
$$I_{de} = \frac{V_{ca}}{Z_{de}} = \frac{100\epsilon^{j0}}{10\epsilon^{j0}} = 10\epsilon^{j0} = 10 + j0$$
$$I_{bc} = \frac{V_{bc}}{Z_{bc}} = \frac{100\epsilon^{j120}}{5\sqrt{2}\epsilon^{-j45}} = 14.14\epsilon^{j165} = -13.66 + j3.66$$

and the line currents required to determine the wattmeter indications are

$$I_{3d} = I_{de} + I_{ca} + I_{cb} = 32.32 - j8.66$$
$$I_{2b} = I_{bc} = -13.66 + j3.66$$

The wattmeter indications are

$$P_{ca}{}^{3d} = V_{ca} \cdot I_{3d} = (100 + j0) \cdot (32.32 - j8.66) = 3232 \text{ watts}$$
$$P_{ba}{}^{2b} = V_{ba} \cdot I_{2b} = (50 + j86.6) \cdot (-13.66 + j3.66) = -683 + 317$$
$$= -366 \text{ watts}$$

The total power absorbed by the load is the sum of these two meter indications

$$P_0 = P_{ca}{}^{3d} + P_{ba}{}^{2b} = 2866 \text{ watts}$$

As a check on this result, consider the sum of the $|I|^2R$ losses

$$|I_{ed}|^2R_{ed} = \left|\frac{100}{10}\right|^2 10 = 1000 \text{ watts}$$
$$|I_{ac}|^2R_{ac} = \left|\frac{100}{10}\right|^2 8.66 = 866 \text{ watts}$$
$$|I_{cb}|^2R_{ab} = \left|\frac{100}{5\sqrt{2}}\right|^2 5 = \frac{1000 \text{ watts}}{2866 \text{ watts}}$$

Equation 12–5 may be extended to represent the power absorbed by any set of N wires on which a mesh load is connected by simply adding more terms with the proper subscripts. The resultant equation can be modified in exactly the same fashion as equation 12–5, with a result which shows that *N–1 wattmeters in N–1 lines, with the remaining line as the common wattmeter voltage connection*, will measure the power absorbed by the load. The same conclusions may be reached for star-connected loads; hence, in general, N–1 wattmeters will measure the power of an N-wire load.

12.5 Measurement of Three-Phase Three-Wire Power with Three Wattmeters.

The use of three wattmeters to measure power in a three-phase three-wire system is not of importance in practice, but a consideration of this method will lead to some interesting conclusions and will permit a further development of the technique of computing wattmeter indications.

Because of the brevity of the expressions, the scalar, or dot, product of the current and voltage vectors will be used instead of the integral of the instantaneous values, as in equation 12–5. The dot product form is, of course, applicable only to pure sine waves of current and voltage, but the conversion of the expressions derived to instantaneous values of any wave form is not difficult, and the derivation of results is much easier in vector form.

The sum of the wattmeter indications of Fig. 12–8 is

$$P_{10}{}^{1a} + P_{20}{}^{2b} + P_{30}{}^{3c} = V_{10} \cdot I_{1a} + V_{20} \cdot I_{2b} + V_{30} \cdot I_{3c} \quad (12\text{–}14)$$

Since the wattmeter voltage coils are connected in wye,

$$V_{10} = V_{12} + V_{20}$$
$$V_{30} = -V_{23} + V_{20} \tag{12–15}$$

and equation 12–14 becomes, on substituting these values,

$$P_{10}{}^{1a} + P_{20}{}^{2b} + P_{30}{}^{3c} = V_{12} \cdot I_{1a} + V_{32} \cdot I_{3c} + V_{20} \cdot (I_{1a} + I_{2b} + I_{3c})$$

which, because the sum of the currents is zero, is

$$P_{10}{}^{1a} + P_{20}{}^{2b} + P_{30}{}^{3c} = V_{12} \cdot I_{1a} + V_{32} \cdot I_{3c} \tag{12–16}$$

giving an expression representing a *two-wattmeter* combination of the kind derived in equation 12–9. But such a two-wattmeter combination measures the power into the load. Hence, the combination of wattmeters given in Fig. 12–8 will also measure the power absorbed by the

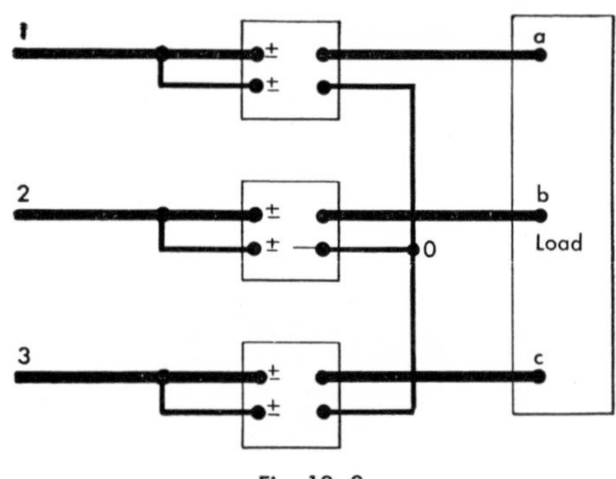

Fig. 12–8.

load *even though the common point of the wattmeter potential coils is free of the system.* Furthermore, note that no restrictions have been placed on the resistances of the wattmeter potential coils. The voltages across the wattmeter potential coils may, therefore, vary widely, thus making the individual wattmeter indications vary widely. The sum of these indications, however, will always give the total power of the load.

If N wattmeters are connected with potential coils in star (wye) to an N-wire system, the sum of the indications will give the total power absorbed by any load connected to the N-wire system. The N–1 wattmeter method of the preceding article is a special case of the N wattmeter method of this article with one of the potential coil resistances equal to zero. This zero potential coil resistance is evidently equivalent to connecting the common point of the potential coils to one of the wires of the system.

Example 12:3 (*a*) Determine the indications of the three wattmeters in the circuit of Fig. 12–9*a*. The resistance of the wattmeter voltage coils are R_{01} = 15,000 ohms, R_{02} = 10,000 ohms, and R_{03} = 8000 ohms. Phase sequence is *a–b–c*. (*b*) Suppose the connection in the wattmeter lead 1,0 breaks at *x*. Find the wattmeter indications.

Solution (*a*) It will be necessary to determine the current in each wattmeter and the voltage across each voltage coil to find the wattmeter indication.

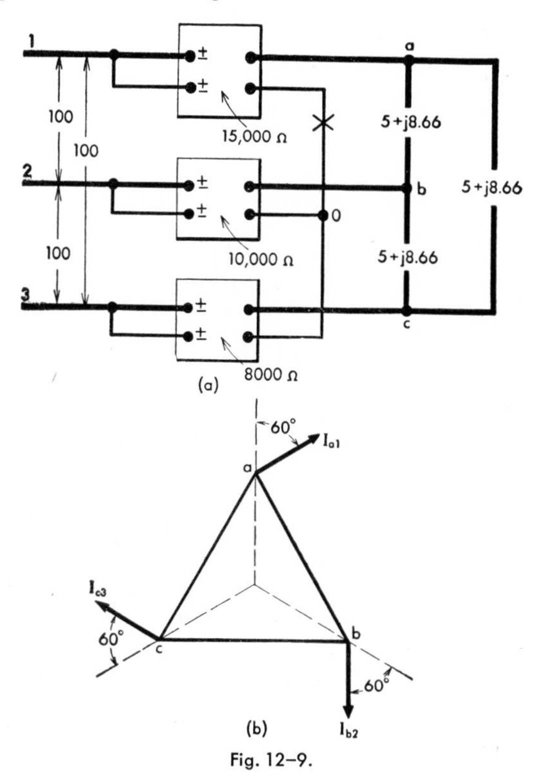

Fig. 12–9.

Since the delta-connected load is balanced, the currents are easily determined from the relations developed in Chapter 11. The line currents are

$$|I_l| = \sqrt{3}\,|I_p| = \sqrt{3}\,\tfrac{100}{10} = 17.32 \text{ amp}$$

Furthermore, the currents are located vectorially as indicated in Fig. 12–9*b*. This location of the currents follows from the relation, deduced in Chapter 11, that the line currents of a balanced impedance load have the same phase angle with the ideal neutral voltages as the phase currents have with the phase voltages.

The line currents are, therefore, if V_{cb} is chosen as the reference (see Fig. 12–9*b*),

$$I_{a1} = \frac{|V_p|}{|Z_p|}\sqrt{3}\,\epsilon^{j30} = \tfrac{100}{10}\sqrt{3}\,\epsilon^{j30} = 15 + j8.66$$

$$I_{b2} = \frac{|V_p|}{|Z_p|}\sqrt{3}\,\epsilon^{-j90} = \tfrac{100}{10}\sqrt{3}\,\epsilon^{-j90} = 0 - j17.32$$

$$I_{c3} = \frac{|V_p|}{|Z_p|}\sqrt{3}\,\epsilon^{j150} = \tfrac{100}{10}\sqrt{3}\,\epsilon^{j150} = -15 + j8.66$$

The voltages across the wattmeter voltage coils must be obtained by solving the unbalanced wye formed by these voltage coils. The equations for this wye circuit are

$$V_{ab} = 25{,}000I_{10} - 10{,}000I_{03}$$
$$V_{bc} = -10{,}000I_{10} + 18{,}000I_{03}$$

From the vector diagram of Fig. 12–9*b*,

$$V_{ab} = 100\epsilon^{-j60} = 50 - j86.6$$
$$V_{bc} = 100\epsilon^{j180} = -100 + j0$$

so that, solving for the currents,

$$I_{10} = (-2.9 - j44.5)10^{-4}$$
$$I_{03} = (-57.1 - j24.8)10^{-4}$$

The current I_{20} is

$$I_{20} = I_{01} + I_{03} = (-54.2 + j19.7)10^{-4}$$

Therefore, the voltages across the wattmeter voltage coils are

$$V_{10} = R_{10}I_{10} = -4.35 - j66.75$$
$$V_{20} = R_{20}I_{20} = -54.2 + j19.7$$
$$V_{30} = R_{30}I_{30} = 45.68 + j19.84$$

The wattmeter indications may now be computed as

$$P_{10}{}^{1a} = V_{10} \cdot \mathrm{I}_{1a} = (-4.35)(-15) + (-66.75)(-8.66) = 643.3 \text{ watts}$$
$$P_{20}{}^{2b} = V_{20} \cdot I_{2b} = (-54.2)(0) + (19.7)(17.32) = 341.2 \text{ watts}$$
$$P_{30}{}^{3c} = V_{30} \cdot I_{3c} = (45.7)(15) + (19.8)(-8.66) = 513.4 \text{ watts}$$
$$P_0 = P_{10}{}^{1a} + P_{20}{}^{2b} + P_{30}{}^{3c} = 1498 \text{ watts}$$

The total power absorbed by the load is, from the balanced load power formula,

$$P_0 = \sqrt{3}|V_l|\ |I_l|\cos\theta_p = \sqrt{3}(100)(17.32)(0.5) = 1500 \text{ watts}$$

which checks the sum of the three wattmeter indications, even though the individual indications do not represent the power absorbed by any part of the circuit.

(*b*) The load and, therefore, wattmeter currents will not be affected by the breaking of the wattmeter potential circuit of the meter in line *a*. The wattmeter voltages will be affected and, from the fact that the potential coils of the wattmeters in lines *b* and *c* are now in series across the line *bc*, these voltages will be

$$V_{10} = 0$$
$$V_{20} = \tfrac{10}{18}V_{bc} = -55.5 + j0$$
$$V_{30} = \tfrac{8}{18}V_{cb} = 44.4 + j0$$

The wattmeters now indicate

$$P_{10}{}^{1a} = 0$$
$$P_{20}{}^{2b} = (-55.5)(0) + (0)(17.32) = 0$$
$$P_{30}{}^{3c} = (44.4)(15) + (0)(-8.66) = 666$$

These indications have no significance so far as the load is concerned.

12.6 Measurement of Power and Energy in a Four-Wire Three-Phase System.

As has already been indicated, the power of any four-wire circuit can be measured by three wattmeters. The single unit of commercial practice consisting of three meters in vertical alignment operating on one shaft is illustrated in Fig. 12–10. The electrical connections are illustrated in Fig. 12–11. From a practical standpoint, the use of the three-element meter is to be avoided wherever possible because of its size, cost, and the weight which the jeweled lower bearing must support. If the system is likely to be much unbalanced, there is no choice in the matter; the three-element meter must be used. If, however, the system voltages remain balanced, as they frequently do even though the load impedances are not balanced, a meter employing two disks, known as a split-coil, or $2\frac{1}{2}$-element, meter is used.

Fig. 12–10a. Front view of three-element three-phase watthour meter. (Courtesy, General Electric Co.)

The electrical connections of the split-coil meter are shown in Fig. 12–12. Two current elements are active in each meter. The two elements in series connected in line $2b$ each have the same number of turns as the other two current coils, and are each wound *oppositely* to the other coil of the element in which they are located. The conditions under which this meter will measure correctly the energy absorbed by a balanced-voltage four-wire three-phase load can be determined by writing the equations for the total registration of the meter.

The upper element indicates

$$P_u = V_{an} \cdot I_{1a} + V_{an} \cdot I_{b2} \tag{12–17}$$

and the lower element indicates

$$P_l = V_{cn} \cdot I_{3c} + V_{cn} \cdot I_{b2} \tag{12–18}$$

Fig. 12–10*b*. Installation of three-element three-phase meter. (Courtesy, Public Service Co. of Colorado)

The sum of these indications appears on the dials so that

$$P_0 = P_u + P_l = V_{an} \cdot I_{1a} + (V_{an} + V_{cn}) \cdot I_{b2} + V_{cn} \cdot I_{3c} \quad (12\text{–}19)$$

But for balanced line-to-neutral voltages of the load

$$V_{an} + V_{cn} = -V_{bn}$$

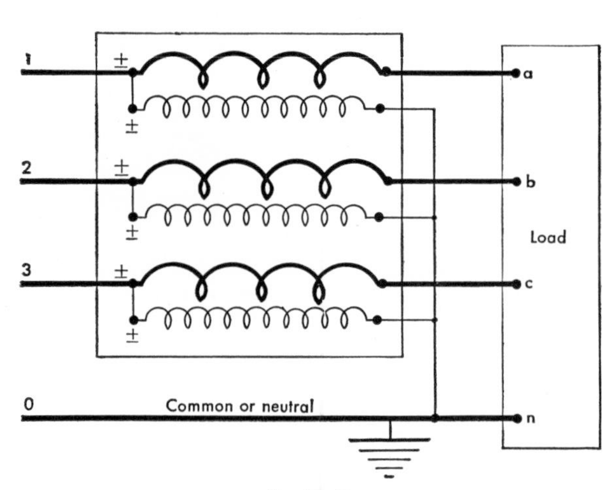

Fig. 12–11.

and equation 12–19 becomes

$$P_0 = V_{an} \cdot I_{1a} + V_{bn} \cdot I_{2b} + I_{cn} \cdot I_{3c} \tag{12–20}$$

which is exactly the power absorbed by the load. Accordingly, if the voltages are maintained in a balanced condition, the split-coil meter of *two* elements measures the four-wire three-phase power.

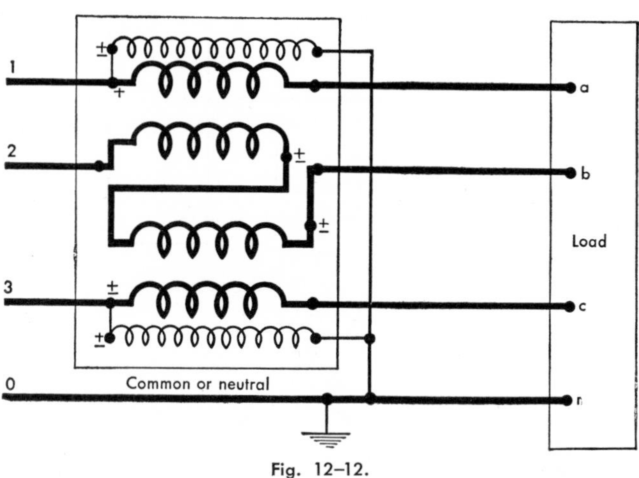

Fig. 12–12.

12.7 Two-Wattmeter Method for Balanced Loads.

Since commercial three-phase systems are usually balanced, a consideration of the two-wattmeter method of measuring power in a balanced three-phase system leads to useful results.

Suppose two wattmeters are connected as in Fig. 12–13*a* and that the load is as represented by the vector diagram of Fig. 12–13*b*. Whether the load is wye or delta connected is not important. From the circuit and vector diagram, the meter indications may be expressed as—$\theta < 0$ for lagging power factor—

$$P_{ab}{}^{1a} = |V_l|\,|I_l| \cos (30 + \theta) \tag{12–21}$$
$$P_{cb}{}^{3c} = |V_l|\,|I_l| \cos (30 - \theta) \tag{12–22}$$

The effect of a change in power factor or in phase sequence on the two balanced-load wattmeter indications may be deduced by means of vector diagrams. If the power factor changes from lag to lead, all the radiating current vectors of Fig. 12–13*b* will be moved counterclockwise past the dotted extension of the ideal neutral voltages, and

$$P_{ab}{}^{1a} = |V_l|\,|I_l| \cos (30 - \theta)$$
$$P_{cb}{}^{3c} = |V_l|\,|I_l| \cos (30 + \theta) \tag{12–23}$$

These meter indications are those of equations 12–21 and 12–22 interchanged because θ has changed sign—$\theta > 0$ for leading power factor.

A change of phase sequence will have the same effect on the two wattmeter indications as does a change in power factor from lead to lag or vice versa, i.e., it will interchange the formulas to be used for computing the wattmeter indications. This fact is easily deduced from the vector

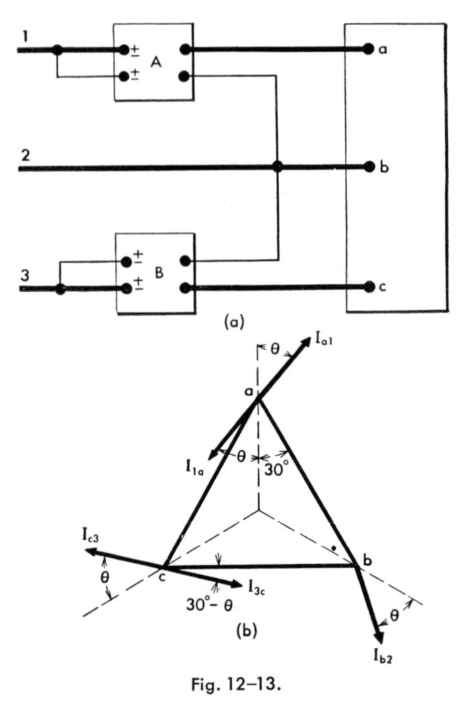

Fig. 12–13.

diagram because changing the phase sequence has the effect in Fig. 12–13*b* of simply interchanging all *b*'s and *c*'s on the diagram. Then

$$
\begin{aligned}
P_{ab}{}^{1a} &= |V_l|\,|I_l| \cos (30 - \theta) \\
P_{cb}{}^{3c} &= |V_l|\,|I_l| \cos (30 + \theta)
\end{aligned} \tag{12–24}
$$

These equations are once more the same *pair* of equations as deduced for leading and lagging power factor and for the other, or *a–b–c*, sequence. Evidently, therefore, if the load is balanced for any power factor or phase sequence, the two wattmeters will never indicate anything but the two results

$$
\begin{aligned}
P_1 &= |V_l|\,|I_l| \cos (30 + \theta) \\
P_2 &= |V_l|\,|I_l| \cos (30 - \theta)
\end{aligned} \tag{12–25}
$$

Furthermore, if either the power factor (lead or lag) or phase sequence are not known it is not possible to predict which meter will indicate which result.

The manner in which these two possible wattmeter indications vary is shown in Fig. 12–14. These curves are plotted for a volt-ampere product of unity. The actual wattmeter indications may be obtained for any θ by multiplying the ordinates of Fig. 12–14 by $|V_l|\,|I_l|$. These curves indicate that at unity power factor the two wattmeters indicate the same amount, and also that the indications are both positive for $0 \leqslant |\theta| < 60°$.

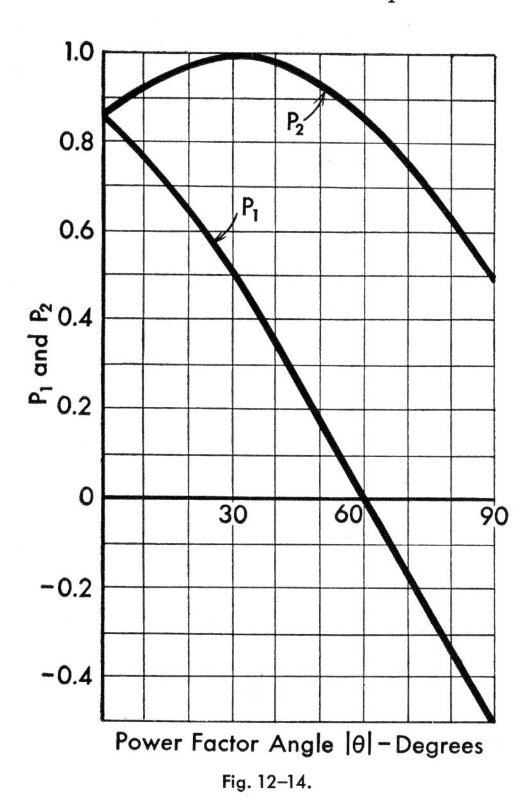

Fig. 12–14.

At $|\theta| = 60$ degrees one of the indications is zero and for $|\theta| > 60°$ one of the meter indications is negative. The total power of the system will, therefore, be the difference in the magnitudes of P_1 and P_2 for $60° < |\theta| \leqslant 90°$. At $|\theta| = 90°$ the two meter indications are equal in magnitude but of opposite sign so that the total power, given by the sum, is zero.

12.8 Power-Factor Determination by the Two Wattmeter Indications in a Balanced Three-Phase System.

An expression for the *magnitude* of the phase power factor angle of a balanced three-phase system, in terms of two wattmeter indications, may be derived as follows. Expanding equations 12–25 gives

$$P_1 = |V_l|\,|I_l|\,(\cos 30 \cos \theta - \sin 30 \sin \theta)$$
$$P_2 = |V_l|\,|I_l|\,(\cos 30 \cos \theta + \sin 30 \sin \theta)$$

Then

$$\frac{|P_1 - P_2|}{|P_1 + P_2|} = \left|\frac{2 \sin 30 \sin \theta}{2 \cos 30 \cos \theta}\right| = \frac{|\tan \theta|}{\sqrt{3}}$$

and

$$|\tan \theta| = \sqrt{3}\,\frac{|P_1 - P_2|}{|P_1 + P_2|} \tag{12–26}$$

The absolute values or magnitudes are used since, as has already been indicated in the preceding article, the magnitudes which a particular pair of wattmeter indications assume depends not only on the power factor, but also on the phase sequence, so that the sign of the power factor angle cannot be determined from the formula of equation 12–26.

12.9 Determination of the Correctness of Connection of Two Wattmeters.

Many methods have been devised for checking the correctness of the indications of the wattmeters for the two-wattmeter method of measuring three-phase power. If the load is not very nearly balanced, the tests are not very simple and will not be discussed here because of the special nature of the problem. If, on the other hand, the load is practically balanced some simple tests are easily applied and easily explained.

That there is need for a check as to whether the two wattmeters are correctly connected is evident because for a power factor below 0.5 one of the meters should indicate negatively. Thus, if nothing is known of the load, and it usually is not in practice without some test, it is not possible to tell whether a meter is indicating negatively because of low power factor or because of an incorrect connection.

One very simple test may be carried out by opening the line of one of the wattmeter current coils. Disconnecting the circuit in this manner causes the load to operate single phase. If the wattmeter remaining indicates positively, it is correctly connected since it is measuring a single-phase load. When this test is repeated with the other meter, it must also indicate positively when alone on the single-phase load in order to be correct in the three-phase system. Even though each meter alone on single phase indicates positively, on reconnecting three phase one of the meters may indicate negatively. The total power is, in any case, the algebraic sum of the two indications taken simultaneously.

The method of test just discussed is not restricted to a consideration of balanced loads, but it does have the practical disadvantage of requiring the interruption of service to the load. In many applications such an interruption is not permissible; hence the method cannot always be applied.

Another simple method of checking for the correctness of the wattmeter connections, but for balanced load only, may be deduced as follows. Refer to Fig. 12–13 and consider meter A, for which

$$P_{ab}{}^{1a} = |V_l|\,|I_l| \cos(30 - \theta)$$

Suppose that the potential coil lead of the meter which is connected to line b is connected instead to line c. Then, from the vector diagram,

$$P_{ac}^{1a} = |V_l|\,|I_l| \cos (30 + \theta)$$

But these two meter indications are the correct two-wattmeter indications; hence their algebraic sum is the total power being absorbed by the load. Therefore, if the two indications of meter A are obtained for its common-wire potential lead connected successively to the two wires in which the current coil is *not* located, their sum is the power absorbed by the load. If this sum is negative, meter A is connected backwards. Meter B connected as in Fig. 12–13 must indicate the same as meter A with the voltage coil of A connected to line c as in the foregoing; otherwise meter B is connected backwards.

The foregoing discussion by no means exhausts the possibilities of the methods for checking the correctness of the connections of two wattmeters,* but perhaps it gives some idea of the problems confronting the meterman.

12.10 Reactive Volt-Ampere Measurement in Three-Phase Systems.

The measurement of reactive volt-amperes in three-phase systems has at the present time become practically as important as measuring power because the total volt-amperes can be determined from the combination of power and reactive volt-amperes. The total volt-amperes are important because it is this factor which determines the size of the equipment required to deliver energy to a load. In the final analysis, an alternator will deliver energy up to the point where it gets too hot for safe operation. But the current carried by the alternator determines to a very great extent its heating, so if the power factor is low enough—reactive volt-amperes high enough—an alternator can be overheated on any energy load whatever. The size of the equipment in the power house, therefore, depends on the reactive volt-amperes it must supply as well as the actual watts required. But the cost of the equipment, and thus the financing charges, increases with its size, so that it seems equitable to charge higher rates for loads which operate at lower power factors. The present-day sale of large blocks of power is based on such increased charge for loads of relatively high reactive volt-ampere content. The measurement of reactive volt-amperes has accordingly become a necessity.

The measurement of single-phase reactive volt-amperes has already been considered in Art. 12–2. It was found possible to use a *standard power meter* by connecting an auxiliary network in series with the voltage coil. The use of a standard power meter for three-phase measurements is also possible and, of course, very desirable. Two methods of measuring

---

* Edison Electric Institute, *Electric Meterman's Handbook*, 5th Edition, 1940.

reactive volt-amperes in a three-phase three-wire circuit will now be considered.

A method known as "cross-phasing" consists in simply connecting a standard two-element watthour meter as shown in Fig. 12–15a. That this

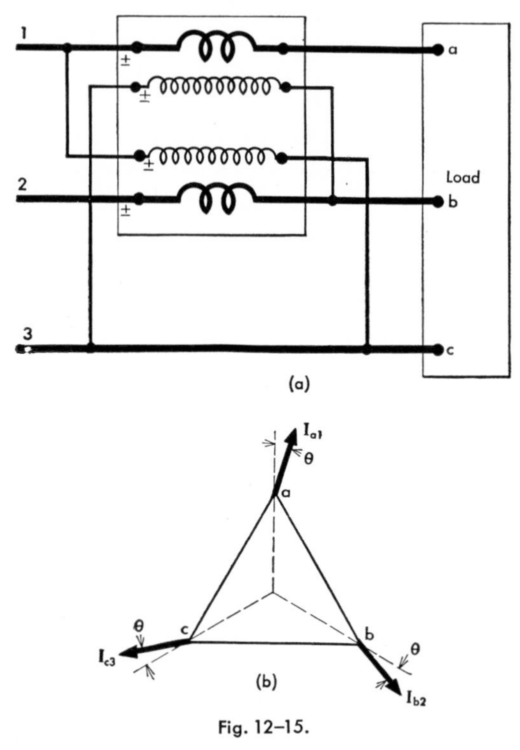

Fig. 12–15.

meter measures reactive volt-amperes on a balanced system follows immediately from the sum of the two meter indications. Thus

$$P_{ac}{}^{2b} + P_{cb}{}^{1a} = V_{ac} \cdot I_{2b} + V_{cb} \cdot I_{1a} = P' \tag{12–27}$$

Reference to the vector diagram of Fig. 12–15b is the simplest way to see what these meters represent. First, recalling that $\theta < 0$ for lagging power factor,

$$V_{ac} \cdot I_{2b} = |V_l|\,|I_l| \cos(90 + \theta) = -\,|V_l|\,|I_l| \sin\theta \tag{12–28}$$

and

$$V_{cb} \cdot I_{1a} = |V_l|\,|I_l| \cos(90 + \theta) = -\,|V_l|\,|I_l| \sin\theta \tag{12–29}$$

Both of these meters will indicate the same amount and both will indicate in the same direction—positively for lagging power factor. Their sum, however, is not the reactive volt-amperes of the balanced system because the latter is

$$Q = \sqrt{3}\,|V_l|\,|I_l| \sin\theta \tag{12–30}$$

But Q can be expressed in terms of the indication of the standard watt-hour meter connected as in Fig. 12–15a by multiplying the sum of the indications of the two elements by $\sqrt{3}/2$. Thus

$$Q = \frac{\sqrt{3}}{2} P' = \frac{\sqrt{3}}{2} (-2|V_l|\,|I_l| \sin \theta) \qquad (12\text{–}31)$$
$$= -\sqrt{3}\,|V_l|\,|I_l| \sin \theta$$

The minus sign in this equation merely shows that the meter deflection is positive for negative or lagging power factor loads (θ negative); and, of course, the indication is negative for leading power factor loads. This result corresponds to the scheme used in actual practice because most commercial loads are lagging power factor and a positive meter deflection is desired.

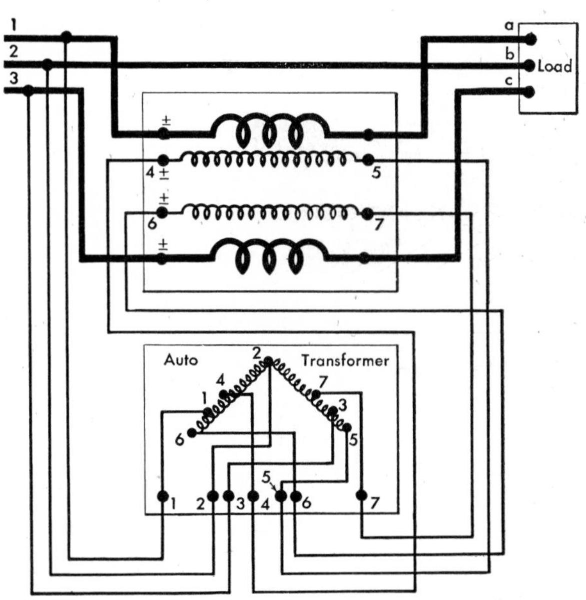

Fig. 12–16.

The "cross-phasing" method of measuring reactive volt-amperes is not in common usage because the meter indication must be multiplied by the factor $\sqrt{3}/2 = 0.866$, and it has been found by experience that this odd factor leads to confusion in the routine process of billing the customer. Instead, therefore, of cross-phasing, a simple, inexpensive autotransformer is used to produce the connection diagram of Fig. 12–16. This circuit looks a bit formidable as a means of avoiding a simple multiplying factor 0.866, but the autotransformer and its seven terminals are constructed and connected internally at the factory and, if the external connections from the lines and meter to the seven binding posts are examined, it will be seen that the connection process is actually simple.

Now to examine the autotransformer scheme in detail. First, the autotransformer itself consists of two iron-core coils with taps as shown. If the number of turns on these coils is high so that the impedance is high enough to reduce the currents to a very low value, the voltage between any two points on a coil is directly proportional to the number of turns between the points. This statement is true even for the turns between 1 and 6 and 3 and 5, which are outside of the 1 to 2 and 2 to 3 ranges where the source voltages are connected, because the magnetic field of each coil set up by small currents from the lines connected to points 1, 2, and 3 induces a voltage in all turns very nearly alike. This induced voltage, for practical purposes—negligible currents—, exactly balances the line voltages wherever they are connected. Therefore, the voltages from, say, 2 to 6 of the autotransformer is greater than the voltage 1 to 2 in proportion to the number of turns from 1 to 6.

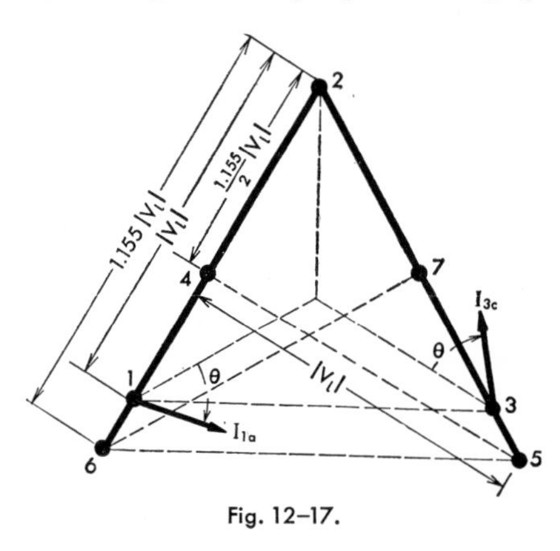

Fig. 12–17.

The vector diagram for the voltages of the autotransformer for a positive (1–2–3) sequence is shown in Fig. 12–17. The currents in the current coils of the meter are superimposed on this diagram. The points 4 and 7 are midpoints of the autotransformer coils and also of the voltage vectors 2–6 and 2–5. The points 1 and 3 will be located later in the discussion so that the meter registers reactive volt-amperes.

Considering the meter elements of Fig. 12–16 one at a time, and remembering that θ is negative for lagging power factor, and also using the vector diagram of Fig. 12–17, gives

$$\begin{aligned} P_{45}{}^{1a} &= V_{45} \cdot I_{1a} = |V_{45}|\,|I_l| \cos(60 + \theta) \\ &= |V_{45}|\,|I_l|[\cos 60 \cos\theta - \sin 60 \sin\theta] \\ &= |V_{45}|\,|I_l| \left(\tfrac{1}{2}\cos\theta - \frac{\sqrt{3}}{2}\sin\theta\right) \end{aligned} \qquad (12\text{–}32)$$

Also

$$\begin{aligned} P_{67}{}^{3c} &= V_{67} \cdot I_{3c} = |V_{67}|\,|I_l| \cos(120 + \theta) \\ &= |V_{67}|\,|I_l| \cos 120 \cos\theta - \sin 120 \sin\theta \\ &= |V_{67}|\,|I_l| \left[-\tfrac{1}{2}\cos\theta - \frac{\sqrt{3}}{2}\sin\theta\right] \end{aligned} \qquad (12\text{–}33)$$

The total registration of the meter will be the sum of these last two equations so that, if $|V_{67}| = |V_{45}| = |V_l|$

$$Q = -\sqrt{3}\,|V_l|\,|I_l| \sin \theta \tag{12–34}$$

This result is exactly the total reactive volt-amperes of a balanced three-phase system. The meter registration will be positive for lagging power factor corresponding to commercial practice.

The location of taps 1 and 3 on the autotransformers is determined from the fact that $|V_{45}| = |V|_{67} = |V_l|$ is required. Because $|V_{45}| = |V_{67}| = |V_l|$ are the altitudes of equilateral triangles, the sides of the triangles are

$$|V_{26}| = |V_{25}| = |V_l|\frac{2}{\sqrt{3}} = 1.155|V_l|$$

Accordingly, if there are n turns between points 1 and 2, or 2 and 3, of the autotransformers, there must be $1.155n$ turns for the whole winding; or the points 1 and 3 are 86.6 per cent taps.

Both of the methods of measuring reactive volt-amperes which have been discussed depend for their validity on the system being balanced. Actually there is little cause for concern over this result because reactive volt-amperes have little or no meaning for systems which are very much unbalanced anyway. For example, it is easily possible to unbalance a system so that none of the phases have unity power factor and yet the sum of the reactive volt-amperes of the three phases may be *zero*. However, the large power loads for which reactive volt-ampere measurements are desired are nearly enough balanced for the autotransformer method to be satisfactory.

12.11 Measurement of Total Volt-Amperes in Three-Phase Three-Wire Systems.

The measurement of total volt-amperes directly is rather difficult. Essentially, a meter for such a measurement must be able to operate independently of the power factor. Thus far, no satisfactory two-element volt-ampere meter has been devised with any such property. Instead, total volt-ampere meters in commercial use are devices which *mechanically* combine the power and reactive volt-ampere results of power and reactive volt-ampere meters in accordance with the right-triangle relations. The meter pictured in Fig. 1–19 is one of the several varieties of such meters used in practice. Because of the special nature of the problem, nothing more will be included here. The reader may find it interesting to consult other sources for details of operation of some of the principal types of volt-ampere meters.

PROBLEMS

12–1 Obtain from the library the information necessary to write a brief report on the compensated wattmeter. Explain in detail how this meter works and state the precautions which must be observed in using such a meter.

12–2 From measurements which the reader should take in the laboratory on an indicating wattmeter, determine the size capacitor which could be used to replace the series resistor of the voltage coil to make the meter an indicating reactive volt-ampere meter. Discuss the accuracy of such a reactive volt-ampere meter.

12–3 A watthour meter potential coil has a Q of 6 at 60 cps with a current of 10 mils at 110 volts. Determine the value of R_C and C of Fig. 12–2*b* so that the current through Z_V is the same in both circuits of Fig. 12–2, and the current of Fig. 12–2*b* leads that of Fig. 12–2*a* by 90 degrees. Two equations will be required to solve for the two unknowns R_C and C. Would R and C in series be satisfactory in place of the arrangement of Fig. 12–2*b*?

12–4 The impedances of Fig. 12–3 are $Z_{ab} = 3 + j4$, $Z_{bc} = 10 + j10$, $Z_{ac} = \infty + j\infty$. Find the indications of all the meters in this circuit and show that the indications of the two meters connected in the line wires, when added, give the total power absorbed by the load. Note that P_{bc}^{2b} and P_{ac}^{1a} individually do not give the power absorbed by any resistor. The generator terminal voltages are constant at $V_{ac} = 100 + j0$, $V_{cb} = 100 + j0$.

12–5 Repeat Problem 12–4 if the generator terminal voltages are three-phase, constant, and balanced at 100 volts between wires and the phase sequence is *a–b–c*. Use V_{ab} as reference.

12–6 Show that the two wattmeters connected in the lines of Fig. 12–3 will measure the total power absorbed by any wye-conected load. *Hint.* Write an equation similar to equation 12–5 in terms of wye load currents and voltages, and then use the voltage equations relating line-to-neutral and line-to-line voltages of the wye load instead of equation 12–6.

12–7 A wye-connected load has impedances $Z_{an} = 8 + j6$, $Z_{bn} = 10 + j0$, $Z_{cn} = \infty + j\infty$. Find the indication of two wattmeters connected in lines 1*a* and 2*b* as in Fig. 12–3. Add these indications and show that the sum is the total power absorbed by the system. The generator terminal voltages are constant and balanced at 200 volts and the phase sequence is *acb*.

12–8 Repeat Problem 12–4 if $Z_{ab} = 3 + j4$, $Z_{bc} = \infty + j\infty$, and $Z_{ac} = \infty + j\infty$.

12–9 A wye load of $Z_{na} = 4 + j3$, $Z_{nb} = 10 + j0$, $Z_{nc} = 3 + j4$ is paralleled with a single-phase load of $Z_{ab} = 10 + j10$. The generator terminal voltages are constant and balanced at 100 volts and the phase sequence is *a–b–c*. Find P_{ab}^{1a} and P_{cb}^{3c}, and show that the sum is the total power absorbed by the system.

12–10 Show that N–1 wattmeters will measure a mesh or star load connected to an N-wire system.

12–11 Three wattmeters with potential coil resistances of $R_{10} = 15{,}000$ ohms, $R_{20} = 13{,}000$ ohms, and $R_{30} = 10{,}000$ ohms are connected as in Fig. 12–8. Determine the indications of each meter if the load is as given in Fig. 12–7.

Show that the sum of these indications is the total power absorbed by the load. The voltage between lines is 100 volts, three-phase, of positive sequence.

12–12 Show that N wattmeters with their potential coils connected in star on an N-wire system will measure the total power absorbed by that system.

12–13 Suppose, in the circuit of Problem 12–9, that line $2b$ opens at the load point b. Determine the wattmeter indications if the resistances of the potential coils are related by $R_{12} = 0.75R_{23}$.

12–14 Repeat Problem 12–13 if in addition line $2b$ opens at the source.

12–15 In the circuit of Fig. 12–9a the line $1a$ breaks off near the load junction and the meter voltage circuit is open at x. Find the two-meter indications if the voltage coil resistances are equal.

12–16 Repeat Problem 12–15 if the line $1a$ opens at the generator and the meter voltage circuit is not open at x.

12–17 Compute the indication of each element of the meter of Fig. 12–12, and the total registration, if the phase voltages are kept constant and balanced at 100 volts each with a phase sequence a–c–b; and if the phase impedances are $Z_{na} = 10 + j0$, $Z_{nb} = 10 + j10$, $Z_{nc} = 6 - j8$.

12–18 Two wattmeters are connected as in lines $1a$ and $2b$ of Fig. 12–3 to a balanced delta-connected load of which the phase impedance is $Z_p = 3 + j4$. The line voltages are 200 and the phase sequence is a–c–b. Find the wattmeter indications and check against the total power absorbed by the load.

12–19 Suppose that a capacitor of 10,000 ohms reactance is inserted in series with the 15,000 ohm potential coils of each of the wattmeters of Fig. 12–3. Compute the meter indications for the load and voltages of Prob. 12–18.

12–20 Several wattmeter indications are taken in a three-phase system of phase sequence a–b–c and balanced line voltages of 200 volts. These indications are $P_{13}{}^{b2} = 0$, $P_{23}{}^{2b} = 3000$, $P_{13}{}^{1a} = 1000 = P_{32}{}^{1a}$. Find the line currents.

12–21 The three line currents are equal in magnitude and the three line voltages are equal in magnitude in a three-wire three-phase system. A wattmeter in line c connected to different voltages indicates $P_{cb}{}^{3c} = 1732$, $P_{ca}{}^{3c} = 866$. What is the total power of the system?

12–22 If a balanced three-phase load of pure inductance is connected to a 200-volt a–c–b sequence system, and if the line currents are $|I_l| = 10$ amp, what will each of the two wattmeters connected to measure the power indicate?

12–23 A balanced three-phase synchronous motor measured by two wattmeters gives meter indications of 1732 watts and 866 watts. What is the system power factor? Suppose that two meters indicate 1732 and -866. What is the system power factor?

12–24 Two wattmeters in a three-wire three-phase system indicate $P_{ab}{}^{1a} = 1732$, $P_{cb}{}^{3c} = 866$. The potential coil lead of the wattmeter in line $1a$ is disconnected from line b and connected to line c. Then $P_{ac}{}^{1a} = 866$. Were the meters originally correctly connected?

12–25 If a certain balanced three-phase system is measured by two wattmeters, $P_1 = 2000$, $P_2 = 1000$. The line voltage is 100 volts. What are the line currents?

12–26 Compute the indications of all the meters shown in Fig. 12–18. The meters marked A_1 and V_1 are D'Arsonval type and those marked A_2 and V_2 are dynamometer type.

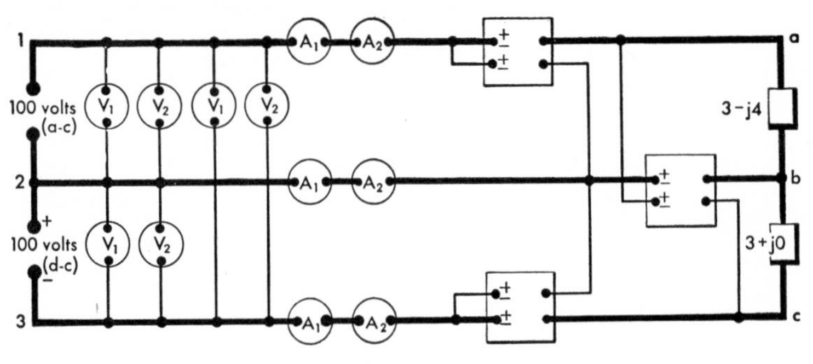

Fig. 12–18.

12–27 Determine the wattmeter indications for Fig. 12–19. Assume the sequence is *a–b–c*, and the line voltage balanced at 100 volts.

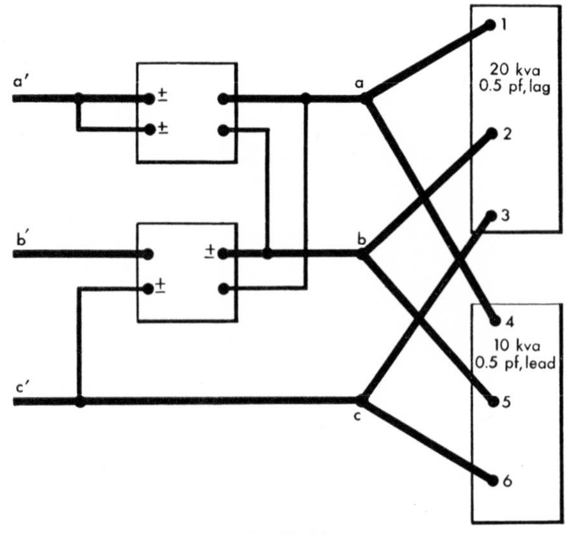

Fig. 12–19.

12–28 Repeat Problem 12–27 if a single-phase load of 5 kva at 0.707 power factor lag is connected to the points *ab* in addition to the balanced three-phase loads shown.

12–29 Repeat Problem 12–27 if a capacitor of 10,000 ohms reactance is placed in series with the potential coil of the upper wattmeter. The potential coil resistance is 10,000 ohms.

12–30 Suppose the phase sequence of the line voltages of Fig. 12–16 is *a–c–b*. Determine symbolically the indication of the meter. What is the effect of a change in phase sequence on the indication of the reactive volt-ampere meter. If a change in phase sequence affects the meter indication, how could the situation be handled in practice?

12–31 Suppose that the load in Fig. 12–16 is 5 kva at 0.8 power factor lag. The sequence is *a–b–c* and the voltage between lines 200 volts. Suppose that the leads which are shown at 5 and 6 actually get interchanged at the autotransformer. Compute the meter indication.

12–32 Repeat the preceding problem if leads 2 and 3 are accidentally interchanged at the autotransformer.

12–33 Write a brief report on two or three methods, used in practice, of making total volt-ampere meters. State their limitations.

CHAPTER 13

Symmetrical Components

The method of electric circuit analysis known as symmetrical components was first introduced by Fortescue as a result of studying the behavior of three-phase rotating machines connected to unbalanced voltages. The symmetrical component method of computation has assumed a position of such outstanding importance in problems dealing with the short circuit analysis of existing power networks, or extensions of them, that virtually all other methods have been abandoned. The complicated behavior of rotating machinery is, of course, almost entirely responsible for the fact that the usual Kirchhoff equations cannot be used directly to calculate fault currents on a power system. The mutual induction between the phases, the iron of the machines, the air gap, and the rotating field structure together present a very complicated problem for analysis. Even if the short-circuited phases can be assumed to be operating under a condition of saturation and thus practical linearity, the problem of determining the ordinary internal impedances of the rotating machine under faults on the system is more or less unsolvable. However, symmetrical components state unbalanced conditions in terms of balanced ones. It has been found that the symmetrical component balanced impedances of rotating machines can be determined with considerable accuracy, because the unbalanced magnetic fields of the rotating machine can be expressed in symmetrical component form as balanced rotating fields and a stationary pulsing field. The reactances, accordingly, for each of the sequences may be expected to be different, as in fact they are, because of different degrees of saturation and different direction of rotation of the magnetic fields.

Unquestionably large is the amount of time and effort engineers have expended in their search to develop a technique for computing fault conditions on power networks. The resultant effect of their united efforts has been to establish symmetrical components in a dominant position for all fault computations, whether steady state or transient. Development work on symmetrical component application and theory, both steady state and transient, is still going on and will continue for some time.

In addition to facilitating fault calculations on power systems, symmetrical components have been found useful as a basis on which to study the interference of power lines with near-by telephone lines, a problem obviously of considerable interest to telephone engineers. Power engineers are also interested in transmission line interference problems because they do not want to cripple either the regular telephone systems or their own private intersystem communication networks.

The full story of symmetrical components is a topic for a book not one chapter in a book. Necessarily, therefore, only their basic elements can be presented in this chapter with a few simple applications. Further knowledge and possible applications must be sought in other works.*

13.1 Definition of Symmetrical Components.

The simplicity of the calculations for balanced three-phase systems, where each phase acts with apparent independence of the others and where the numerical multiplying factor $\sqrt{3}$ converts from phase to line quantities, led directly to the definition of symmetrical components. The symmetry of balanced three-phase systems, whether magnetic fields, electric fields, currents, or voltages always produces very marked simplifications both in behavior and computations. It seems logical, therefore, to expect that, if the unbalanced magnetic fields of a short-circuited alternator can be resolved into balanced systems of magnetic fields, some simplifying ideas should develop from the resolution, as well as some computational aids and probably short cuts. Such is, in fact, exactly what has happened. The full details of the resolution of the magnetic fields and the attendant results can be understood only after a study of the alternator. However, without such a study, it is possible to show what the results obtainable are and to show how they may be used. But even this explanation had best be reserved until the concept of symmetrical component resolutions has been mastered. Consequently, the symmetrical component definitions are now given here.

The well-known and accepted defining equations for the symmetrical components of a set of *unbalanced* three-phase currents, I_a, I_b, and I_c, may be written in one form as

$$\begin{aligned} I_a &= I_{a0} + I_{a1} + I_{a2} \\ I_b &= I_{b0} + I_{b1} + I_{b2} \\ I_c &= I_{c0} + I_{c1} + I_{c2} \end{aligned} \tag{13–1}$$

* Wagner and Evans, *Symmetrical Components*, McGraw-Hill Book Co., 1933; Lyons, *Applications of the Methods of Symmetrical Components*, McGraw-Hill Book Co., 1937; Edith Clarke, *Circuit Analysis of A–C Power Systems*, vol. I, John Wiley & Sons, 1943.

This set of *three* equations is obviously not sufficient to define the *nine* elements on the right from a given set of three known unbalanced currents on the left. In fact, additional relations must be established so that *six* of these right-hand terms may be expressed in terms of the remaining *three*. The possible relations of this sort are limitless, but, because balanced systems of three-phase currents are to be used if possible, certain restrictions are immediately placed on the relations of symmetrical components on the right of equations 13–1. As a start the following six defining equations will be used:

$$\begin{aligned} I_{a1} &= I_{a1} \\ I_{b1} &= a^2 I_{a1} \\ I_{c1} &= a I_{a1} \end{aligned} \tag{13–2}$$

which is a *positive sequence of balanced* currents if $a = \epsilon^{j120}$; and

$$\begin{aligned} I_{a2} &= I_{a2} \\ I_{b2} &= a I_{a2} \\ I_{c2} &= a^2 I_{a2} \end{aligned} \tag{13–3}$$

which is a set of *negative sequence balanced* currents. The third set of symbols on the right of equation 13–1, I_{a0}, I_{b0}, and I_{c0}, will for the moment be expressed in terms of arbitrary a_{ij} and I_{a0} so that equations 13–1, as a result of the foregoing definitions, may be expressed as

$$\begin{aligned} I_a &= a_{11} I_{a0} + I_{a1} + I_{a2} = a_{11} I_0 + I_1 + I_2 \\ I_b &= a_{21} I_{a0} + a^2 I_{a1} + a I_{a2} = a_{21} I_0 + a^2 I_1 + a I_2 \\ I_c &= a_{31} I_{a0} + a I_{a1} + a^2 I_{a2} = a_{31} I_0 + a I_1 + a^2 I_2 \end{aligned} \tag{13–4}$$

where, by common consent, the subscript a is omitted from the a-phase symmetrical components as a matter of convenience.

There are only two possible phase sequences of a three-phase system so that one of these sequences must be used again if a third set of balanced currents are to be used. It is easy to show, however, that the determinant of the set of equations 13–4 is zero if each of a_{11}, a_{21}, and a_{31} is taken as any one of 1, a, or a^2. If symmetry is to be used, therefore, some other sort of symmetry must be employed from that of balanced three-phase. There is certainly no point in defining symmetrical components so that another unbalanced three-phase system is used because it would be rather useless to express an unbalanced system in terms of *another* unbalanced system *plus two* balanced systems. But suppose $a_{11} = a_{21} = a_{31} = 1$; i.e.,

$$\begin{aligned} I_{a0} &= I_{a0} \\ I_{b0} &= I_{a0} \\ I_{c0} &= I_{a0} \end{aligned} \tag{13–5}$$

Then a certain symmetry is obtained, the determinant of equations 13–4 is now not zero, and these equations become

$$\begin{aligned} I_a &= I_{a0} + I_{a1} + I_{a2} = I_0 + I_1 + I_2 \\ I_b &= I_{a0} + a^2 I_{a1} + a I_{a2} = I_0 + a^2 I_1 + a I_2 \\ I_c &= I_{a0} + a I_{a1} + a^2 I_{a2} = I_0 + a I_1 + a^2 I_2 \end{aligned} \qquad (13\text{–}6)$$

The unbalanced currents are thus expressed as *two balanced three-phase sets of currents of opposite phase sequence and a single phase set of currents consisting of three currents equal and in phase.*

Other forms of symmetrical component have been suggested,* but the definition given in equations 13–6 is the one which has had widespread and effective use in power systems.

The set of equations 13–6, with the additional defining relations of equations 13–2, 13–3, and 13–5 have reduced the set of 13–1 from three equations in nine unknowns to three equations in three unknowns. Furthermore, because the definitions have been established to make the determinant of equations 13–6 different from zero, these equations are independent and can be solved for the symmetrical components with the result

$$\begin{aligned} I_0 &= I_{a0} = \frac{I_a + I_b + I_c}{3} \\ I_1 &= I_{a1} = \frac{I_a + a I_b + a^2 I_c}{3} \\ I_2 &= I_{a2} = \frac{I_a + a^2 I_b + a I_c}{3} \end{aligned} \qquad (13\text{–}7)$$

The first of these equations defines the *equal single-phase* symmetrical components of *all three* phases according to equations 13–5. These components are known as *zero sequence* components. Of particular importance is the fact, evident from equation 13–7, that *the zero sequence components are zero if the sum of the three unbalanced currents is zero.* The line currents of a three-phase, three-wire, ungrounded circuit, therefore, can never have a zero sequence component.

The second of equations 13–7 defines the a-phase component of the *positive* sequence of symmetrical components, and the last of equations 13–7 defines the a-phase component of the *negative* sequence of symmetrical components. The b-phase and c-phase positive and negative sequence symmetrical components may be easily determined from equations 13–2 and 13–3 once the a-phase components are known.

---

* E. Clarke, "Problems Solved by Modified Symmetrical Components," *General Electric Review*, vol. 41, November, December, 1938, pp. 488–494, 545–549; L. A. Pipes, *A.I.E.E. Transactions*, August, 1940, p. 467; E. Clarke, *Circuit Analysis of A–C Power Systems*, John Wiley & Sons, 1943, vol. I, chaps. V, X.

Example 13:1 Suppose that the three unbalanced currents in the three phases of a three-phase network are

$$I_a = 10 + j0$$
$$I_b = 0 + j10$$
$$I_c = 0 - j20$$

as in Fig. 13–1*a*. Determine the symmetrical components of these currents and show the results graphically. Also show that these symmetrical components represent the original set of equations.

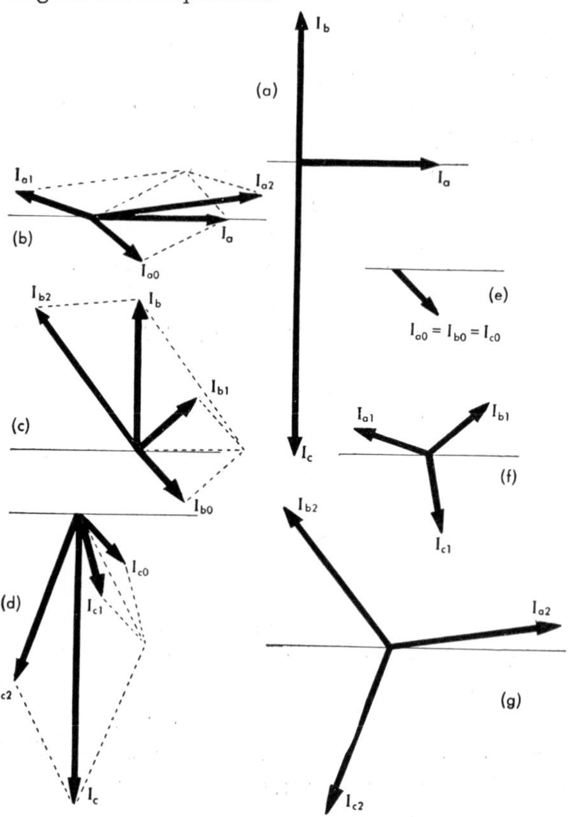

Fig. 13–1.

Solution Equations 13–7 define the *a*-phase symmetrical components for *any* set of currents so that

$$I_0 = \frac{I_a + I_b + I_c}{3} = \frac{10 - j10}{3} = 3.33 - j3.33 = 4.71\epsilon^{-j45}$$

$$I_1 = \frac{I_a + aI_b + a^2I_c}{3} = \frac{-15.98 + j5}{3} = -5.33 + j1.67 = 5.59\epsilon^{j162.6}$$

$$I_2 = \frac{I_a + a^2I_b + aI_c}{3} = \frac{35.98 + j5}{3} = 11.99 + j1.67 = 12.11\epsilon^{j7.9}$$

These results are shown graphically in Fig. 13–1*b*.

The b-phase symmetrical components are immediately, from equations 13–2, 13–3, and 13–5,

$$I_{b0} = I_0 = 3.33 - j3.33 = 4.71\epsilon^{-j45}$$
$$I_{b1} = a^2 I_1 = 4.11 + j3.78 = 5.59\epsilon^{j42.6}$$
$$I_{b2} = aI_2 = -7.44 + j9.55 = 12.11\epsilon^{j127.9}$$

as shown graphically in Fig. 13–1c; and the c-phase symmetrical components are

$$I_{c0} = I_0 = 3.33 - j3.33 = 4.71\epsilon^{-j45}$$
$$I_{c1} = aI_1 = 1.22 - j5.45 = 5.59\epsilon^{j282.6}$$
$$I_{c2} = a^2 I_2 = -4.55 - j11.22 = 12.11\epsilon^{j247.9}$$

as shown graphically in Fig. 13–1d.

The three symmetrical component sets are shown in Figs. 13–1e, f, and g. These three systems add to form the original set of unbalanced currents as Figs. 13–1b, c, and d indicate, and as required by equations 13–1.

A second example illustrates further the application of the symmetrical component defining equations.

Example 13:2 Determine the expressions for the symmetrical components of the line currents of an unbalanced delta in terms of the symmetrical components of the phase currents of the unbalanced delta.

Solution Because the sum of the line currents of a three-wire, three-phase circuit is zero there can be no zero sequence component of these currents. The delta phase currents may have a zero sequence component because their sum need not be zero. In any event, applying the defining equations 13–7 will determine the symmetrical components.

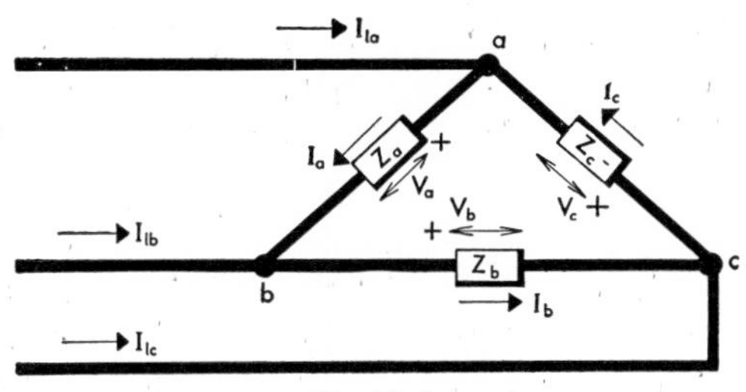

Fig. 13–2.

To solve the present problem, the line and phase currents of a delta network must first be established. These relations are (Fig. 13–2)

$$\begin{aligned} I_{la} &= I_a - I_c \\ I_{lb} &= -I_a + I_b \\ I_{lc} &= -I_b + I_c \end{aligned} \tag{13–8}$$

Next, using the defining equations 13–6 on the left side of this set of equations leads to

$$I_{la0} + I_{la1} + I_{la2} = I_{l0} + I_{l1} + I_{l2} = I_{la}$$
$$I_{lb0} + I_{lb1} + I_{lb2} = I_{l0} + a^2 I_{l1} + aI_{l2} = I_{lb}$$
$$I_{lc0} + I_{lc1} + I_{lc2} = I_{l0} + aI_{l1} + a^2 I_{l2} = I_{lc}$$

Similarly, if the right side of equations 13–8 is transformed

$$\begin{aligned} I_{la} &= I_0 + I_1 + I_2 \qquad\qquad\qquad\qquad\qquad - I_{c0} - I_{c1} - I_{c2} \\ I_{lb} &= -I_0 - I_1 - I_2 + I_{b0} + I_{b1} + I_{b2} \\ I_{lc} &= \qquad\qquad\qquad - I_{b0} - I_{b1} - I_{b2} + I_{c0} + I_{c1} + I_{c2} \end{aligned}$$

Equating these two groups of equations

$$\begin{aligned} I_{l0} + I_{l1} + I_{l2} &= I_0 + I_1 + I_2 \qquad\qquad\qquad\qquad - I_0 - aI_1 - a^2 I_2 \\ I_{l0} + a^2 I_{l1} + aI_{l2} &= -I_0 - I_1 - I_2 + I_0 + a^2 I_1 + aI_2 \qquad\qquad (13\text{–}9) \\ I_{l0} + aI_{l1} + a^2 I_{l2} &= \qquad\qquad - I_0 - a^2 I_1 - aI_2 + I_0 + aI_1 + a^2 I_2 \end{aligned}$$

Since it is the symmetrical components of the line currents which are being sought, these equations are to be solved for these components, I_{l0}, I_{l1}, and I_{l2}.

Simply adding the equations 13–9 gives

$$I_{l0} = 0$$

Multiplying equations 13–9 in order from top to bottom by 1, a, a^2, respectively, and adding gives

$$I_{l1} = (1 - a)I_1 = \sqrt{3}\,\epsilon^{-j30}\,I_1$$

Similarly, multiplying equations 13–9 from top to bottom by 1, a^2, a, respectively, and adding gives

$$I_{l2} = (1 - a^2)I_2 = \sqrt{3}\,\epsilon^{j30}\,I_2$$

These results show that the positive and negative sequences of line and phase currents are related in exactly the same way as the line and phase currents of exactly balanced systems of the same phase sequence. Furthermore, the zero sequence of line current is zero no matter what the zero sequence of phase currents. Also of importance is the fact that the zero sequence of phase currents has no effect on the line currents. A further examination of equations 13–9 reveals that the determinant of these equations, viewed as equations in the unknowns I_0, I_1, and I_2, is zero. Accordingly *the symmetrical components of phase currents cannot be determined from the symmetrical components of line currents of a delta connection.*

The explanation of the important uses of symmetrical components, the assumptions made in their applications, and similar questions which arise in the development and use of symmetrical components can all be derived in terms of the usual manipulations of linear equations. Keeping all the details in their proper places, however, by the usual methods is such a tremendous task that rarely, if ever, are all these details given. Matrix algebra is precisely the tool which overcomes these difficulties.

13.2 Matrix Formulation of Symmetrical Components.

The abbreviating potentialities of matrix algebra, if used to formulate symmetrical components, permit equations 13–7 to be written as

$$\begin{bmatrix} I_0 \\ I_1 \\ I_2 \end{bmatrix} = \frac{1}{3}\begin{bmatrix} 1 & 1 & 1 \\ 1 & a & a^2 \\ 1 & a^2 & a \end{bmatrix}\begin{bmatrix} I_a \\ I_b \\ I_c \end{bmatrix}$$

$$\mathcal{I}_s = \mathcal{A}\mathcal{I} \qquad (13\text{–}10)$$

Script symbols are used to represent matrices because they are simple to write and easily distinguishable from other symbols. This defining equation (13–10) indicates that obtaining the symmetrical components of a system of currents is mainly a matter of multiplying by the transformation matrix

$$\mathcal{A} = \frac{1}{3}\begin{bmatrix} 1 & 1 & 1 \\ 1 & a & a^2 \\ 1 & a^2 & a \end{bmatrix} \tag{13–11}$$

Since the same defining equation is used for voltages as for currents, the symmetrical components of a set of three voltages are

$$\mathcal{V}_s = \begin{bmatrix} V_0 \\ V_1 \\ V_2 \end{bmatrix} = \mathcal{A}\mathcal{V} = \frac{1}{3}\begin{bmatrix} 1 & 1 & 1 \\ 1 & a & a^2 \\ 1 & a^2 & a \end{bmatrix}\begin{bmatrix} V_a \\ V_b \\ V_c \end{bmatrix} \tag{13–12}$$

Because the transformation matrix $\mathcal{A}$ has a non-zero determinant $|\mathcal{A}| \neq 0$, i.e., $\mathcal{A}$ is non-singular, the actual currents and voltages are

$$\mathcal{A}^{-1}\mathcal{I}_s = \mathcal{A}^{-1}\mathcal{A}\mathcal{I} = \mathcal{U}\mathcal{I} = \mathcal{I}$$
$$\mathcal{I} = \mathcal{A}^{-1}\mathcal{I}_s$$

or

$$\mathcal{A}^{-1}\mathcal{V}_s = \mathcal{A}^{-1}\mathcal{A}\mathcal{V} = \mathcal{U}\mathcal{V} = \mathcal{V} \tag{13–13}$$
$$\mathcal{V} = \mathcal{A}^{-1}\mathcal{V}_s$$

Reference to equations 13–6, or computation of $\mathcal{A}^{-1}$, shows that in detail the currents are

$$\mathcal{I} = \begin{bmatrix} I_a \\ I_b \\ I_c \end{bmatrix} = \mathcal{A}^{-1}\mathcal{I}_s = \begin{bmatrix} 1 & 1 & 1 \\ 1 & a^2 & a \\ 1 & a & a^2 \end{bmatrix}\begin{bmatrix} I_0 \\ I_1 \\ I_2 \end{bmatrix} \tag{13–14}$$

The matrices $\mathcal{A}$ and $\mathcal{A}^{-1}$, therefore, transform respectively the unbalanced currents or voltages into the a-phase symmetrical component form, or the a-phase symmetrical components into the actual currents or voltages.

Situations arise in which the b-phase and c-phase symmetrical components are desired. Examination of equations 13–2, 13–3, and 13–5 indicates that the b-phase symmetrical components, in terms of those of the a-phase, are

$$\mathcal{I}_{bs} = \begin{bmatrix} I_{b0} \\ I_{b1} \\ I_{b2} \end{bmatrix} = \begin{bmatrix} 1 & 0 & 0 \\ 0 & a^2 & 0 \\ 0 & 0 & a \end{bmatrix}\begin{bmatrix} I_0 \\ I_1 \\ I_2 \end{bmatrix} = \mathcal{A}_r\mathcal{I}_s = \mathcal{A}_r\mathcal{A}\mathcal{I} \tag{13–15}$$

The c-phase symmetrical components are in terms of this same transformation matrix $\mathcal{A}_r$

$$\mathcal{I}_{cs} = \begin{bmatrix} I_{c0} \\ I_{c1} \\ I_{c2} \end{bmatrix} = \mathcal{A}_r\mathcal{I}_{bs} = \mathcal{A}_r\mathcal{A}_r\mathcal{I}_s = \mathcal{A}_r\mathcal{A}_r\mathcal{A}\mathcal{I} \tag{13–16}$$

Of interest is the fact that continuing as the last two transformations suggest, the round may be completed, so that

$$\mathcal{I}_s = \mathcal{A}_r\mathcal{I}_{cs} = \mathcal{A}_r\mathcal{A}_r\mathcal{I}_{bs} = \mathcal{A}_r\mathcal{A}_r\mathcal{A}_r\mathcal{I}_s = \mathcal{U}\mathcal{I}_s = \mathcal{I}_s \qquad (13\text{–}17)$$

Example 13:3 Suppose that the problem of Example 13:1 is now reworked in matrix form.

Solution The unbalanced currents are

$$\mathcal{I} = \begin{bmatrix} I_a \\ I_b \\ I_c \end{bmatrix} = \begin{bmatrix} 10 + j0 \\ 0 + j10 \\ 0 - j20 \end{bmatrix}$$

Determination of the symmetrical components of these currents is simply a matter of applying the $\mathcal{A}$ matrix. Thus

$$\mathcal{I}_s = \begin{bmatrix} I_0 \\ I_1 \\ I_2 \end{bmatrix} = \tfrac{1}{3}\begin{bmatrix} 1 & 1 & 1 \\ 1 & a & a^2 \\ 1 & a^2 & a \end{bmatrix}\begin{bmatrix} 10+j0 \\ 0+j10 \\ 0-j20 \end{bmatrix} = \tfrac{1}{3}\begin{bmatrix} (10+j0)+(0+j10)+(0-j20) \\ (10+j0)+a(0+j10)+a^2(0-j20) \\ (10+j0)+a^2(0+j10)+a(0-j20) \end{bmatrix}$$

$$= \tfrac{1}{3}\begin{bmatrix} 10 - j10 \\ -15.98 + j5 \\ 35.98 + j5 \end{bmatrix} = \begin{bmatrix} 4.71\epsilon^{-j45} \\ 5.59\epsilon^{j162.6} \\ 12.11\epsilon^{j7.9} \end{bmatrix}$$

as already computed in Example 13:1.

The b-phase and c-phase symmetrical components follow immediately by application of the $\mathcal{A}_r$ transformation matrix. Accordingly,

$$\mathcal{I}_{bs} = \begin{bmatrix} I_{b0} \\ I_{b1} \\ I_{b2} \end{bmatrix} = \mathcal{A}_r\mathcal{I}_s = \begin{bmatrix} 1 & 0 & 0 \\ 0 & a^2 & 0 \\ 0 & 0 & a \end{bmatrix}\begin{bmatrix} 4.71\epsilon^{-j45} \\ 5.59\epsilon^{j162.6} \\ 12.11\epsilon^{j7.9} \end{bmatrix} = \begin{bmatrix} 4.71\epsilon^{-j45} \\ 5.59\epsilon^{j42.6} \\ 12.11\epsilon^{j127.9} \end{bmatrix}$$

and

$$\mathcal{I}_{cs} = \begin{bmatrix} I_{c0} \\ I_{c1} \\ I_{c2} \end{bmatrix} = \mathcal{A}_r\mathcal{I}_{bs} = \begin{bmatrix} 1 & 0 & 0 \\ 0 & a^2 & 0 \\ 0 & 0 & a \end{bmatrix}\begin{bmatrix} 4.71\epsilon^{-j45} \\ 5.59\epsilon^{j42.6} \\ 12.11\epsilon^{j127.9} \end{bmatrix} = \begin{bmatrix} 4.71\epsilon^{-j45} \\ 5.59\epsilon^{282.6} \\ 12.11\epsilon^{j247.9} \end{bmatrix}$$

The advantage of the matrix formulation over the usual manipulations of linear equations is not very great in the simple problems of Examples 13:1 and 13:3. The advantage becomes a little more evident if Example 13:2 is stated in matrix form.

Example 13:4 The symmetrical components of line currents of an unbalanced delta connection are to be computed in terms of the phase current symmetrical components.

Solution First the relations between the line and phase currents are

$$\mathcal{I}_l = \begin{bmatrix} I_{la} \\ I_{lb} \\ I_{lc} \end{bmatrix} = \begin{bmatrix} I_a - I_c \\ I_b - I_a \\ I_c - I_b \end{bmatrix} = \begin{bmatrix} 1 & 0 & -1 \\ -1 & 1 & 0 \\ 0 & -1 & 1 \end{bmatrix}\begin{bmatrix} I_a \\ I_b \\ I_c \end{bmatrix} = \mathcal{B}\mathcal{I} \qquad (13\text{–}18)$$

Applying the $\mathcal{A}$ transformation matrix gives

$$\mathcal{I}_{ls} = \mathcal{A}\mathcal{I}_l = \mathcal{A}\mathcal{B}\mathcal{I} \qquad (13\text{–}19)$$

Then to express $\mathcal{I}_{ls}$ in terms of the symmetrical components of the phase currents, $\mathcal{I}$ of equation 13–19 can be replaced by $\mathcal{A}^{-1}\mathcal{I}_s$ (equation 13–14) so that

$$\mathcal{I}_{ls} = \mathcal{A}\mathcal{B}\mathcal{A}^{-1}\mathcal{I}_s \tag{13–20}$$

which, in detail, is

$$\mathcal{I}_{ls} = \begin{bmatrix} I_{l0} \\ I_{l1} \\ I_{l2} \end{bmatrix} = \frac{1}{3}\begin{bmatrix} 1 & 1 & 1 \\ 1 & a & a^2 \\ 1 & a^2 & a \end{bmatrix}\begin{bmatrix} 1 & 0 & -1 \\ -1 & 1 & 0 \\ 0 & -1 & 1 \end{bmatrix}\begin{bmatrix} 1 & 1 & 1 \\ 1 & a^2 & a \\ 1 & a & a^2 \end{bmatrix}\begin{bmatrix} I_0 \\ I_1 \\ I_2 \end{bmatrix} \tag{13–21}$$

The routine multiplication of the $\mathcal{A}\mathcal{B}\mathcal{A}^{-1}$ product gives the desired relations as

$$\mathcal{I}_{ls} = \begin{bmatrix} I_{l0} \\ I_{l1} \\ I_{l2} \end{bmatrix} = \begin{bmatrix} 0 & 0 & 0 \\ 0 & 1-a & 0 \\ 0 & 0 & 1-a^2 \end{bmatrix}\begin{bmatrix} I_0 \\ I_1 \\ I_2 \end{bmatrix} = \begin{bmatrix} 0 & 0 & 0 \\ 0 & \sqrt{3}\epsilon^{-j30} & 0 \\ 0 & 0 & \sqrt{3}\epsilon^{-j30} \end{bmatrix}\begin{bmatrix} I_0 \\ I_1 \\ I_2 \end{bmatrix} \tag{13–22}$$

These results are, of course, identical with those given in Example 13:2, but the thread of the argument is more evident in the matrix formulation, and the expressions are simpler.

13.3 Symmetrical Components of a Four-Wire Wye (or Three-Wire Grounded) System.

The symmetrical component form of the generated voltages of a four-wire wye connection show an important circuit relation when expressed

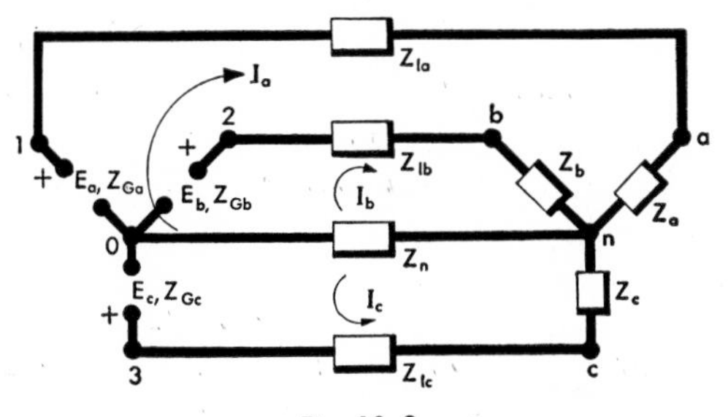

Fig. 13–3.

in terms of the symmetrical components of current and impedance. First, the matrix voltage equation for any circuit is

$$\mathcal{E} = \mathcal{Z}\mathcal{I}$$

which, in detail, for Fig. 13–3 is

$$\begin{bmatrix} E_a \\ E_b \\ E_c \end{bmatrix} = \begin{bmatrix} Z_a' + Z_n & Z_n & Z_n \\ Z_n & Z_b' + Z_n & Z_n \\ Z_n & Z_n & Z_c' + Z_n \end{bmatrix}\begin{bmatrix} I_a \\ I_b \\ I_c \end{bmatrix} \tag{13–23}$$

where

$$\begin{aligned} Z_a' &= Z_{Ga} + Z_{la} + Z_a \\ Z_b' &= Z_{Gb} + Z_{lb} + Z_b \\ Z_c' &= Z_{Gc} + Z_{lc} + Z_c \end{aligned} \tag{13–24}$$

The current and voltage systems can be expressed in symmetrical components by multiplying $\mathcal{E}$ by $\mathcal{A}$ according to equation 13–10, and by substituting for $\mathcal{I}$ according to equation 13–14. Thus

$$\mathcal{E}_s = \mathcal{A}\mathcal{E} = \mathcal{A}\mathfrak{Z}\mathcal{A}^{-1}\mathcal{I}_s = \mathfrak{Z}_s\mathcal{I}_s \tag{13–25}$$

If a further shortening of symbolism is used, namely,

$$\begin{aligned} Z_{a0}' &= Z_0' = \frac{Z_a' + Z_b' + Z_c'}{3} \\ Z_{a1}' &= Z_1' = \frac{Z_a' + aZ_b' + a^2Z_c'}{3} \\ Z_{a2}' &= Z_2' = \frac{Z_a' + a^2Z_b' + aZ_c'}{3} \end{aligned} \tag{13–26}$$

and, if the product $\mathcal{A}\mathfrak{Z}\mathcal{A}^{-1}$ indicated by equation 13–25 is carried out in full, the result is

$$\mathcal{E}_s = \begin{bmatrix} E_0 \\ E_1 \\ E_2 \end{bmatrix} = \begin{bmatrix} Z_0' + 3Z_n & Z_2' & Z_1' \\ Z_1' & Z_0' & Z_2' \\ Z_2' & Z_1' & Z_0' \end{bmatrix} \begin{bmatrix} I_0 \\ I_1 \\ I_2 \end{bmatrix} = \mathfrak{Z}_s\mathcal{I}_s \tag{13–27}$$

Each symmetrical component of voltage is a function of *all* the symmetrical components of current. Such an interrelation is spoken of as coupling between the sequences. General three-phase systems, in which coupling between the sequences exists, have not been found useful. The calculations involved are as complex in every way as the calculations of the circuit without the symmetrical component transformations. Consequently, there is no point in using symmetrical components on such a network because it simply means more work with no compensating advantage. Fortunately, power systems are such that coupling between the sequences can be eliminated because of balanced conditions.

Just how system balance eliminates the coupling between the sequences can be demonstrated by applying the condition for balance to the impedance matrix of equation 13–27. Thus, if the impedances of the circuit of Fig. 13–3 are balanced, i.e., if the impedances of equations 13–24 are related by $Z_a' = Z_b' = Z_c' = Z'$, then from equations 13–26 $Z_0' = Z'$, $Z_1' = 0$, and $Z_2' = 0$, so that

$$\mathcal{E}_s = \begin{bmatrix} E_0 \\ E_1 \\ E_2 \end{bmatrix} = \begin{bmatrix} Z' + 3Z_n & 0 & 0 \\ 0 & Z' & 0 \\ 0 & 0 & Z' \end{bmatrix} \begin{bmatrix} I_0 \\ I_1 \\ I_2 \end{bmatrix} \tag{13–28}$$

or, in detail,

$$\begin{aligned} E_0 &= (Z' + 3Z_n)I_0 \\ E_1 &= Z'I_1 \\ E_2 &= Z'I_2 \end{aligned}$$

But now there is no sequence coupling, for each sequence of voltage determines the corresponding sequence of current only, and vice versa. Power systems in general, therefore, have just the impedance characteristics required to make symmetrical component application most useful and effective.

Also of major importance in the application of symmetrical components is the fact that three times the fourth, or *common, wire impedance* Z_n appears in the zero sequence current-voltage relation.

If the system under consideration does not have a fourth wire, but instead is grounded through impedances at the generator and load common points, three times the total grounding impedance will take the place of three times the fourth wire impedance in the zero sequence current-voltage relation.

13.4 Symmetrical Component Voltage Relations of a Three-Wire, Wye, Ungrounded System.

The application of the symmetrical component transformation matrix $\mathcal{A}$ (equation 13–10) obviously requires three currents or voltages, so for a symmetrical component development the *two*-mesh circuit of Fig. 13–4

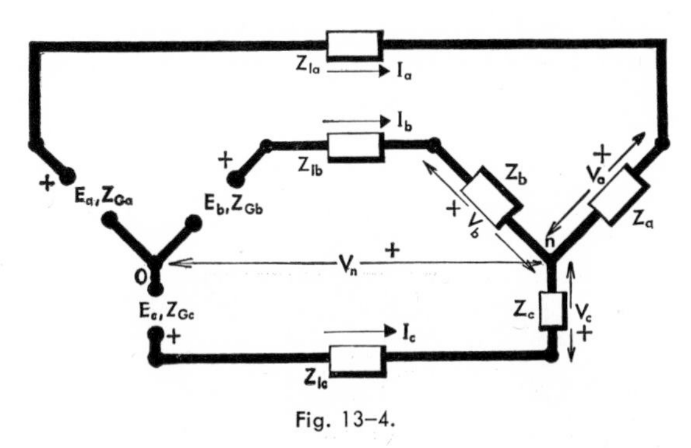

Fig. 13–4.

requires some special consideration. Three equations can be obtained for this circuit, if they are written in terms of three meshes closed by the voltage V_n. Thus, using the definitions of equations 13–24 gives

$$\mathcal{E} = \begin{bmatrix} E_a \\ E_b \\ E_c \end{bmatrix} = \begin{bmatrix} Z_a' & 0 & 0 \\ 0 & Z_b' & 0 \\ 0 & 0 & Z_c' \end{bmatrix} \begin{bmatrix} I_a \\ I_b \\ I_c \end{bmatrix} + \begin{bmatrix} V_n \\ V_n \\ V_n \end{bmatrix} \tag{13–29}$$

or

$$\mathcal{E} = \mathfrak{Z}\mathcal{I} + \mathcal{V}_n \tag{13–30}$$

The $\mathcal{A}$ transformation can now be applied to give the symmetrical component form of the voltages as

$$\mathcal{E}_s = \mathcal{A}\mathfrak{Z}\mathcal{A}^{-1}\mathcal{I}_s + \mathcal{A}\mathcal{B}_n \tag{13–31}$$

which, on multiplying and using the substitutions of equations 13–26, gives

$$\mathcal{E}_s = \begin{bmatrix} E_0 \\ E_1 \\ E_2 \end{bmatrix} = \begin{bmatrix} Z_0' & Z_2' & Z_1' \\ Z_1' & Z_0' & Z_2' \\ Z_2' & Z_1' & Z_0' \end{bmatrix} \mathcal{I}_s + \begin{bmatrix} 1 \\ 0 \\ 0 \end{bmatrix} V_n$$

or

$$\mathcal{E}_s = \mathfrak{Z}_s \mathcal{I}_s + \mathcal{V}_{ns} \tag{13–32}$$

Once more coupling between the sequences occurs, and, as before, if the circuit impedances are balanced, the impedances Z_1' and Z_2' (equations 13–26) become zero and Z_0' becomes Z' the total impedance per phase, so that equation 13–32 becomes, for balanced impedances,

$$\mathcal{E}_s = \begin{bmatrix} E_0 \\ E_1 \\ E_2 \end{bmatrix} = \begin{bmatrix} Z' & 0 & 0 \\ 0 & Z' & 0 \\ 0 & 0 & Z' \end{bmatrix} \begin{bmatrix} I_0 \\ I_1 \\ I_2 \end{bmatrix} + \begin{bmatrix} 1 \\ 0 \\ 0 \end{bmatrix} V_n$$

or

$$\mathcal{E}_s = Z' \mathcal{U} \mathcal{I}_s + \mathcal{V}_{ns} = Z_p \mathcal{I}_s + \mathcal{V}_{ns} \tag{13–33}$$

and again coupling between the sequences is eliminated by balanced impedances. Note particularly that the impedance of the circuit to both positive and negative sequence current is the total phase impedance. Furthermore, because the sum of the circuit currents is

Fig. 13–5. Destruction caused by a short circuit. (Courtesy, Utah Power & Light Co.)

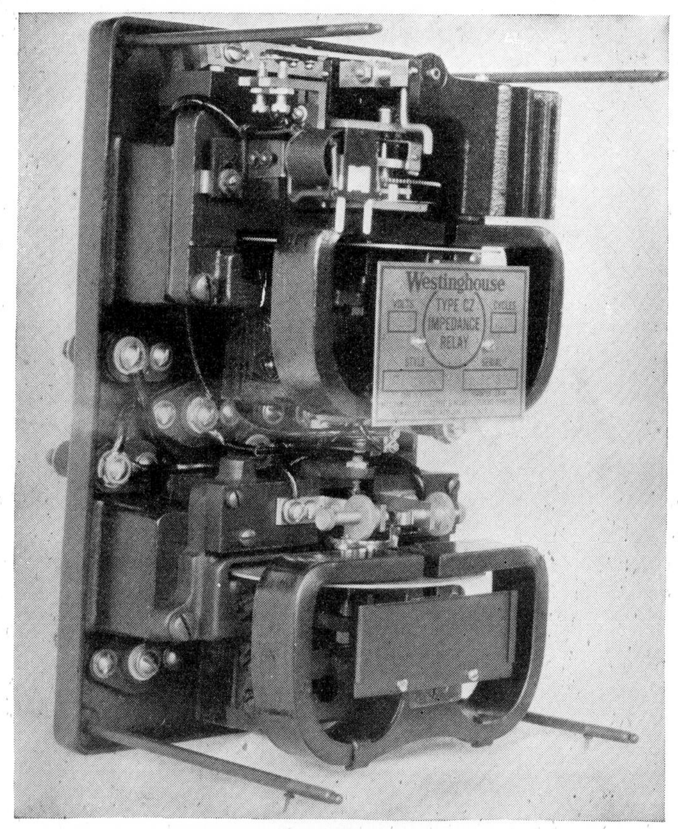

Fig. 13–6a. Power system protective relay. (Courtesy, Westinghouse Electric & Mfg. Co.)

zero, the zero sequence of current I_0 is zero, and equation 13–33 reduces to

$$\begin{bmatrix} E_0 \\ E_1 \\ E_2 \end{bmatrix} = \begin{bmatrix} 0 \\ Z'I_1 \\ Z'I_2 \end{bmatrix} + \begin{bmatrix} V_n \\ 0 \\ 0 \end{bmatrix} = \begin{bmatrix} 0 \\ Z_pI_1 \\ Z_pI_2 \end{bmatrix} + \begin{bmatrix} V_n \\ 0 \\ 0 \end{bmatrix} \qquad (13\text{–}34)$$

The zero sequence of the generated voltages E_0, therefore, is identical with the voltage V_n between the generator and load common points 0 and n. Consequently, if the generated voltages add to zero and the impedances are balanced, the points 0 and n of Fig. 13–4 are at the same potential.

13.5 Basis for the Use of Symmetrical Components.

Power systems tend to feed the tremendous amounts of energy, which they normally transfer from generator to load, into short-circuiting defects in the system. Short circuits, therefore, are usually very destructive, not infrequently causing oil circuit breakers, transformers, etc.,

Fig. 13–6*b*. Power system protective relay. (Courtesy, Westinghouse Electric & Mfg. Co.)

Fig. 13–7*a*. Circuit breaker contactors. (Courtesy, Roller Smith Co.)

Fig. 13–7b. Semisection showing oil blast at a current zero. (Courtesy, General Electric Co.)

to blow up as though high explosives had been set off (see Fig. 13–5). Even short circuits which do not cause any extensive damage disrupt service by causing low voltages to appear all over the system, or actually cause an interruption of service while the power system is shut down to clear the fault. Because of the years of practical experience that power engineers have and particularly because of the effectiveness of symmetrical components in permitting the calculation of system currents and voltages to be expected during short circuits, it is possible to install equipment which generally will not fail during short circuits. Of equal importance with having the proper size equipment at the proper point is the extensive network of protective relays which are part of all present-day power systems. If these protective relays (Fig. 13–6) are properly adjusted they cause circuit breakers to open and disconnect the fault before enough

Fig. 13–7c. Air blast circuit breaker. (Courtesy, I.T.E. Circuit Breaker Co.)

time can elapse to disrupt the system. Until the advent of symmetrical components calculations, setting relays was largely a matter of experience and experiment. Now, symmetrical component calculations permit accurate adjustment of protective relays without employing the difficult and expensive experimental method.

If it were not for the fact that the internal impedances of a-c generators vary considerably with current (non-linear) rather than remaining independent of current (linear), the usual set of Kirchhoff equations could be written and solved. But the value of the internal impedance of the generator is not known until the current is known, and, of course, the current cannot be determined until the impedance is known. The linear transformation of symmetrical components actually does not relieve

Fig. 13–7*d*. High-voltage oil circuit breakers. (Courtesy, Westinghouse Electric & Mfg. Co.)

this situation without some adjustment, as the appearance of all the circuit impedances in relations such as equation 13–27 indicates. Burying the undetermined generator impedances in more complicated expressions is no solution to the non-linearity difficulty. So, theoretically, symmetrical components offer no solution to the problem of calculating the behavior of non-linear rotating machinery. But as a result of many years of experimental and mathematical work on the part of many men, certain assumptions may be made which change the actual *non-linear* problem into a *linear* problem which can be solved. The results obtained are not exact, but they are accurate enough to be very effective as a basis on which to adjust relays and determine the rating required for circuit-interrupting apparatus, such as that shown in Figs. 13–7.

The basis of symmetrical component application can be explained from equation 13–28. This equation, it will be recalled, is for *balanced* impedances which are required to eliminate coupling between the sequences. But note that the zero sequence impedance is different from the other two sequence impedances even for balanced circuit impedances. Suppose, to extend this idea, that equation 13–28 is written as

$$\mathcal{E}_s = \begin{bmatrix} E_0 \\ E_1 \\ E_2 \end{bmatrix} = \begin{bmatrix} Z_0 & 0 & 0 \\ 0 & Z_1 & 0 \\ 0 & 0 & Z_2 \end{bmatrix} \begin{bmatrix} I_0 \\ I_1 \\ I_2 \end{bmatrix} \tag{13-35}$$

where Z_0, Z_1, and Z_2 are now the zero, positive, and negative sequence impedances of the network and are *not* determined by equations 13–26. Instead, as years of experience and experiment with actual power systems and machines have shown, these impedances can be established at such particular values that the *non-linear behavior of the power system under short circuit* can be determined with considerable accuracy from *linear equations* similar to 13–35. The remainder of this chapter will show how symmetrical components are used to calculate fault currents and voltages on power systems in terms of the three *different* sequence impedances Z_0, Z_1, and Z_2.

13.6 Single Line-to-Ground Fault.

A short circuit from one wire to ground is perhaps the most common fault on three-phase systems. A simple illustration of such a short circuit is shown in Fig. 13–8. Symmetrical components may be used to express the behavior of this circuit as follows. The use of three-phase symmetrical

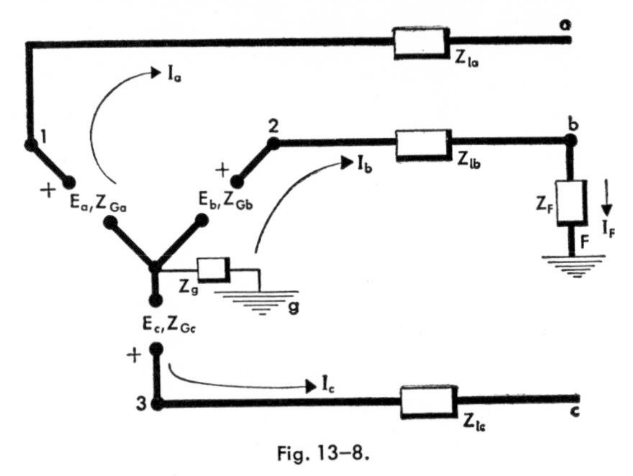

Fig. 13–8.

components, of course, requires three equations. Three equations may be written from Fig. 13–8 by using three paths consisting of one phase and the ground return for each equation. Thus, if for convenience the shortening symbolism $Z_a = Z_{Ga} + Z_{la}$, $Z_b = Z_{Gb} + Z_{lb}$, etc., is used

$$\begin{bmatrix} E_a \\ E_b \\ E_c \end{bmatrix} = \begin{bmatrix} Z_a + Z_g & Z_g & Z_g \\ Z_g & Z_b + Z_g & Z_g \\ Z_g & Z_g & Z_c + Z_g \end{bmatrix} \begin{bmatrix} I_a \\ I_b \\ I_c \end{bmatrix} + \begin{bmatrix} V_{aF} \\ Z_F I_F \\ V_{cF} \end{bmatrix} \tag{13–36}$$

which in more compact form may be expressed as

$$\mathcal{E} = \mathfrak{Z}\mathcal{I} + \mathcal{V}_F \tag{13–37}$$

In terms of symmetrical components this equation becomes

$$\mathcal{E}_s = \mathcal{A}\mathcal{E} = \mathcal{A}\mathfrak{Z}\mathcal{A}^{-1}\mathcal{I}_s + \mathcal{A}\mathcal{V}_F = \mathfrak{Z}_s\mathcal{I}_s + \mathcal{V}_{Fs} \tag{13–38}$$

which is a very compact equation expressing the behavior of the grounded machine in terms of symmetrical components. Writing this equation from the circuit, and expressing it in symmetrical component form, was not at all difficult. Obtaining the general expression for other types of faults is correspondingly simple. In fact, the ease with which the matrix equation is obtained and the symmetrical component behavior of a faulted system is expressed is one of the principal virtues of the matrix method. In addition, the matrix equation contains within it all the current and voltage relations sought as a solution to the faulted system behavior. *Obtaining these relations is simply a matter of evaluating the different matrices in the complete and general matrix expression.*

Symbolically at least, the symmetrical components of fault currents can be expressed from equations 13–38, as

$$\mathcal{I}_s = \mathcal{A}\mathfrak{Z}^{-1}\mathcal{A}^{-1}(\mathcal{E}_s - \mathcal{A}\mathcal{V}_F) \tag{13–39}$$

and the symmetrical components of voltages at the fault as

$$\mathcal{V}_{Fs} = \mathcal{A}\mathcal{V}_F = \mathcal{E}_s - \mathcal{A}\mathfrak{Z}\mathcal{A}^{-1}\mathcal{I}_s \tag{13–40}$$

Neither of these last two equations can be used immediately to determine either the fault currents or the fault voltages because both sets of unknowns are in each equation. Instead, as already indicated, the general expression of 13–38 will be evaluated first by considering its matrix elements one at a time and then combining the conclusions.

To start on the left of equation 13–38, the generator voltages are

$$\mathcal{E}_s = \mathcal{A}\mathcal{E} = \mathcal{A}\begin{bmatrix} E_a \\ E_b \\ E_c \end{bmatrix} = \begin{bmatrix} E_0 \\ E_1 \\ E_2 \end{bmatrix} \tag{13–41}$$

If, as is the usual assumption in accordance with the ordinary operating condition of the generator, the generator voltages are balanced and of positive sequence, this last equation becomes

$$\mathcal{E}_s = \mathcal{A}\mathcal{E} = \begin{bmatrix} 0 \\ E_1 \\ 0 \end{bmatrix} \tag{13–42}$$

Next consider the impedance matrix of equation 13–38. The discussion will be simpler if this matrix is expressed as the sum

$$\begin{aligned} \mathfrak{Z} &= \mathfrak{Z}_G + \mathfrak{Z}_l + \mathfrak{Z}_g \\ &= \begin{bmatrix} Z_{Ga} & 0 & 0 \\ 0 & Z_{Gb} & 0 \\ 0 & 0 & Z_{Gc} \end{bmatrix} + \begin{bmatrix} Z_{la} & 0 & 0 \\ 0 & Z_{lb} & 0 \\ 0 & 0 & Z_{lc} \end{bmatrix} + Z_g\begin{bmatrix} 1 & 1 & 1 \\ 1 & 1 & 1 \\ 1 & 1 & 1 \end{bmatrix} \end{aligned} \tag{13–43}$$

Because of the distributive property of matrices, the symmetrical component form of this sum is

$$\begin{aligned} \mathfrak{Z}_s &= \mathcal{A}\mathfrak{Z}\mathcal{A}^{-1} = \mathcal{A}(\mathfrak{Z}_G + \mathfrak{Z}_l + \mathfrak{Z}_g)\mathcal{A}^{-1} \\ &= \mathcal{A}\mathfrak{Z}_G\mathcal{A}^{-1} + \mathcal{A}\mathfrak{Z}_l\mathcal{A}^{-1} + \mathcal{A}\mathfrak{Z}_g\mathcal{A}^{-1} = \mathfrak{Z}_{Gs} + \mathfrak{Z}_{ls} + \mathfrak{Z}_{gs} \end{aligned}$$

In accordance with the discussion leading to equation 13–35, the impedance matrix $\mathfrak{A}\mathfrak{Z}_G\mathfrak{A}^{-1}$, containing the generator impedances, will be empirically expressed as

$$\mathfrak{Z}_{Gs} = \begin{bmatrix} Z_{G0} & 0 & 0 \\ 0 & Z_{G1} & 0 \\ 0 & 0 & Z_{G2} \end{bmatrix} \tag{13–44}$$

The sequence impedance matrix for the transmission line will be

$$\mathfrak{Z}_{ls} = \mathfrak{A}\mathfrak{Z}_l\mathfrak{A}^{-1} = \begin{bmatrix} Z_{l0} & 0 & 0 \\ 0 & Z_{l1} & 0 \\ 0 & & Z_{l2} \end{bmatrix} \tag{13–45}$$

where $Z_{l0} = Z_{l1} = Z_{l2}$ and is equal to $Z_{la} = Z_{lb} = Z_{lc}$, as straight multiplication of this matrix equation would produce.

It may be well to point out, what possibly the reader has concluded, that determining the values of sequence impedances for generators, transmission lines, etc., is a very important part of symmetrical component applications, and also a relatively complicated process. Nothing more will be done with determining these sequence impedances here than to accept their existence.

Also by routine multiplication

$$\mathfrak{Z}_{gs} = \mathfrak{A}\mathfrak{Z}_g\mathfrak{A}^{-1} = \begin{bmatrix} 3Z_g & 0 & 0 \\ 0 & 0 & 0 \\ 0 & 0 & 0 \end{bmatrix} \tag{13–46}$$

Adding the results obtained in equations 13–44, 13–45, and 13–46 gives the symmetrical component form of equation 13–43 as

$$\mathfrak{Z}_s = \mathfrak{A}\mathfrak{Z}\mathfrak{A}^{-1} = \begin{bmatrix} Z_{G0} + Z_{l0} + 3Z_g & 0 & 0 \\ 0 & Z_{G1} + Z_{l1} & 0 \\ 0 & 0 & Z_{G2} + Z_{l2} \end{bmatrix} \tag{13–47}$$

Continuing the evaluation of equation 13–38, the current matrix $\mathfrak{I}_s$, for the fault currents, becomes, because (from Fig. 13–8) $I_a = 0$, $I_b = I_F$, and $I_c = 0$,

$$\mathfrak{I}_s = \begin{bmatrix} I_0 \\ I_1 \\ I_2 \end{bmatrix} = \mathfrak{A}\mathfrak{I} = \frac{1}{3}\begin{bmatrix} 1 & 1 & 1 \\ 1 & a & a^2 \\ 1 & a^2 & a \end{bmatrix}\begin{bmatrix} 0 \\ I_F \\ 0 \end{bmatrix} = \frac{I_F}{3}\begin{bmatrix} 1 \\ a \\ a^2 \end{bmatrix} \tag{13–48}$$

Finally, the last term of equation 13–38 contains the three unknown elements of the present problem: V_{aF}, V_{cF}, and I_F. The matrix equation 13–38 has, therefore, now been reduced to a set of three equations in three unknowns by equations 13–42, 13–47, and 13–48. Substituting from these equations into equation 13–38 gives

$$\mathcal{E}_s = \begin{bmatrix} 0 \\ E_1 \\ 0 \end{bmatrix} = \begin{bmatrix} Z_{G0} + Z_{l0} + 3Z_g & 0 & 0 \\ 0 & Z_{G1} + Z_{l1} & 0 \\ 0 & 0 & Z_{G2} + Z_{l2} \end{bmatrix} \begin{bmatrix} 1 \\ a \\ a^2 \end{bmatrix} \frac{I_F}{3}$$
$$+ \tfrac{1}{3} \begin{bmatrix} 1 & 1 & 1 \\ 1 & a & a^2 \\ 1 & a^2 & a \end{bmatrix} \begin{bmatrix} V_{aF} \\ Z_F I_F \\ V_{cF} \end{bmatrix} \qquad (13\text{–}49)$$

Any valid method can be used to solve this set of three linear equations in three variables—determinants, elimination of variables, substitution of equations, etc. Because of the characteristics of the a-operator, the current can be obtained immediately by multiplying equation 13–49 by the matrix $[1, a^2, a]$. Thus,

$$[1, a^2, a]\mathcal{E}_s = [1, a^2, a]\mathfrak{z}_s \mathcal{I}_s + [1, a^2, a]\mathcal{A}\mathcal{V}_F \qquad (13\text{–}50)$$

gives, because $a^2 E_1 = E_{b1}$,

$$a^2 E_1 = E_{b1} = [(Z_{G0}+Z_{l0}+3Z_g)+(Z_{G1}+Z_{l2})+(Z_{G2}+Z_{l2})]\frac{I_F}{3} + Z_F I_F$$

which, solved for I_F and using the current relations of equation 13–48, leads to

$$\frac{I_F}{3} = I_{F0} = I_0 = \frac{E_{b1}}{(Z_{G0}+Z_{l0}+3Z_g)+3Z_F+(Z_{G1}+Z_{l1})+(Z_{G2}+Z_{l2})} \qquad (13\text{–}51)$$

The fault voltages follow immediately from equations 13–40 and 13–48 in terms of the now determined fault current as

$$\mathcal{V}_{Fs} = \begin{bmatrix} 0 \\ E_1 \\ 0 \end{bmatrix} - \begin{bmatrix} Z_{G0}+Z_{l0}+3Z_g & 0 & 0 \\ 0 & Z_{G1}+Z_{l1} & 0 \\ 0 & 0 & Z_{G2}+Z_{l2} \end{bmatrix} \begin{bmatrix} 1 \\ a \\ a^2 \end{bmatrix} \frac{I_F}{3} \qquad (13\text{–}52)$$

or

$$V_{F0} = -(Z_{G0} + Z_{l0} + 3Z_g)\frac{I_F}{3}$$
$$V_{F1} = E_1 - (Z_{G1} + Z_{l1})a\frac{I_F}{3} \qquad (13\text{–}53)$$
$$V_{F2} = -(Z_{G2} + Z_{l2})a^2\frac{I_F}{3}$$

A certain very important symmetry and simplicity is hidden in these solutions by the fact that the a-phase has been used as the reference phase to determine the symmetrical components for a fault on the b-phase. This fact will appear immediately, if the b-phase symmetrical components of fault currents and voltages are determined. Applying the $\mathcal{A}_r$ matrix transformation

$$\mathcal{I}_{bs} = \mathcal{A}_r \mathcal{I}_s = \begin{bmatrix} 1 & 0 & 0 \\ 0 & a^2 & 0 \\ 0 & 0 & a \end{bmatrix} \begin{bmatrix} 1 \\ a \\ a^2 \end{bmatrix} \frac{I_F}{3} = \begin{bmatrix} 1 \\ 1 \\ 1 \end{bmatrix} \frac{I_F}{3} \qquad (13\text{–}54)$$

and the b-phase symmetrical components of fault current are *all alike.*

Applying the $\mathfrak{A}_r$ operator to the a-phase symmetrical components of voltage of equation 13–52 gives

$$\mathcal{V}_{Fbs} = \begin{bmatrix} V_{bF0} \\ V_{bF1} \\ V_{bF2} \end{bmatrix} = \begin{bmatrix} 0 \\ E_{b1} \\ 0 \end{bmatrix} - \begin{bmatrix} Z_{G0} + Z_{l0} + 3Z_g \\ Z_{G1} + Z_{l1} \\ Z_{G2} + Z_{l2} \end{bmatrix} \frac{I_F}{3} \qquad (13\text{–}55)$$

The disappearance of the a-operator from equations 13–54 and 13–55 suggests that perhaps an equivalent circuit can be established for the faulted line and generator in terms of the sequence impedances. Such an equivalent circuit is shown in Fig. 13–9. An examination of this network in conjunction with the relations derived in the foregoing will show that the *series connection* of sequence networks can be used to determine the complete behavior of the faulted system of Fig. 13–8. Note that the zero sequence current is in the zero sequence network, as are the positive and negative sequence currents in their respective networks. Also the sequence voltages at the fault appear directly across the corresponding sequence networks if the fault impedance is placed *outside* the sequence networks. There is no particular reason for locating $3Z_F$ as three impedances as shown in Fig. 13–9, except for symmetry. An impedance equal to $3Z_F$ may be located anywhere in the circuit *external* to the sequence networks.

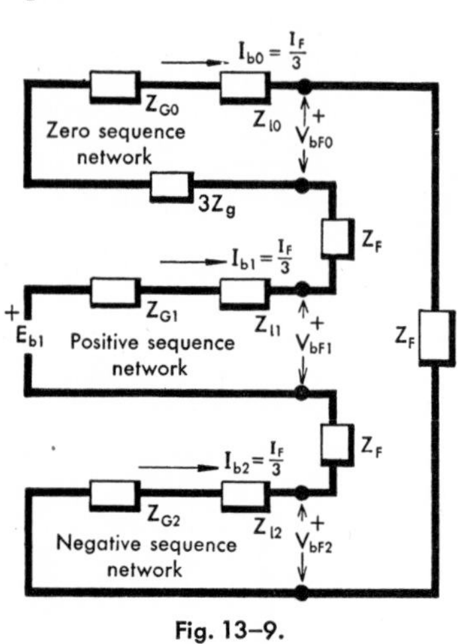

Fig. 13–9.

Symmetrical component usage is based entirely on determining and interconnecting the sequence networks. Obviously there are only a finite number of different ways a fault can occur on three wires. If all these possibilities are listed and the sequence network interconnection is computed for each possibility and listed along with the kind of fault, the determination of the symmetrical component behavior of a faulted system is merely a routine computation job as soon as the sequence impedances are all known.* It need hardly be mentioned that once the symmetrical component behavior at the fault is determined, applying $\mathfrak{A}^{-1}$ to the symmetrical component sets of currents and voltages establishes the actual currents and voltages to be found at the fault.

A further point which should be noted is that, if line a is grounded, exactly the same equivalent circuit will arise as in Fig. 13–9 except that

* Westinghouse Electric and Manufacturing Co., Pittsburgh, Pa., *Electric Transmission and Distribution Reference Book*, 2nd Edition, pp. 11–28, 1943.

E_{a1} will be in the positive sequence network, and currents I_{a0}, I_{a1} and I_{a2} will all be equal and may be considered as in the corresponding networks. Similarly, for line c grounded, E_{c1} and I_{c0}, I_{c1}, and I_{c2} will appear in their respective networks, and these networks will be the same as for line a or b faulted. (See Problems 13–12 and 13–13.)

The network of Fig. 13–9 is, of course, very much simpler than any power network in commercial practice for which symmetrical component computations or measurements would be used. However, the basic principles are given in the foregoing, and the following example illustrates an application of symmetrical components to a more extensive circuit.

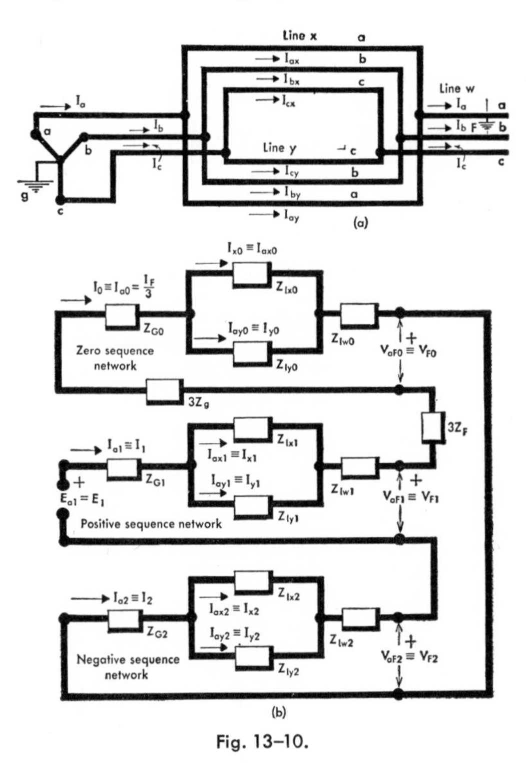

Fig. 13–10.

Example 13:5 The three-phase network shown in Fig. 13–10a has a short circuit (ground) on phase a. Sketch the sequence networks properly connected. Also determine the voltages from lines to fault, the fault current, the generator current, and the line currents, if $Z_{G0} = j0.14$ ohms, $Z_{G1} = j3.3$ ohms, $Z_{G2} = j2.1$ ohms, $Z_{lx1} = Z_{lx2} = j7$ ohms, $Z_{lx0} = j10$ ohms, $Z_{ly1} = Z_{ly2} = j5$ ohms, $Z_{ly0} = j7$ ohms, $Z_{lw1} = Z_{lw2} = j2$ ohms, $Z_{lw0} = j3$ ohms. It has been found sufficiently accurate to ignore the resistance of the usual power circuit. The generator is solidly grounded through zero impedance, and the fault also has negligible impedance. The generator voltage is 6930 between lines and of positive sequence.

Solution The circuit of Fig. 13–10*b* represents the sequence networks, connected in *series corresponding to a single line-to-ground fault.* The fault current may be determined immediately by solving for the currents in these interconnected sequence networks, since $I_0 = I_1 = I_2 = I_F/3$. Accordingly, using the subscript *e* to indicate *equivalent* impedances,

$$\frac{I_F}{3} = \frac{E_1}{Z_{e0}+Z_{e1}+Z_{e2}+3Z_F} = \frac{E_1}{(Z_{G0}+Z_{l0}+3Z_g)+(Z_{G1}+Z_{l1})+(Z_{G2}+Z_{l2})+3Z_F}$$

where Z_{l0} is the series-parallel combination of the zero sequence line impedances, etc.; hence

$$Z_{e0} = Z_{G0} + \frac{Z_{lx0}Z_{ly0}}{Z_{lx0} + Z_{ly0}} + Z_{lw0} + 3Z_g = j0.14 + \frac{j10j7}{j17} + j3 + 0 = j7.26$$

$$Z_{e1} = Z_{G1} + \frac{Z_{lx1}Z_{ly1}}{Z_{lx1} + Z_{ly1}} + Z_{lw1} = j3.3 + \frac{j7j5}{j12} + j2 = j8.22$$

$$Z_{e2} = Z_{G2} + \frac{Z_{lx2}Z_{ly2}}{Z_{lx2} + Z_{ly2}} + Z_{lw2} = j2.1 + \frac{j7j5}{j12} + j2 = j7.02$$

$$Z_F = 0$$

and where, for convenience, the reference axis may be taken so that

$$E_{a1} = E_1 = \frac{6930 + j0}{\sqrt{3}} = 4000 + j0$$

The fault current is, then,

$$I_F = \frac{3 \times 4000}{j22.5} = -j533 \text{ amperes}$$

and

$$I_0 = I_1 = I_2 = \frac{-j533}{3} = -j177.8 \text{ amperes, i.e.,}$$

$$\mathcal{I}_s = \mathcal{I}_{as} = \begin{bmatrix} I_0 \\ I_1 \\ I_2 \end{bmatrix} = \begin{bmatrix} -j177.8 \\ -j177.8 \\ -j177.8 \end{bmatrix}$$

The other symmetrical components of current into the fault are

$$\mathcal{I}_{bs} = \mathcal{A}_r \mathcal{I}_s = \begin{bmatrix} 1 & 0 & 0 \\ 0 & a^2 & 0 \\ 0 & 0 & a \end{bmatrix} \begin{bmatrix} -j177.8 \\ -j177.8 \\ -j177.8 \end{bmatrix} = \begin{bmatrix} -j177.8 \\ -153.9 + j88.9 \\ 153.9 + j88.9 \end{bmatrix}$$

$$\mathcal{I}_{cs} = \mathcal{A}_r \mathcal{A}_r \mathcal{I}_s = \begin{bmatrix} 1 & 0 & 0 \\ 0 & a & 0 \\ 0 & 0 & a^2 \end{bmatrix} \begin{bmatrix} -j177.8 \\ -j177.8 \\ -j177.8 \end{bmatrix} = \begin{bmatrix} -j177.7 \\ 153.9 + j88.9 \\ -153.9 + j88.9 \end{bmatrix}$$

The currents in the lines at the fault are already known as

$$\mathcal{I}_F = \begin{bmatrix} -j533 \\ 0 \\ 0 \end{bmatrix}$$

which also follows from equations 13–14, i.e.,

$$\mathcal{I}_F = \begin{bmatrix} I_a \\ I_b \\ I_c \end{bmatrix} = \mathcal{A}^{-1}\mathcal{I}_{Fs} = \begin{bmatrix} 1 & 1 & 1 \\ 1 & a^2 & a \\ 1 & a & a^2 \end{bmatrix} \begin{bmatrix} -j177.8 \\ -j177.8 \\ -j177.8 \end{bmatrix} = \begin{bmatrix} -j533 \\ 0 \\ 0 \end{bmatrix}$$

These currents also represent the generator currents—533 amp in phase a and no current in phases b and c.

The currents in the lines x and y may be obtained by computing the sequence currents in the sequence networks of Fig. 13–10*b*. Using the current-impedance relations of parallel circuits gives

$$\frac{I_{x0}}{I_0} = \frac{\dfrac{Z_{lx0}Z_{ly0}}{Z_{lx0} + Z_{ly0}}}{Z_{lx0}} = \frac{j4.12}{j10} = 0.412$$

from which

$$I_{x0} = (-j177.8)0.412 = -j73.3 \text{ amperes}$$

From this result, the zero sequence current of line y is

$$I_0 - I_{x0} = I_{y0} = -j177.8 + j73.3 = -j104.5 \text{ amperes}$$

Similarly,

$$I_{x1} = I_1 \frac{\dfrac{Z_{lx1}Z_{ly1}}{Z_{lx1} + Z_{ly1}}}{Z_{lx1}} = (-j177.8)0.417 = -j74.1 \text{ amperes}$$

from which

$$I_{y1} = I_1 - I_{x1} = -j177.8 + j74.1 = -j103.7 \text{ amperes}$$

and

$$I_{x2} = I_2 \frac{\dfrac{Z_{lx2}Z_{ly2}}{Z_{lx2} + Z_{ly2}}}{Z_{lx2}} = (-j177.8)0.417 = -j74.1 \text{ amperes}$$

from which

$$I_{y2} = -j103.7 \text{ amperes}$$

In matrix form these a-phase sequence currents of the lines x and y are

$$\mathcal{I}_{xs} = \begin{bmatrix} I_{x0} \\ I_{x1} \\ I_{x2} \end{bmatrix} = \begin{bmatrix} -j73.2 \\ -j74.1 \\ -j74.1 \end{bmatrix}$$

and

$$\mathcal{I}_{ys} = \begin{bmatrix} I_{y0} \\ I_{y1} \\ I_{y2} \end{bmatrix} = \begin{bmatrix} -j104.5 \\ -j103.7 \\ -j103.7 \end{bmatrix}$$

The sequence currents of these same lines for phases b and c are

$$\mathcal{I}_{bxs} = \mathcal{A}_r \mathcal{I}_{xs} = \begin{bmatrix} 1 & 0 & 0 \\ 0 & a^2 & 0 \\ 0 & 0 & a \end{bmatrix} \begin{bmatrix} -j73.3 \\ -j74.1 \\ -j74.1 \end{bmatrix} = \begin{bmatrix} -j73.3 \\ -64.2 + j37.1 \\ 64.2 + j37.1 \end{bmatrix}$$

and

$$\mathcal{I}_{cxs} = \mathcal{A}_r \mathcal{A}_r \mathcal{I}_{xs} = \begin{bmatrix} 1 & 0 & 0 \\ 0 & a & 0 \\ 0 & 0 & a^2 \end{bmatrix} \begin{bmatrix} -j73.3 \\ -j74.1 \\ -j74.1 \end{bmatrix} = \begin{bmatrix} -j73.3 \\ 64.2 + j37.1 \\ -64.2 + j37.1 \end{bmatrix}$$

Also

$$\mathcal{I}_{bys} = \mathcal{A}_r \mathcal{I}_{ys} = \begin{bmatrix} 1 & 0 & 0 \\ 0 & a^2 & 0 \\ 0 & 0 & a \end{bmatrix} \begin{bmatrix} -j104.5 \\ -j103.7 \\ -j103.7 \end{bmatrix} = \begin{bmatrix} -j104.5 \\ -89.8 + j51.9 \\ 89.8 + j51.9 \end{bmatrix}$$

and

$$\mathcal{I}_{cys} = \mathcal{A}_r \mathcal{A}_r \mathcal{I}_{ys} = \begin{bmatrix} 1 & 0 & 0 \\ 0 & a & 0 \\ 0 & 0 & a^2 \end{bmatrix} \begin{bmatrix} -j104.5 \\ -j103.7 \\ -j103.7 \end{bmatrix} = \begin{bmatrix} -j104.5 \\ 89.8 + j51.9 \\ -89.8 + j51.9 \end{bmatrix}$$

The currents in lines x and y are, from equation 13–14

$$\mathcal{I}_x = \begin{bmatrix} I_{ax} \\ I_{bx} \\ I_{cx} \end{bmatrix} = \mathcal{A}^{-1} \mathcal{I}_{xs} = \begin{bmatrix} 1 & 1 & 1 \\ 1 & a^2 & a \\ 1 & a & a^2 \end{bmatrix} \begin{bmatrix} -j73.3 \\ -j74.1 \\ -j74.1 \end{bmatrix} = \begin{bmatrix} -j221.5 \\ 0 \\ 0 \end{bmatrix}$$

and

$$\mathcal{I}_y = \begin{bmatrix} I_{ay} \\ I_{by} \\ I_{cy} \end{bmatrix} = \mathcal{A}^{-1} \mathcal{I}_{ys} = \begin{bmatrix} 1 & 1 & 1 \\ 1 & a^2 & a \\ 1 & a & a^2 \end{bmatrix} \begin{bmatrix} -j104.5 \\ -j103.7 \\ -j103.7 \end{bmatrix} = \begin{bmatrix} -j311.9 \\ 0 \\ 0 \end{bmatrix}$$

All the currents of the network have now been determined, and there remain the voltages at the fault yet to be determined.

The network combination of Fig. 13–10b may be used, or equation 13–55 altered to express phase-a voltages, may be used. Thus, directly from the circuit diagram,

$$\mathcal{V}_{Fs} = \begin{bmatrix} V_{F0} \\ V_{F1} \\ V_{F2} \end{bmatrix} = \begin{bmatrix} 0 \\ E_1 \\ 0 \end{bmatrix} - \begin{bmatrix} Z_{e0} I_0 \\ Z_{e1} I_1 \\ Z_{e2} I_2 \end{bmatrix}$$

$$= \begin{bmatrix} 0 \\ 4000 + j0 \\ 0 \end{bmatrix} - \begin{bmatrix} j7.26(-j177.8) \\ j8.22(-j177.8) \\ j7.02(-j177.8) \end{bmatrix} = \begin{bmatrix} -1290 + j0 \\ 2538 + j0 \\ -1248 + j0 \end{bmatrix}$$

The sequence fault voltages of phases b and c are, from these voltages,

$$\mathcal{V}_{Fbs} = \mathcal{A}_r \mathcal{V}_{Fs} = \begin{bmatrix} 1 & 0 & 0 \\ 0 & a^2 & 0 \\ 0 & 0 & a \end{bmatrix} \begin{bmatrix} -1290 + j0 \\ 2538 + j0 \\ -1248 + j0 \end{bmatrix} = \begin{bmatrix} -1290 + j0 \\ -1269 - j2200 \\ 624 - j1080 \end{bmatrix}$$

and

$$\mathcal{V}_{Fcs} = \mathcal{A}_r \mathcal{A}_r \mathcal{V}_{Fs} = \begin{bmatrix} 1 & 0 & 0 \\ 0 & a & 0 \\ 0 & 0 & a^2 \end{bmatrix} \begin{bmatrix} -1290 + j0 \\ 2538 + j0 \\ -1248 + j0 \end{bmatrix} = \begin{bmatrix} -1290 + j0 \\ -1269 + j2200 \\ 624 + j1080 \end{bmatrix}$$

which lead to the voltages from lines to ground at the fault

$$\mathcal{V}_F = \begin{bmatrix} V_{aF} \\ V_{bF} \\ V_{cF} \end{bmatrix} = \mathcal{A}^{-1}\mathcal{V}_{Fs} = \begin{bmatrix} 1 & 1 & 1 \\ 1 & a^2 & a \\ 1 & a & a^2 \end{bmatrix} \begin{bmatrix} -1290 + j0 \\ 2538 + j0 \\ -1248 + j0 \end{bmatrix} = \begin{bmatrix} 0 \\ -1935 - j3280 \\ -1935 + j3280 \end{bmatrix}$$

In studying power systems and their response to faults at various points, in terms of sequence networks, small power networks can be studied by numerical calculation of the currents and voltages of these sequence networks. For extensive networks, however, calculation becomes so time consuming and tedious that test boards are used. These boards can be adjusted and interconnected to represent the sequence networks properly interconnected, and the sequence currents and voltages can be determined immediately by measuring the currents and voltages in the test board network. The test board shown in Fig. 11–26 suggests the extent to which these boards are used, from the size and, therefore, obvious expense of building such a board. The few largest of these test boards are in such demand that they are under contract for six to eight months in advance.

13.7 Short, or Fault, Between Two Lines — Double-Line (DL) Fault.

A short circuit between two of the lines of a three-phase system occurs frequently. The circuit of Fig. 13–11 represents a simple form of such a fault. The symmetrical component requirement of three equations can be satisfied by writing equations following the currents of Fig. 13–11 and continuing through the point m to the starting point g. The fault will be assumed to occur through the impedance $2Z_F$ between points b and c, with the point m at the midpoint of $2Z_F$. This assumption maintains a certain amount of symmetry in the equations and so facilitates the solution. If Z_a, Z_b, and Z_c represent the total impedance in the respective phases, the required three equations are

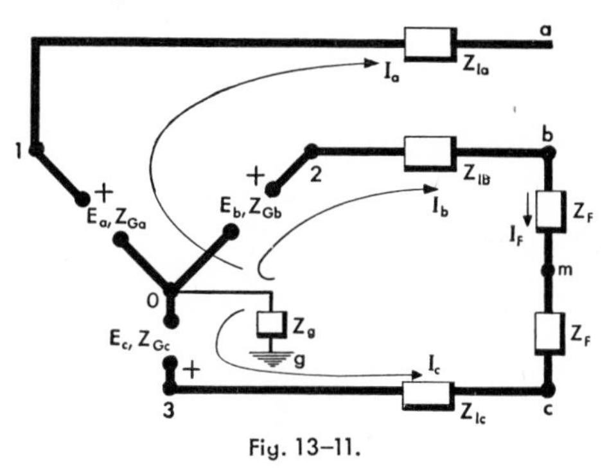

Fig. 13–11.

$$\begin{bmatrix} E_a \\ E_b \\ E_c \end{bmatrix} = \begin{bmatrix} Z_a+Z_g & Z_g & Z_g \\ Z_g & Z_b+Z_g+Z_F & Z_g \\ Z_g & Z_g & Z_c+Z_g+Z_F \end{bmatrix} \begin{bmatrix} I_a \\ I_b \\ I_c \end{bmatrix} + \begin{bmatrix} V_{am}+V_{mg} \\ V_{mg} \\ V_{mg} \end{bmatrix} \qquad (13\text{–}56)$$

or

$$\mathcal{E} = \mathcal{Z}\mathcal{I} + \mathcal{V} \qquad (13\text{–}57)$$

The symmetrical component form of this equation is

$$\mathcal{E}_s = \mathcal{A}\mathcal{E} = \mathcal{A}\mathfrak{Z}\mathcal{A}^{-1}\mathcal{I}_s + \mathcal{A}\mathcal{V} \qquad (13\text{–}58)$$

Just as for the single line-to-ground fault, this equation expresses the complete behavior of the faulted generator of Fig. 13–11. And, as before, evaluating each of the matrix combinations of the general equation leads to a set of simultaneous equations from which the fault currents and voltages can be determined.

Proceeding to the evaluation of the matrices of equation 13–58, consider first the source voltage matrix. Because only positive sequence voltages are assumed to be generated in the alternator,

$$\mathcal{E}_s = \mathcal{A}\mathcal{E} = \begin{bmatrix} 0 \\ E_1 \\ 0 \end{bmatrix} \qquad (13\text{–}59)$$

The impedance matrix can be handled most effectively by considering it as the sum

$$\mathfrak{Z} = \mathfrak{Z}_G + \mathfrak{Z}_l + \mathfrak{Z}_g + \mathfrak{Z}_F = \mathfrak{Z}_G + \mathfrak{Z}_l + Z_g \begin{bmatrix} 1 & 1 & 1 \\ 1 & 1 & 1 \\ 1 & 1 & 1 \end{bmatrix} + Z_F \begin{bmatrix} 0 & 0 & 0 \\ 0 & 1 & 0 \\ 0 & 0 & 1 \end{bmatrix} \qquad (13\text{–}60)$$

Then, to recall the assumptions made in the preceding article regarding the sequence impedance of alternators and transmission lines,

$$\mathcal{A}\mathfrak{Z}\mathcal{A}^{-1} = \begin{bmatrix} Z_{G0} & 0 & 0 \\ 0 & Z_{G1} & 0 \\ 0 & 0 & Z_{G2} \end{bmatrix} + \begin{bmatrix} Z_{l0} & 0 & 0 \\ 0 & Z_{l1} & 0 \\ 0 & 0 & Z_{l2} \end{bmatrix} + \mathcal{A}\mathfrak{Z}_g\mathcal{A}^{-1} + \mathcal{A}\mathfrak{Z}_F\mathcal{A}^{-1} \qquad (13\text{–}61)$$

Evaluating each of these last two matrix products results in

$$\mathfrak{Z}_s = \mathcal{A}\mathfrak{Z}\mathcal{A}^{-1} = \begin{bmatrix} Z_{G0} & 0 & 0 \\ 0 & Z_{G1} & 0 \\ 0 & 0 & Z_{G2} \end{bmatrix} + \begin{bmatrix} Z_{l0} & 0 & 0 \\ 0 & Z_{l1} & 0 \\ 0 & 0 & Z_{l2} \end{bmatrix} + \begin{bmatrix} 3Z_g & 0 & 0 \\ 0 & 0 & 0 \\ 0 & 0 & 0 \end{bmatrix} + \frac{Z_F}{3} \begin{bmatrix} 2 & -1 & -1 \\ -1 & 2 & -1 \\ -1 & -1 & 2 \end{bmatrix}$$

Adding the first three matrices, and using the subscript e to denote the sum (equivalent), gives

$$\mathfrak{Z}_s = \mathcal{A}\mathfrak{Z}\mathcal{A}^{-1} = \begin{bmatrix} Z_{e0} + 3Z_g & 0 & 0 \\ 0 & Z_{e1} & 0 \\ 0 & 0 & Z_{e2} \end{bmatrix} + Z_F \begin{bmatrix} 2 & -1 & -1 \\ -1 & 2 & -1 \\ -1 & -1 & 2 \end{bmatrix} \qquad (13\text{–}62)$$

Next, the symmetrical components of the currents, on applying the $\mathcal{A}$ transformation to the currents of Fig. 13–11, are

$$\mathcal{I}_s = \mathcal{A}\mathcal{I} = \tfrac{1}{3} \begin{bmatrix} 1 & 1 & 1 \\ 1 & a & a^2 \\ 1 & a^2 & a \end{bmatrix} \begin{bmatrix} 0 \\ I_F \\ -I_F \end{bmatrix} = \frac{I_F}{3} \begin{bmatrix} 0 \\ j\sqrt{3} \\ -j\sqrt{3} \end{bmatrix} = \begin{bmatrix} I_0 \\ I_1 \\ I_2 \end{bmatrix} \qquad (13\text{–}63)$$

which shows that

$$I_{0n} = 0$$

$$I_1 = -I_2 = j\frac{I_F}{\sqrt{3}} \tag{13–64}$$

The symmetrical components of the voltage matrix $\mathcal{V}$ of equations 13–56 and 13–57 are

$$\mathcal{V}_s = \mathcal{A}\mathcal{V} = \tfrac{1}{3}\begin{bmatrix} 1 & 1 & 1 \\ 1 & a & a^2 \\ 1 & a^2 & a \end{bmatrix}\begin{bmatrix} V_{am} + V_{mg} \\ V_{mg} \\ V_{mg} \end{bmatrix} = \tfrac{1}{3}\begin{bmatrix} V_{am} + 3V_{mg} \\ V_{am} \\ V_{am} \end{bmatrix} \tag{13–65}$$

Combining the results obtained in equations 13–59, 13–62, 13–63, and 13–65 gives

$$\begin{bmatrix} 0 \\ E_1 \\ 0 \end{bmatrix} = \begin{bmatrix} Z_{e0} + 3Z_g & 0 & 0 \\ 0 & Z_{e1} & 0 \\ 0 & 0 & Z_{e2} \end{bmatrix}\begin{bmatrix} 0 \\ I_1 \\ I_2 \end{bmatrix} + \frac{Z_F}{3}\begin{bmatrix} 2 & -1 & -1 \\ -1 & 2 & -1 \\ -1 & -1 & 2 \end{bmatrix}\begin{bmatrix} 0 \\ I_1 \\ I_2 \end{bmatrix} + \tfrac{1}{3}\begin{bmatrix} V_{am} + 3V_{mg} \\ V_{am} \\ V_{am} \end{bmatrix} \tag{13–66}$$

If certain evident combinations are made, and equations 13–64 are used, this last equation becomes

$$0 = \frac{V_{am}}{3} + V_{mg} \tag{13–67}$$

$$\begin{bmatrix} E_1 \\ 0 \end{bmatrix} = \begin{bmatrix} Z_{e1} + Z_F & 0 \\ 0 & Z_{e2} + Z_F \end{bmatrix}\begin{bmatrix} I_F \\ -I_F \end{bmatrix}\frac{j}{\sqrt{3}} + \frac{1}{3}\begin{bmatrix} V_{am} \\ V_{am} \end{bmatrix} \tag{13–68}$$

The two unknown elements at the fault, namely I_F and V_{am} can be determined from this last matrix equation.

In correspondence with the sequence network interconnection of the *SLG* fault already considered, a sequence network interconnection can be established for a double-line (*DL*) fault. In the first place, examination of Fig. 13–12 and the matrix equation 13–68 shows that this equation expresses exactly the behavior of the shown interconnection of sequence networks. Such an interconnection is considered as a parallel connection, and from it the fault current I_F and voltage V_{am} from the open line a to the center m of the fault impedance can be measured.

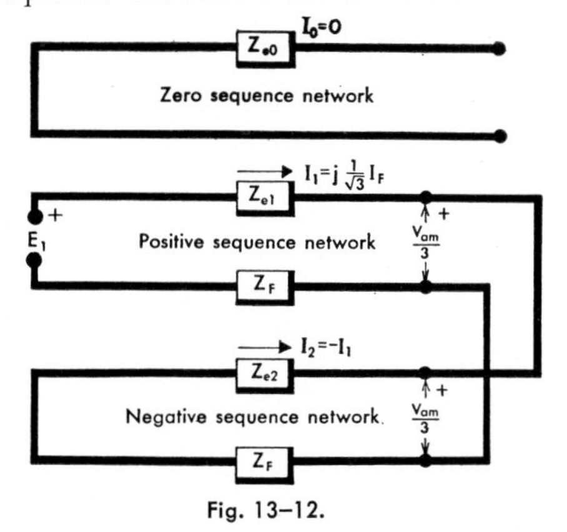

Fig. 13–12.

For actual interconnection on test boards, it is more useful to remove the fault impedance from the sequence network and make the interconnection as shown in Fig. 13–13. The question then immediately arises as to the meaning of the voltages across the terminals of the sequence

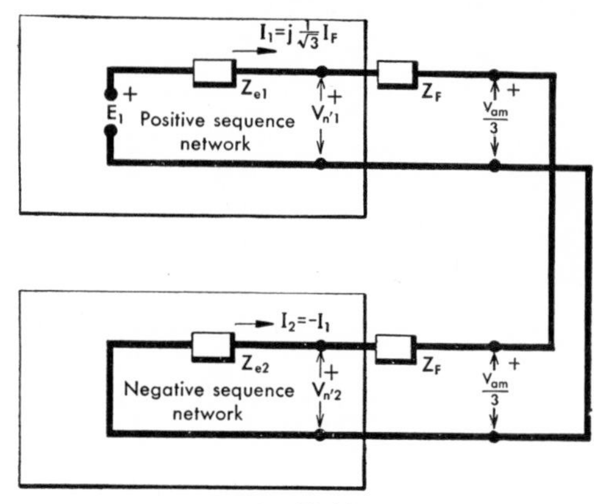

Fig. 13–13.

networks. These voltages are actually positive and negative sequence voltages at the fault as will now be shown.

The voltages from the three points a, b, and c at the fault (Fig. 13–11) to the ideal neutral n' of the line voltages at the fault are (equations 11–13) if use is made of the fact that $V_{bm} = I_F Z_F$ and $V_{mc} = I_F Z_F$

$$V_{an'} = \frac{V_{ab} + V_{ac}}{3} = \frac{V_{am} + V_{mb} + V_{am} + V_{mc}}{3} = \frac{2}{3} V_{am} \tag{13–69}$$

$$V_{bn'} = \frac{V_{ba} + V_{bc}}{3} = \frac{V_{bm} + V_{ma} + V_{bm} + V_{mc}}{3} = -\frac{V_{am}}{3} + I_F Z_F \tag{13–70}$$

$$V_{cn'} = \frac{V_{ca} + V_{cb}}{3} = \frac{V_{cm} + V_{ma} + V_{cm} + V_{mb}}{3} = -\frac{V_{am}}{3} - I_F Z_F \tag{13–71}$$

In matrix form these results are

$$\mathcal{V}_{n'} = \begin{bmatrix} V_{an'} \\ V_{bn'} \\ V_{cn'} \end{bmatrix} = \frac{V_{am}}{3} \begin{bmatrix} 2 \\ -1 \\ -1 \end{bmatrix} + I_F Z_F \begin{bmatrix} 0 \\ 1 \\ -1 \end{bmatrix} \tag{13–72}$$

The symmetrical component form of this equation is

$$\mathcal{V}_{n's} = \mathcal{A}\mathcal{V}_{n'} = \frac{V_{am}}{9} \begin{bmatrix} 1 & 1 & 1 \\ 1 & a & a^2 \\ 1 & a^2 & a \end{bmatrix} \begin{bmatrix} 2 \\ -1 \\ -1 \end{bmatrix} + \frac{I_F Z_F}{3} \begin{bmatrix} 1 & 1 & 1 \\ 1 & a & a^2 \\ 1 & a^2 & a \end{bmatrix} \begin{bmatrix} 0 \\ 1 \\ -1 \end{bmatrix}$$

$$\mathcal{V}_{n's} = \begin{bmatrix} V_{n'0} \\ V_{n'1} \\ V_{n'2} \end{bmatrix} = \frac{V_{am}}{3} \begin{bmatrix} 0 \\ 1 \\ 1 \end{bmatrix} + j \frac{I_F Z_F}{\sqrt{3}} \begin{bmatrix} 0 \\ 1 \\ -1 \end{bmatrix} \tag{13–73}$$

But reference to Fig. 13–13 will show that $V_{n'1}$ and $V_{n'2}$ are exactly the voltages which appear across the terminals of the parallel-connected sequence networks. The sequence network connection of Fig. 13–14 may, therefore, be used and the sequence currents and voltages appear in and across the network exactly as they did in the series connection for the *SLG* fault.

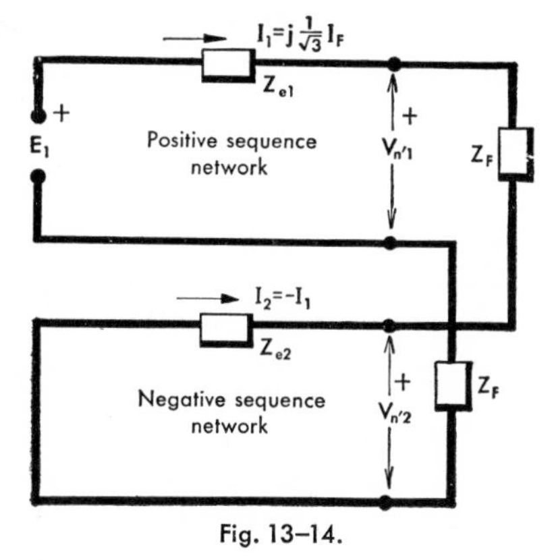

Fig. 13–14.

The line voltages at the fault can be determined directly from V_{am} and $I_F Z_F$, or from $V_{n'1}$ and $V_{n'2}$ by means of

$$\begin{bmatrix} V_{ab} \\ V_{bc} \\ V_{ca} \end{bmatrix} = \begin{bmatrix} 1 & -1 & 0 \\ 0 & 1 & -1 \\ -1 & 0 & 1 \end{bmatrix} \begin{bmatrix} V_{an'} \\ V_{bn'} \\ V_{cn'} \end{bmatrix} = \begin{bmatrix} 1 & -1 & 0 \\ 0 & 1 & -1 \\ -1 & 0 & 1 \end{bmatrix} \mathfrak{A}^{-1} \begin{bmatrix} 0 \\ V_{n'1} \\ V_{n'2} \end{bmatrix}$$

which is

$$\begin{bmatrix} V_{ab} \\ V_{bc} \\ V_{ca} \end{bmatrix} = \sqrt{3} \begin{bmatrix} 0 & \epsilon^{j30} & \epsilon^{-j30} \\ 0 & \epsilon^{j90} & \epsilon^{-j90} \\ 0 & \epsilon^{j150} & \epsilon^{-j150} \end{bmatrix} \begin{bmatrix} 0 \\ V_{n'1} \\ V_{n'2} \end{bmatrix} \tag{13–74}$$

The line voltages at the fault, therefore, can be determined from the measured or calculated symmetrical component voltages of the network of Fig. 13–14.

The impedances Z_{e1}, and Z_{e2}, of course, represent the equivalent positive and negative sequence impedances of all linear portions of any three-phase power network. For example, if the network of Fig. 13–10*a* has a line-to-line fault between lines *b* and *c* on line *w* in place of the ground

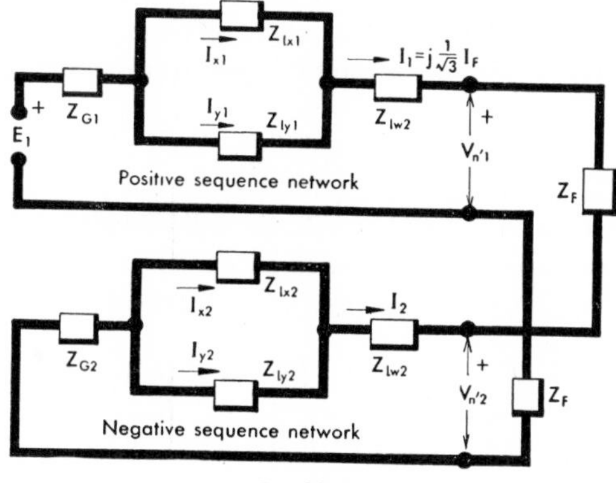

Fig. 13–15.

shown, the *same sequence networks* as given in Fig. 13–10*b* should be connected in parallel, as shown in Fig. 13–15, to represent the line-to-line fault behavior. This circuit, then, determines the *DL* fault behavior of the network of Fig. 13–10*a*.

PROBLEMS

13–1 Determine the *a*-, *b*-, and *c*-phase symmetrical components of the unbalanced set of currents $I_a = 10 + j0$, $I_b = -10 + j0$, and $I_c = 10 + j10$. Show these components graphically and show that they add to form the original set of currents.

13–2 Repeat Problem 13–1 for the three unbalanced, three-phase currents $I_a = 10 + j0$, $I_b = -10 + j0$, and $I_c = 0 + j0$.

13–3 Multiply equation 13–25 in detail and show that the result given in equation 13–27 is correct.

13–4 Suppose three equal impedances $8 + j6$ are connected in wye. To these impedances a regulated wye-connected generator of positive sequence phase voltages $V_a = 100 + j0$, $V_b = 0 - j100$, and $V_c = 100 + j100$ is connected. Compute the symmetrical components of generator phase voltages, of line voltages, and of line currents.

13–5 Suppose three impedances $Z_a = 10 + j0$, $Z_b = 8 - j6$, and $Z_c = 0 + j10$ are connected in wye across the same regulated generator as specified in Problem 13–4. Compute the impedance matrix of equation 13–32. Also compute $\mathcal{I}_s$ and $\mathcal{V}_{ns}$.

13–6 The line and phase voltages of a wye generator are

$$\mathcal{E}_l = \begin{bmatrix} E_{ab} \\ E_{bc} \\ E_{ca} \end{bmatrix} = \begin{bmatrix} E_a - E_b \\ E_b - E_c \\ E_c - E_a \end{bmatrix} = \begin{bmatrix} 1 & -1 & 0 \\ 0 & 1 & -1 \\ -1 & 0 & 1 \end{bmatrix} \begin{bmatrix} E_a \\ E_b \\ E_c \end{bmatrix}$$

Determine the symmetrical components of the line voltages in terms of the symmetrical components of phase voltages. Show that the zero sequence of phase generated voltage cannot be expressed in terms of the zero sequence of line voltage, but that the positive and negative sequences of phase and line voltages can be expressed in terms of each other and that they are related by the usual balanced voltage angle of 30 degrees and the numerical factor $\sqrt{3}$.

13–7 Show symbolically that the symmetrical components of currents in a balanced three-wire wye circuit are related to the generator phase voltages by

$$\mathcal{I}_s = \begin{bmatrix} I_0 \\ I_1 \\ I_2 \end{bmatrix} = \begin{bmatrix} 0 & 0 & 0 \\ 0 & Y_p & 0 \\ 0 & 0 & Y_p \end{bmatrix} \begin{bmatrix} E_0 \\ E_1 \\ E_2 \end{bmatrix}$$

where Y_p is the total admittance of each balanced phase.

13–8 Show that the phase voltages of a three-wire wye load are related by

$$\begin{bmatrix} V_0 \\ V_1 \\ V_2 \end{bmatrix} = \begin{bmatrix} V_{a0} \\ V_{a1} \\ V_{a2} \end{bmatrix} = \begin{bmatrix} 0 & 0 & 0 \\ 0 & Z_p & 0 \\ 0 & 0 & Z_p \end{bmatrix} \begin{bmatrix} I_0 \\ I_1 \\ I_2 \end{bmatrix}$$

where Z_p is the total impedance per balanced phase.

13–9 Show that, if the impedances of a delta load are balanced, the zero sequence of phase currents is zero. Assume constant *unbalanced* voltages connected to the delta load.

13–10 The transpose of a matrix is formed by interchanging rows and columns. Thus if

$$\mathfrak{D} = \begin{bmatrix} d_{11} \\ d_{21} \\ d_{31} \end{bmatrix}, \text{ the transpose } \mathfrak{D}_t = [d_{11}, d_{21}, d_{31}]$$

or if

$$\mathcal{B} = \begin{bmatrix} b_{11} & b_{12} \\ b_{21} & b_{22} \end{bmatrix}, \text{ the transpose } \mathcal{B}_t = \begin{bmatrix} b_{11} & b_{21} \\ b_{12} & b_{22} \end{bmatrix}$$

The average apparent power of a three-phase system can be expressed in terms of voltage conjugates and currents as

$$\mathrm{U} = \hat{\mathcal{E}}_t \mathcal{I} = [\hat{E}_a, \hat{E}_b, \hat{E}_c] \begin{bmatrix} I_a \\ I_b \\ I_c \end{bmatrix} = \hat{E}_a I_a + \hat{E}_b I_b + \hat{E}_c I_c$$

If the symmetrical component transformation is used, the average apparent power is

$$\mathrm{U} = (\hat{\mathcal{A}}^{-}\hat{\mathcal{E}}^{1}{}_{s})_t \mathcal{A}^{-1} \mathcal{I}_s$$

Carry out this multiplication and show that the average apparent power is

$$\mathrm{U} = 3\hat{\mathcal{E}}_{st} \mathcal{I}_s = 3(\hat{E}_0 I_0 + \hat{E}_1 I_1 + \hat{E}_2 I_2)$$

13–11 Use of the matrix property of Art. 9–6, namely,

$$(\mathcal{A}\mathcal{B})' = \mathcal{B}'\mathcal{A}'$$

on the average apparent power expression of Problem 13–10,

$$\mathrm{U} = (\hat{\mathcal{A}}^{-1}\hat{\mathcal{E}}_s)' \mathcal{A}^{-1} \mathcal{I}_s = \hat{\mathcal{E}}_s{}' \hat{\mathcal{A}}^{-1} \mathcal{A}^{-1} \mathcal{I}_s$$

Show that this relation gives the correct average apparent power expression.

13–12 Derive the equation for the zero sequence of line currents as given in equation 13–51, if the short circuit is on phase a instead of phase b as in Fig. 13–8. Show that the only difference between the result for a short circuit on phase a or b is that the voltage E_{a1} or E_{b1} is used, depending on whether a-phase or b-phase is shorted. Also show that $I_{a0} = I_{a1} = I_{a2} = I_F/3$ for phase a grounded.

13–13 Repeat Problem 13–12 for phase c grounded, and thus with Problem 13–12 and equation 13–51 show that E_{a1}, E_{b1}, or E_{c1} appears in the numerator of equation 13–51, otherwise unchanged, depending on whether phase a, b, or c is grounded. Also show that $I_{c0} = I_{c1} = I_{c2} = I_F/3$ for phase c grounded and, therefore, that Fig. 13–9 represents a single line-to-ground (*SLG*) fault on any phase if the proper current and generated voltage are assumed in the network.

13–14 Sketch the sequence networks to be used to solve for the fault current on the system of Fig. 13–10a if it has a fault on phase b of line y in place of the fault shown on line w. The fault is at the center of line y. Calculate the fault currents and voltages between the lines and ground at the fault. Refer to Example 13–5 for the characteristics of this network.

13–15 Assume a fault on phase *c* of the system of Example 13–5 instead of phase *a* and find the fault current and voltages.

13–16 (*a*) Derive the sequence network interconnection as in Art. 13.7 for a line-to-line short between phases *a* and *b* of Fig. 13–11. (*b*) Repeat part (*a*) for a short between lines *a* and *c*. Compare the results of this problem with Art. 13.7 and state how to set up the sequence networks depending on the phase shorted.

13–17 Calculate the fault current and the fault voltages for a line-to-line short circuit between phases *a* and *b* at the end of line *w* of Fig. 13–10*a*. The ground is to be removed.

13–18 Calculate the fault currents and voltages for the circuit of Fig. 13–10*a* for a short between lines *b* and *c* on line *y* halfway between the generator and the line *w*. Line *w* is open.

13–19 Determine the method of interconnecting the sequence networks for a line-to-line fault which is also grounded.

13–20 Design a symmetrical component ammeter to measure all three sequences. Specify a set of values of resistance and inductance and show a switching arrangement and circuit diagram so that one ammeter can be used to measure all three sequences of currents. It will be necessary to use current transformers. The solution of the problem may be based on the fact that because a current divides inversely as the impedances of a two-branch parallel circuit, the phase relation of the total current and the branch currents can be controlled by altering the parameter values of the two branches. If one branch current is 60 degrees from the total, a reversal of this branch current will give a 120-degree phase relation which is just the relation required in the symmetrical component defining equations.

13–21 Design a symmetrical component voltmeter to measure all three sequences. Use resistors and capacitors in parallel, also use potential transformers if necessary.

13–22 Devise a graphical scheme for determining the symmetrical components from known unbalanced vectors representing a system of currents. Will one of the vectors equal to zero affect the scheme derived?

CHAPTER **14**

Steady State Operation of a Transmission Line

A transmission line consisting of two or more wires is one of the most important links in the utilization of electricity. The vast communication network which reaches to nearly all parts of the earth consists largely of transmission lines. The immense quantities of energy taken from coal, oil, gas, and falling water are available, far from the source of energy, only because of the transmission line. Indeed, the simplicity and the flexibility of the transmission line, as much as anything else, have made possible the widespread use of electricity.

Some knowledge of the behavior of a transmission line is, therefore, essential to the student of electrical engineering. This chapter is devoted to a study of the basic elements of the steady state behavior of transmission lines.

14.1 The Constants of a Transmission Line.

Examined superficially, the electrical behavior of a transmission line should require a consideration of its resistance because of the metallic conductors, a consideration of its capacitance because of the separation of these conductors by a dielectric, a consideration of its inductance because of the magnetic field which surrounds the conductors, and a consideration of the conductance which is a measure of the leakage current between wires. A detailed study of these transmission line constants, R, L, C, and G, will not be carried out here. The reader should refer to other books * for such discussions. For the purposes of this chapter the various factors which affect the R, L, C, and G of a transmission line will simply be pointed out.

The resistance of a transmission line is not, strictly speaking, a constant, but is a function of the spacings of the wires, the diameter of the

---

* M. B. Reed, *Fundamentals of Electrical Engineering*, International Textbook Co., 1938; L. F. Woodruff, *Principles of Electrical Power Transmission*, John Wiley & Sons, 1938; E. A. Guillemin, *Communication Networks*, John Wiley & Sons, 1935, vol. II, Chap. 1.

wires, the frequency, and the current in the wires. The spacing and size of the wires as well as the current magnitude affect the distribution of the current in the wires and, therefore, the resistance. The frequency, because of the "skin effect"—crowding of current toward the surface of the conductor—also affects the resistance, increasing the resistance as the frequency increases.

The inductance is computed for the one-turn coil formed by a unit of length of the two-wire line. In order for the inductance to mean anything, the current must be the same throughout the unit length of line, because of the definition

$$L \equiv \frac{n\phi}{I}$$

As will be seen in what follows, the current, except for direct current, is not the same throughout any length of line. Hence any computation of inductance is certain to be an approximation. The approximation is *very good,* however, for all power and most telephonic communication systems and is, therefore, widely assumed.

The line capacitance is computed for the capacitor formed by a unit length of the two wires separated by the insulating air as dielectric. Because of the definition of capacitance as

$$C \equiv \frac{Q}{V}$$

the voltage between the electrodes of the capacitor must be the *same at all points of the unit length* for the definition to mean anything. Such a condition exists exactly for d-c systems only; hence the use of the capacitance per unit length in computing the a-c behavior of a line must also lead to an approximate result. As for the corresponding approximation for the inductance, this approximation is very good for power and telephonic transmission lines and is widely employed.

The leakage current of the line is introduced into line computations by means of the conductance symbol G and the formula

$$G \equiv \frac{I}{V}$$

There is less justification for assuming G a constant than any of the factors R, L, or C. The leakage current increases markedly at a certain instantaneous voltage and is high for all greater voltages. The leakage current response to a sinusoidal voltage is, therefore, very different from sinusoidal. Fortunately, the voltages used on communication lines are too low to produce leakage current of relatively important magnitudes, and power lines are specially designed to operate at high voltages without producing excessive leakage current.

The fact that the so-called transmission line constants are not constants but are assumed so for many purposes parallels the assumption of constant R, L and C of the many *lumped constant* networks already considered. Such assumptions, of necessity, limit the application of the conclusions reached on the basis of these assumptions, but without postulating constant R, L, C, and G it is found that no satisfactory solution can be reached for any of our problems. The really essential point for the reader to keep in mind is that the formulas already derived in this book, as well as the ones yet to be formulated, *do not apply to all networks under all conditions*. If this fact is kept in mind, the approximate results obtained are extremely useful and cover the majority of situations with sufficient accuracy, as well as serving as a guide for the treatment of many of the more difficult non-linear networks which are used.

14.2 Partial Differential Equations of a Transmission Line.

A two-wire transmission line is physically one of the simplest structures possible. It is this simplicity which has permitted the formulation and solution of the behavior of transmission lines in a more complete form than for any other type of electrical equipment. A pair of partial differential equations is the starting point for the present discussion.

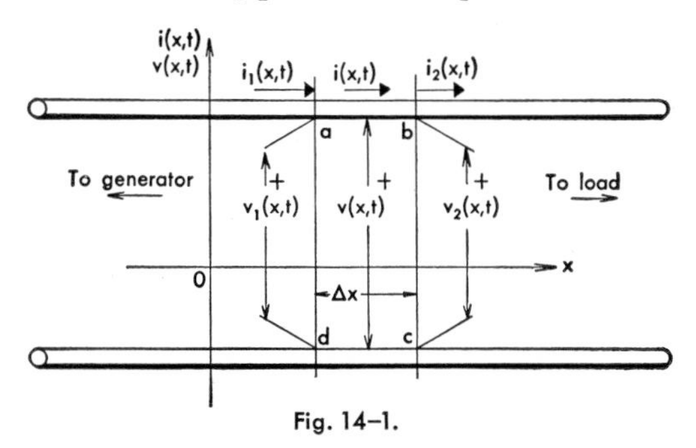

Fig. 14–1.

These equations may be deduced as follows. Figure 14–1 represents a section of a two-wire line on which is superimposed a two-dimensional coordinate system. To employ the well-known differential approximation, if it is assumed that the *current is constant* over a length Δx of a line, the voltage equation around the mesh *abcd* is

$$(R\,\Delta x)i(x,t) + (L\,\Delta x)\frac{\partial i\,(x,t)}{\partial t} + v_2(x,t) - v_1(x,t) = 0 \qquad (14\text{–}1)$$

where the R and L are evaluated per *unit length* of the two-wire line.

Next, if it is assumed that the *voltage between wires is constant* over the interval Δx the current equation at point a is

$$i_1(x,t) = i_2(x,t) + (G\,\Delta x)v(x,t) + (C\,\Delta x)\frac{\partial v\,(x,t)}{\partial t} \qquad (14\text{–}2)$$

where C and G are, respectively, the capacitance *between* wires and the conductance *between* wires, both per unit length of two-wire line.

Assuming that the voltage or current does not change over the interval Δx is, of course, an approximation which is progressively less in error as Δx is reduced. In the limit, therefore, as Δx approaches zero the error may be said to be zero. While such a consideration is not the complete justification for writing equations 14–1 and 14–2, it suggests that in the limit they might be valid. The mathematician's and experimentalist's proofs, which amply justify the process, are also available to increase confidence in the usefulness of these equations.

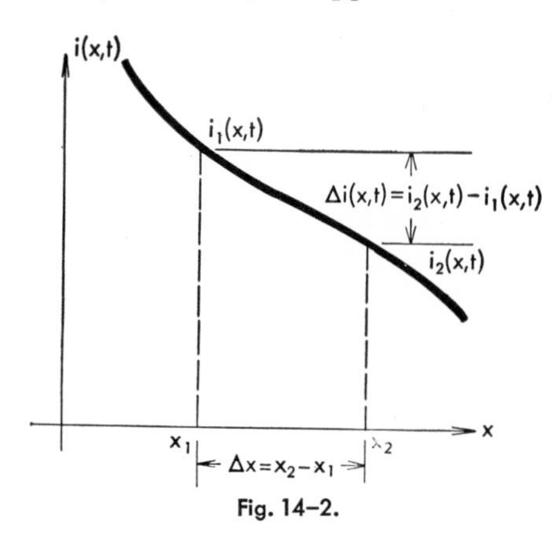

Fig. 14–2.

If the currents and voltages are considered as functions of x, it follows from the assumed positive x-direction and the calculus *definition* of the differential of the dependent variable (see Fig. 14–2) that

$$\Delta i\,(x, t) = i_2(x, t) - i_1(x, t)$$

and

$$\Delta v\,(x, t) = v_2(x, t) - v_1(x, t) \tag{14–3}$$

Equations 14–1 and 14–2, on dividing by Δx and rearranging, may, therefore, be written as

$$\frac{-\Delta v\,(x, t)}{\Delta x} = Ri(x, t) + L\frac{\partial i\,(x, t)}{\partial t} \tag{14–4}$$

$$\frac{-\Delta i\,(x, t)}{\Delta x} = Gv(x, t) + C\frac{\partial v\,(x, t)}{\partial t} \tag{14–5}$$

If the limit of the ratio of differentials exists as Δx approaches zero, and it will be assumed to do so, these equations become

$$\frac{-\partial v\,(x, t)}{\partial x} = Ri(x, t) + L\frac{\partial i\,(x, t)}{\partial t} \tag{14–6}$$

$$\frac{-\partial i\,(x, t)}{\partial x} = Gv(x, t) + C\frac{\partial v\,(x, t)}{\partial t} \tag{14–7}$$

These partial differential equations represent the interrelations of current, voltage, and line constants on a transmission line in terms of the two independent variables, time and distance from the generator. These equations, because of the assumptions made regarding the line constants, obviously do not represent the line behavior for all conditions, but, as already pointed out, they are sufficiently accurate for a great variety of purposes and are exact as long as constant R, L, C, and G exist or can be assumed to exist for practical purposes.

14.3 Steady State Solution of the Transmission Line Partial Differential Equations.

The complete solution—transient and steady state—of the differential equations obtained in the preceding article has been obtained only through the use of such devices as experimental means or Fourier integrals.* If only the steady state is desired it may be obtained from the partial differential equations.

Assume that the generated voltage is sinusoidal, and that this voltage in complex number form is

$$E(t) = E_m \epsilon^{j\omega t} \tag{14-8}$$

Equations 14–6 and 14–7, in complex variable form, are

$$\frac{-\partial V\,(x, t)}{\partial x} = RI(x, t) + L\frac{\partial I\,(x, t)}{\partial t} \tag{14-9}$$

$$\frac{-\partial I\,(x, t)}{\partial x} = GV(x, t) + C\frac{\partial V\,(x, t)}{\partial t} \tag{14-10}$$

The steady state solution of these equations is most easily obtained by establishing an equation in terms of *one* dependent variable. Thus if equation 14–9 is differentiated partially with respect to x,

$$\frac{-\partial^2 V\,(x, t)}{\partial x^2} = R\frac{\partial I\,(x, t)}{\partial x} + L\frac{\partial^2 I\,(x, t)}{\partial t\,\partial x} \tag{14-11}$$

Then if equation 14–10 is differentiated partially with respect to t,

$$\frac{-\partial^2 I\,(x, t)}{\partial x\,\partial t} = G\frac{\partial V\,(x, t)}{\partial t} + C\frac{\partial^2 V\,(x, t)}{\partial t^2} \tag{14-12}$$

Substituting, on the right-hand side of equation 14–11, for the first derivative from equation 14–10 and the second derivative from equation 14–12—the order of differentiation will be assumed immaterial—and rearranging gives

$$\frac{\partial^2 V\,(x, t)}{\partial x^2} = LC\frac{\partial^2 V\,(x, t)}{\partial t^2} + (RC + LG)\frac{\partial V\,(x, t)}{\partial t} + RGV(x, t) \tag{14-13}$$

an equation in terms of the voltage only.

By a very similar process from equations 14–9 and 14–10,

$$\frac{\partial^2 I\,(x, t)}{\partial x^2} = LC\frac{\partial^2 I\,(x, t)}{\partial t^2} + (RC + LG)\frac{\partial I\,(x, t)}{\partial t} + RGI(x, t) \tag{14-14}$$

* E. A. Guillemin, *Communication Networks*, John Wiley & Sons, 1935, vol. II; L. F. Woodruff, *Principles of Electrical Power Transmission*, Wiley, 1938.

which is just like equation 14–13 except that the current is now the only dependent variable present.

The steady state, or particular integral, part of the solution of these equations may be established by assuming the form the solution is to take. Since a sinusoidal voltage is connected to the line, the current or voltage at any point on the line may also be expected to be sinuosidal. Also, the current and voltage maximum value may be expected to be a function of x. Hence, suppose that the voltage is assumed to be of the form

$$V(x, t) = V_m(x)\epsilon^{j\omega t} \tag{14–15}$$

Substituting this assumed solution into equation 14–13 and canceling the common non-zero factor $\epsilon^{j\omega t}$ leads to

$$\frac{d^2V_m(x)}{dx^2} = (R + j\omega L)(G + j\omega C)V_m(x) \tag{14–16}$$

which, if, for convenience, the abbreviation

$$\alpha = \alpha_1 + j\alpha_2 = \sqrt{(R + j\omega L)(G + j\omega C)} = \sqrt{ZY} \tag{14–17}$$

is used, becomes

$$\frac{d^2V_m(x)}{dx^2} - \alpha^2 V_m(x) = 0 \tag{14–18}$$

The solution of this equation—value of $V_m(x)$—substituted into equation 14–15 will establish the steady state space and time solution for the voltage distribution of the transmission line.

Similarly, assuming

$$I(x, t) = I_m(x)\epsilon^{j\omega t} \tag{14–19}$$

equation 14–14 produces

$$\frac{d^2I_m(x)}{dx^2} - \alpha^2 I_m(x) = 0 \tag{14–20}$$

Equations 14–18 and 14–20 are now of exactly the same general form—linear with constant coefficients and in terms of *one* independent variable—as the equations solved in Chapter 8, and the same method of solution may, therefore, be used. Hence assume that

$$V_m(x) = V_m\epsilon^{mx} \tag{14–21}$$

and substitute into equation 14–18. The result, after canceling the non-zero exponential and the non-zero constant V_m, is

$$m^2 - \alpha^2 = 0$$

and

$$\begin{aligned} m_1 &= \alpha \equiv \sqrt{ZY} \\ m_2 &= -\alpha \equiv -\sqrt{ZY} \end{aligned} \tag{14–22}$$

The solution of equation 14–18 is, then,

$$V_m(x) = V_{m1}\epsilon^{\sqrt{ZY}\,x} + V_{m2}\epsilon^{-\sqrt{ZY}\,x} \tag{14–23}$$

Similarly the solution of equation 14–20 is

$$I_m(x) = I_{m1}\epsilon^{\sqrt{ZY}\,x} + I_{m2}\epsilon^{-\sqrt{ZY}\,x} \tag{14–24}$$

These last two equations substituted into equations 14–15 and 14–19, respectively, express the steady state behavior of a two-wire transmission line in terms of *four* constants. Thus

$$V(x, t) = [V_{m1}\epsilon^{\sqrt{ZY}\,x} + V_{m2}\epsilon^{-\sqrt{ZY}\,x}]\,\epsilon^{j\omega t} \tag{14–25}$$

and

$$I(x, t) = [I_{m1}\epsilon^{\sqrt{ZY}\,x} + I_{m2}\epsilon^{-\sqrt{ZY}\,x}]\,\epsilon^{j\omega t} \tag{14–26}$$

The evaluation of the arbitrary integration constants must be accomplished, as always for differential equation solutions, by using known values of the dependent variables for specified values of the independent variable. The number of such conditions required is equal to the number of *arbitrary* constants in the general solution—apparently *four* for the present problem.

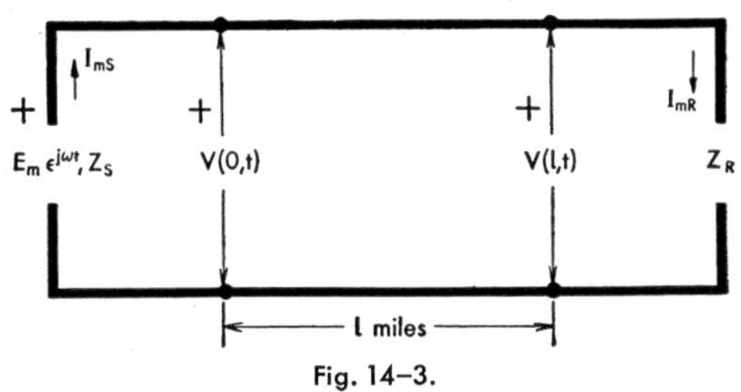

Fig. 14–3.

The steady state conditions of the line which may be specified are (Fig. 14–3): at the generator end of the line the voltage between lines is, of course, equal at all times to the generated voltage minus the internal impedance voltage of the generator

$$\begin{aligned} V(0, t) &= E_m\epsilon^{j\omega t} - Z_S I(0, t) \\ &= E_m\epsilon^{j\omega t} - Z_S I_{mS}\epsilon^{j\omega t} \end{aligned} \tag{14–27}$$

and at the receiving or load end of a line of length l

$$V(l, t) = Z_R I(l, t) = Z_R I_{mR}\epsilon^{j\omega t} \tag{14–28}$$

Since no other conditions can be specified, apparently only half enough boundary conditions are available. However, to retrace the steps employed in solving the original pair of differential equations, equations 14–13 and 14–14 were established by *eliminating an interrelation between current and voltage* appearing in the original equations, i.e., forming one equation from the pair of equations 14–9 and 14–10 inevitably eliminates a current and voltage interrelation evident in these equations, and completely absent in equations 14–13 and 14–14. Because the original differential equations do indicate a relation between currents and voltages, these two equations can be used to eliminate any *two* of the arbitrary constants of the current and voltage solutions as follows. On substituting equations 14–25 and 14–26 into equations 14–9 and 14–10, two equations in terms of the four constants will result. But since these equations are independent, *two* of the constants can be determined in terms of the other two, then the two boundary conditions already specified can be used to determine the value of these two remaining arbitrary constants and thus the steady state solution can be obtained.

If equations 14–9, 14–10, 14–25, and 14–26 are used, it may be shown that

$$V_{m1} = -\sqrt{\frac{R + j\omega L}{G + j\omega C}}\, I_{m1} = -\sqrt{\frac{Z}{Y}}\, I_{m1}$$

$$V_{m1} = -Z_0 I_{m1} \tag{14–29}$$

where, for brevity,

$$Z_0 \equiv \sqrt{\frac{R + j\omega L}{G + j\omega C}} \equiv \sqrt{\frac{Z}{Y}} \tag{14–30}$$

Also

$$V_{m2} = \sqrt{\frac{R + j\omega L}{G + j\omega C}}\, I_{m2} = \sqrt{\frac{Z}{Y}}\, I_{m2} = Z_0 I_{m2} \tag{14–31}$$

Equations 14–25 and 14–26 then become

$$V(x, t) = (V_{m1}\epsilon^{\alpha x} + V_{m2}\epsilon^{-\alpha x})\epsilon^{j\omega t} \tag{14–32}$$

$$I(x, t) = \left(-\frac{V_{m1}}{Z_0}\,\epsilon^{\alpha x} + \frac{V_{m2}}{Z_0}\,\epsilon^{-\alpha x}\right)\epsilon^{j\omega t} \tag{14–33}$$

These two equations may now be used to solve for the two arbitrary constants V_{m1} and V_{m2} by using the initial conditions of equations 14–27 and 14–28 substituted in equations 14–32 and 14–33 for the proper values of x, so that

$$V(0, t) = \left(E_m - Z_S\left[-\frac{V_{m1}}{Z_0} + \frac{V_{m2}}{Z_0}\right]\right)\epsilon^{j\omega t} = (V_{m1} + V_{m2})\epsilon^{j\omega t} \tag{14–34}$$

$$V(l, t) = Z_R\left(-\frac{V_{m1}}{Z_0}\,\epsilon^{\alpha l} + \frac{V_{m2}}{Z_0}\,\epsilon^{-\alpha l}\right)\epsilon^{j\omega t} = (V_{m1}\epsilon^{\alpha l} + V_{m2}\epsilon^{-\alpha l})\epsilon^{j\omega t} \tag{14–35}$$

Dividing these equations by the common non-zero exponential, and solving the resultant linear equations for V_{m1} and V_{m2}, gives

$$V_{m1} = \frac{E_m(Z_0 - Z_R)Z_0\epsilon^{-\alpha l}}{(Z_0 - Z_S)(Z_0 - Z_R)\epsilon^{-\alpha l} - (Z_0 + Z_S)(Z_0 + Z_R)\epsilon^{\alpha l}} \tag{14–36}$$

$$V_{m2} = \frac{-E_m(Z_0 + Z_R)Z_0\epsilon^{\alpha l}}{(Z_0 - Z_S)(Z_0 - Z_R)\epsilon^{-\alpha l} - (Z_0 + Z_S)(Z_0 + Z_R)\epsilon^{\alpha l}} \tag{14–37}$$

These constants, as is to be expected, are functions of the terminal impedances, generated voltage, line constants, and line length. Substituting the values thus obtained for the integration constants into the current and voltage equations 14–32 and 14–33, after making certain combinations and after a certain amount of rearranging to establish a form which has been found convenient, leads to the final equations for voltage and current. The steady state solution of the transmission line differential equations is then

$$V(x,t) = \left\{ \frac{E_m Z_0[(Z_R+Z_0)\epsilon^{\alpha(l-x)}+(Z_R-Z_0)\epsilon^{-\alpha(l-x)}]}{(Z_S+Z_0)(Z_R+Z_0)\epsilon^{\alpha l}-(Z_S-Z_0)(Z_R-Z_0)\epsilon^{-\alpha l}} \right\} \epsilon^{j\omega t} \quad (14\text{–}38)$$

$$I(x,t) = \left\{ \frac{E_m[(Z_R+Z_0)\epsilon^{\alpha(l-x)}-(Z_R-Z_0)\epsilon^{-\alpha(l-x)}]}{(Z_S+Z_0)(Z_R+Z_0)\epsilon^{\alpha l}-(Z_S-Z_0)(Z_R-Z_0)\epsilon^{-\alpha l}} \right\} \epsilon^{j\omega t} \quad (14\text{–}39)$$

The formal steady state, or particular integral, solution of the transmission line differential equations is thus complete, subject, of course, to the various restrictions stated, such as constant line coefficients R, L, C, and G, a load termination of constant impedance, Z_R, and a constant, internal impedance generator with constant sinusoidal generated voltage. The interpretation of these equations is the topic of discussion for the remainder of this chapter.

14.4 Wave Characteristics of the Current and Voltage on a Transmission Line.

The current and voltage solutions of a transmission line expressed in instantaneous, real variable form establishes the simplest equations from which to show the wave characteristics of these solutions. To this end, recalling the complex nature of α (equation 14–17), equations 14–38 and 14–39 may be written as

$$V(x,t) = V_{md}\epsilon^{\alpha_1(l-x)}\epsilon^{j[\omega t+\alpha_2(l-x)]} + V_{mr}\epsilon^{-\alpha_1(l-x)}\epsilon^{j[\omega t-\alpha_2(l-x)]} \quad (14\text{–}40)$$

and

$$I(x,t) = I_{md}\epsilon^{\alpha_1(l-x)}\epsilon^{j[\omega t+\alpha_2(l-x)]} + I_{mr}\epsilon^{-\alpha_1(l-x)}\epsilon^{j[\omega t-\alpha_2(l-x)]} \quad (14\text{–}41)$$

where

$$V_{md} = \frac{E_m Z_0(Z_R+Z_0)}{(Z_S+Z_0)(Z_R+Z_0)\epsilon^{\alpha l}-(Z_S-Z_0)(Z_R-Z_0)\epsilon^{-\alpha l}} = |V_{md}|\epsilon^{j\phi_d} \quad (14\text{–}42)$$

$$V_{mr} = \frac{E_m Z_0(Z_R-Z_0)}{(Z_S+Z_0)(Z_R+Z_0)\epsilon^{\alpha l}-(Z_S-Z_0)(Z_R-Z_0)\epsilon^{-\alpha l}} = |V_{mr}|\epsilon^{j\phi_r} \quad (14\text{–}43)$$

$$I_{md} = \frac{E_m(Z_R+Z_0)}{(Z_S+Z_0)(Z_R+Z_0)\epsilon^{\alpha l}-(Z_S-Z_0)(Z_R-Z_0)\epsilon^{-\alpha l}} = |I_{md}|\epsilon^{j\delta_d} \quad (14\text{–}44)$$

$$I_{mr} = \frac{-E_m(Z_R-Z_0)}{(Z_S+Z_0)(Z_R+Z_0)\epsilon^{\alpha l}-(Z_S-Z_0)(Z_R-Z_0)\epsilon^{-\alpha l}} = |I_{mr}|\epsilon^{j\delta_r} \quad (14\text{–}45)$$

If the significance of rotating vectors is recalled in terms of instantaneous values, the instantaneous values of current and voltage along the line are, therefore, the j-components of the complex variable expressions of equations 14–40 and 14–41, namely,

$$v(x, t) = |V_{md}|\epsilon^{\alpha_1(l-x)} \sin [\omega t + \phi_d + \alpha_2(l - x)] + |V_{mr}|\epsilon^{-\alpha_1(l-x)} \sin [\omega t + \phi_r - \alpha_2(l - x)] \quad (14\text{–}46)$$

$$i(x, t) = |I_{md}|\epsilon^{\alpha_1(l-x)} \sin [\omega t + \delta_d + \alpha_2(l - x)] + |I_{mr}|\epsilon^{-\alpha_1(l-x)} \sin [\omega t + \delta_r - \alpha_2(l - x)] \quad (14\text{–}47)$$

These equations may best be discussed by examining the separate terms. To anticipate conclusions which will shortly be reached, the first

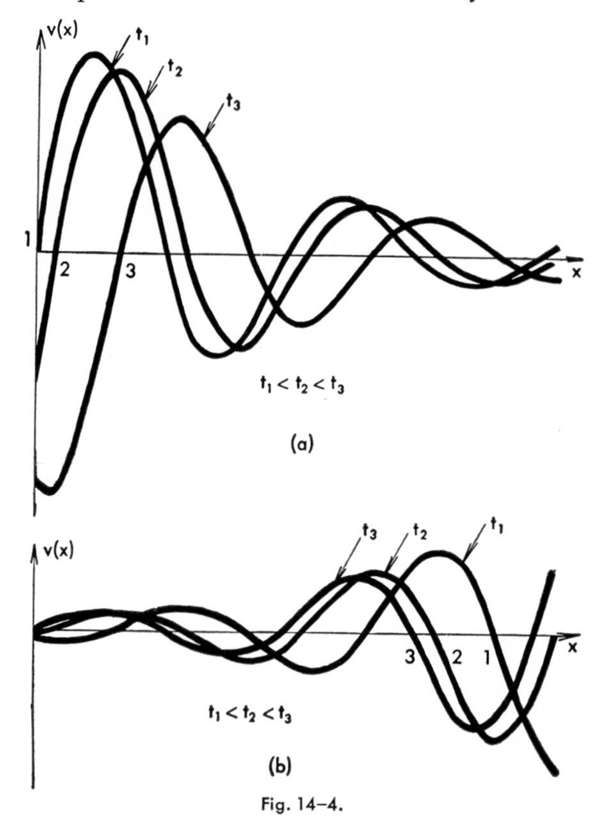

Fig. 14–4.

term on the right of each equation will be designated as the direct wave and the second term on the right as the reflected wave. The behavior of the line current or voltage of the direct wave of equations 14–46 and 14–47 is easily established by noting that, to keep the sine unchanged as time increases, x must increase, i.e., if $\omega t + \phi_d + \alpha_2(l - x)$ is to remain constant, as ωt increases x—$x \leqslant l$—must increase to reduce $\alpha_2(l - x)$. But this means that a constant angle value of direct wave of voltage, or current, moves down the line—from generator to load—with increase in time. Hence, the direct wave is a damped sine wave traveling toward the load. Three instantaneous positions of a direct wave of voltage are shown in Fig. 14–4*a*. The time indicated by t_1, t_2, and t_3 is successively later, and the sine waves of space distribution of voltage are shown advanced along the line for each increase in time.

Analogously, the second term on the right of equations 14–46 and 14–47 is a damped sine wave moving from *load to generator*, since as time *increases* x must *decrease* to keep the angle constant. The damping exponential also increases from load to generator, thus indicating a reduction in magnitude of the wave moving from *load to generator* (Fig. 14–4*b*).

The two terms of the current and voltage solution may thus be interpreted as direct and reflected waves, the total current or voltage thereby being the sum of these two waves. Particular note should be taken of the fact that *it is the component parts—direct and reflected waves—which have the traveling wave characteristics just discussed, and not the actual current or voltage.*

Whether the component parts of the solutions can be considered as actually existing is perhaps a matter of doubt. Under certain circumstances, to be discussed subsequently, the direct wave only is present and thus actually exists. In any event, analyzing the solution in the basis of the existence of direct and reflected waves is extremely useful and, therefore, is in general use.

14.5 Reflection Coefficients.

If the numerator and denominator of equations 14–38 and 14–39 are divided by $(Z_R + Z_0)(Z_S + Z_0)$ and if the symbolism

$$r_R \equiv \frac{Z_R - Z_0}{Z_R + Z_0} \tag{14–48}$$

$$r_S \equiv \frac{Z_S - Z_0}{Z_S + Z_0} \tag{14–49}$$

is used, the voltage and current equations become

$$V(x, t) = \frac{E_m Z_0[\epsilon^{\alpha(l-x)} + r_R\epsilon^{-\alpha(l-x)}]}{(Z_S+Z_0)(\epsilon^{\alpha l} - r_S r_R \epsilon^{-\alpha l})}\epsilon^{j\omega t} = [V_{md}\epsilon^{\alpha(l-x)} + V_{mr}\epsilon^{-\alpha(l-x)}]\epsilon^{j\omega t} \tag{14–50}$$

$$I(x, t) = \frac{E_m[\epsilon^{\alpha(l-x)} - r_R\epsilon^{-\alpha(l-x)}]}{(Z_S+Z_0)(\epsilon^{\alpha l} - r_S r_R \epsilon^{-\alpha l})}\epsilon^{j\omega t} = [I_{md}\epsilon^{\alpha(l-x)} + I_{mr}\epsilon^{-\alpha(l-x)}]\epsilon^{j\omega t} \tag{14–51}$$

where the factors V_{md}, V_{mr}, I_{md}, and I_{mr}, already defined in the preceding article, have a modified form which these last equations define.

The coefficients r_R and r_S are known as *reflection* coefficients. The reason for this name may be seen by examining the easily verified relations—determined from these last two equations—

$$V_{mr} = r_R V_{md} \tag{14–52}$$

$$I_{mr} = -r_R I_{md} \tag{14–53}$$

in the light of the meaning which will now be assigned to V_{md}, V_{mr}, I_{md}, and I_{mr}. If $x = l$, equations 14–40 and 14–41 show that V_{md} and I_{md} are the *receiving end* values of the direct waves, at $t = 0$. Similarly, V_{mr} and I_{mr} are the *receiving end* values of the reflected waves at $t = 0$. The reflection factor, r_R, therefore, according to equations 14–52 and 14–53, specifies the reflecting properties of the load, since it specifies the magnitude and phase of the reflected wave leaving the load in terms of the magnitude and phase of the direct wave reaching the load. For example, if in the current relation (equation 14–53) r_R should be real, the current wave is reflected exactly reversed as well as increased or decreased, depending on the magnitude of r_R.

14.6 Characteristic Impedance.

The impedance

$$Z_0 = \sqrt{\frac{R + j\omega L}{G + j\omega C}} = \sqrt{\frac{Z}{Y}}$$

defined during the process of solving the differential equations (equation 14–30) is known as the characteristic, or sometimes surge, impedance. This impedance, determined by the transmission line constants, is very important both in application and interpretation. Reference to the definition of the receiving end reflection factor (equation 14–48) shows that *if the line is terminated in a load impedance Z_R which is equal to the characteristic impedance Z_0, the reflection factor is zero.* But a zero reflection factor means *no reflection* term, as reference to equations 14–50 and 14–51 will show. Such a terminating condition is very desirable in communication work since it eliminates an *echo* which would otherwise be present. Communication engineers strive, therefore, to terminate their lines in Z_0. Power transmission line operators, on the other hand, are not at all concerned with reducing echoes. Furthermore, a power load is controlled almost entirely by the customer being served; hence the characteristic impedance is not quite so important to the power engineer as to the communication engineer. However, the surge impedance concept has been found to be distinctly useful in the study of lightning and switching surges on power lines.

If the line is terminated in Z_0, the current and voltage equations take on the relatively simple form

$$V(x, t) = \frac{E_m Z_0 \epsilon^{-\alpha x}}{Z_S + Z_0} \epsilon^{j\omega t} \tag{14–54}$$

$$I(x, t) = \frac{E_m \epsilon^{-\alpha x}}{Z_S + Z_0} \epsilon^{j\omega t} \tag{14–55}$$

which instantaneously are

$$v(x, t) = \left|\frac{E_m Z_0}{Z_S + Z_0}\right| \epsilon^{-\alpha_1 x} \sin(\omega t + \phi - \alpha_2 x) \tag{14–56}$$

$$i(x, t) = \left|\frac{E_m}{Z_S + Z_0}\right| \epsilon^{-\alpha_1 x} \sin(\omega t + \delta - \alpha_2 x) \tag{14–57}$$

The *total* current and voltage, not just one of their components, are now represented by sine waves traveling from generator to load.

The fact that termination in the characteristic impedance eliminates reflection suggests that such a termination might represent an infinitely long line, since certainly no reflections would occur on such a line. To examine the transmission line equations in such a light, consider the limit of equation 14–50 as the line length becomes infinite. Before taking the limit the numerator and denominator of this equation should be divided by $\epsilon^{\alpha l}$. After being so divided, equation 14–50 becomes

$$V(x, t) = \frac{E_m Z_0[\epsilon^{-\alpha x} + r_R \epsilon^{-\alpha(2l-x)}]\epsilon^{j\omega t}}{(Z_S + Z_0)(1 - r_S r_R \epsilon^{-2\alpha l})}$$

Now on taking the limit of this expression as $l \rightarrow \infty$, part of both numerator and denominator, i.e., the last term of each, approaches zero, hence

$$\lim_{l \to \infty} V(x, t) = \frac{E_m Z_0}{Z_S + Z_0} \epsilon^{-\alpha x} \epsilon^{j\omega t} \tag{14–58}$$

which is exactly the voltage equation when the line is terminated in its characteristic impedance. Evidently, then, *an infinite line may be simulated by terminating a finite line in its characteristic impedance.*

A result which has been found very useful in practice arises from the formula for the impedance looking away from the source, of an infinite line or a characteristic impedance terminated line. To determine such an impedance formula, the ratio of voltage and current at any point on the line may be used (equations 14–54 and 14–55). Thus

$$\frac{V(x)}{I(x)} = \frac{\dfrac{E_m Z_0 \epsilon^{-\alpha x}}{Z_S + Z_0}}{\dfrac{E_m \epsilon^{-\alpha x}}{Z_S + Z_0}} = Z_0 \tag{14–59}$$

Since this same result arises from the voltage-current ratio of an infinite line, it follows that the impedance looking away from the source at *any* point on a line terminated in Z_0 or an infinite line is Z_0.

14.7 Propagation Function.

The factor

$$\alpha = \alpha_1 + j\alpha_2 = \sqrt{(R + j\omega L)(G + j\omega C)} = \sqrt{ZY}$$

which was introduced in the process of solving the differential equations of the transmission line (equation 14–17) is known as the propagation factor, or function. That this factor is important in expressing the behavior of transmission lines has already been amply shown by its appearance in all current and voltage formulas. Each of the real and imaginary components of the propagation factor has a particular significance in expressing the behavior of the line. They have been given particular names because of this fact. The real component, α_1, is known as the *attenuation function*, and the imaginary component, α_2, is known as the *wave length function*. These two factors will now be discussed.

The attenuation factor, α_1, is so named because it expresses, through the exponential ϵ^{α_1}, the change in the magnitude of the *direct* or *reflected* waves as they move a unit distance along the line. This fact may be shown by evaluating the ratio of the direct or reflected waves of voltage or current between any two points along the line. Thus, from the ratio of the *magnitudes* of the *direct* waves of voltages or currents (first term of equation 14–40 or 14–41) at distances x_1 and x_2 ($x_1 < x_2$) from the generator,

$$\left|\frac{V_d(x_1, t)}{V_d(x_2, t)}\right| = \left|\frac{V_{md}\epsilon^{\alpha_1(l-x_1)}}{V_{md}\epsilon^{\alpha_1(l-x_2)}}\right| = \epsilon^{\alpha_1(x_2-x_1)} \tag{14–60}$$

and if, in particular, x_1 and x_2 are points unit distances apart, this ratio is

$$\left|\frac{V_d(x_1, t)}{V_d(x_2, t)}\right| = \epsilon^{\alpha_1}, \ (x_2 - x_1 = 1) \tag{14–61}$$

Hence α_1 is such a factor that ϵ^{α_1} gives the ratio of the magnitudes of the *direct wave* components separated by unit length of line. This ratio is always greater than unity since $\epsilon^{\alpha_1} > 1$ if $\alpha_1 > 0$ (see Problem 14–11). The direct wave thus decreases in magnitude as it travels down the line. This same exponential factor also expresses the ratio of the magnitudes of the *reflected* waves at any two points on the line separated by unit distance. Particular notice should be taken of the fact that ϵ^{α_1} determines the ratio of direct or reflected waves and *not* the actual current or voltage except for characteristic impedance termination. Note also that this equation shows that *the voltage of the direct wave always decreases in the direction from source to load.* Therefore, the rms voltage or current of an infinite line, a Z_0 terminated line, or the direct wave on any line always decreases from source to load. On the contrary, as is shown subsequently, the rms voltage or current on a line not terminated in Z_0 does not necessarily steadily increase or decrease, but may have either or both forms of variation on the same line, depending on the line length and on Z_R.

The factor α_2, known as the wave length function, may be interpreted from the ratio of the phase position exponentials of the direct wave of equations 14–40 or 14–41, namely,

$$\frac{\epsilon^{j\psi_d(x_1,\,t)}}{\epsilon^{j\psi_d(x_2,\,t)}} = \frac{\epsilon^{j[\omega t+\alpha_2(l-x_1)]}\epsilon^{j\phi_d}}{\epsilon^{j[\omega t+\alpha_2(l-x_2)]}\epsilon^{j\phi_d}} = \epsilon^{j\alpha_2(x_2-x_1)} \tag{14–62}$$

and, once more, if x_1 and x_2 are unit distance apart, with $x_2 > x_1$, from this equation,

$$\frac{\epsilon^{j\psi_d(x_1,\,t)}}{\epsilon^{j\psi_d(x_2,\,t)}} = \epsilon^{j\alpha_2}, \ (x_2 - x_1 = 1) \tag{14–63}$$

The wave length factor, α_2, therefore, is the phase difference of the *direct* wave at points unit distance apart on the line. Whether the direct wave at different points on the line lags or leads as x increases depends, of course, on the sign of α_2. But, since the phase angle α_2 is restricted by $90 > \alpha_2 \geqslant 0$, as an examination of equation 14–17 shows, and since the phase angle resulting from a ratio of two complex numbers is the phase difference of the two complex numbers *measured from the vector represented by the complex number in the denominator*, the positive phase angle of equation 14–63 represents a lag of the direct wave of voltage, or current, vector at x_2 with respect to a corresponding vector at x_1. But x_2 is farther from the generator. Hence the farther a point is down the line from the generator, the more the vectors lag. Just the opposite is true of the reflected wave. Therefore, the voltage and current on an infinite line, a Z_0 terminated line, or the direct wave on any line, lag the voltage and current at the source steadily farther at points farther down the line. If, however, the line is not Z_0 terminated, the length of line and nature of Z_R determine whether voltages and currents at any point on the line lead or lag the voltage and current at any point closer to the source. The discussion of polar plots in the next article will further demonstrate the phase relations along the line.

The wave length function may be used to establish further what may be considered as the velocity of travel of the direct or reflected waves along the line. This velocity is known as the phase velocity. If a section of line is long enough so that $\alpha_2(x_2 - x_1) = 2\pi$, then

$$x_2 - x_1 = \lambda \equiv \frac{2\pi}{\alpha_2} \tag{14–64}$$

where λ is designated as the wave length and is the length of line on which the *direct* or *reflected* components at the opposite ends of the line are exactly one cycle apart in time phase. But the direct or reflected waves must travel just this distance λ in the time of one cycle, of $1/f$

seconds. Hence the phase velocity with which the component waves move along the line is

$$v = \frac{\lambda}{\frac{1}{f}} = \lambda f = \frac{2\pi f}{\alpha_2} = \frac{\omega}{\alpha_2} \tag{14–65}$$

Of interest is the fact that the phase velocity, v, is a function of the frequency, since ω is linear in f and α_2 is not. The phase velocity of propagation is, therefore, different for each frequency. Verification of this fact and the manner in which the frequency affects the velocity will be left for the reader to establish (see Problems 14–10, 14–11).

While bearing all the earmarks of a velocity, the phase velocity of equation 14–65 is still an artificial concept and does not necessarily represent the velocity of propagation of the electric impulses of the line. As already pointed out, the direct and reflected wave interpretation is an arbitrary splitting of the voltage and current equations into two parts. These parts need not correspond to any physical reality, and a velocity established from them also need not represent the velocity of any actual impulse on the line. In actual fact, the velocity of propagation of an electrical impulse on a line is not given by equation 14–65. It is for this reason that the designation phase velocity is used.

14.8 Polar Plots.

Probably the simplest way to visualize the current and voltage relations on a transmission line, when considered as a function of both time and distance, is by means of polar plots. While it is not possible to represent, in two dimensions, the three-dimensional configuration required for three variables, still the polar plot permits an effective visualization of the line behavior.

Polar plots can best be established by plotting the direct and reflected components and adding the results vectorially. The direct wave according to equation 14–40 is

$$V_d(x, t) = V_{md}\epsilon^{\alpha(l-x)}\epsilon^{j\omega t} \tag{14–66}$$

This equation, since V_{md} is complex, represents, for any fixed x, a rotating vector of constant magnitude $|V_{md}\epsilon^{\alpha_1(l-x)}|$; and for fixed t it represents a spiral of the kind shown by the larger of the two dashed spirals in Fig. 14–5a for exactly one wave length at $t = 0$. This spiral may be considered as generated by a vector decreasing in magnitude and rotating clockwise as x increases. The reflected wave for $t = 0$ is shown by the smaller spiral of Fig. 14–5a, and is generated by an increasing vector rotating counterclockwise as x increases.

The locus of the actual voltage between lines, $V(x, 0)$, according to equation 14–40, is the vector sum of the direct and reflected wave vectors.

In forming the vector sum, care must be taken to add vectors which correspond to the same distance on the line. As a guide in this connection, note that, on the component spirals, distances along the line are directly proportional to angles, i.e., the vectors representing the direct or reflected wave, which are 90 degrees apart at any particular instant, represent direct or reflected wave conditions on the line one quarter of a wave length apart at that instant.

The resultant voltage locus, formed by adding direct and reflected components, is shown by the flattened spiral of Fig. 14–5*a*. While the transmission line represented by this diagram is just one wave length long so far as the direct and reflected components are concerned, the *total voltage* is *more* than one cycle out of phase at the two ends. If the line termination is different so that $V_d(0, 0)$ is lagging $V_r(0, 0)$ sufficiently, the actual voltage at points one wave length distant from each other will be *less* than one cycle apart. This fact can be demonstrated by a vector diagram, or by solving Problem 14–14. These results show once more the artificiality of the wave length and velocity factors when attempts are made to interpret them in terms of the total current or voltage of the line.

The locus diagram of Fig. 14–5*a*, as the method of constructing it indicates, is the locus of the maximum-value vectors representing, at $t = 0$, the voltage at all points along the line. The whole locus, therefore, should be considered as rotating counterclockwise f times per second, and any vector from the origin to the locus will form a circle which represents the sinusoidal time variation at the particular point chosen.

The fact that the total voltage or current locus is a flattened spiral indicates that the current and voltage maximum values go through successive maxima and minima as x increases since the vectors represent maximum values. Needless to say, the effective values also undergo a similar variation. The curve *a* of Fig. 14–5*b* shows the variation of maximum or effective value of voltage with x, for a line which has the locus diagram of Fig. 14–5*a*. This curve is simply the length of the vectors of the locus diagram plotted against distance down the line. Of interest is the fact that maxima and minima are separated by $\lambda/4$. From this diagram it is apparent that because of low voltage a line of about one quarter wave length may be very undesirable, particularly as a power line. If a power line is not over $\lambda/16$ in length, the voltage at the receiving end may be greater or less than at the generator end, as suggested by curves *a* and *b* in Fig. 14–5*b*; but if the line is about one quarter wave length the voltage at the receiver is definitely and probably seriously less than at the generator. Actually this particular difficulty has never arisen because at 60 cps the wave length is about 3300 miles and $\lambda/4$ is about 825 miles, which is much longer than any power line in existence or contemplation. Note that $\lambda/16$, about 206 miles, is a little shorter than the Boulder Dam–Los Angeles line, which is 266 miles in length.

14.9 Standing Waves.

The term *standing wave* is used to designate a condition somewhat more extreme, so far as maxima and minima are concerned, than that shown in Fig. 14–5*b*. In a sense at least, standing waves may be considered as existing on any line which has a behavior similar to that illustrated in this figure, and any line will have such a behavior except one

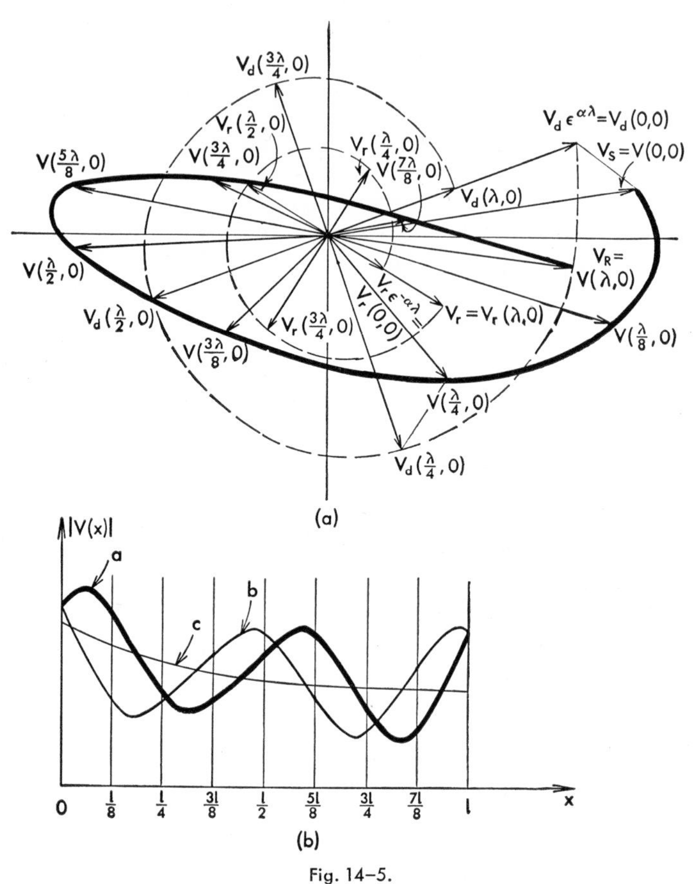

Fig. 14–5.

terminated in its characteristic impedance. Then only the direct wave spiral exists, and the curve corresponding to curves *a* and *b* of Fig. 14–5*b* is the exponential of curve *c* of Fig. 14–5*b*, decreasing as x increases. Standing waves, however, are ordinarily defined as existing on a line when the minimum values of voltage on the line are practically or exactly zero. This latter requirement will be used here, and the possibility of line conditions to produce zero voltage at all times at certain points on the line will now be considered.

The condition which will make the voltage zero at some point on the line for all values of time may be written from equation 14–50 by equating the numerator to zero, which gives

$$\epsilon^{\alpha(l-x)} + r_R \epsilon^{-\alpha(l-x)} = 0 \tag{14–67}$$

If the two terms of this equation are viewed as vectors, their sum can be zero only when they are equal in magnitude and oppositely directed. Since these vectors rotate in opposite directions with increase of x, and since one vector decreases and the other increases with increase of x, at most there can be but *one* value of x which satisfies equation 14–67. From this equation and the definition of Z_R, such a value of x would be $x = l$ with $Z_R = 0$, i.e., the voltage is zero at the short-circuited end of the line.

In order that the two vectors of equation 14–67 add to zero for more than one x, first of all the real part of α must be equal to zero ($\alpha_1 = 0$), since only under this condition can the magnitudes be constant so as to give periodic vector cancellation. If $\alpha_1 = 0$, equation 14–67 becomes

$$\epsilon^{j\alpha_2(l-x)} + r_R \epsilon^{-j\alpha_2(l-x)} = 0 \tag{14–68}$$

which consists of two rotating vectors of *constant* but not necessarily *equal* magnitudes. However, if $|r_R| = 1$, these vectors are equal in magnitude and will, because of rotation in the opposite direction for increasing x, add to zero for each half revolution, or at points, along the line, separated by $x = \lambda/2$. In recapitulation, therefore, if $\alpha_1 = 0$ and $|r_R| = 1$, the current and voltage *magnitudes* will be zero for all values of time at points along the line separated by one half wave length. The current and voltage will not be zero at the same point, however, as an examination of the current and voltage equations will show.

It will be necessary to consider the conditions $\alpha_1 = 0$ and $|r_R| = 1$ in terms of the line parameters R, L, C, and G in order to determine whether standing waves can actually occur on a line. First a condition which will make $\alpha_1 = 0$ is $R = G = 0$, as substitution in equation 14–83 derived below will demonstrate. Second, to make $|r_R| = 1$, an examination of the expression for r_R (equation 14–48) shows that

$$\begin{aligned} &\text{if } Z_R = 0, \text{ then } r_R = -1 \\ &\text{if } Z_R = \infty, \text{ then } r_R = 1 \text{ (see equation 14–71)} \\ &\text{if } Z_R = 0 + jX_R, \text{ then } r_R = \epsilon^{j\phi} \end{aligned} \tag{14–69}$$

all of which satisfy the condition $|r_R| = 1$. Therefore, standing waves, i.e., actual zero values of voltage and current for all values of time at periodic points along a line can occur if $R = G = 0$, and if the line is shorted, open-circuited, or terminated in a pure reactance. There is no difficulty about obtaining the load conditions required for standing waves, but obviously no line is possible for which $R = G = 0$. But R and G

can be made small so that the standing wave condition will be approached as R and G are reduced.

Figure 14–6 is a graph of the standing wave condition for an open-circuited line, where the effective or maximum values of voltage and current are plotted against distance. The behavior of this pattern with change in termination and length of line is of importance for certain applications at high frequencies.

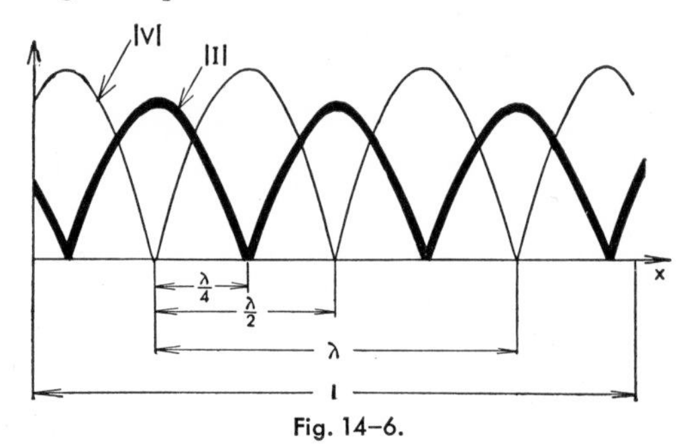

Fig. 14–6.

Consider, for example, a short-circuited line of varying length. A maximum of current magnitude and a zero of voltage magnitude are maintained at the end of any length of line by the short circuit. Also the voltage at the source terminals will be assumed as held constant. Shortening the length of the shorted line, therefore, will move the standing wave pattern toward the source. The spacing of zeros and maximum values will not change, but the magnitudes will change—the magnitudes increasing indefinitely as the fixed relation at the end of the line—maximum current and zero voltage—forces a zero nearer and nearer the fixed source voltage; or decreasing as the maximum of the standing wave pattern of voltage is moved closer to the source.

A similar situation appears if a line, open at the receiving end, is shortened or if a line terminated in a pure reactance is shortened.

As might be suspected from this discussion, dissipationless lines have peculiar impedance properties. For example, the impedance looking from the source into an open-circuited line as given in general by equation 14–70 of the next article, when specialized for a dissipationless, open-circuited line, is

$$Z_{oc} = \sqrt{\frac{L}{C}} \frac{\epsilon^{j\alpha_2 l} + \epsilon^{-j\alpha_2 l}}{\epsilon^{j\alpha_2 l} - \epsilon^{-j\alpha_2 l}} = -j\sqrt{\frac{L}{C}} \frac{\cos \alpha_2 l}{\sin \alpha_2 l}$$

Since $\alpha_2 l = 2\pi l/\lambda$, from this equation:

$$\text{for } l = \frac{\lambda}{4}, \; Z_{oc} = -j\sqrt{\frac{L}{C}} \frac{\cos \dfrac{\pi}{2}}{\sin \dfrac{\pi}{2}} = 0$$

and $\quad$ for $0 < l < \frac{\lambda}{4}, \frac{Z_{oc}}{j} < 0$, hence capacitive;

$$\text{for } l = \frac{2\lambda}{4},\ Z_{oc} = -j\sqrt{\frac{L}{C}}\frac{\cos \pi}{\sin \pi} = \infty$$

and $\quad$ for $\frac{\lambda}{4} < l < \frac{\lambda}{2}, \frac{Z_{oc}}{j} > 0$; hence inductive;

$$\text{for } l \doteq \frac{3\lambda}{4},\ Z_{oc} = -j\sqrt{\frac{L}{C}}\frac{\cos \frac{3\pi}{2}}{\sin \frac{3\pi}{2}} = 0$$

$$\text{for } l = \frac{4\lambda}{4},\ Z_{oc} = -j\sqrt{\frac{L}{C}}\frac{\cos 2\pi}{\sin 2\pi} = \infty$$

Consequently, an open line of very little dissipation, and of odd quarter wave lengths from source to open circuit, appears as a short circuit to the source; whereas the same type of line of even quarter wave lengths from source to open circuit appears as an open circuit to the source. Note furthermore that the impedance of an open line is such that, if the line is less than $\lambda/4$ in length, it is capacitive and so can be used as capacitor of any desired size depending on the length. Similarly a coil of any size can be simulated by a line of length l where l is somewhere in the range $\lambda/4$ to $\lambda/2$.

A short-circuited line will have similar characteristics for even quarter wave length lines.

14.10 Experimental Determination of the Constants of a Transmission Line.

The constants of a transmission line may be determined, as will now be shown, from two simple impedance measurements, namely, from the sending end impedance measured when the line is short-circuited and when the line is open-circuited.

First, with the load end of the line open—Z_R infinite—the impedance, looking into the sending end of the line, is the ratio

$$Z_{oc} = \frac{V_{ms}}{I_{ms}} = \frac{V(0, 0)_{oc}}{I(0, 0)_{oc}} = Z_o \frac{\epsilon^{\alpha l} + r_R \epsilon^{-\alpha l}}{\epsilon^{\alpha l} - r_R \epsilon^{-\alpha l}} \tag{14–70}$$

but for Z_R infinite, the reflection factor is

$$r_{Roc} = \lim_{Z_R \to \infty} r_R = \lim_{Z_R \to \infty} \frac{Z_R - Z_0}{Z_R + Z_0} = \underset{Z_R \to \infty}{L} \frac{1 - \dfrac{Z_0}{Z_R}}{1 + \dfrac{Z_0}{Z_R}} = 1 \tag{14–71}$$

hence

$$Z_{oc} = Z_0 \frac{\epsilon^{\alpha l} + \epsilon^{-\alpha l}}{\epsilon^{\alpha l} - \epsilon^{-\alpha l}} = Z_0 \coth \alpha l \tag{14–72}$$

Second, if the line is short-circuited at the load end,

$$r_{Rsc} = -1 \tag{14–73}$$

and

$$Z_{sc} = \frac{V(0, 0)_{sc}}{I(0, 0)_{sc}} = Z_0 \frac{\epsilon^{\alpha l} - \epsilon^{-\alpha l}}{\epsilon^{\alpha l} + \epsilon^{-\alpha l}} = Z_0 \tanh \alpha l \tag{14–74}$$

Multiplying equations 14–72 and 14–74, and extracting the square root, establishes

$$Z_0 = \sqrt{Z_{oc} Z_{sc}} \tag{14–75}$$

Thus if the open circuit and short circuit impedances are known, the characteristic impedance is easily determined.

The propagation factor can also be determined from equations 14–72 and 14–74 by taking the ratio of these equations to produce

$$\frac{Z_{sc}}{Z_{oc}} = \tanh^2 \alpha l \tag{14–76}$$

which eliminated Z_0. Then to solve for αl

$$\sqrt{\frac{Z_{sc}}{Z_{oc}}} = \frac{\epsilon^{\alpha l} - \epsilon^{-\alpha l}}{\epsilon^{\alpha l} + \epsilon^{-\alpha l}} = \frac{\epsilon^{2\alpha l} - 1}{\epsilon^{2\alpha l} + 1} \tag{14–77}$$

Solving this equation for $\epsilon^{2\alpha l}$ gives

$$\epsilon^{2\alpha l} = \frac{1 + \sqrt{\dfrac{Z_{sc}}{Z_{oc}}}}{1 - \sqrt{\dfrac{Z_{sc}}{Z_{oc}}}}$$

which, on taking logarithms and dividing by $2l$, becomes

$$\alpha = \frac{1}{2l} \ln \frac{1 + \sqrt{\dfrac{Z_{sc}}{Z_{oc}}}}{1 - \sqrt{\dfrac{Z_{sc}}{Z_{oc}}}} \tag{14–78}$$

the propagation factor per unit length.

Since

$$\alpha Z_0 = \sqrt{ZY} \sqrt{\frac{Z}{Y}} = Z \tag{14–79}$$

and

$$\frac{\alpha}{Z_0} = \sqrt{ZY} \sqrt{\frac{Y}{Z}} = Y \tag{14–80}$$

it is a simple matter to express the line admittance and impedance in terms of the open circuit and short circuit impedances of the line. Thus the line constants may be completely established from two impedance measurements, and from the constants so derived the behavior of the line may be established.

14.11 Distortionless Transmission—Loading.

The properties of a transmission line as discussed in the foregoing are based on a single-frequency impulse in the generator. The properties deduced apply to telephone lines or power lines equally well except that power lines are so short and the frequency so low that such phenomena as standing waves, or extreme variations of voltage and current as illustrated in Fig. 14–5*b* do not occur. In fact, the load voltage may actually be higher at the *load* than at the *generator* of a power line. Telephone line operation differs from that of power lines also because of the very irregular wave form of the impulse generated in the telephone transmitter by speech impulses. Telephone lines must, therefore, be considered as transmitting impulses made up of a wide band of frequencies, i.e., impulses consisting of many harmonics. The problem of the telephone engineer is, consequently, to transmit non-sine wave impulses of high harmonic content in such a manner that the wave form is changed as little as possible by its passage over the line.

The line conditions to produce no distortion can be established by examining the current and voltage equations of the line (equations 14–50 and 14–51). If the line is terminated in Z_0—$r_R = 0$—and if $\alpha = k_1 + jk_2\omega$, where k_1 and k_2 are constants, equation 14–50, for example, becomes

$$V(x, t) = V(x)\epsilon^{j\omega t} = \frac{E_m Z_0}{Z_S + Z_0}\epsilon^{-k_1 x}\epsilon^{-jk_2\omega x}\epsilon^{j\omega t} \qquad (14\text{–}81)$$

which is also the equation of the direct wave only. If in addition to the foregoing restrictions, Z_S and Z_0 are constants, the magnitude of *all* harmonics decrease as x increases and in the same proportion, and each harmonic is shifted in phase as x increases, in proportion to the order of the harmonic, i.e., the nth harmonic is shifted in phase n times as much as the fundamental. But this is exactly the condition required for the input and output voltages (or currents) of the line to have the same wave form, i.e., for all the harmonics to have the same relative magnitudes and phase positions at each end of the line. If any one of these conditions

$$\begin{aligned} \alpha &= k_1 + j\omega k_2 \\ Z_0 &= \text{constant} \\ Z_S &= \text{constant} \\ r_R &= 0, \text{ i.e., } Z_R = Z_0 \end{aligned} \qquad (14\text{–}82)$$

does not hold, an examination of equations 14–50 and 14–51 will show that the magnitude of $V(x)$ or $I(x)$ is a function of frequency; hence each harmonic component of E_m must be multiplied by a *different* factor for each frequency to determine the line current and voltage at that frequency. Thus each harmonic will be treated differently, both in phase shift and magnitude, so that the line output will be of different wave shape from that of the input.

The conditions given by equation 14–82, therefore, are required to assure distortionless transmission. Whether these relations can be satisfied or not can be determined only by examining the equations for α_1, α_2, Z_0, and r_R.

The equations for α_1 and α_2 may be derived from

$$\alpha \equiv \alpha_1 + j\alpha_2 = \sqrt{(R + j\omega L)(G + j\omega C)}$$

If this equation is solved for α_1, and α_2, the results are

$$\alpha_1 \equiv \sqrt{\frac{RG - \omega^2 LC + \sqrt{(R^2 + \omega^2 L^2)(G^2 + \omega^2 C^2)}}{2}} \tag{14–83}$$

$$\alpha_2 \equiv \sqrt{\frac{\omega^2 LC - RG + \sqrt{(R^2 + \omega^2 L^2)(G^2 + \omega^2 C^2)}}{2}} \tag{14–84}$$

When these equations are examined, it is apparent that if R and G are zero—line dissipationless—

$$\alpha_1 = 0$$
$$\alpha_2 = \omega\sqrt{LC} \tag{14–85}$$

Furthermore, if R and G are zero,

$$Z_0 = \sqrt{\frac{j\omega L}{j\omega C}} = \sqrt{\frac{L}{C}} \tag{14–86}$$

which is a *non-inductive* resistance. Therefore, if R and G are zero, the conditions of equations 14–82 are satisfied if the line is terminated in the constant, non-reactive Z_0 and if Z_S is constant.

The foregoing dissipationless line is not possible to approximate in practice although its study shows the tendency of the line behavior under reduction of R and G. A more useful result may be obtained by assuming α_1 a constant and under this condition establishing a relation connecting R, L, G, and C to make α_1 constant. To this end, equation 14–83 may be written as

$$\alpha_1^2 - \frac{RG}{2} + \frac{\omega^2 LC}{2} = \sqrt{\frac{(R^2 + \omega^2 L^2)(G^2 + \omega^2 C^2)}{2}} \tag{14–87}$$

Squaring both sides of this equation and rearranging leads to

$$\alpha_1{}^4 - \alpha_1{}^2RG = \frac{\omega^2}{4}[(RC + LG)^2 - 4\alpha_1{}^2LC] \tag{14-88}$$

If now α_1 is to be a constant, the term multiplying ω must be zero; hence

$$(RC + LG)^2 - 4\alpha_1{}^2LC = 0$$

from which

$$\alpha_1{}^2 = \frac{(RC + LG)^2}{4LC} \tag{14-89}$$

Substituting this result into the left side of equation 14–88 gives

$$\frac{(RC + LG)^2}{4LC}\left[\frac{(RC + LG)^2}{4LC} - RG\right] = 0 \tag{14-90}$$

The term in brackets must be zero to satisfy this relation, therefore,

$$\frac{(RC + LG)^2}{4LC} - RG = 0 \tag{14-91}$$

from which

$$RC = LG \tag{14-92}$$

This parameter relation has the remarkable property of making a transmission line distortionless, as will be shown by an examination of α_1, α_2, and Z_0 under its conditions.

The propagation factor α_1 is, of course, a constant, because equation 14–92 was established on the assumption of constant α_1. Substituting the relation of equation 14–91 into equation 14–89 gives the constant value of

$$\alpha_1 = \sqrt{RG} \tag{14-93}$$

If the relation given by equation 14–92 is substituted in the equation for α_2 (equation 14–84)

$$\alpha_2 = \omega\sqrt{LC} \tag{14-94}$$

and if $\sqrt{L/C}$ is factored from equation 14–30, the remainder will be found equal to unity under the condition of equation 14–92, so that

$$Z_0 = \sqrt{\frac{L}{C}} \tag{14-95}$$

But these conditions (equations 14–93, 14–94, and 14–95) are, according to equations 14–82, just the parameter conditions to make the line distortionless if the line is terminated in Z_0 and if Z_S is a constant.

Actual transmission lines usually have a parameter relation

$$\frac{R}{L} > \frac{G}{C} \tag{14–96}$$

rather than

$$RC = LG$$

Evidently increasing L or G or decreasing R or C sufficiently will bring this relation to the desired equality. The practical feasibility of making these changes as well as the effect such changes have on other aspects of the line behavior determine which one or more of the parameters should be changed.

Increasing L is feasible and may be accomplished by adding inductance coils of low resistance in series with the lines. Increasing G is also feasible and may be accomplished by using poor insulators. However, according to equation 14–93, increasing G also increases the attenuation factor and is, therefore, not particularly desirable. Decreasing R is also practical and is done for telephone lines by using copper wire instead of iron wire and by having the copper wire diameter as large as is practically possible.

The addition of inductance coils of low resistance is known as loading. These coils should be added at regular and frequent intervals to simulate an increase in the actual distributed L on the line.

Because of the extreme effectiveness of amplifiers in restoring very weak signals to normal, present-day practice is outmoding the technique of loading. Instead amplifiers are placed at frequent intervals along the line, thus periodically restoring the signal to normal. Corrective networks are used in addition to bring the total effect to as near distortionless transmission as desired.

14.12 Three-Phase Lines—General Remarks.

As has already been pointed out, power lines are short electrically. In fact, the longest power line in this country—Boulder Dam to Los Angeles—is about one-twelfth of a wave length between terminals. Some of the behavior characteristics to be noted on longer communication lines, therefore, are not evident on a power line. Such things as standing waves and extreme differences between voltages at different points on the line, as in Fig. 14–5*b*, do not occur. In fact, the voltage may actually be higher at the load than at the generator of a power line, as these curves show for $\lambda/12$ or less.

Power lines are almost universally three phase (see Fig. 14–7). An individual circuit on a power line will, for this reason, consist of at least three wires, and often six wires connected at load and generator in three groups of two wires in parallel. Figure 14–7 shows typical three-phase lines and substations. The lines terminate at the substations for trans-

Fig. 14–7*a*. High-voltage three-phase power line with lightning protection wires. (Courtesy, Westinghouse Electric & Mfg. Co.)

Fig. 14–7*b*. Wooden pole three-phase line. (Courtesy, Utah Power & Light Co.)

Fig. 14–7c. Typical large substation. (Courtesy, Westinghouse Electric & Mfg. Co.)

Fig. 14–7*d*. Substation showing incoming line, lightning arresters, transformers, and oil circuit breakers. (Courtesy, General Electric Co.)

formation of the voltages to the value desired for distribution to the loads being supplied. The three wires universally present in three-phase systems are evident in all these illustrations.

The wires of a three-phase system may be transposed, i.e., each of three wires placed in each of the three positions of the circuit one third of the line length. Transposition, by placing each conductor in each of the possible positions for the same distance, makes the capacitive and inductive effects the same for each wire, thus making a three-phase line a balanced impedance link in the chain of power distribution. Telephone lines are also transposed, much more frequently and more consistently than power lines. Interference with the conversation on a pair of wires, by other conversations on other pairs of wires, makes transposition of telephone lines absolutely necessary to keep this interference at as low a level as possible.

The values of inductance and capacitance factors to be used for a three-phase line are not immediately evident nor is it immediately evident how the solution of a two-wire line may be used for the three wires of a three-phase line. This particular problem is discussed at length in many of the textbooks which consider power lines* and will not be discussed here beyond giving the results ordinarily derived.

---

* L. F. Woodruff, *Principles of Electric Power Transmission*, John Wiley & Sons, 1938; Bingham and Norris, *Electrical Characteristics of Power and Telephone Transmission Lines*, International Textbook Co., 1936; Bryant, Correll, and Johnson, *Alternating Current Circuits*, McGraw-Hill Book Co., 1939.

A transposed three-phase line is calculated for one of the three balanced phases and the line conditions are determined by the usual multiplier and rotator—$\sqrt{3}$ and ϵ^{j120}. A balanced phase is based on one line and the voltage to neutral. There may not be a voltage to neutral if, for example, the equipment at the ends of the lines is connected delta. However, a hypothetical phase voltage, or the ideal neutral voltage, may be obtained by dividing the balanced line voltage by $\sqrt{3}$, and this voltage may be assumed as the voltage connected to a two-wire line. One wire of this phase—the neutral is resistanceless and inductanceless—has the actual inductance of one wire of the three-phase line, and the capacitance of this hypothetical phase is twice the line-to-line capacitance of the three-phase line.

14.13 Current and Voltage Relations on a Three-Phase Line.

According to the discussion of the preceding article, a three-phase power line which is transposed is not essentially different from a telephone line, so far as the equations to be used to study the line are concerned. It is merely necessary to modify the values of R, L, C, and G to be used—R and L are the values for a single wire, C is twice the capacitance between two wires, and G may be determined from one-third of the total leakage loss of the three-wire line divided by the voltage to neutral.

Equation 14–50 will, accordingly, express the behavior of the hypothetical phase-to-neutral section of the three-phase line from which the line behavior follows by applying the balanced three-phase factors to the neutral voltage. Equation 14–51 will express the current behavior of one of the lines.

As power lines are ordinarily operated, voltage regulators or control devices are located at the generator and usually at the load, and the line is studied on the basis of a fixed generator or load terminal voltage. In order to establish the equations for such a study, note that equations 14–50 and 14–51 give at the load ($x = l$)

$$V_R(t) = V(l, t) = \frac{E_m Z_0(1 + r_R)}{(Z_S + Z_0)[\epsilon^{\alpha l} - r_S r_R \epsilon^{-\alpha l}]} \epsilon^{j\omega t} \tag{14–97}$$

$$I_R(t) = I(l, t) = \frac{E_m(1 - r_R)}{(Z_S + Z_0)[\epsilon^{\alpha l} - r_S r_R \epsilon^{-\alpha l}]} \epsilon^{j\omega t} \tag{14–98}$$

Also at the generator ($x = 0$),

$$V_S(t) = V(0, t) = \frac{E_m Z_0[\epsilon^{\alpha l} + r_R \epsilon^{-\alpha l}]}{(Z_S + Z_0)[\epsilon^{\alpha l} - r_S r_R \epsilon^{-\alpha l}]} \epsilon^{j\omega t} \tag{14–99}$$

$$I_S(t) = I(0, t) = \frac{E_m[\epsilon^{\alpha l} - r_R \epsilon^{-\alpha l}]}{(Z_S + Z_0)[\epsilon^{\alpha l} - r_S r_R \epsilon^{-\alpha l}]} \epsilon^{j\omega t} \tag{14–100}$$

If now equation 14–97 is multiplied by

$$\cosh \alpha l = \frac{\epsilon^{\alpha l} + \epsilon^{-\alpha l}}{2} \tag{14–101}$$

and equation 14–98 is multiplied by

$$Z_0 \sinh \alpha l = Z_0 \frac{\epsilon^{\alpha l} - \epsilon^{-\alpha l}}{2} \tag{14–102}$$

and the resultant equations added, the sum will be exactly equation 14–99. So, omitting the time variation, for convenience, and dividing by $\sqrt{2}$ to express the equation in rms form, gives

$$V_S = V_R \cosh \alpha l + Z_0 I_R \sinh \alpha l \tag{14–103}$$

Similarly, if equation 14–97 is multiplied by

$$\frac{\sinh \alpha l}{Z_0} = \frac{\epsilon^{\alpha l} - \epsilon^{-\alpha l}}{2Z_0} \tag{14–104}$$

and equation 14–98 multiplied by cosh αl and the resultant equations added, and divided by $\sqrt{2}$, the sum will be exactly equation 14–100, i.e.,

$$I_S = \frac{V_R}{Z_0} \sinh \alpha l + I_R \cosh \alpha l \tag{14–105}$$

The behavior of a three-phase, transposed line expressed to *neutral* in rms values is, therefore,

$$\begin{aligned} V_{SN} &= V_{RN} \cosh \alpha l + I_R Z_0 \sinh \alpha l \\ I_S &= V_{RN} \frac{\sinh \alpha l}{Z_0} + I_R \cosh \alpha l \end{aligned} \tag{14–106}$$

These equations are sometimes written as

$$\begin{aligned} V_{SN} &= V_{RN} A + I_R B \\ I_S &= V_{RN} C + I_R D \end{aligned} \tag{14–107}$$

and A, B, C, and D are designated as general circuit parameters. The determinant of these equations is not zero, but is in fact

$$\begin{vmatrix} A & B \\ C & D \end{vmatrix} = 1 \tag{14–108}$$

and, therefore, equations 14–106 can be solved for the load conditions for given generator terminal conditions as

$$\begin{aligned} V_{RN} &= V_{SN} D - I_S B \\ I_R &= -V_{SN} C + I_S A \end{aligned} \tag{14–109}$$

and

$$V_{RN} = V_{SN} \cosh \alpha l - I_S Z_0 \sinh \alpha l \tag{14-110}$$

$$I_R = -V_{SN} \frac{\sinh \alpha l}{Z_0} + I_S \cosh \alpha l$$

If two lines are joined, one at the end of the other (see Fig. 14–8) it is evident that, using matrices,

$$\begin{bmatrix} V_{RN1} \\ I_{R1} \end{bmatrix} = \begin{bmatrix} V_{SN2} \\ I_{S2} \end{bmatrix} \tag{14-111}$$

Therefore, using equation 14–107, for each line

$$\begin{bmatrix} V_{SN1} \\ I_{S1} \end{bmatrix} = \begin{bmatrix} A_1 & B_1 \\ C_1 & D_1 \end{bmatrix} \begin{bmatrix} V_{RN1} \\ I_{R1} \end{bmatrix} \tag{14-112}$$

and

$$\begin{bmatrix} V_{SN2} \\ I_{S2} \end{bmatrix} = \begin{bmatrix} A_2 & B_2 \\ C_2 & D_2 \end{bmatrix} \begin{bmatrix} V_{RN2} \\ I_{R2} \end{bmatrix} \tag{14-113}$$

If equation 14–113 is substituted into equation 14–112, as equation 14–111 permits, the result is

$$\begin{bmatrix} V_{SN1} \\ I_{S1} \end{bmatrix} = \begin{bmatrix} A_1 & B_1 \\ C_1 & D_1 \end{bmatrix} \begin{bmatrix} A_2 & B_2 \\ C_2 & D_2 \end{bmatrix} \begin{bmatrix} V_{RN2} \\ I_{R2} \end{bmatrix} \tag{14-114}$$

This equation points out the interesting fact that connecting two transmission lines in cascade, as shown in Fig. 14–8, leads to a combined line the characteristics of which may be determined from the product of the individual A, B, C, D matrices.

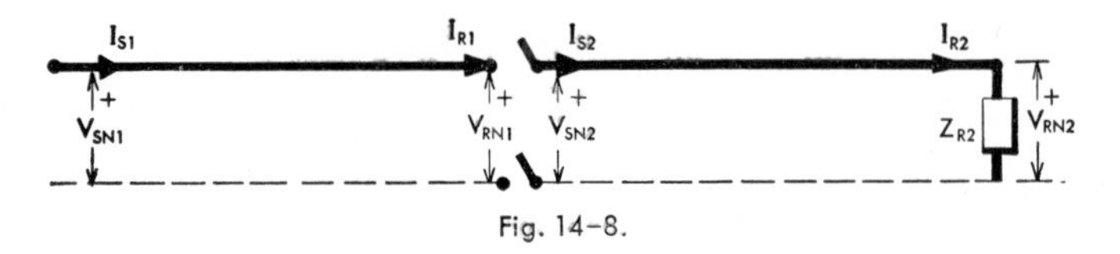

Fig. 14–8.

14.14 Lumped Constant Representations of a Smooth Transmission Line.

A laboratory study of the behavior of a transmission line is rendered rather difficult by the distance and expense required for the installation of a line. Considerable work has been done in the past on lumped constant equivalents of a smooth transmission line. These equivalent circuits are constructed of coils, capacitors, and resistors and, therefore, offer no real difficulties so far as either expense or space requirements are concerned. The test boards of the type shown in Fig. 11–26 are particularly useful for representing transmission lines in a restricted space.

A lumped constant network can be made equivalent to a transmission line at only one frequency, or at most a certain group of frequencies. The reason for this is that while the transmission line parameters R, L, G, and

C are functions of frequency as are the corresponding lumped parameters which may be used to represent the line, the manner of variation with frequency of these two sets of parameters is not the same, hence the lack of equivalence for all frequencies, even though the two systems are equivalent at one frequency. Also, independently of this fact, frequency response of a fixed lumped network is not at all like that of a fixed transmission line.

Such a condition naturally restricts the usefulness of equivalent networks. However, since considerable use has been made of lumped structures equivalent to a transmission line, these networks will be considered briefly. In passing, it may be well to note that miniature representations of lines have been built which are exact, i.e., miniature networks which have distributed constants also.

If it is recalled that the smooth line consists of series resistance and inductance and shunt capacitance and conductance, it seems immediately evident that structures like the T of Fig. 14–9a and the π of Fig. 14–9b could be built so as to represent a smooth line.

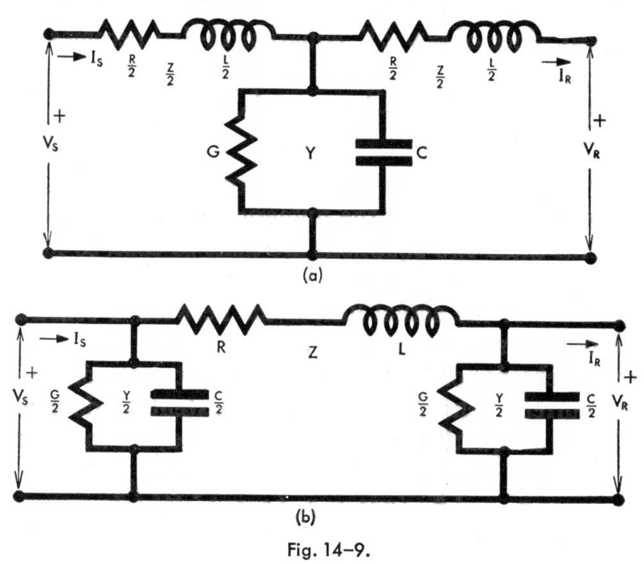

Fig. 14–9.

The problem of finding the T or π network to represent a transmission line may be approached in two ways. First these structures may simply be made so that the impedance Z and admittance Y of the equivalent network are

$$\begin{aligned} Z &= R + j\omega L \\ Y &= G + j\omega C \end{aligned} \tag{14–115}$$

where R, L, G, and C are simply the constants of a smooth line calculated from the open circuit and short circuit impedances of the line. The T or

π networks so constructed are not *exactly equivalent* to the transmission line, but are fair approximations as will now be shown for the T circuit.

The equations for this circuit will be expressed in terms of the same currents and voltages as equations 14–103 and 14–105. To start at the sending end of Fig. 14–9*a*,

$$V_S = I_S \frac{Z}{2} + I_R \frac{Z}{2} + V_R \tag{14–116}$$

To eliminate I_S from this equation, the current equation of Fig. 14–9*a* is

$$I_S = \left(\frac{Z}{2} I_R + V_R\right) Y + I_R \tag{14–117}$$

which on substitution into equation 14–116, and rearranging, gives

$$V_S = V_R\left(1 + \frac{(\sqrt{ZY})^2}{2}\right) + I_R Z_0\left(\sqrt{ZY} + \frac{(\sqrt{ZY})^3}{4}\right) \tag{14–118}$$

If the first two terms of the infinite series expansion of cosh αl and sinh αl are used, since $\alpha l = \sqrt{ZY}$, equation 14–103 becomes

$$V_S \simeq V_R\left(1 + \frac{(\sqrt{ZY})^2}{2}\right) + I_R Z_0\left(\sqrt{ZY} + \frac{(\sqrt{ZY})^3}{2 \cdot 3}\right) \tag{14–119}$$

A comparison of this equation and the corresponding equation for a T network shows that except for the numerical factor in the denominator of the last term these two equations are alike so that, so far as voltage is concerned, the T network of Fig. 14–9*a* may be expected to *approximate* the behavior of the actual line, if the network is constructed with the Z and Y of the line.

The current behavior of the T section does not approximate the transmission line current behavior to the same extent as does the voltage behavior. Thus, if equation 14–117 is rearranged, for the T section

$$I_S = \frac{V_R}{Z_0}\sqrt{ZY} + I_R\left(1 + \frac{(\sqrt{ZY})^2}{2}\right) \tag{14–120}$$

which, as far as it goes, is an approximation to the transmission line behavior, given by equation 14–106. However, the second term of the sinh αl expansion is missing entirely in this approximation.

A similar result can be obtained for the π section of Fig. 14–9*b*, as the reader should show (see Problem 14–28), as well as for other approximate sections (see Problem 14–29).

A second and more effective and useful approach to forming lumped networks, which are equivalent to a transmission line, is to establish a network which is *exactly* equivalent to a line at some particular frequency.

Evidently, if the coefficients of V_R and I_R of equations 14–103 and 14–105 are equated to the corresponding coefficients of the equations for the lumped network, the values of the lumped network constants may perhaps be calculated. For example, from equations 14–103 and 14–118 and equations 14–105 and 14–120, the following three equations can be written relating the line constants and T network constants:

$$\begin{aligned} \cosh \alpha l &= 1 + \frac{Z_N Y_N}{2} \\ Z_0 \sinh \alpha l &= Z_N + \frac{Z_N{}^2 Y_N}{4} \\ \frac{\sinh \alpha l}{Z_0} &= Y_N \end{aligned} \qquad (14\text{–}121)$$

From the last of these equations, the T network parallel admittance is

$$Y_N = \frac{\sinh \alpha l}{Z_0} \qquad (14\text{–}122)$$

and from this result and the first of equations 14–121,

$$\frac{Z_N}{2} = Z_0 \frac{\cosh \alpha l - 1}{\sinh \alpha l} = Z_0 \tanh \frac{\alpha l}{2} \qquad (14\text{–}123)$$

The second one of equations 14–121 is also satisfied by the results given in these last two equations. Therefore, if a T network is formed which has the shunt admittance Y_N of equation 14–122, and two series arms of impedance $Z_N/2$, of equation 14–123, both determined from measured line parameters α and Z_0, the T structure and the line will be exactly equivalent at the frequency at which α and Z_0 are computed. Note that this equivalence is valid only at the two ends, and *not* at any intermediate position.

By using a process similar to the foregoing, other lumped structures may be obtained which are equivalent to a line at a particular frequency. These lumped constant networks, at a particular frequency, permit a laboratory demonstration of the behavior of a transmission line without requiring a great outlay of time and money.

PROBLEMS

14–1 Derive equation 14–14.

14–2 Show that equation 14–16 may be derived as suggested in the text.

14–3 Derive equations 14–29 and 14–31. Give full details and justify each step. Then determine that equations 14–36 and 14–37 are correct.

14–4 Determine the solution of a two-wire transmission line as in equations 14–38 and 14–39 if the origin of coordinates is at the receiving end of the line.

14–5 Determine the equations for current and voltage of a two-wire transmission line if the generators with different sinusoidal voltages of the same frequency are connected to the two ends of the lines. This condition has the effect of changing the boundary conditions. Discuss the nature of the component waves of the solution. What is the direction of reflection and of damping? What is the meaning of r_S from the equations derived?

14–6 Plot curves of distance vs. the magnitude of the direct and reflected waves of voltage between wires and their sum, at the $t = 0$ instant, for the transmission line of $R = 10.44$ ohms, $G = 0.3 \times 10^{-6}$ mho; $L = 0.00393$ henry; $C = 0.00794 \times 10^{-6}$ farad, all per loop mile, with the terminal conditions of $E(t) = 100\epsilon^{j5000t}$ and $Z_R = Z_0 = 748\epsilon^{-j14}$. Plot the curve for at least 1000 miles of line.

14–7 Repeat Problem 14–6 for $Z_R = 1500 + j0$, $R = 1.0$ ohm, $G = 0$.

14–8 Repeat Problem 14–6 for $Z_R = 100 + j100$, $R = 1.0$ ohm, $G = 0$.

14–9 Determine the reflection factor r_R for the line and terminations of Problems 14–6, 14–7, and 14–8. Assume any convenient V_{md} and I_{md} and show on a vector diagram their relations to V_{mr} and I_{mr}.

14–10 Determine α_1 and α_2 symbolically in terms of the line constants R, L, C, and G.

14–11 Show that α_1 and α_2 increase with the frequency and that both are always positive for positive frequency. From the manner of variation of α_2 show how the phase velocity varies with frequency.

14–12 Determine Z_0 and α for the line of Problem 14–6. Also find the phase velocity and the wave length.

14–13 Plot α_1, α_2, phase velocity, and λ vs. frequency (0 to 3000 cps) for the line of Problem 14–6.

14–14 Draw diagrams similar to the ones of Fig. 14–5 for the transmission line of $R = 0.113$ ohms, $L = 0.00212$ henry, $C = 0.0136 \times 10^{-6}$ farad, $G = 0$, all per loop mile. The voltage between lines is maintained at $V_s = 165{,}500$ volts, and assume $Z_S = 0$ and $Z_R = 571.2 + j54.7$. Plot the diagrams for at least one wave length of line at the power frequency of 60 cps.

The longest stretch of such a line as here described is 270 miles. Show that maximum and minimum values as in Fig. 14–5*b* will not occur on this line. In fact, by calculating the load voltage for $Z_R = 424 + j424$, and $Z_R = 424 - j424$, show that the voltage may increase or decrease from source to load.

14–15 Outline in careful detail all the properties of a transmission line which are given in Arts. 14–4 to 10, inclusive.

14–16 Suppose the line of Problem 14–14 is terminated in its characteristic impedance. Sketch a curve corresponding to Fig. 14–5*b* for a wave length of line.

14–17 Sketch curves of the form shown in Fig. 14–5 for the line of Problem 14–6 if R and G are assumed zero. Note that the maxima and minima of voltage or current are separated by exactly one quarter wave length.

14–18 Show that relations 14–69 are valid. Also show that if Z_R has a real part, $r_R \neq 1$. Make use of the fact that Z_0 is a non-inductive resistance for R and G zero. What is the value of ϕ of 14–69?

14–19 Assume R and G zero for the line of Problem 14–6. Plot the standing wave of voltage-maximum and current-maximum values vs. distance along a double wave length of line for $Z_R = 0$. What is the phase relation between current and voltage at any point on the line? Repeat for $Z_R = \infty$. Repeat for $Z_R = 100 + j100$. Also plot the polar diagram for each case.

14–20 Suppose that a dissipationless line—$R = G = 0$—is shorted by a copper bar. The generator terminal voltage and line length are maintained constant as the copper bar is moved from the end of the line toward the generator. Sketch the standing wave pattern for several positions of the short circuit. Sketch both current and voltage magnitude patterns. Explain the effect on the standing wave sketches of shortening the short-circuited line. Consider lines of length: odd number of quarter wave lengths, even number, and neither.

14–21 Use sketches of standing wave patterns of current and voltage to illustrate in complete detail the discussion immediately preceding Art. 14–10. Consider shorted and reactance terminated lines.

14–22 Show that α_2 is as given by equation 14–94 if $RC = LG$.

14–23 (*a*) Assume that the line of Problem 14–6 is to be made approximately distortionless by adding coils of 8 ohms resistance and 0.1 henry inductance. Determine the number of coils per mile. (*b*) Assume this same line is to be made approximately distortionless by decreasing the resistance. Determine the required resistance per mile and from this the size of copper wire required.

14–24 Express equations 14–50 and 14–51 in terms of $\cosh \alpha(l - x)$ and $\sinh \alpha(l - x)$. Then derive equations 14–103 and 14–105.

14–25 A 135-mile three-phase line has the constants per mile per phase: $R = 0.118$ ohm, $L = 0.00106$ henry, $C = 0.0284$ microfarad. Plot a curve of $|V_R|$ vs. load power factor if the load is kept constant in magnitude at 60,000 kva. The generator terminal voltage is constant at 132,000 volts between lines. Assume values of power factor from 85 degrees lead to 85 degrees lag. Note the effect of load power factor on the load voltage and discuss briefly the feasibility of controlling the load voltage by paralleling the load with a synchronous motor which acts as a capacitor or inductor at the operator's behest.

14–26 The line of Problem 14–25 connects to two other lines at 135 miles from the generator. If one of these lines is disconnected and the other has (per mile) $R = 0.098$ ohm, $L = 0.00101$ henry, $C = 0.03$ microfarad, what is the voltage at the load, and what is the generator current if a 30,000-kva load of 0.8 power factor lag is at the end of the second line 60 miles from the junction? Find the current and voltage at the junction.

14–27 Assume that the 30,000-kva load of Problem 14–26 is required to operate at 130,000 volts. Determine the generator voltage and current if the second branch line—50 miles in length—is connected at the junction. There is no load in the second line. Determine the voltage at the junction and the current into each line.

14–28 Show that a π section is an approximation to a smooth line by comparing approximations to equations 14–103 and 14–105 with the corresponding equations for the π network, as was done for the T network in Art. 14–14.

14–29 Repeat Problem 14–28 for the structure shown in Fig. 14–10.

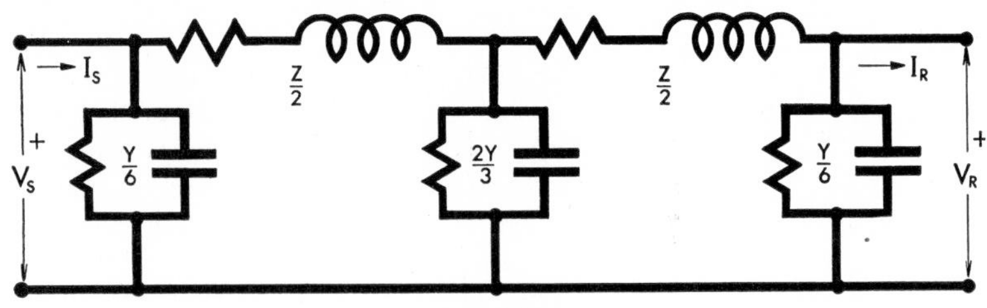

Fig. 14–10.

14–30 Determine a T network equivalent to the line of Problem 14–6.

14–31 Repeat Problem 14–30 for a π network.

14–32 Plot the impedance looking into a two-wire transmission line as the length of line varies. Consider the line of Problem 14–6: (*a*) open-circuited, (*b*) short-circuited. Plot the phase angle of the impedance also.

14–33 Plot the impedance vs. length of an open and shorted line which has the same L and C as in Problem 14–6. Assume $R = G = 0$. Plot the phase angle of the impedance.

CHAPTER 15

Electric Filters

Electric filters are electric networks—four-terminal, as used at present—placed between the *non-sinusoidal output* of some network or generating device and the input of some other network. The filter is designed to feed into the receiving network an input which differs from the output of the original source network in some particular and specified manner. For example, the output of a rectifier—two-electrode electron tubes or piles of oxide-covered copper plates which conduct in only one direction and so produce a pulsating direct current from alternating current—does not produce a very steady direct current, as is easy to imagine. But because rectifiers are so simple physically when compared with the common rotary rectifying device, it is very desirable that rectifiers be used wherever possible. Inserting a filter between the rectifier and the load requiring direct current is just the circuit addition which makes the widespread use of rectifiers possible. How such a scheme works can be briefly stated as follows. Take for granted first the characteristic of filters, to be shown subsequently in this chapter; namely, the ability practically to prevent the appearance at the two output terminals of the filter of any specified group of harmonics of voltages which appear at the input to the filter. Then, if the pulsating d-c output of a rectifier (Figs. 6–16 and 6–17) is considered on the basis of the Fourier series analysis, it will consist of a d-c component plus many harmonics. The filter can be designed to suppress practically all harmonics, leaving the d-c component, which is just the result desired. Filters are thus an essential part of the majority of rectifiers.

Filters have also made it possible for telephone engineers to crowd the electrical impulses of many conversations onto the same pair of wires, or cable. These signals, as many as 480 on a coaxial cable, are impressed on the transmission line at the sending end, and at the receiving end filters separate the conversations and feed them into the proper receivers. The saving thus effected in labor, material, time, and complexity of the communication system is so obvious as hardly to need mention.

The filters used in communication systems are often made of quartz crystals. Such filters will not be considered here, but the background which may be acquired in this chapter is necessary to understand the action of crystal filters, and will make the understanding of the behavior of such filters relatively easy.

Filters are also the basis of all radio reception and transmission. It is possible to "tune out" all but one radio station, of all those impressing their signal on each antenna, only by means of variable filters which suppress all but the band of frequencies desired.

Filters are also becoming important in control of power networks. Switches are being controlled, machines started, systems interconnected, etc., by means of various bands of frequency impulses, or harmonics, which must be separated at the operation end by filters.

Because there is no doubt, therefore, that filtering networks are one of the most important classes of electrical networks, a study of such networks is included in this book.

As is true of the construction of all electrical networks which are built for a particular purpose, filtering networks can be built to produce only an approximation to a specified change between the output and input of a network, but the approximations obtainable are good, very useful, and very widely used. It is possible, on the basis of the elementary a-c behavior of inductors and capacitors, to reach an understanding of the fundamental behavior of filters. Such a development is now presented, before a more rigorous and complete mathematical study is undertaken.

15.1 Basic Filter Behavior—Low-Pass Filters.

In the present discussion of filters, the terminating impedances—Z_S and Z_R of Fig. 15–1—will be considered as resistive—non-reactive. While this assumption may seem to be unnecessarily restrictive, a great many of the actual applications of filters are just so restricted. The behavior of filters as deduced on the basis of resistive terminations must, of necessity, be modified if the terminations are reactive, but the required modification is only one of change in degree of effectiveness rather than in basic concepts. The use of resistive terminations corresponds also to the ideal requirements, as will be seen, and so will be assumed in what follows whenever the discussion requires a consideration of the terminal impedances.

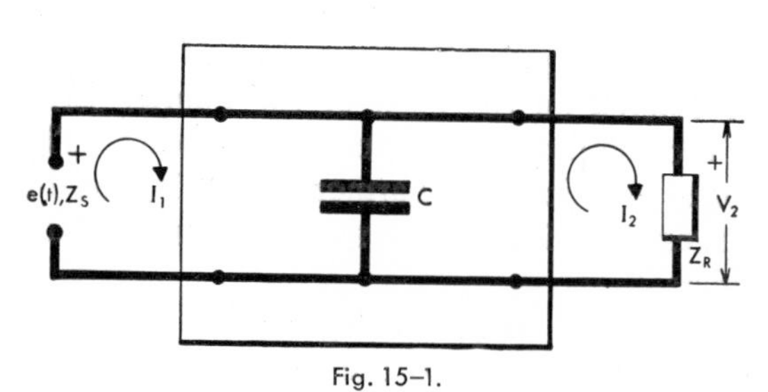

Fig. 15–1.

An understanding of the basic principles of filter behavior can best be reached by first studying some very simple filter elements. The four-terminal network shown between the load and generator of Fig. 15–1, consisting of a shunt capacitor, is designated as a "by-pass" element or as a "low-pass" filter. The meaning of both these terms will become apparent as this circuit is considered in detail.

If Z_S is considered as zero and $e(t)$ as unchanged by the current through the generator, the capacitor obviously has no effect on the voltage appearing at the load impedance Z_R. Suppose, on the other hand, that Z_S is not zero and that the generated voltage is non-sinusoidal. The behavior of the network may then be established for the kth harmonic from the two mesh equations ($Z_S = R_S$, and $Z_R = R_R$):

$$E_k = I_{1k}\left(R_S + \frac{1}{j\omega_k C}\right) - \frac{1}{j\omega_k C} I_{2k}$$

$$0 = I_{1k}\left(\frac{-1}{j\omega_k C}\right) + \left(R_R + \frac{1}{j\omega_k C}\right) I_{2k} \tag{15–1}$$

The solution of this pair of equations for the currents is

$$I_{1k} = \frac{R_R + \dfrac{1}{j\omega_k C}}{R_S R_R + \dfrac{R_S}{j\omega_k C} + \dfrac{R_R}{j\omega_k C}} E_k \tag{15–2}$$

$$I_{2k} = \frac{\dfrac{1}{j\omega_k C}}{R_S R_R + \dfrac{R_S}{j\omega_k C} + \dfrac{R_R}{j\omega_k C}} E_k \tag{15–3}$$

The voltage across the load, for the kth harmonic, is

$$V_{2k} = I_{2k} R_R = \frac{R_R\left(-j\dfrac{1}{\omega_k C}\right)}{R_S R_R - j\dfrac{R_S + R_R}{\omega_k C}} E_k \tag{15–4}$$

In order to compare this voltage with the load voltage for no filter, which is

$$V_{2k}' = \frac{R_R}{R_S + R_R} E_k \tag{15–5}$$

their ratio will be considered. Thus

$$\frac{V_{2k}}{V_{2k}'} = \frac{-j\dfrac{1}{\omega_k C}}{\dfrac{R_S R_R}{R_S + R_R} - j\dfrac{1}{\omega_k C}} \tag{15–6}$$

If this ratio is considered as a function of frequency,

$$\lim_{\omega_k \to 0} \frac{V_{2k}}{V_{2k}'} = 1 \quad \text{and} \quad \lim_{\omega_k \to \infty} \frac{V_{2k}}{V_{2k}'} = 0 \tag{15-7}$$

Also the magnitude of this ratio of voltages is always less than unity for $\omega_k > 0$, except at zero frequency, because the derivative of the ratio is always negative (see Problem 15–1). The effect of the "low-pass" filter can now be formulated from the foregoing results.

According to equation 15–5 the same fraction of each harmonic of generated voltage appears across the load resistor, R_R, if the filter is not in the circuit. If the filter is placed in the circuit, equation 15–7 and the statement immediately following show it is only for zero frequency that the voltage V_{2k} (filter in place) across the load resistor R_R is the same as the voltage V_{2k}' (filter removed) across the load resistor R_R, and that for all other frequencies the voltage V_{2k} is reduced by the presence of the filter. Furthermore, since the slope of the curve representing the magnitude of the ratio given by equation 15–6 is always negative, the maximum value of this ratio for $\omega_k > 0$ occurs at $\omega_k = 0$. Therefore, in *ascending* order, each harmonic of generated voltage is less effective in producing a current of that harmonic order in the load resistor.

The shunt capacitor of Fig. 15–1 may, therefore, be thought of as a filter which, as the harmonic order increases, is increasingly effective in suppressing the reaction on the load of the generated voltage. Such a filter is known as "low-pass" because it has less effect on the lower frequency than on the higher frequency harmonics and appears, in a sense at least, to pass the lower frequency effects of the generator most effectively.

A second simple by-pass filter is shown by the series inductor of Fig. 15–2. The mathematical treatment of this filter will be left for the reader to work out (Problem 15–2). The general properties may be stated rather easily from an examination of the circuit. At zero frequency the inductor offers no impedance and therefore does not affect the load action of a d-c component of generated voltage. At infinite frequency the inductor acts as an open circuit and therefore has the effect of separating the generator and the load as does the short-circuiting capacitor of Fig. 15–1. Thus the two limiting frequencies are treated alike by a series inductor

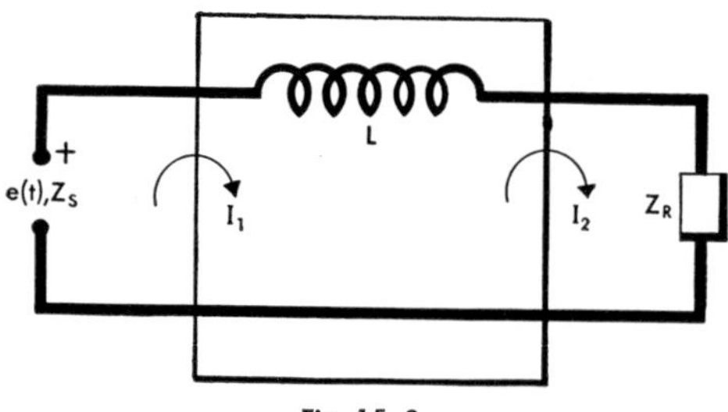

Fig. 15–2.

or a shunt capacitor. At intermediate frequencies, as the order of the harmonic increases, the series inductor is increasingly effective in reducing the fraction of the generated voltage appearing at the load, because the increased impedance of the inductor reduces the current and so the voltage $I_{2k}R_R = V_{2k}$ which appears across the load.

15.2 Basic Filter Behavior—High-Pass Filter.

If a *shunt inductor* or *series capacitor* is used as a filter, the effect is just the opposite of the low-pass shunt capacitor and series inductor. For at zero frequency the series capacitor acts as an open circuit, thus preventing any d-c component of generated voltage from appearing at the load; and at infinite frequency the series capacitor has no effect on the circuit. Similarly, the shunt inductor, by short-circuiting the load at zero frequency, prevents any effect on the load by a d-c voltage component of the generator, and at infinite frequency the shunt inductor is simply an open circuit and has no effect on the circuit. Furthermore, since as a function of ω the slope of the ratio corresponding to equation 15–6 is always *positive* ($\omega > 0$), each harmonic of generated voltage, in *descending* order, has less effect on the load than the preceding one. A shunt inductor or series capacitor, therefore, acts as a high-pass filter.

15.3 Simple Capacitor and Inductor Combination to Form a Filter.

As a further qualitative discussion of filter behavior, consider the π and T networks shown in Fig. 15–3. The particular parameter designa-

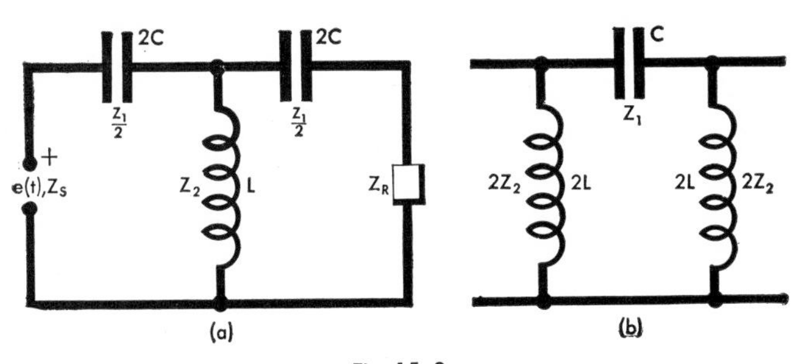

Fig. 15–3.

tions shown on this circuit are used in order that the results obtained may correspond to the usual practice in filter theory studies. Both these networks are evidently high-pass filters because they are constructed on a high-pass arrangment of inductors and capacitors. These two networks can be established so that they are equivalent and, apparently therefore, it is immaterial which network is used as a filter.

The T and π networks of Fig. 15–4 illustrate low-pass filter sections.

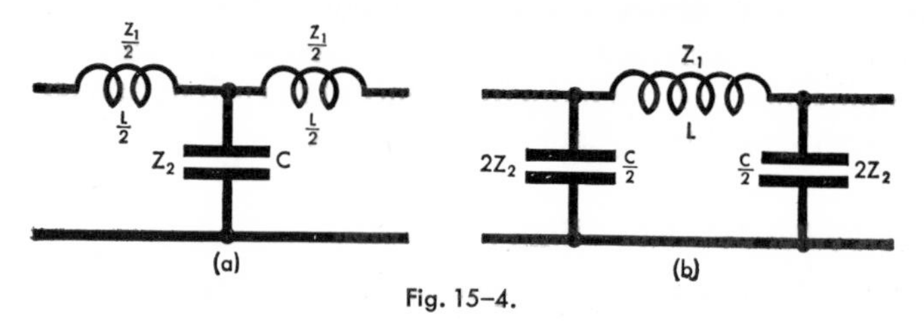

Fig. 15–4.

15.4 Simple Band-Pass Filter.

A simple four-terminal network which, placed between source and load, has less reductive effect over a band of frequencies, not at zero or infinite frequency, is shown in Fig. 15–5a. At the resonant frequency of the L-C series circuit the generator is connected directly to the load terminals, and at *zero* and *infinite* frequency the filter opens the circuit; hence the title "band pass" when applied to such a filter.

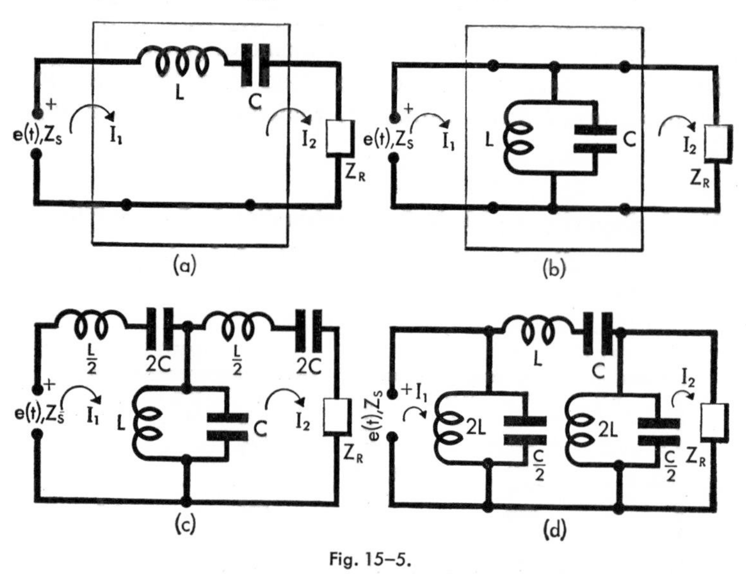

Fig. 15–5.

The four-terminal network shown in Fig. 15–5b is also a band-pass filter. At the resonant frequency of the parallel L and C circuit, the generator is once more connected directly to the load, because L and C in parallel is equivalent to an open circuit at resonant frequency. Also, at zero and infinite frequency the shunt L and C, respectively, short-circuit the generator.

Band-pass filters may also be formed by establishing T and π networks of the band-pass elements of Fig. 15–5a and b. Such networks are shown in Figs. 15–5c and d.

15.5 Simple Band-Elimination Filter.

Simple filters may also be constructed which will reduce, or practically eliminate, the effect on the load of a certain group or band of harmonics of the generated source voltage. Such simple filters are shown in Fig. 15–6. At the resonant frequencies of the L, C combinations of these

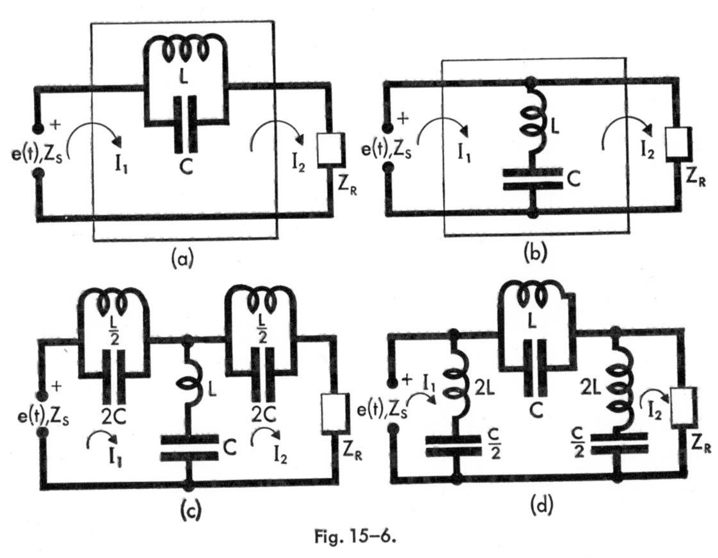

Fig. 15–6.

circuits the generator is disconnected from the load of Fig. 15–6*a* and the generator is shorted in Fig. 15–6*b*. Also, at zero and infinite frequency, the generator of Figs. 15–6*a* and *b* is directly connected to the load. Thus the harmonics near the resonant frequency are more nearly ineffective, so far as the load is concerned, than are harmonics far removed from the resonant frequency.

Obviously, π and T networks can be formed of the filter elements of Figs. 15–6*a* and *b* to constitute band-elimination filters as shown in Figs. 15–6*c* and *d*.

The qualitative treatment thus far considered should be effective in leading to an understanding and appreciation of some of the whys of filter behavior. However, pursuing the analysis further in this direction has not been found very fruitful. In fact, the equations get very involved with amazing rapidity on adding more filtering elements. As a result, an entirely different approach has been developed—suggested by the solution of the transmission line equations—which forms the basis of much of the filter design of the present time, whether it is ordinary coils and capacitors, quartz crystals, or brass and copper tubes that are used to make the filters. The types of filters to be discussed are those already qualitatively characterized in the foregoing—low-pass, high-pass, band-pass, band-block. The low-pass, symmetric lattice is the basic four-terminal network and the formulas for the image-impedance functions and image-transfer function (image parameters) are the basic mathematical relations for the discussion.

15.6 Image Parameters of Four-Terminal Networks.

The method of filter design based on the image parameters—two image-impedance functions and one image-transfer function—is the oldest formal method as well as still the most widely used. First, consider briefly the status of the image parameters. As indicated by equation 10–21, a set of three mathematical relations specify the T-equivalent of a four-terminal network and so the electrical properties at the terminals of the four-terminal network. These T-equivalent relations are in no sense unique, for the three relations of equation 10–15 are another such set. The three image parameters are still a different set of mathematical relations which specify the electrical behavior of a four-terminal network. The image parameters are particularly effective because, in addition to specifying the electrical behavior of a four-terminal network (analysis), they also permit, with considerable effectiveness, *the establishment of a four-terminal network with certain electrical properties* (synthesis). It is this synthesis aspect, i.e., determination of a network from specified image parameters, which is of interest in filter design.

There are various ways of introducing the image parameters into a discussion. Historically, the three image parameters were introduced by analogy with and extension of the two relations, attenuation and characteristic impedance, used to characterize transmission lines. There is little utility in attempting, in the brief discussion given here, to trace this devious historical pattern. Let it suffice here simply to define the three image parameters and then show their relation with and use in filter design.

By *definition*, then, the image impedance-functions $Z_{I1}(\omega)$ and $Z_{I2}(\omega)$—one for each end of a 4TN (four-terminal network)—are

$$Z_{I1}(\omega) = \pm\sqrt{Z_{s1}(\omega)\, Z_{o1}(\omega)} \tag{15–8}$$

$$Z_{I2}(\omega) = \pm\sqrt{Z_{s2}(\omega)\, Z_{o2}(\omega)} \tag{15–9}$$

where $Z_{s1}(\omega)$ and $Z_{s2}(\omega)$ are short-circuit impedance functions determined respectively at the left end of Fig. 15–7 with the right end shorted and at the right end with the left end shorted;

$Z_{o1}(\omega)$ and $Z_{o2}(\omega)$ are open-circuit impedance functions determined similarly from the open-circuited 4TN.

On the basis of the general T-equivalent of Fig. 10–8e, it can be shown that

$$\frac{Z_{s1}(\omega)}{Z_{o1}(\omega)} = \frac{Z_{s2}(\omega)}{Z_{o2}(\omega)} \tag{15–10}$$

in general; see Problem 15–9 for suggested illustrations. The image-transfer functions for the two ends of the four-terminal network, $P_{I1}(\omega)$ and $P_{I2}(\omega)$, as expressed in terms of the equal ratios of equation 15–10, are defined and related by

$$\epsilon^{P_I(\omega)} = \epsilon^{A_I(\omega)+jB_I(\omega)} = \epsilon^{P_{I1}(\omega)} = \pm\sqrt{\frac{1+\sqrt{\dfrac{Z_{s1}(\omega)}{Z_{o1}(\omega)}}}{1-\sqrt{\dfrac{Z_{s1}(\omega)}{Z_{o1}(\omega)}}}} = \epsilon^{P_{I2}(\omega)} = \pm\sqrt{\frac{1+\sqrt{\dfrac{Z_{s2}(\omega)}{Z_{o2}(\omega)}}}{1-\sqrt{\dfrac{Z_{s2}(\omega)}{Z_{o2}(\omega)}}}} \tag{15–11}$$

Note particularly that $P_I(\omega)$ is independent of the end of the 4TN used to define it, whereas the image-impedance functions are not. Also note particularly that these *three* image-parametric functions are dependent only on and are fully determined by the 4TN.

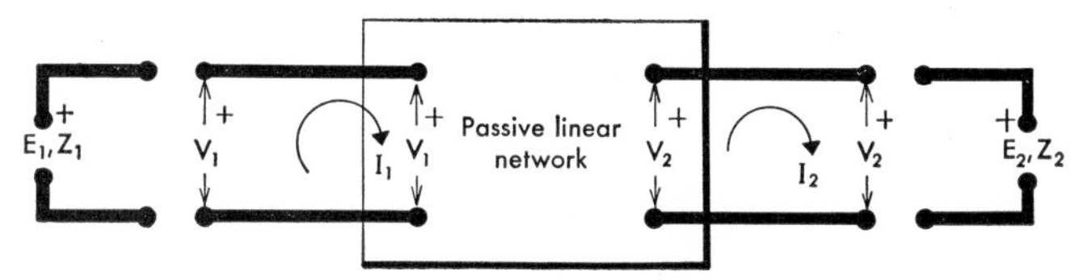

Fig. 15–7.

As a consequence of a certain amount of algebraic manipulation with the equations for a 4TN,* it can be shown, for Fig. 15–7 with *image-impedance termination*—i.e., $Z_1 = Z_{I1}(\omega)$, $Z_2 = Z_{I2}(\omega)$, with $E_2 = 0$, and the gaps closed—that

$$\frac{I_1}{I_2} = \sqrt{\frac{Z_{I2}(\omega)}{Z_{I1}(\omega)}}\epsilon^{P_I(\omega)} \tag{15–12}$$

$$\frac{V_1}{V_2} = \sqrt{\frac{Z_{I1}(\omega)}{Z_{I2}(\omega)}}\epsilon^{P_I(\omega)} \tag{15–13}$$

In addition to these last two relations, the V-relation and the I-relation, the image-impedance functions have a very useful relation with respect to impedance observations on the 4TN. These relations are indicated by Fig. 15–8 and are to be interpreted as follows: (1) If switch *a* is

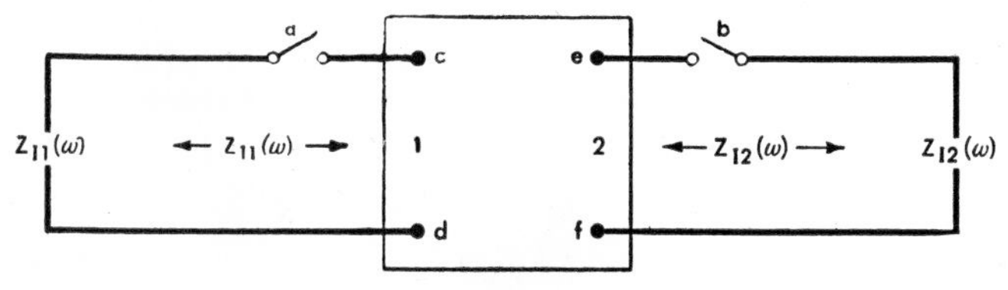

Fig. 15–8.

* Myril B. Reed, *Electric Network Synthesis—Image Parameter Method,* Prentice-Hall, Inc., 1955.

open and switch b is closed onto $Z_{I2}(\omega)$, then $Z_{I1}(\omega)$ is observed at terminals c–d; (2) if switch b is open and switch a is closed onto $Z_{I1}(\omega)$, then $Z_{I2}(\omega)$ is observed at terminals e–f. It is this pattern of image-impedance function relations that has given the term "image" to the three functions defined in the foregoing.

The general idea of *image-impedance terminations and approximations thereto* is the basis of the image-parameter method of filter design.

A special and very important case of equations 15–12 and 15–13 occurs when they are associated with symmetric 4TN. A 4TN is symmetric if interchanging its input terminals (V_1 terminals of Fig. 15–7) and its output terminals (V_2 terminals of Fig. 15–7) has no effect on V_1, I_1, V_2, and I_2. For such a 4TN, $Z_{s1} = Z_{s2} = Z_s$, and $Z_{o1} = Z_{o2} = Z_o$; i.e., there is only one open-circuit impedance function and only one short-circuit impedance function. None of the 4TN represented by Fig. 10–9 are symmetric. Omitting all E's and setting $Z_2 = Z_4$, $Z_5 = Z_8$, $Z_6 = Z_7$ in Fig. 9–3 specifies a symmetric 4TN.

Equations 15–12 and 15–13 take on the simple form, for a symmetric 4TN, of

$$\frac{I_1}{I_2} = \epsilon^{P_I(\omega)} = \epsilon^{A_I(\omega)+jB_I(\omega)} \tag{15–14}$$

$$\frac{V_1}{V_2} = \epsilon^{P_I(\omega)} = \epsilon^{A_I(\omega)+jB_I(\omega)} \tag{15–15}$$

and equations 15–8 and 15–9 specify only one image-impedance function for a symmetric 4TN as

$$Z_I(\omega) = \pm\sqrt{Z_s(\omega)Z_o(\omega)} \tag{15–16}$$

This last image-impedance function, together with equation 15–11 altered by taking the natural logarithm to specify the image transfer function, $P_I(\omega)$, as

$$P\ (\omega) = A_I(\omega) + jB_I(\omega) = ln(\pm)\sqrt{\frac{1 + \sqrt{\dfrac{Z_s(\omega)}{Z_o(\omega)}}}{1 - \sqrt{\dfrac{Z_s(\omega)}{Z_o(\omega)}}}} \tag{15–17}$$

defines the two image-parameter relations for a symmetric 4TN.

15.7 Image-Parametric Functions for a Symmetric Lattice.

The most effective approach to electric filter design is based on a symmetric lattice represented by the two entirely equivalent diagrams in Fig. 15–9, the dashed lines being abbreviations. The image-parametric functions take on a particularly simple form for this type of 4TN and so greatly facilitate design techniques. In addition, the symmetric lattice has very general electrical characteristics. This symmetric lattice is considered to be such that it may be designed to exhibit the electrical characteristics of almost any symmetric non-lattice 4TN. Moreover, many electrical characteristics are available from a symmetric lattice which are not available from non-lattice types. It is to be expected, therefore, that

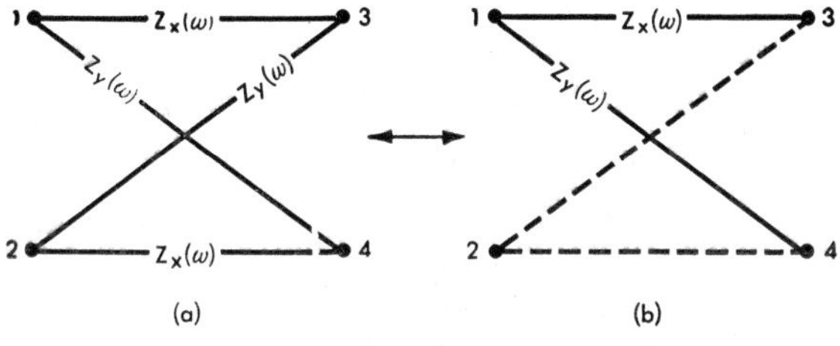

Fig. 15–9.

a symmetric lattice should provide an excellent basis for 4TN synthesis, as indeed it does.

Consider the symmetric lattice in Fig. 15–9. The open-circuit and short-circuit impedance functions for this lattice are

$$Z_o(\omega) = \frac{Z_x(\omega) + Z_y(\omega)}{2} \tag{15–18}$$

$$Z_s(\omega) = \frac{2Z_x(\omega)Z_y(\omega)}{Z_x(\omega) + Z_y(\omega)} \tag{15–19}$$

Hence the image-impedance function for the symmetric lattice is—equations 15–16, 15–18, 15–19—

$$Z_I(\omega) = \pm\sqrt{Z_x(\omega)Z_y(\omega)} \tag{15–20}$$

Then from equations 15–17, 15–18, 15–19 the image-transfer function for a symmetric lattice is, after some algebraic manipulation,

$$P_I(\omega) = A_I(\omega) + jB_I(\omega) = ln\frac{1 \pm \sqrt{\dfrac{Z_x(\omega)}{Z_y(\omega)}}}{1 \mp \sqrt{\dfrac{Z_x(\omega)}{Z_y(\omega)}}} = ln\,\frac{1 + H(\omega)}{1 - H(\omega)} \tag{15–21}$$

where

$$H(\omega) = \pm\sqrt{\frac{Z_x(\omega)}{Z_y(\omega)}} \tag{15–22}$$

The image-impedance function and the image-transfer function of a symmetric lattice are thus simply expressed in terms of the ratio and product of $Z_x(\omega)$ and $Z_y(\omega)$ of the lattice. The real and imaginary parts of $P_I(\omega)$ play a dominant role in filter design and so must be considered in all that follows.

Consider first the real part of $P_I(\omega)$, namely, $A_I(\omega)$, the transfer loss function as defined by equation 15–21 (see Art. 2.10)

$$A_I(\omega) = ln \left| \frac{1 + H(\omega)}{1 - H(\omega)} \right| \qquad (15\text{–}23)$$

This function is zero if the ratio is unity, and infinite if the ratio is infinite. Note in particular that if $1 + H(\omega)$ and $1 - H(\omega)$ are conjugates, then $A_I(\omega)$ is zero; and if $H(\omega) = 1$, $A_I(\omega)$ is infinite. These salient properties of $A_I(\omega)$ are of major importance for filter design.

The transfer-phase function, the imaginary part of $P_I(\omega)$, is defined from equation 15–21 (again see Art. 2–10) as

$$B_I(\omega) = \text{angle of } [1 + H(\omega)] - \text{angle of } [1 - H(\omega)] \qquad (15\text{–}24)$$

The forms which this last equation takes when $H(\omega)$ is real and when it is pure imaginary are of considerable interest.

First, when $H(\omega)$ is real, $1 + H(\omega)$ and $1 - H(\omega)$ are both real and may be positive or negative depending on the magnitude and sign of $H(\omega)$. Since the angle of a positive real number is $\pm k2\pi$ $(k = 1,2,3, \cdots)$ and of a negative real number is $\pm\ (2k - 1)\pi(k = 1,2,3, \cdots)$, the transfer phase (equation 15–24) for real $H(\omega)$ is an integral multiple of π, i.e.,

$$B_I(\omega) = \pm k\pi(k = 0,1,2, \cdots), \text{ if } H(\omega) \text{ is real} \qquad (15\text{–}25)$$

Second, when $H(\omega)$ is pure imaginary, $H(\omega) = \pm j|H(\omega)|$, the transfer-phase function (equation 15–24) becomes

$$B_I(\omega) = \tan^{-1} \pm |H(\omega)| - \tan^{-1} \mp |H(\omega)|$$
$$= 2 \tan^{-1} \frac{H(\omega)}{j} \qquad (15\text{–}26)$$

15.8 Purely Reactive Symmetric Lattices.

Beyond restricting consideration to 4TN which are symmetric lattices, a still further restriction on the 4TN being considered, dictated once more by the mathematical simplicity obtained thereby, is next imposed. All resistance is neglected in the symmetric lattice.

Consider, therefore, $Z_x(\omega) = jX_x(\omega)$ and $Z_y(\omega) = jX_y(\omega)$. The pattern of the character of $Z_I(\omega)$ under this reactive restriction is given in Table 15–1—$Z_I(\omega) = \pm\sqrt{jX_x(\omega)\, jX_y(\omega)}$. The sign before the radical is used:

TABLE 15–1

$Z_x(\omega)$	$Z_y(\omega)$	$Z_I(\omega)$
$+j\|X_x(\omega)\|$	$+j\|X_y(\omega)\|$	$0 + jX_I(\omega)$, pure reactance
$+j\|X_x(\omega)\|$	$-j\|X_y(\omega)\|$	$R_I(\omega) + j0$, pure resistance
$-j\|X_x(\omega)\|$	$+j\|X_y(\omega)\|$	$R_I(\omega) + j0$, pure resistance
$-j\|X_x(\omega)\|$	$-j\|X_y(\omega)\|$	$0 + jX_I(\omega)$, pure reactance

(1) which makes $Z_I(\omega)$ positive when it is *real* (pure resistance; i.e. $X_x(\omega)$ and $X_y(\omega)$ of opposite sign), or (2) which makes $Z_I(\omega)$ and $X_x(\omega)$ have the same sign when $Z_I(\omega)$ is *imaginary* (pure reactance; i.e. $X_x(\omega)$ and $X_y(\omega)$ of the same sign).

Consider next the transfer function as given by equation 15–21. Note that when $jX_x(\omega)$ and $jX_y(\omega)$ are of opposite sign, the numerator and denominator of this equation are conjugates. The magnitude of this ratio is then unity and the real part of the logarithm is zero. Consequently, the character of $P_I(\omega)$ for purely reactive $Z_x(\omega)$ and $Z_y(\omega)$ is given by Table 15–2. The feature of this table which is of extreme importance is the fact that the real part of $P_I(\omega)$, namely, the transfer loss $A_I(\omega)$, is zero when $X_x(\omega)$ and $X_y(\omega)$ are of opposite sign. Reference to equations 15–14 and 15–15 shows that $|I_1| = |I_2|$ and $|V_1| = |V_2|$ for $A_I(\omega) = 0$.

TABLE 15–2

$Z_x(\omega)$	$Z_y(\omega)$	$P_I(\omega) = A_I(\omega) + jB_1(\omega)$
$+j\|X_x(\omega)\|$	$+j\|X_y(\omega)\|$	$A_I(\omega) \pm jk\pi,\ k = 0, 1, 2, \cdots$
$+j\|X_x(\omega)\|$	$-j\|X_y(\omega)\|$	$0 + jB_I(\omega)$
$-j\|X_x(\omega)\|$	$+j\|X_y(\omega)\|$	$0 + jB_I(\omega)$
$-j\|X_x(\omega)\|$	$-j\|X_y(\omega)\|$	$A_I(\omega) \pm jk\pi,\ k = 0, 1, 2, \cdots$

By definition, the value or values of ω for which $A_I(\omega) = 0$ are called *pass frequencies*. Further, as is seen in various places in the remainder of

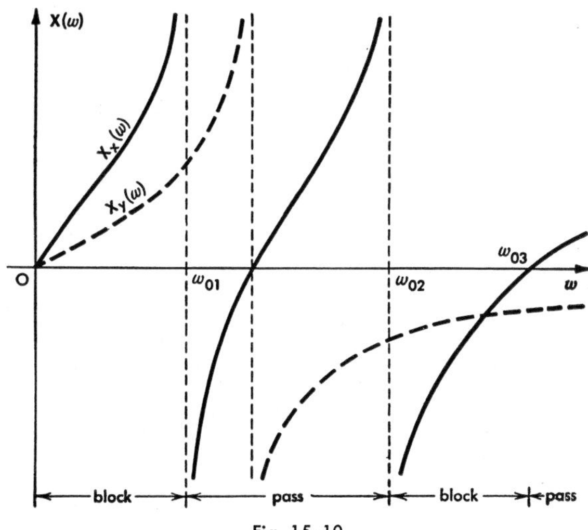

Fig. 15–10.

this chapter, it is possible to specify not points, but ranges of ω for which $A_I(\omega) = 0$, i.e., pass ranges or pass bands as they are called. See Fig. 15–10 for an example.

15.9 The Impedance and Ratio Functions.

A more convenient pair of functions with which to consider the symmetric lattice, as it is used in filter design, are here called the impedance function and the ratio function. The impedance function is defined by

$$Z(\omega) = \frac{Z_I(\omega)}{R} = \pm\frac{\sqrt{Z_x(\omega)Z_y(\omega)}}{R} \tag{15–27}$$

where R, a positive constant, is the terminating impedance (resistance) of the 4TN. Common practical usage is to terminate filters in pure resistance because of the greater simplicity and effectiveness, of both control and design, of the networks. The technique considered here is based entirely on resistance termination.

The ratio function $H(\omega)$, as defined by equation 15–22, is the second of the two basic functions used here to set forth the techniques of filter design.

Briefly, the impedance function $Z(\omega)$ and the ratio function $H(\omega)$ are basic to filter design because the closer to unity each can be made, the better the filter. Thus if $Z(\omega)$ is unity, from equation 15–27 the 4TN is image-impedance terminated—$R = Z_I(\omega)$—and the simple relations of equations 15–14 and 15–15 describe the electrical behavior of the 4TN. Control and design are both thereby very greatly facilitated.

Consider unit values of the ratio function, $H(\omega)$, next. According to equation 15–23, if $H(\omega) = 1$, $A_I(\omega) = \infty$. But $A_I(\omega) = \infty$ is the ideal block-band behavior for a filter, since for any I_1 or V_1, if $A_I(\omega) = \infty$, I_2 and V_2 are zero, i.e., the filter blocks completely—equations 15–12 and 15–13 for an *image-impedance* terminated 4TN. It can also be shown that for *any* terminations, if $A_I(\omega) = \infty$, the filter blocks completely. Certainly, therefore, the circumstances which lead to $H(\omega) = 1$ are very important in filter design. The following discussion of filters makes use of this salient aspect of $H(\omega) = 1$.

One other simplification in the mathematical formulation of the relations used hereafter is that of changing the independent variable by the relation

$$x = \frac{\omega}{\omega_0} \tag{15–28}$$

where ω_0 is a *cut-off* value of ω. Cut-off is defined as the ω value at the boundary of pass and block bands—ω_{01}, ω_{02}, ω_{C3} of Fig. 15–10. The virtues of this change of variable are discussed as the design method is developed in the following sections of this chapter.

15.10 Simple Symmetric Lattice and Symmetric Ladder Equivalents—Half-Section Basis.

It can be shown* that the tandem combination (cascading) of two identical 4TN, symmetric or not as illustrated by Fig. 15–11*a*, in the manner of Figs. 15–11*b* and *d*, has exactly the same transmission prop-

* *Ibid.*, Chap. 5.

erties, i.e., the same impedance function and ratio function, as the corresponding symmetric lattices (constructed from four of these identical 4TN) of Figs. 15–11c and e respectively. Furthermore, on the basis of such equivalences, the $Z_x(\omega)$ and $Z_y(\omega)$ of the symmetric lattice equivalent are obtainable as shown by Fig. 15–11c and e by open circuiting and short circuiting the basic 4TN. This equivalence of Fig. 15–11, applied to three particular non-symmetric 4TN, is the basis of the following discussion.

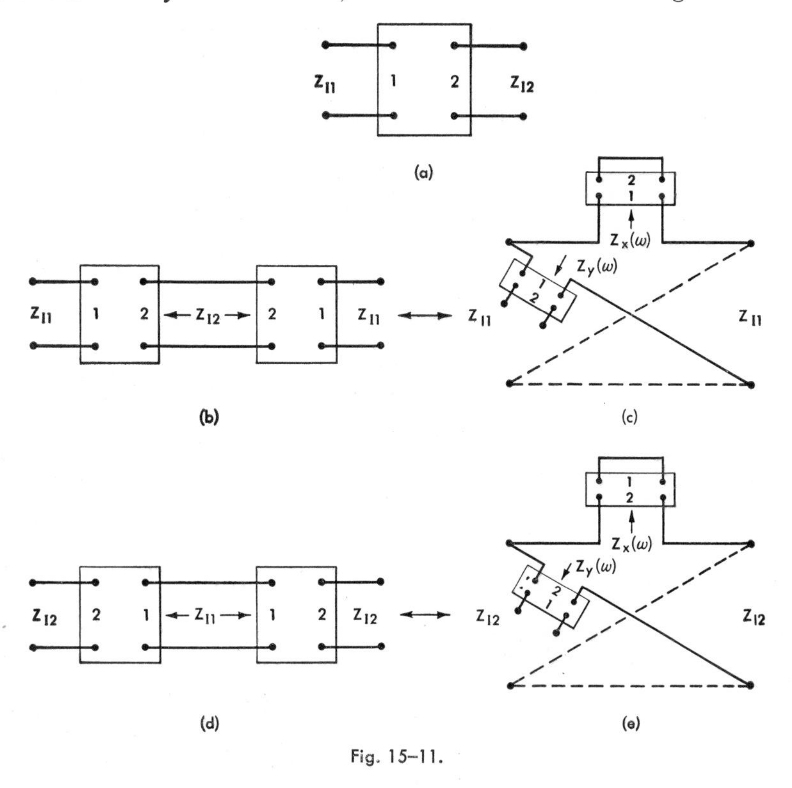

Fig. 15–11.

An important aspect of the cascading of 4TN and formation of an equivalent symmetric lattice, as on Fig. 15–11, is the pattern of image-impedance functions for these 4TN shown on the diagram. The scheme in Fig. 15–11 indicates that the image-impedance functions of a non-symmetric 4TN may be studied by means of two symmetric lattices. Thus the lattices in Figs. 15–11c and e have the image-impedance functions separately of the unsymmetric 4TN in Fig. 15–11a. Therefore, these two lattices can be studied to obtain the properties of these image-impedance functions of the unsymmetric 4TN. This scheme is used because the mathematical simplicity of the impedance function of a symmetric lattice is such that two lattices are easier to consider than one non-symmetric, non-lattice 4TN.

The pattern of cascading 4TN of Fig. 15–11b and d is designated as image-impedance matched cascading. Image-impedance matching is considered in more detail in the next section.

15.11 Cascading 4TN on the Basis of Image-Impedance Matching.

Consider the diagram in Fig. 15–12 to represent the cascading of n 4TN. Consider also the relation

$$\frac{I_1}{I_n} = \frac{I_{11}}{I_{2n}} = \frac{I_{11}}{I_{21}} \frac{I_{12}}{I_{22}} \frac{I_{13}}{I_{23}} \frac{I_{14}}{I_{24}} \cdots \frac{I_{1(n-1)}}{I_{2(n-1)}} \frac{I_{1n}}{I_{2n}} \tag{15–29}$$

valid for this diagram since $I_{21} = I_{12}$, $I_{22} = I_{13}$, $\cdots$ $I_{2(n-2)} = I_{1(n-1)}$, $I_{2(n-1)} = I_{1n}$. If equations 15–12 and 15–13 are used with the appropriate

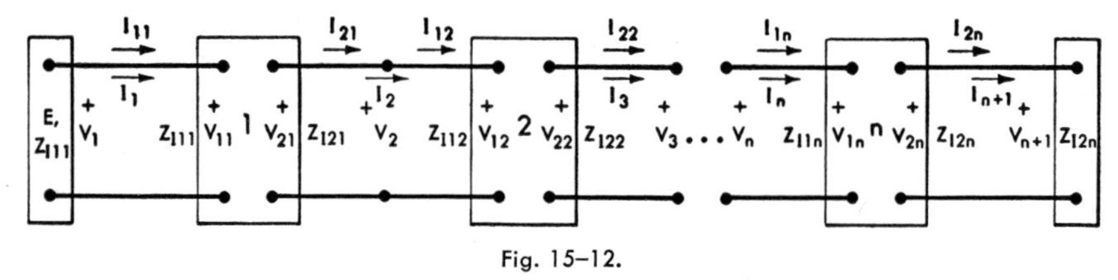

Fig. 15–12.

alterations to replace the ratios on the right of this last equation, the result is

$$\frac{I_1}{I_n} = \sqrt{\frac{Z_{I21}(\omega)}{Z_{I11}(\omega)}}\epsilon^{P_{I1}(\omega)} \sqrt{\frac{Z_{I22}(\omega)}{Z_{I12}(\omega)}}\epsilon^{P_{I2}(\omega)} \sqrt{\frac{Z_{I23}(\omega)}{Z_{I13}(\omega)}}\epsilon^{P_{I3}(\omega)} \cdots$$

$$\sqrt{\frac{Z_{I2(n-1)}(\omega)}{Z_{I1(n-1)}(\omega)}}\epsilon^{P_{I(n-1)}(\omega)} \sqrt{\frac{Z_{I2n}(\omega)}{Z_{I1n}(\omega)}}\epsilon^{P_{In}(\omega)} \tag{15–30}$$

However, this replacement in equation 15–29 is only valid for image-impedance function match at the junctions. Therefore,

$$Z_{I21} = Z_{I12}, Z_{I22} = Z_{I13}, Z_{I23} = Z_{I14}, \cdots Z_{I2(n-1)} = Z_{I1n}$$

and so equation 15–30, after cancellation of the equal image-impedance functions, becomes

$$\frac{I_1}{I_n} = \sqrt{\frac{Z_{I2n}(\omega)}{Z_{I11}(\omega)}}\epsilon^{P_{I0}(\omega)} \tag{15–31}$$

where

$$P_{I0}(\omega) = P_{I1}(\omega) + P_{I2}(\omega) + P_{I3}(\omega) + \cdots + P_{In}(\omega) \tag{15–32}$$

A corresponding result for the ratio V_1/V_2 can be established as

$$\frac{V_1}{V_n} = \sqrt{\frac{Z_{I11}(\omega)}{Z_{I2n}(\omega)}}\epsilon^{P_{I0}(\omega)} \tag{15–33}$$

Again note that the results in equations 15–31, 15–32, and 15–33 are contingent on *image-impedance function match* at each junction of 4TN.

Also note that under this condition of image-impedance function match at all junctions, (*a*) only the input and output image-impedance functions appear in the ratios I_1/I_n and V_1/V_n; and (*b*) the image-transfer function for the total combination 4TN is simply the sum of all the $P_I(\omega)$ of the individual 4TN cascaded. Finally, note that the only requirement in this impedance function matching is that the matching be effected at each junction. These functions can be different in any possible manner at different junctions of the 4TN.

If there is a key property of the image-parameter method it is the foregoing: that under matching of impedance functions at junctions the $P_I(\omega)$ add and all $Z_I(\omega)$ at the matched junctions of the 4TN vanish from consideration.

15.12 Low-Pass Half-Sections—General Discussion.

The discussion thus far in this chapter has been on a fairly broad basis. Through this and several succeeding sections a restricted class of 4TN is considered, namely, low-pass and reactive. Such discussion as is presented here covers the usual pattern of constant-*k* and *m*-derived filters as well as a much broader and more basic approach to filter design.

The basic idea used here is that of combining non-symmetric 4TN (half-sections) on an image-impedance function match basis. First, this matched cascading of the basic half-sections is used to establish equivalent symmetric lattices. These lattices are then used to establish the image-parameter properties of the half-sections. Second, filters are then studied in terms of the match cascading of these half-sections of known properties.

The basic half-sections (non-symmetric) considered here are shown at the top of Table 15–3 and are designated as the A-, B-, and C-sections. A discussion of the B-section is given next to illustrate the manner of establishing the relations in Table 15–3 and to explain the general significance of this table.

15.13 Low-Pass, Reactive, Peak Half-Section (B-Section).

Consider the B-section in Table 15–3. If this section is used to form symmetric sections by cascading two B-sections on an impedance function match basis, the T-section and π-section of the third and fourth columns result. In addition, use of Fig. 15–11 specifies the two lattice networks equivalent to the T-section and the π-section of the same column. The designation "peak-section" is sometimes used for sections with one "peak" of A_I.

On the basis of the discussion in Art. 15.11, the image-transfer function of the B-section (half-section) is just one-half that of the T-section, π-section, or either, of the equivalent lattices; i.e., the image-transfer loss,

Table 15–3

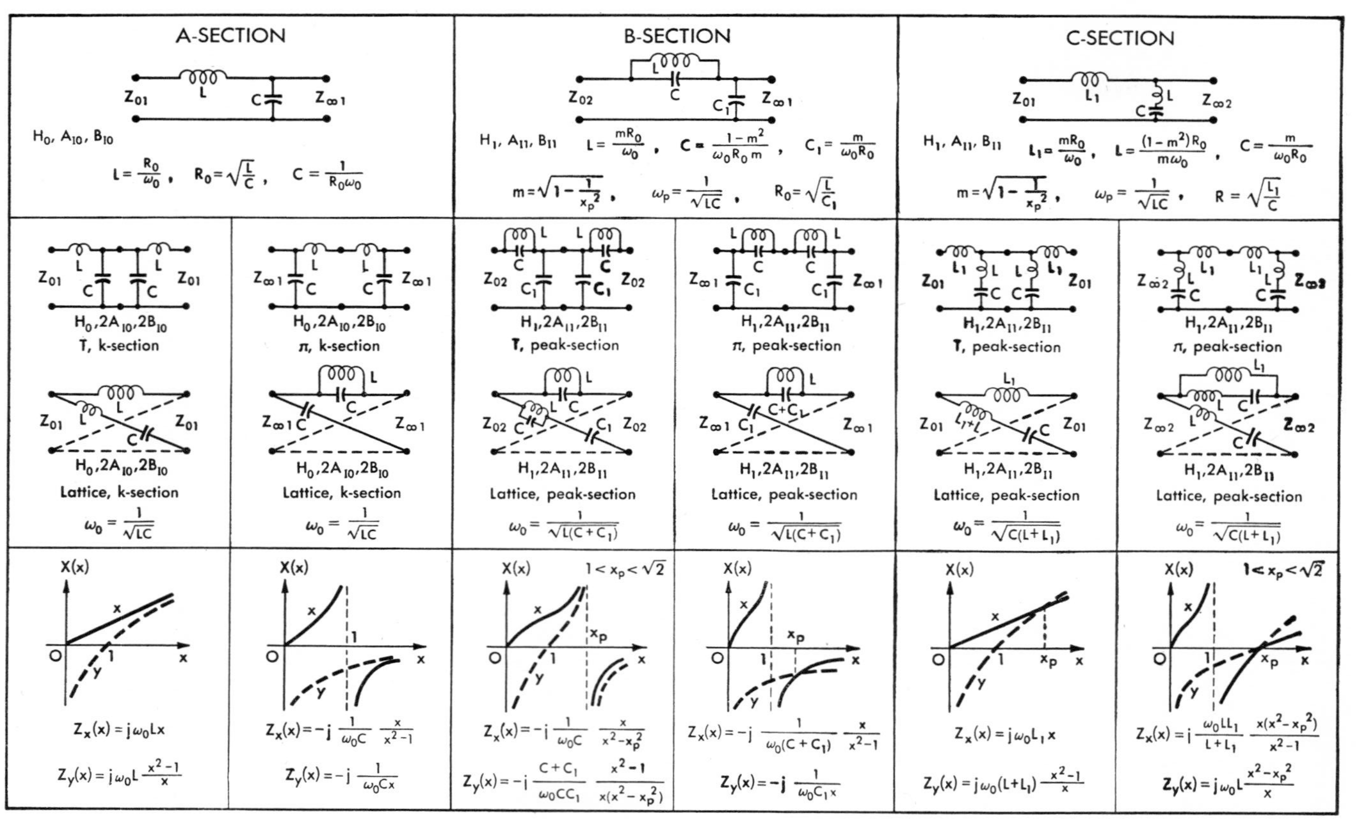

A-SECTION
Z_{01} L C $Z_{\infty 1}$
H_0, A_{10}, B_{10}
$L = \frac{R_0}{\omega_0}$, $R_0 = \sqrt{\frac{L}{C}}$, $C = \frac{1}{R_0 \omega_0}$
B-SECTION
Z_{02} L C C_1 $Z_{\infty 1}$
H_1, A_{11}, B_{11}
$L = \frac{mR_0}{\omega_0}$, $C = \frac{1-m^2}{\omega_0 R_0 m}$, $C_1 = \frac{m}{\omega_0 R_0}$
$m = \sqrt{1 - \frac{1}{x_p^2}}$, $\omega_p = \frac{1}{\sqrt{LC}}$, $R_0 = \sqrt{\frac{L}{C_1}}$
C-SECTION
Z_{01} L_1 C L $Z_{\infty 2}$
H_1, A_{11}, B_{11}
$L_1 = \frac{mR_0}{\omega_0}$, $L = \frac{(1-m^2)R_0}{m\omega_0}$, $C = \frac{m}{\omega_0 R_0}$
$m = \sqrt{1 - \frac{1}{x_p^2}}$, $\omega_p = \frac{1}{\sqrt{LC}}$, $R = \sqrt{\frac{L_1}{C}}$
$H_0, 2A_{10}, 2B_{10}$
T, k-section
$H_0, 2A_{10}, 2B_{10}$
Lattice, k-section
$\omega_0 = \frac{1}{\sqrt{LC}}$
$H_0, 2A_{10}, 2B_{10}$
π, k-section
$H_0, 2A_{10}, 2B_{10}$
Lattice, k-section
$\omega_0 = \frac{1}{\sqrt{LC}}$
$H_1, 2A_{11}, 2B_{11}$
T, peak-section
$H_1, 2A_{11}, 2B_{11}$
Lattice, peak-section
$\omega_0 = \frac{1}{\sqrt{L(C+C_1)}}$
$H_1, 2A_{11}, 2B_{11}$
π, peak-section
$H_1, 2A_{11}, 2B_{11}$
Lattice, peak-section
$\omega_0 = \frac{1}{\sqrt{L(C+C_1)}}$
$H_1, 2A_{11}, 2B_{11}$
T, peak-section
$H_1, 2A_{11}, 2B_{11}$
Lattice, peak-section
$\omega_0 = \frac{1}{\sqrt{C(L+L_1)}}$
$H_1, 2A_{11}, 2B_{11}$
π, peak-section
$H_1, 2A_{11}, 2B_{11}$
Lattice, peak-section
$\omega_0 = \frac{1}{\sqrt{C(L+L_1)}}$
$Z_x(x) = j\omega_0 Lx$
$Z_y(x) = j\omega_0 L \frac{x^2-1}{x}$
$Z_x(x) = -j \frac{1}{\omega_0 C} \frac{x}{x^2-1}$
$Z_y(x) = -j \frac{1}{\omega_0 Cx}$
$1 < x_p < \sqrt{2}$
$Z_x(x) = -j \frac{1}{\omega_0 C} \frac{x}{x^2 - x_p^2}$
$Z_y(x) = -j \frac{C+C_1}{\omega_0 CC_1} \frac{x^2-1}{x(x^2-x_p^2)}$
$Z_x(x) = -j \frac{1}{\omega_0 (C+C_1)} \frac{x}{x^2-1}$
$Z_y(x) = -j \frac{1}{\omega_0 C_1 x}$
$Z_x(x) = j\omega_0 L_1 x$
$Z_y(x) = j\omega_0 (L+L_1) \frac{x^2-1}{x}$
$1 < x_p < \sqrt{2}$
$Z_x(x) = j \frac{\omega_0 LL_1}{L+L_1} \frac{x(x^2-x_p^2)}{x^2-1}$
$Z_y(x) = j\omega_0 L \frac{x^2-x_p^2}{x}$

TABLE 15–3 (*continued*)

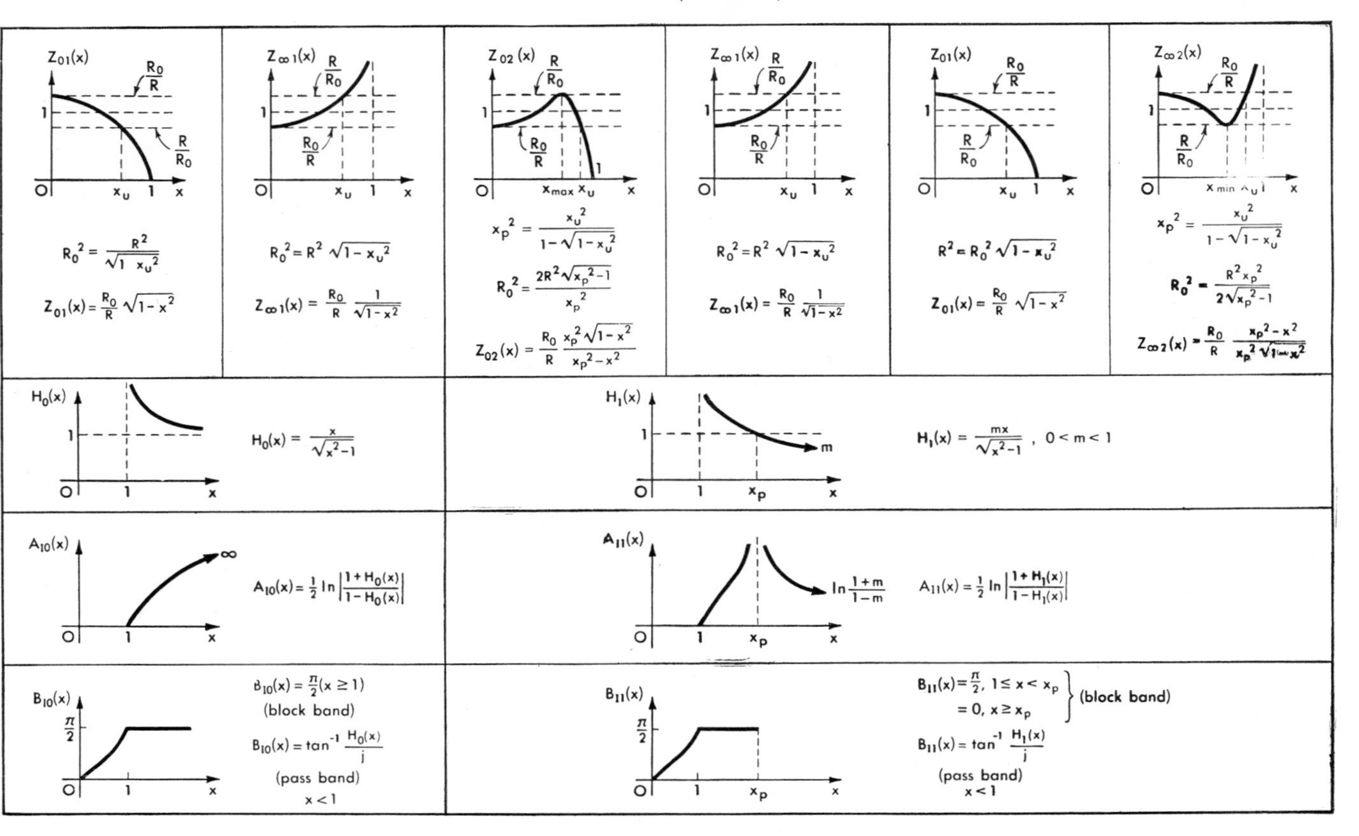

$Z_{01}(x)$	$Z_{\infty 1}(x)$	$Z_{02}(x)$	$Z_{\infty 1}(x)$	$Z_{01}(x)$	$Z_{\infty 2}(x)$
$R_0^2 = \frac{R^2}{\sqrt{1\ x_u^2}}$	$R_0^2 = R^2\sqrt{1-x_u^2}$	$x_p^2 = \frac{x_u^2}{1-\sqrt{1-x_u^2}}$	$R_0^2 = R^2\sqrt{1-x_u^2}$	$R^2 = R_0^2\sqrt{1-x_u^2}$	$x_p^2 = \frac{x_u^2}{1-\sqrt{1-x_u^2}}$
		$R_0^2 = \frac{2R^2\sqrt{x_p^2-1}}{x_p^2}$			$R_0^2 = \frac{R^2 x_p^2}{2\sqrt{x_p^2-1}}$
$Z_{01}(x) = \frac{R_0}{R}\sqrt{1-x^2}$	$Z_{\infty 1}(x) = \frac{R_0}{R}\frac{1}{\sqrt{1-x^2}}$	$Z_{02}(x) = \frac{R_0}{R}\frac{x_p^2\sqrt{1-x^2}}{x_p^2-x^2}$	$Z_{\infty 1}(x) = \frac{R_0}{R}\frac{1}{\sqrt{1-x^2}}$	$Z_{01}(x) = \frac{R_0}{R}\sqrt{1-x^2}$	$Z_{\infty 2}(x) = \frac{R_0}{R}\frac{x_p^2-x^2}{x_p^2\sqrt{1-x^2}}$

$H_0(x) = \frac{x}{\sqrt{x^2-1}}$	$H_1(x) = \frac{mx}{\sqrt{x^2-1}}$, $0 < m < 1$
$A_{10}(x) = \frac{1}{2}\ln\left\lvert\frac{1+H_0(x)}{1-H_0(x)}\right\rvert$	$A_{11}(x) = \frac{1}{2}\ln\left\lvert\frac{1+H_1(x)}{1-H_1(x)}\right\rvert$
$B_{10}(x) = \frac{\pi}{2} (x \geq 1)$ (block band) $B_{10}(x) = \tan^{-1}\frac{H_0(x)}{j}$ (pass band) $x < 1$	$B_{11}(x) = \frac{\pi}{2}$, $1 \leq x < x_p$; $= 0$, $x \geq x_p$ (block band) $B_{11}(x) = \tan^{-1}\frac{H_1(x)}{j}$ (pass band) $x < 1$

$A_I(\omega)$, and the image-transfer phase, $B_I(\omega)$, are each, for a half-section, half that for a full section. Note also that the end of viewing the half-section does not affect this half-image transfer function property.

Consider next the lattices for the B-section and their reactance patterns. On the basis of the discussion in Art. 10.11, the reactance curves in Fig. 15–13 can at least tentatively be accepted as those for these lat-

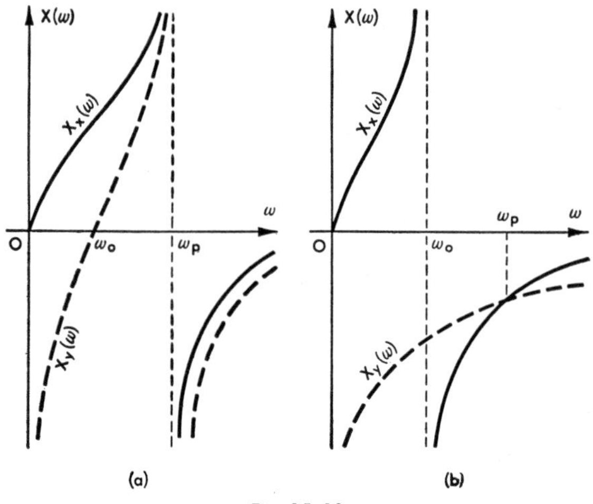

Fig. 15–13.

tices. Now to show that in fact these reactance curves do fit, consider the left-hand lattice. The pole of $Z_x(\omega)$ and of $Z_y(\omega)$ occur at the same $\omega = \omega_p$ (same L and C in parallel). Also, as ω increases indefinitely, the L's tend toward an open circuit and the C's toward a short circuit. The C's thus dominate. Then since C and C_1 in series has a larger reactance than C alone, $|X_y(\omega)| > |X_x(\omega)|$ for $\omega > \omega_p$, as shown in Fig. 15–13*a*. Evidently this lattice, and so the T-section and B-section, is low-pass—$X_x(\omega)$ and $X_y(\omega)$ of *opposite* sign for $0 \leq \omega \leq \omega_0$. The point ω_0 is the cut-off (boundary between the pass and block bands).

The reactance curves of Fig. 15–13*b* are for the right-hand lattice of the B-section in Table 15–3. With an argument similar to that in the immediately preceding discussion, it follows for this second lattice that $|X_y(\omega)| > |X_x(\omega)|$ for very large values of ω. Hence the reactance curves cross at some ω, indicated as ω_p.

Consider next the formula for $Z_x(\omega)$ and $Z_y(\omega)$. On the basis of the well-known pattern of series and parallel circuit combinations, for the left-hand lattice of the B-section

$$Z_y(\omega) = \frac{1}{j\omega C_1} + \frac{j\omega L \dfrac{1}{j\omega C}}{j\omega L + \dfrac{1}{j\omega C}} \tag{15–34}$$

which may be expressed as

$$Z_y(\omega) = -j\frac{C+C_1}{\omega CC_1}\frac{\omega^2 - \dfrac{1}{L(C+C_1)}}{\omega^2 - \dfrac{1}{LC}} \tag{15–35}$$

Similarly

$$Z_x(\omega) = -j\frac{1}{\omega C}\frac{\omega^2}{\omega^2 - \dfrac{1}{LC}} \tag{15–36}$$

But since cut-off is at the zero of $Z_y(\omega)$ and ω_p is the pole of both $Z_x(\omega)$ and $Z_y(\omega)$,

$$\omega_0^2 = \frac{1}{L(C+C_1)} \tag{15–37}$$

$$\omega_p^2 = \frac{1}{LC} \tag{15–38}$$

Equations 15–35 and 15–36 may then be expressed as

$$Z_y(\omega) = -j\frac{C+C_1}{\omega CC_1}\frac{\omega^2 - \omega_0^2}{\omega^2 - \omega_p^2} \tag{15–39}$$

$$Z_x(\omega) = -j\frac{1}{\omega C}\frac{\omega^2}{\omega^2 - \omega_p^2} \tag{15–40}$$

Use of the transformation of variable $x = \omega/\omega_0$ then specifies $Z_x(x)$ and $Z_y(x)$ as shown in Table 15–3, third column. Similar treatment leads to the $Z_x(x)$ and $Z_y(x)$ formulas of Table 15–3 for all the other lattices shown.

15.14 Impedance Functions of the B-Section.

On the basis of years of experience, it is convenient to impose the general requirement that at $\omega = 0$ the impedance function of equation 15–27 shall be

$$Z(0) = \frac{R_0}{R} \tag{15–41}$$

where R_0, a positive constant called the design resistance, is used as shown throughout the remainder of this chapter.

The impedance function for the left-hand end of the B-section in Table 15–3 is (equation 15–27, and $Z_x(x)$ and $Z_y(x)$ from the table)

$$Z_{02}(x) = \pm\frac{\sqrt{Z_x(x)Z_y(x)}}{R} = \pm\frac{1}{R}\sqrt{\left(\frac{-j}{\omega_0 C}\right)^2\frac{C+C_1}{C_1}\frac{(x^2-1)}{(x^2-x_p^2)^2}} \tag{15–42}$$

But since in the pass band where $Z(x)$ is real and is to be chosen as *positive*, this last expression becomes, because also $x < 1 < x_p$,

$$Z_{02}(x) = \frac{1}{R\omega_0 C}\sqrt{\frac{C + C_1}{C_1}} \frac{\sqrt{1 - x^2}}{x_p^2 - x} \tag{15-43}$$

The design resistance R_0 is introduced at this point by using equation 15–41. Thus

$$Z_{02}(0) = \frac{R_0}{R} = \frac{1}{R\omega_0 C}\sqrt{\frac{C + C_1}{C_1}} \frac{1}{x_p^2} \tag{15-44}$$

from which, by means of equations 15–37 and 15–38 and also $x_p = \omega_p/\omega_0$,

$$R_0 = \frac{1}{\omega_0 C}\sqrt{\frac{C + C_1}{C_1}} \frac{1}{x_p^2} = \sqrt{\frac{L}{C_1}} \tag{15-45}$$

Finally, then, in the pass band,

$$Z_{02}(x) = \frac{R_0}{R} \frac{x_p^2\sqrt{1 - x^2}}{x_p^2 - x^2} \tag{15-46}$$

This last expression for $Z_{02}(x)$ contains the three parameters R, R_0, and x_p. The terminating resistance, R, is fixed by other than filter-design considerations and is here assumed as known. The parameters R_0 and x_p are then available for shaping the $Z_{02}(x)$ curve. The generally most useful form of the $Z_{02}(x)$ curve is that shown in the third column of Table 15–3. Such a variation has the following important properties: it approximates unity on a geometric mean basis for $0 \leq x \leq x_u$, crosses the unity line twice—hence the subscript 2 on $Z_{02}(x)$—and is zero at cut-off—hence the subscript 0 on $Z_{02}(x)$. The mathematical requirements which assure that $Z_{02}(x)$ will have the graphical equivalent shown in Table 15–3 are:

$$Z_{02}(x_{\max}) = \frac{R}{R_0} \tag{15-47}$$

$$Z_{02}(x_u) = \frac{R_0}{R} \tag{15-48}$$

and from the vanishing of $dZ_{02}(x)/dx$

$$x_{\max} = \sqrt{2 - x_p^2} \tag{15-49}$$

Equation 15–48

$$x_p^2 = \frac{x_u^2}{1 - \sqrt{1 - x_u^2}} \tag{15-50}$$

and equations 15–47 and 15–49 lead to

$$R_0^2 = \frac{2R^2\sqrt{x_p^2 - 1}}{x_p^2} \tag{15-51}$$

Based on fixing R and x_u, these last two equations specify x_p and R_0 of $Z_{02}(x)$ of equation 15–46 such that $Z_{02}(x)$ varies on a geometric mean basis for $0 \leq x \leq x_u$ (see column three of Table 15–3). Curves such as suggested by Problem 15–25 facilitate choosing x_u. Ultimately, however, x_u can be chosen only on the basis of experience in the design and operation of filters.

Other impedance functions available from the A-, B-, and C-sections are shown in Table 15–3. Fixing x_u and R in each case specifies the pattern of behavior of each of these functions and establishes R_0 and, where relevant, x_p. Both R_0 and x_p are also important parameters in the specification of the ratio function and in turn the two components of the image-transfer function, namely, $A_I(x)$ and $B_I(x)$.

The pattern of impedance functions in Table 15–3, while probably the most generally useful, is not the only one possible for these half-sections. For example, the left end of the B-section can be made (set $x_p > \sqrt{2}$) to resemble $Z_{01}(x)$ in that the derivative is negative throughout the pass band. Likewise the impedance function of the right end of the C-section can be made to resemble $Z_{\infty 1}(x)$ in that it has a positive derivative throughout the pass band. Full consideration of all possible impedance-function variations for the A-, B-, and C-sections, although involving little complexity, is rather voluminous and not worth while in such a brief discussion as is presented here. It is only essential that the reader be aware of the fact that Table 15–3 depicts the most generally useful scheme, not the only one.

15.15 The Ratio Functions $H_0(x)$ and $H_1(x)$.

As indicated by Table 15–3, the A-, B-, and C-sections have two ratio functions, $H_0(x)$ and $H_1(x)$—defined by equation 15–22—when the parameter m, as defined at the top of the table, determined by x_p, is used for the B- and C-sections. Verification of this fact by use of $Z_x(x)$ and $Z_y(x)$ of the table involves ordinary algebra and is not presented here. Note that the ratio function $H_1(x)$ has one and the ratio function $H_0(x)$ has no crossing of the unit line. The unit value of $H_1(x)$ occurs at $x = x_p$. An important point to note is that fixing the pattern of behavior of the impedance function of the B- and C-sections determines x_p and so $H_1(x)$; i.e., there are no free parameters in $H_0(x)$ or $H_1(x)$ for design adjustment if $Z(x)$ is fixed. Arts. 15–19 and 15–20 present further discussion of this idea.

15.16 The Transfer Loss Functions $A_{I0}(x)$ and $A_{I1}(x)$.

The transfer loss function (equation 15–23), since it is directly determined by the ratio function, is the same for all 4TN with the same $H(x)$. Table 15–3 shows the general pattern of the $A_{I0}(x)$ and $A_{I1}(x)$ functions for the A-, B-, and C-sections. The curves show that the $A_{I0}(x)$ function increases indefinitely with x, whereas the $A_{I1}(x)$ function has its indefinitely increasing feature at x_p. Note that the parameter m, and so x_p, also determines the $H_1(\infty)$ value.

15.17 The Transfer-Phase Functions $B_{I0}(x)$ and $B_{I1}(x)$.

The transfer-phase functions for the A-, B-, and C-sections in Table 15–3 are shown adequately, for basic behavior considerations, in the table. The discontinuity in $B_{I1}(x)$ at x_p is the only feature that may require consideration. Since in the block band, $H_1(x)$ is real, equation 15–21 indicates that, as $H_1(x)$ changes from greater than to less than unity, the sign of the ratio of this equation changes. The transfer phase (equation 15–24) then changes by $\pm\pi$ radians for a full section or by $\pm\pi/2$ for a half-section (B- and C-sections). Measurement on actual filters indicates that the change in transfer phase is a reduction, rather than an increase, of $\pi/2$ as shown on Table 15–3 at x_p for the B- and C-sections.

15.18 Element Values of Half-Sections.

The element values, i.e., L and C values, for the filter half-sections depend on the ω-range, not the x-range, of the pass band for which the filter is designed. Hence the x-variable must be replaced by the ω-variable in order to determine these element values. Also the cut-off, ω_0, the parameter m, wherever it is involved, and R_0 are considered the most convenient set of parameters with which to formulate the element values. Incidentally, notice that the specification of x_u and R determines R_0 and m (Table 15–3).

From the definitions of equations 15–22 and 15–27

$$Z_x(x) = RZ(x)H(x) \tag{15–52}$$

$$Z_y(x) = \frac{RZ(x)}{H(x)} \tag{15–53}$$

Therefore, for the B-section

$$Z_x(x) = RZ_{\infty 1}(x)H_1(x) = -jmR_0\frac{x}{x^2 - 1} \tag{15–54}$$

$$Z_y(x) = \frac{RZ_{\infty 1}(x)}{H_1(x)} = -j\frac{R_0}{mx} \tag{15–55}$$

which, on using $x = \omega/\omega_0$ and an algebraic rearrangement, become

$$Z_x(x) = -jmR_0\omega_0\frac{\omega}{\omega^2 - \omega_0{}^2} = \frac{j\dfrac{mR_0}{\omega_0}\omega\, j\dfrac{1}{\dfrac{1}{mR_0\omega_0}}\omega}{j\dfrac{mR_0}{\omega_0}\omega + \dfrac{1}{j\dfrac{1}{mR_0\omega_0}\omega}} \tag{15–56}$$

$$Z_y(x) = -j\frac{R_0\omega_0}{m\omega} = \frac{1}{j\frac{m}{R_0\omega_0}\omega} \tag{15-57}$$

These last two equations are of the form of equations for an L–C parallel combination and of a capacitor, respectively, and from the lattice of column four of Table 15–3

$$C_1 = \frac{m}{R_0\omega_0} \tag{15-58}$$

$$L = \frac{mR_0}{\omega_0} \tag{15-59}$$

$$C_1 + C = \frac{1}{mR_0\omega_0} \quad \text{and so} \quad C = \frac{1 - m^2}{\omega_0 R_0 m} \tag{15-60}$$

as given in the table.

Similar treatment specifies the element values for the A- and C-sections. Note that it is immaterial which of the two lattices is used to determine the L and C formulas for a particular half-section (A-, B-, or C-section); hence the simpler lattice should be used because of the simpler algebra involved.

15.19 Image-Impedance Matching.

The A-, B-, and C-sections, with properties as derived in the foregoing and listed in Table 15–3, can be used in cascade to form a wide variety of low-pass filters. In order that the pattern be predictable in terms of the properties of the individual sections, the cascading must be on an image-impedance match (matched) basis. Combining these three half-sections in a random pattern is obviously possible, but the behavior of the combination is not readily predictable and, indeed, may not even be low-pass. However, if cascaded on a matched basis, the total transfer function is the sum of the individual transfer functions, and the two image impedances of the combination are those of the external terminals of the sections on the ends of the combination (Art. 15.11).

The basis for cascading the A-, B-, and C-sections on a matched basis is given on Fig. 15–14. First, the possible matched combinations, taken two at a time, of these three sections are given. Based on a geometric-mean variation of image-impedance functions which the combinations present, the factors that may be assigned arbitrary values (within the limits specified in preceding discussions) are given below each combination. The assignment of these factors completely determines the two sections in cascade in each case. Where two B-sections or two C-sections are cascaded, x_p can be assigned other than the value to give geometric-mean variation of the common image-impedance function with the assurance that cascading is still on a matched basis.

Also in Fig. 15–14 is an illustration of the cascading of eight half-sections. As shown, the x_u of either end of the combination, R, and two of the x_p's are arbitrary for geometric-mean variation of the $Z_{01}(x)$ and

WAYS OF CONNECTING THE A-, B-, AND C-SECTIONS, TWO AT A TIME, ON AN IMAGE-IMPEDANCE MATCH BASIS

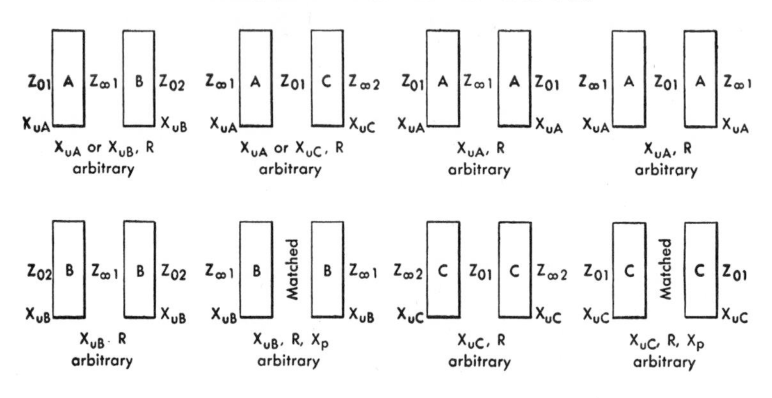

A PARTICULAR PATTERN OF IMAGE-IMPEDANCE MATCHED A-, B-, AND C-SECTIONS

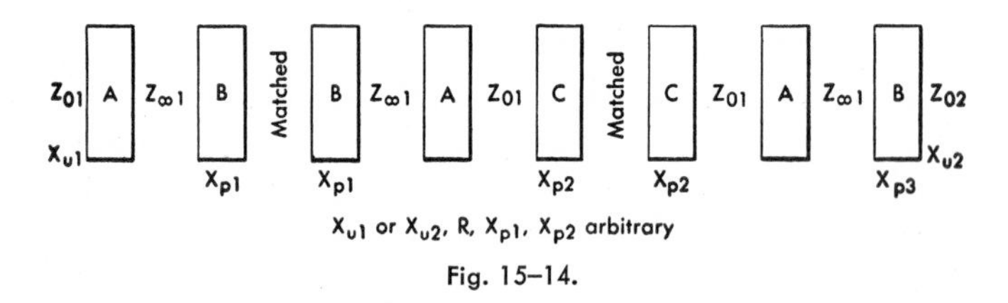

X_{u1} or X_{u2}, R, X_{p1}, X_{p2} arbitrary

Fig. 15–14.

$Z_{02}(x)$ at the ends. The assignment of these four factors completely fixes all the sections.

15.20 A Low-Pass Filter.

For perhaps a majority of practical purposes, cascading of the 4TN of Table 15–3, on an image-impedance function matching basis, is fully adequate for designing filters. As an example of such a process, consider the following filter design.

A filter is to be designed which presents $Z_{02}(x)$ at one end and $Z_{\infty 2}(x)$ at the other, and in addition has a pole (infinite value) of $A_I(x)$ at $x = x_p = 2$. The cascaded set of five sections shown in Fig. 15–15a fits the requirement specified. Thus the B-section on the left and the C-section on the right give the required terminating $Z_{02}(x)$ and $Z_{\infty 2}(x)$. The two interior B-sections with $x_p = 2$ add the pole at $x = 2$. Two such sections and an A-section are required to meet this requirement of a pole at $x = 2$ and to match the required terminating impedance functions, since for the terminating B- and C-sections x_p cannot equal 2 but must be such that $1 < x_p < \sqrt{2}$ to produce $Z_{02}(x)$ and $Z_{\infty 2}(x)$ as required.

The network in Fig. 15–15*b* is the combined form of Fig. 15–15*a*. The curves in Fig. 15–15*c* and *d* indicate the $A_I(x)$ and $B_I(x)$ for the whole filter based on adding the $A_I(x)$ and $B_I(x)$ functions for the five matched half-sections of Fig. 15–15*a*. Completion of the design necessitates determination of the element values.

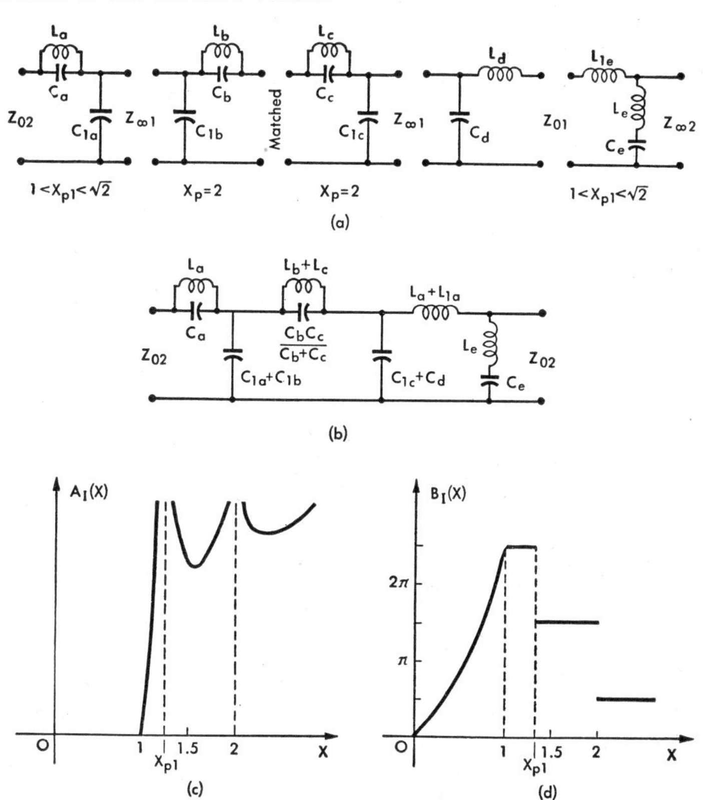

Fig. 15–15.

The formulas of Table 15–3 specify the L's and C's in terms of the factors R_0, m, and ω_0. These three factors are used mainly because of the simplicity of the resulting element-value formulas. For all cases the cut-off, ω_0, and the terminating resistance, R, are specified. The appropriate R_0's and m's then follow from the additional specification of the x_u's and x_p's. In particular, for the filter being considered, specifying x_u, the same one for both Z_{02} and $Z_{\infty 2}$ of the ends of the filter, and R and ω_0 in addition to $x_p = 2$ as already given, completely determines all L's and C's. Thus from x_u, x_{p1} and so m_1 for the terminating B- and C-sections are determined. From x_{p1} the value of R_0 follows. Then from $x_p = 2$ a value of m for the two interior B-sections is fixed. The L- and C-values then follow by direct substitution in the formulas of Table 15–3.

15.21 Low-Pass Equivalent of a High-Pass Filter—High-Pass Design.

All of the foregoing discussion in this chapter is directed essentially toward the design of low-pass filters. Early in this discussion, however, it was indicated that this low-pass pattern forms a basis for the design of high-pass, band-pass, and band-elimination filters. Since space does not permit a complete discussion of the low-pass basis idea, only the results, but results fully adequate for design purposes, are given here.

Consider first the high-pass design. The procedure in designing a high-pass filter is laid out on Fig. 15–16. First the high-pass transfer loss function of Fig. 15–16*a* is transferred into a low-pass form by locating the appropriate ordinate value for each x at the corresponding $1/x$ abscissa, as on Fig. 15–16*b*. The low-pass filter to fit this transfer loss function is then designed to the point of establishing the network and its element values. The high-pass filter is then determined by replacing each L of the low-pass network by C_L, and each C of the low-pass network by an L_C, according to Fig. 15–16*c* and *d*. A high-pass filter is shown in Fig. 15–17. Note that ω_0 is the same for the high-pass and low-pass filters.

15.22 Low-Pass Equivalent of a Band-Pass Filter—Band-Pass Design.

The lay-out of Fig. 15–18 indicates the method of designing a band-pass filter on a low-pass basis. A band-pass $A_I(x)$ curve is shown in Fig. 15–18*a*. It is only band-pass filters with such "symmetric" types of $A_I(x)$ curves that may be conveniently treated on a low-pass basis. One side of the band-pass transfer loss function should be transferred to a low-pass basis as is done in Fig. 15–18*b*. The appropriate low-pass filter is then designed. The band-pass filter then follows by replacing each L of the low-pass filter by L_L and C_L in series, and each C of the low-pass filter by L_C and C_C in parallel, as indicated in Fig. 15–18*c* and *d*. The ω_{01} and ω_{02} are the two cut-offs of the band-pass filter which may be specified arbitrarily. Note that ω_0 of the low-pass filter may be specified as any convenient number, or $\omega_0 L$ and $\omega_0 C$ may be computed for the low-pass filter and used in the band-pass element value formulas. See Fig. 15–19 for a picture of a band-pass filter.

15.23 Low-Pass Equivalent of a Band-Block Filter—Band-Block Design.

The band-block design, in terms of a low-pass basis, is given in Fig. 15–20. The scheme here is so similar to that of the preceding two sections that the figure should convey all the needed information. Briefly, though, the band-block transfer loss curve ("half" of it) is transferred to

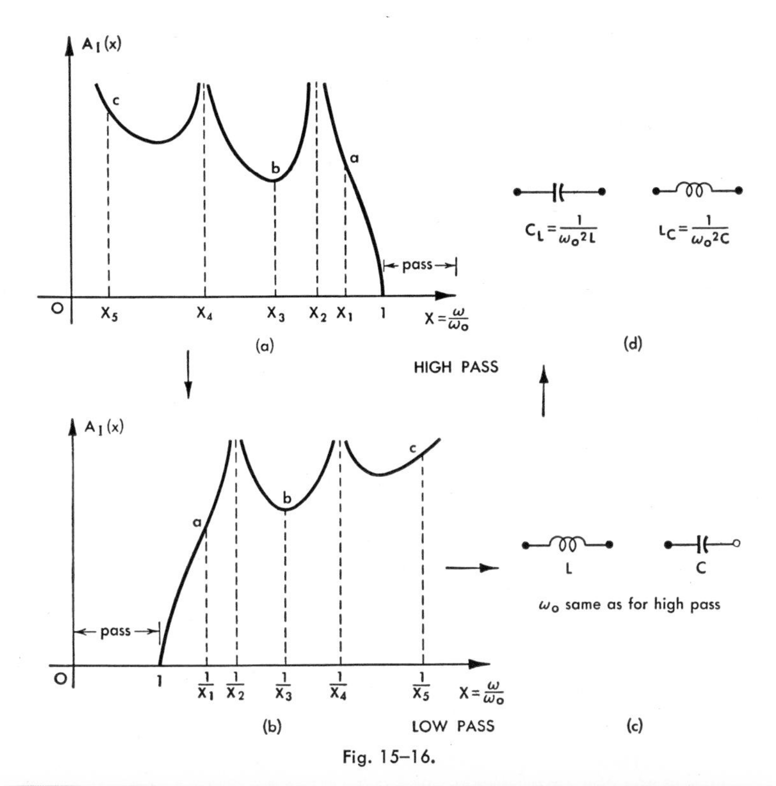

Fig. 15–16.

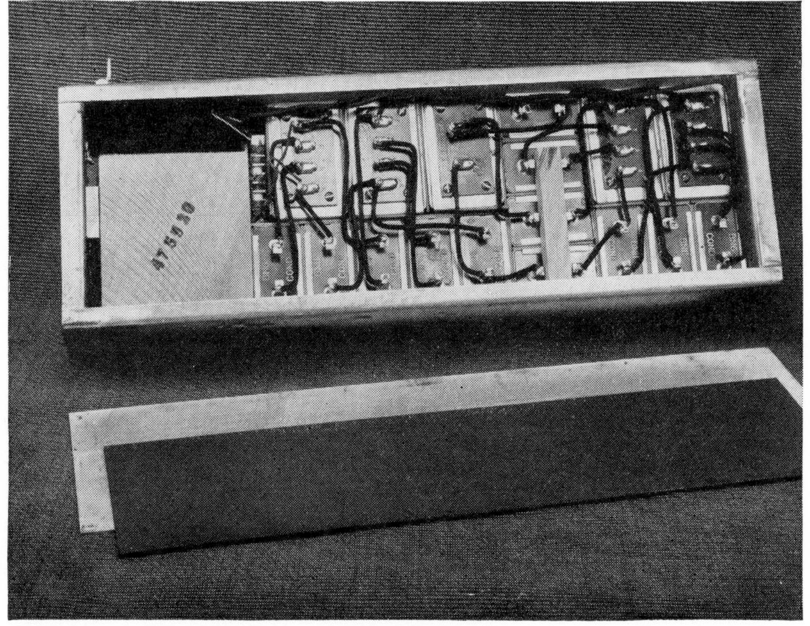

Fig. 15–17.

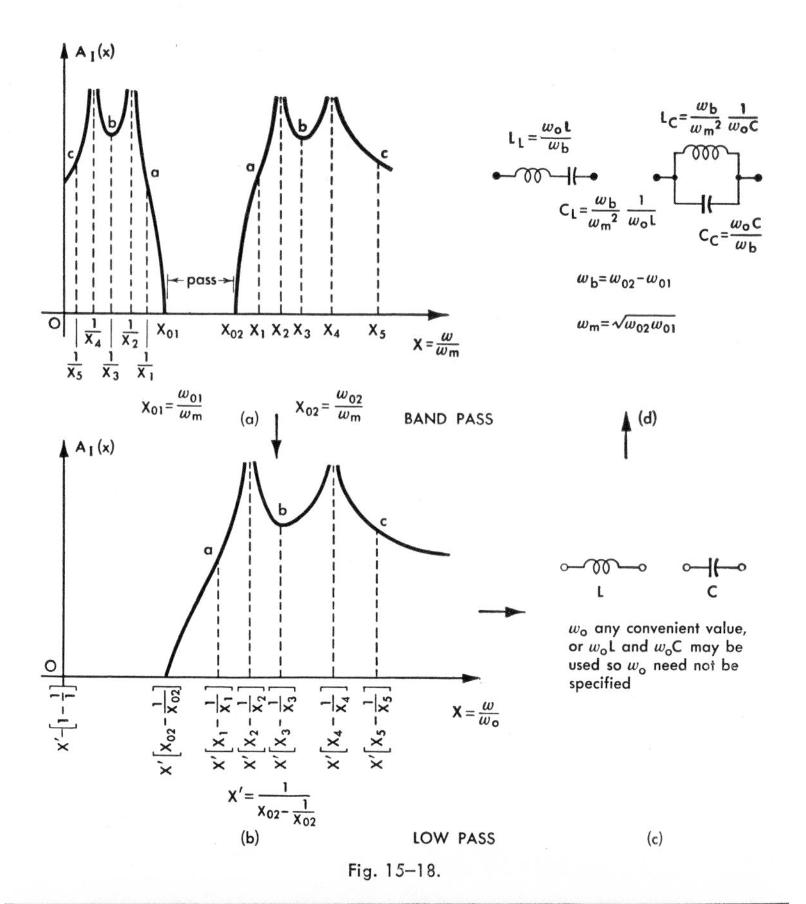

Fig. 15–18.

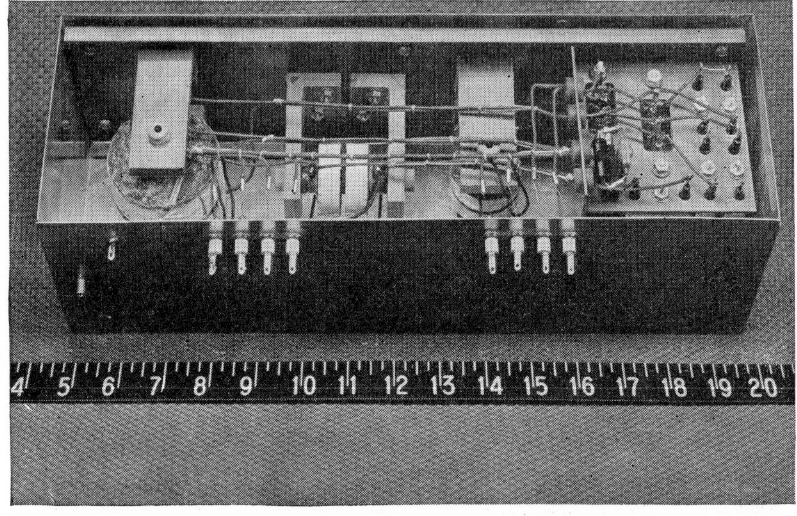

Fig. 15–19.

the low-pass x scale; the formula for doing so is given in Fig. 15–20b. The low-pass filter is then designed, after which the band-block filter is formed by replacing each L of the low-pass network by L_L and C_L in parallel, and each C of the low-pass network by L_C and C_C in series. It is

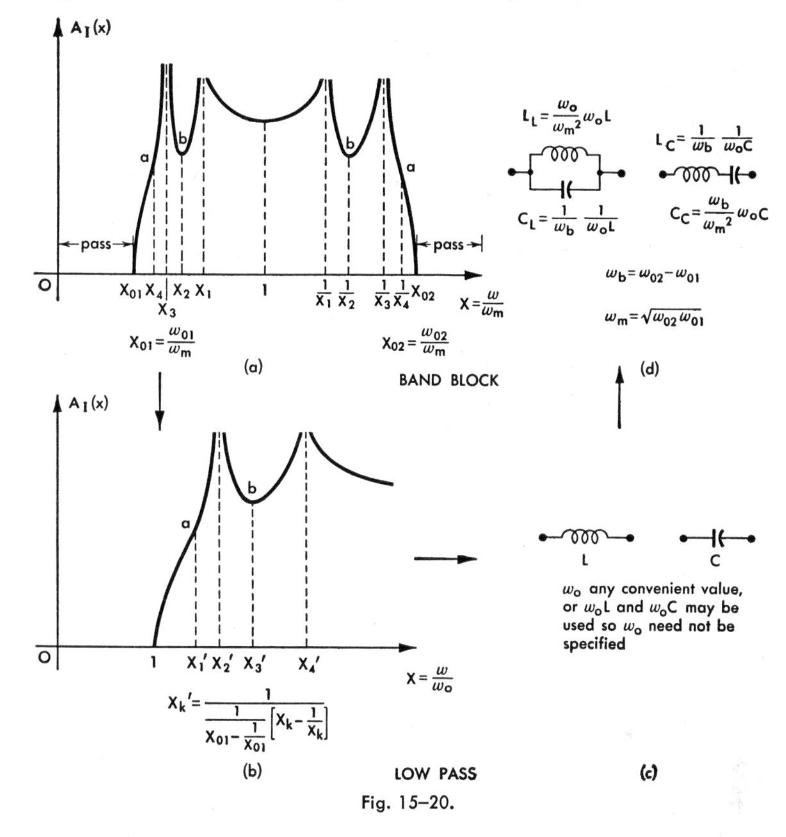

Fig. 15–20.

more convenient to compute $\omega_0 L$ and $\omega_0 C$ than L and C for the low-pass and to use these numbers in the block-band element value formulas.

15.24 Insertion Function.

If the filters designed in accordance with the foregoing techniques *could be* terminated in impedances which varied with frequency as do the image-impedance functions, the ratios in equations 15–12 and 15–13 would apply. However, such terminations are not possible. On the contrary, no attempt is made so to terminate filters. Instead, as pointed out in the preceding, a pure resistance unit is used for termination and this pure resistance is approximated on a geometric-mean basis over some specified range of the pass band. Because of this mismatch at the terminals between the image-impedance function and the terminating impedance, the filter behavior is *not* specified by equations 15–12 and 15–13.

Practical experience has indicated that an effective way of calculating and measuring the actual performance of filters is by means of what is called the *insertion function*. This insertion function, $P_s(\omega)$, is defined by

$$P_s(\omega) = A_s(\omega) + jB_s(\omega) = ln \frac{I_R'}{I_R} \tag{15–61}$$

where I_R' and I_R are associated with the driver, receiver, and filter in accordance with Fig. 15–21. The designation *insertion* function is based on the pattern of this figure; i.e., the insertion function gives a measure of the effect of inserting the filter between receiver and sender.

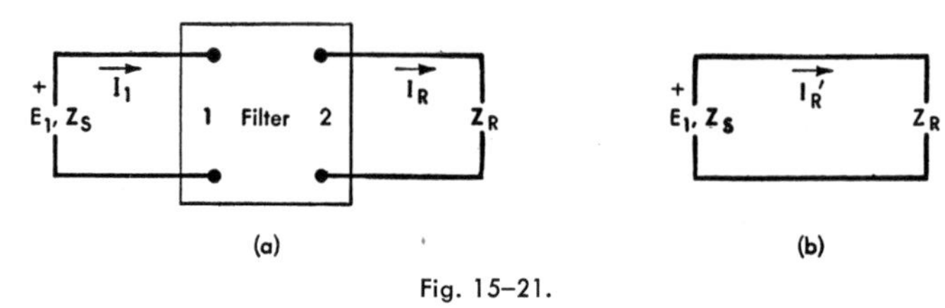

Fig. 15–21.

The algebra required to express the ratio I_R'/I_R in terms of the image-impedance functions, image-transfer functions, and Z_S and Z_R is rather involved although not essentially difficult. The general T-equivalent of Chapter 10 may be used as a base from which to start. The result of performing this manipulation is

$$\frac{I_R'}{I_R} = \frac{2\sqrt{Z_S Z_R}}{Z_S + Z_R} \frac{Z_S + Z_{I1}}{2\sqrt{Z_S Z_{I1}}} \frac{Z_R + Z_{I2}}{2\sqrt{Z_R Z_{I2}}} \epsilon^{P_I}(1 - k_S k_R \epsilon^{-2P_I}) \tag{15–62}$$

where

$$k_S = \frac{Z_S - Z_{I1}}{Z_S + Z_{I1}} \tag{15–63}$$

$$k_R = \frac{Z_R - Z_{I2}}{Z_R + Z_{I2}} \tag{15–64}$$

The insertion function is, therefore, from equations 15–61 and 15–62,

$$P_s(\omega) = A_s(\omega) + jB_s(\omega) = ln \frac{2\sqrt{Z_S Z_R}}{Z_S + Z_R} + ln \frac{Z_S + Z_{I1}(\omega)}{2\sqrt{Z_S Z_{I1}(\omega)}}$$
$$+ ln \frac{Z_R + Z_{I2}(\omega)}{2\sqrt{Z_R Z_{I2}(\omega)}} + P_I(\omega) + ln[1 - k_S(\omega)k_R(\omega)\epsilon^{-2P_I(\omega)}] \tag{15–65}$$

An immediately evident characteristic of this insertion function is that if $Z_S = Z_R$, $Z_S = Z_{I1}$, $Z_R = Z_{I2}$, all the logarithmic terms vanish, since $ln\ 1 = 0$. For the problem being considered here, the first term on the right of equation 15–65 vanishes because $Z_S = Z_R = R$. The last term is also very often, although not always, negligibly small. In any event, the insertion function specifies the effect of the filter on transmission of a signal (input voltage) in terms of mismatches of image-impedance functions and terminations and in terms of the image-transfer function.

The usual method of using the insertion function is to specify this function and then to design a filter which has an insertion function as near the one specified as time and expense allow. Before designing a filter in this true synthesis manner, however, it is essential that the designer have a thorough knowledge of the analysis problem, i.e., know fully the mathematical characteristics of the insertion function of equation 15–65. Since the individual terms of this equation are simple, establishing the elementary and most useful properties of the insertion function is not difficult. Solution of the problems at the end of this chapter will give the reader such a working knowledge of the insertion function.

The techniques of synthesis, i.e., compensation for unavoidable resistance, equalization of the pass-band insertion loss, choice of the particular form of network to be used, etc., cannot be presented here. However, the material in this chapter presents a basis on which a knowledge of synthesis techniques can be built with the aid of other material.*

PROBLEMS

15–1 Show that the derivative with respect to ω of the magnitude of the ratio of equation 15–6 is always negative.

15–2 Derive mathematically the conclusions indicated at the end of Art. 15–1 for the low-pass filter of Fig. 15–2.

15–3 Assume $R_S = 100$ ohms and $R_R = 1000$ ohms for Fig. 15–1. Plot curves of the magnitude of the ratio of equation 15–6 vs. ω for $C = 0.001$, 0.01, 0.1, 1, 10μf.

15–4 Repeat Problem 15–3 for the circuit of Fig. 15–2 for $L = 0.001$, 0.01, 0.1, 1, 10 henrys.

15–5 Derive mathematically the conclusions reached in Art. 15–2 for the high-pass filter consisting of a series capacitor. Repeat for a shunt inductor filter.

15–6 Suppose that $R_S = 10$ ohms, and $R_R = 100$ ohms, that $C = 1\ \mu$f, and $L = 1$ henry (Fig. 15–3*a*). Determine the equivalent π network at $\omega^2 = 4/LC$, then plot the magnitude of the ratio similar to equation 15–6 vs. ω for the π and T networks. Plot these curves with particular care in the neighborhood of $\omega = 2/\sqrt{LC}$. Suppose that $R_S = 10{,}000$ ohms and repeat the plotting of $|V_{2k}/V'_{2k}|$. Compare the curves and, thereby, verify the argument of Art. 15–3.

15–7 Plot the magnitude of the ratio corresponding to equation 15–6 vs. ω for the T network of Fig. 15–5*c*. Assume $R_S = R_R = 100$ ohms, $L = 1$ henry, and $C = 1\ \mu$f.

---

* *Ibid.*

15–8 Plot the magnitude of the ratio corresponding to equation 15–6 vs. ω for a T network made of the band elimination elements of Fig. 15–6c. Assume $R_S = R_R = 100$ ohms, $L = 1$ henry, and $C = 1\mu$f. Plot this curve in the region of $\omega = 1000$ and $\omega = 4 \times 10^6$ with care.

15–9 (a) Show, by using the equivalent-T of Fig. 10–8e to obtain formulas for open-circuit and short-circuit impedances of the general four-terminal network, that equation 15–10 is valid in general.

(b) Show for Fig. 15–22 that

$$\frac{Z_{s1}}{Z_{o1}} = \frac{Z_{s2}}{Z_{o2}}$$

by determining Z_{s1}, Z_{s2}, Z_{o1}, Z_{o2} in terms of the five Z's in the figure.

(c) Repeat (b) for terminals ac and bd of Fig. 10–26.

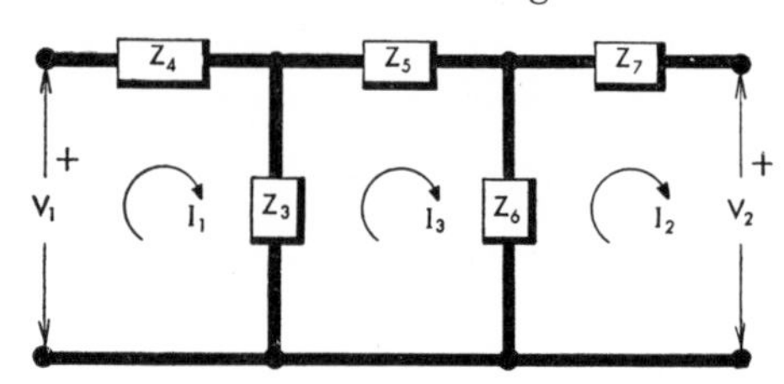

Fig. 15–22.

15–10 Determine Z_{I1}, Z_{I2}, P_I for the diagram in Fig. 15–22 for $Z_3 = 10 + j0$ ohms, $Z_4 = 5 + j0$ ohms, $Z_5 = 8 + j0$ ohms, $Z_6 = 10 + j0$ ohms, and $Z_7 = 4 + j0$ ohms.

15–11 Show, for the diagram and Z-values of the preceding problem, that equations 15–12 and 15–13 are valid. Place the 4TN of Fig. 15–22 in its appropriate place in Fig. 15–7 (gap closed, $E_2 = 0$, etc, as in the discussion preceding equations 15–12 and 15–13). Calculate I_1/I_2 and V_1/V_2 directly from the equations for the network diagram and from the definitions of the image parameters and compare.

15–12 (a) Repeat the preceding problem for Fig. 15–23a.

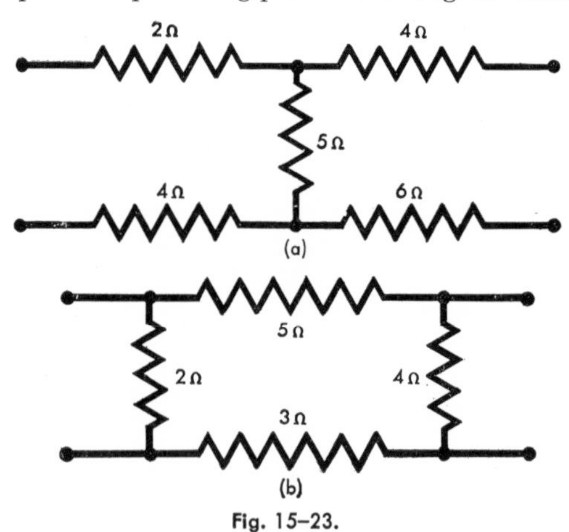

Fig. 15–23.

(*b*) Repeat the preceding problem for Fig. 15–23*b*.

15–13 Show for Fig. 15–22 and the numerical specifications of Problem 15–10 that Z_{I1} and Z_{I2} are related as indicated on Fig. 15–8.

15–14 Repeat Problem 15–13 for the two diagrams in Fig. 15–23.

15–15 Verify equations 15–18, 15–19, 15–20, and 15–21. The last equation may be shown to be valid by forming squares in terms of $Z_x(\omega)$ and $Z_y(\omega)$.

15–16 Discuss in full detail all the features of Tables 15–1 and 15–2.

15–17 Suppose $Z_x(\omega)$ is as given in Fig. 10–20*b* with corresponding reactance curve as on Fig. 10–21*a*, and that $Z_y(\omega)$ is represented by the appropriate reactance curve from Figs. 10–19 or 10–21. Make sketches of these $Z_x(\omega)$ and $Z_y(\omega)$ curves on the same pair of axes, with their poles and zeros located with respect to each other to display the following pattern of pass bands:

(*a*) one pass band from $0 \leq \omega \leq \omega_0$, block band $\omega > \omega_0$.

(*b*) pass hands $0 \leq \omega \leq \omega_{01}$, $\omega_{01} < \omega_{02} \leq \omega$, block band $\omega_{01} < \omega < \omega_{02}$.

(*c*) pass band for all ω, no block band.

(*d*) any three other pass- and block-band arrangements

15–18 Consider the non-symmetric 4TN of Fig. 10–9*b*. (*a*) Determine each of the two symmetric lattices equivalent to the cascading (tandem connection) of this 4TN in accordance with Fig. 15–11*a* and *b*.

(*b*) Determine the two image resistances for the 4TN of Fig. 10–9*b* as well as for the two equivalent lattices. Compare.

(*c*) Determine the image transfer loss of the 4TN of Fig. 10–9*b* and compare with half of the transfer loss of each of the equivalent lattices.

15–19 Repeat the preceding problem for Fig. 10–9*c*.

15–20 Repeat Problem 15–18 for the 4TN of Fig. 10–9*a*.

15–21 Work out in full detail the properties of the A-section of Table 15–3.

15–22 Work out in full detail the properties of the C-section of Table 15–3.

15–23 Show that equation 15–46 for $Z_{02}(x)$ corresponds to either of the plotted forms shown in the first and third columns of Table 15–3, depending on whether $1 < x_p < \sqrt{2}$ or $x_p \geq \sqrt{2}$. The x-values for which the derivative vanishes form a good starting point for the investigation. Find x_m.

15–24 Consider the arithmetic mean and the geometric mean as a basis for approximating unity. Consider the deviations above and below unity. Plot a curve or curves to show conclusions reached.

15–25 Curves of x_p vs. x_u, of R/R_0 and R_0/R vs. x_u, and of $(R - R_0)/R_0$ and $(R - R_0)/R$ are useful for choosing an x_u value to effect a particular half-section design. Plot such curves for $0 < x_u < 1$. Discuss the use of this set of curves in choosing an x_u.

15–26 Work out the details of the last column of Table 15–3.

15–27 Validate the formulas for the element values of Table 15–3. See Art. 15–18 for the pattern of procedure.

15–28 Indicate the filters which present one of each of $Z_{01}(x)$, $Z_{\infty 1}(x)$, $Z_{02}(x)$, and $Z_{\infty 2}(x)$ at one end and one of each of this set of impedance functions at the other end. Combine the inductors and capacitors where possible to reduce the networks to their simplest form. Sketch the $A_I(x)$ and $B_I(x)$ curves for each filter.

15–29 Determine the character of the impedance function at the matched junction in Fig. 15–15*a*. Investigate for the two cases of R_0/R equal to 1.01 and 0.9.

15–30 Determine the element values of a low-pass filter which has the following characteristics: $\omega_0 = 500{,}000$, $R = 100$ ohms, $Z_{\infty 2}(x)$ at one end with $x_u = 0.8$, $Z_{01}(x)$ at the other end, and with poles of $A_I(\omega)$ at $x = 1.6$ and 2.0. Sketch the $A_I(x)$ and $B_I(x)$ curves. Determine the maximum deviation from unity of the $Z_{\infty 2}(x)$ and $Z_{01}(x)$ of the terminating half-sections. Sketch $A_I(x)$ and $B_I(x)$.

15–31 Determine the low-pass filter—network form and element values—which has the properties: $\omega_0 = 10^6$, $R = 500$, $Z_{\infty 1}(x)$ at each end with poles of $A_I(\omega)$ required at $\omega = 1.5 \times 10^6$, 1.7×10^6, 2.1×10^6. Let $x_u = 0.75$ for the terminating sections. Use the least possible number of half-sections. Sketch $A_I(x)$ and $B_I(x)$.

15–32 Determine a high-pass filter with the properties: $Z_{\infty 2}(x)$ at each end, required poles of $A_I(x)$ at $x = 0.95$ and 0.8, $\omega_0 = 500{,}000$, $R = 100$, and $x_u = 1.7$ for the terminating sections. Sketch $A_I(x)$, $B_I(x)$, $Z_{\infty 2}(x)$ for the high-pass filter.

15–33 Determine a high-pass filter with the properties: $Z_{01}(x)$ at one end and $Z_{02}(x)$ at the other, $\omega_0 = 2 \times 10^6$, $R = 1000$, and at each end $x_u = 1.9$. No other poles of $A_I(x)$ are required beyond those required for the impedance function matching. Sketch $A_I(x)$, $B_I(x)$, $Z_{01}(x)$, and $Z_{02}(x)$ for the high-pass filter.

15–34 Design the band-pass filter for which $\omega_{01} = 900{,}000$, $\omega_{02} = 10^6$, $R = 100$, $Z_{\infty 2}(x)$ is to be presented by each end, and $R_0 = 101$. Two poles of $A_I(x)$ must be located at $x = 19.026$, 0.0526. Sketch the $A_I(x)$, $B_I(x)$, and $Z_{\infty 2}(x)$ for the band-pass filter.

15–35 Design a band-block filter for which $Z_{01}(\omega)$ and $Z_{02}(\omega)$ are the end impedance functions, $R = 1000$, $R_0 = 990$, $\omega_{01} = 0.8 \times 10^6$, and $\omega_{02} = 1.2 \times 10^6$. Calculate x_u. Sketch $A_I(x)$, $B_I(x)$, $Z_{01}(x)$, $Z_{02}(x)$.

15–36 Derive the insertion function formula of equation 15–65.

15–37 Plot curves of insertion loss $A_s(x)$ and of insertion phase $B_s(x)$ for:

(*a*) An A-section for which $\omega_0 = 10^6$, $R = 100$, $x_u = 0.8$.

(*b*) A B-section for which $\omega_0 = 10^6$, $R = 100$, $x_u = 0.9$.

(*c*) A C-section for which $\omega_0 = 10^6$, $R = 100$, $x_u = 0.9$.

Plot the insertion loss in *db*, i.e., use $20 \log I'_R/I_R$.

INDEX